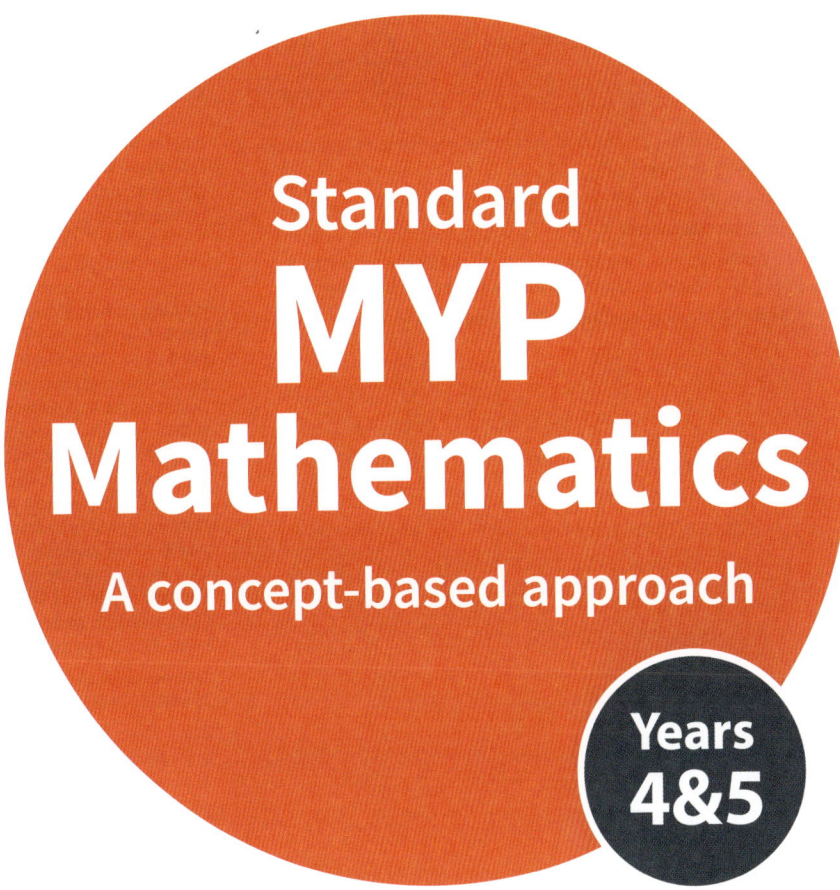

Standard

MYP Mathematics

A concept-based approach

Years 4&5

Rose Harrison
Clara Huizink
Aidan Sproat-Clements
Marlene Torres-Skoumal

OXFORD
UNIVERSITY PRESS

OXFORD
UNIVERSITY PRESS

Great Clarendon Street, Oxford, OX2 6DP, United Kingdom

Oxford University Press is a department of the University of Oxford. It furthers the University's objective of excellence in research, scholarship, and education by publishing worldwide. Oxford is a registered trade mark of Oxford University Press in the UK and in certain other countries

© Oxford University Press 2021

The moral rights of the authors have been asserted

First published in 2021

British Library Cataloguing in Publication Data
Data available

978-1-38-201100-6

7 9 10 8 6

The manufacturing process conforms to the environmental regulations of the country of origin.

Printed in the UK by Bell and Bain Ltd, Glasgow

MIX
Paper | Supporting responsible forestry
FSC
www.fsc.org   FSC® C007785

Acknowledgements

The publisher and authors would like to thank the following for permission to use photographs and other copyright material:

Cover: Nirut Sangkeaw/EyeEm/Getty Images.

Photos: p4: Redfeniks/Shutterstock; **p13:** Waj/Shutterstock; **p17:** Fernando Batista/Shutterstock; **p18:** mark higgins/Shutterstock; **p19:** Cienpies Design/Shutterstock; **p20:** Cristi Matei/Shutterstock; **p41:** Alexander Raths/Shutterstock; **p50:** Dan Briški/Shutterstock; **p64:** dibrova/Shutterstock; **p65:** nohab/Shutterstock; **p66:** Martin M303/Shutterstock; **p70:** louis wulffAlamy Stock Photo; **p77:** andras_csontos/Shutterstock; **p78:** polartern/Shutterstock; **p80:** Olga Danylenko/Shutterstock; **p92:** Chris King/OUP; p93(b): Elnur/ Shutterstock; **p94:** Jason Vandehey/Shutterstock; **p104:** Yerbolat Shadrakhov/Dreamstime; p111(l): imageBROKERAlamy Stock Photo; p111(r): Panther Media GmbHAlamy Stock Photo; **p123:** paul prescott/Shutterstock; **p137:** Nuchylee/Shutterstock; **p139:** dalmingo/Shutterstock; **p140:** Djinn/Shutterstock; **p160:** Stuart Taylor/Shutterstock; **p162:** marekuliasz/Shutterstock; **p177:** Videowokart/Shutterstock; p178, **p195:** icsnaps/Shutterstock; **p183:** Cstock/Alamy Stock Photo; **p194:** gregobagel/iStockphoto; p196(tl): KENNY TONG/Shutterstock; p196(tr): lowefoto/Alamy Stock Photo p196(bl): Pat Tr/Shutterstock; p196(br): James Brittain/ The Image Bank/Getty Images; **p197:** Frank Tozier/Alamy Stock Photo p199(t): Chris Walsh/Relaximages; p199(b): Martyn Vickery/ Alamy Stock Photo **p200:** Media Union/Shutterstock; p218(b): Kanate/Shutterstock; p219(t): AshTproductions/Shutterstock; p219(m): Janelle Lugge/Shutterstock; p219(b): Piotr Krzeslak/ Shutterstock; **p220:** Alexander Rath/Dreamstime; **p234:** K.Wanvisa/Shutterstock; p251(t): Gjermund/Shutterstock; p251(b): bogdan ionescu/Shutterstock; p261(t): njaj/Shutterstock; p261(ml): Eric Milos/Shutterstock; p261(mm): Anton Starikov/Shutterstock; p261(mr): tgunal/Shutterstock; **p262:** EpicStockMedia/ Shutterstock; p261(bl): NASA; p261(bm): NASA; p261(br): NASA; **p268:** Tupungato/Shutterstock; **p277:** Typhoonski/ Dreamstime; p286(a&b): elfinadesign/Shutterstock; p286(c&d): funkyplayer/Shutterstock; p287(a): funkyplayer/Shutterstock; p287(b): Hi-Point/Shutterstock; p287(c): Kjarra/Shutterstock; **p304:** Macrovector/Shutterstock; **p305:** sebaturek/Shutterstock; **p306:** Teo Tarras/Shutterstock; **p308:** AZ Images/Shutterstock; **p325:** Francey/Shutterstock; **p326:** Inna G/Shutterstock; **p337:** maxstockphoto/Shuttertsock; **p348:** Drop of Light/Shutterstock; **p363:** Getmilitaryphotos/Shutterstock; **p364:** Germanskydiver/ Shutterstock; **p374:** rangizzz/Shutterstock; **p378:** Dmitry Pichugin/ Shutterstock; **p379:** sirtravelalot/Shutterstock; **p393:** Christian Heeb/awl-images.com; **p394:** goodynewshoes/iStockphoto; **p408:** Pressmaster/Shutterstock; **p418:** Carlos Caetano/Shutterstock; **p419:** Alena Brozova/Shutterstock; **p432:** Pablo Caridad/ Shutterstock; **p458:** greenland/Shutterstock; p459(tl): Clara Huizink; p459(tr): Clara Huizink; p459(bl): Clara Huizink; p459(br): Clara Huizink; **p460:** Rawpixel.com/Shutterstock; **p477:** Nosha/ Shutterstock; **p487:** wavebreakmedia/Shutterstock.

Artwork by Q2A Media Services Pvt. Ltd, Jon Mackay and Thomson Digital.

Every effort has been made to contact copyright holders of material reproduced in this book. Any omissions will be rectified in subsequent printings if notice is given to the publisher.

The 'in cooperation' logo signifies that the content in the print book has been reviewed by the IB to ensure it fully aligns with the revised MYP framework. The extra online resources found in the digital book offer additional support but are not published in cooperation with the IB.

Contents

 Launch answers and other digital
resources for this book

Introduction

Introduction for students

Studying mathematics is a fundamental part of a balanced education: understanding mathematics can help make sense of the world around us, exploring it can give both the thrill of exploration and the rewards of discovery, and engaging in mathematics can give insightful reflections.

Our aim writing this book was to create a journey of knowing, understanding, investigating and communicating mathematics. The MYP 4&5 Standard book is designed to take you on this wondrous journey and to help your analytical reasoning and problem-solving skills that contribute to strengthening your logical, abstract and critical thinking. All these skills are necessary to participate successfully in an ever-changing world.

Introduction for teachers

We believe that mathematics aims to equip all students with the knowledge, understanding and intellectual capabilities to progress to further study, as well as to prepare them for their life journey, which is why we wanted to showcase authentic examples of how mathematics is useful and relevant to students' lives and encourage them to apply it to new situations. In addition, we wanted them to experience the elegance and beauty of pure mathematics. To achieve this, we entwined content, concepts and contexts throughout the units for the right balance of new and consolidation material, both in the printed book and the extra digital resources.

This second edition of the MYP Mathematics 4&5 Standard book is fully aligned with the latest MYP Mathematics framework, for first teaching in 2020. Unlike the first edition, this book is structured by unit, making it easier for you to use it in the classroom.

How to get the most out of this resource

We also wanted to give you more teaching resources which is why this new edition comes with an enhanced digital online book. Wherever you see this icon, you are able to launch supporting resources:

 Launch additional digital resources for this unit

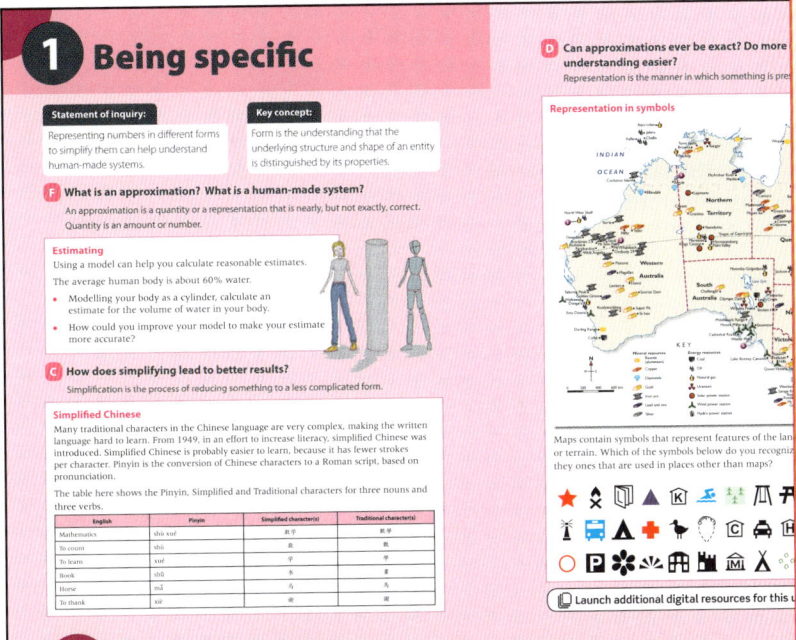

On each unit opening spread you will find a downloadable:

- Formative task - a task rooted in real-life applications of mathematics and led by the unit's global context. The task is in the style of the eAssessment, focused on assessment criteria A and C, and either criterion B or criterion D, depending on the context.

- Summative task - an open-ended task, supporting students with assessment criterion D.

- Answers to the questions in this unit.

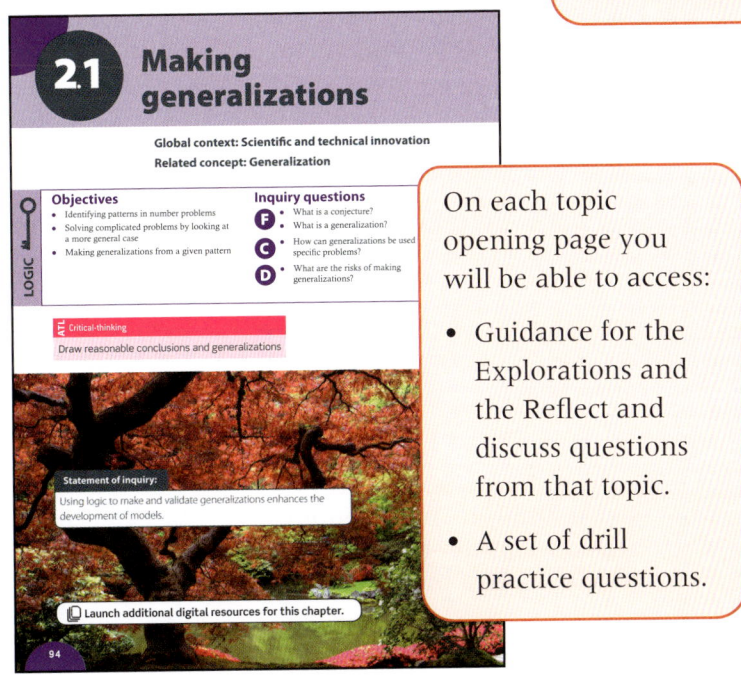

On each topic opening page you will be able to access:

- Guidance for the Explorations and the Reflect and discuss questions from that topic.

- A set of drill practice questions.

Unit	Statement of inquiry	ATL cluster(s)	Key concept
1. Being specific	Representing numbers in different forms to simplify them can help understand human-made systems.	Organization, communication, critical thinking	Form
2. Decisions, decisions	Using logic to make and validate generalizations enhances the development of models.	Critical thinking, transfer	Logic
3. Back to the beginning	Discovering relationships in patterns and studying equivalence between representations can lead to better models.	Communication, critical thinking, creative thinking	Relationships
4. Mathematically speaking	Understanding health and validating life-style choices results from using logical representations and systems.	Communication	Logic
5. Spacious interiors	Representing transformed objects and studying their form helps us enjoy their creativity in space.	Creative thinking	Form
6. A whole range of things	How quantities are represented can help to establish underlying relationships and trends in a population.	Communication, critical thinking	Relationships
7. How do they measure up?	Systems use logic to validate generalizations and increase our appreciation of the aesthetic.	Communication, critical thinking	Logic
8. What comes next?	Representing patterns and change in a variety of forms has helped humans apply their understanding of scientific principles.	Critical thinking, transfer	Form
9. So, what do you think?	Generalizing and representing relationships can help to clarify trends amongst individuals.	Critical thinking	Relationships

Related concepts	Global context	Exploration
Simplification, representation, quantity, approximation	Globalization and sustainability	Exploring different ways of measuring human-made systems
Generalization, validity, models	Scientific and technical innovation	Exploring the natural world by developing realistic models
Representation, patterns, equivalence	Scientific and technical innovation	Exploring systems and methods to create models
Validity, representation	Identities and relationships	Exploring personal and physical health and good lifestyle choices
Representation, space	Personal and cultural expression	Exploring the ways in which we reflect on, extend and enjoy our creativity.
Representation, quantity, generalization	Globalization and sustainability	Exploring trends and the impact of decision-making on the environment
Approximation, generalization, systems	Personal and cultural expression	Exploring the appreciation of the aesthetic.
Patterns, change	Scientific and technical innovation	Exploring how humans apply their understanding of scientific principles to real-life situations
Generalization, representation	Identities and relationships	Exploring trends and characteristics amongst individuals

1 Being specific

F What is an approximation? What is a human-made system?

An approximation is a quantity or a representation that is nearly, but not exactly, correct. Quantity is an amount or number.

Estimating

Using a model can help you calculate reasonable estimates.

The average human body is about 60% water.

- Modelling your body as a cylinder, calculate an estimate for the volume of water in your body.

- How could you improve your model to make your estimate more accurate?

C How does simplifying lead to better results?

Simplification is the process of reducing something to a less complicated form.

Simplified Chinese

Many traditional characters in the Chinese language are very complex, making the written language hard to learn. From 1949, in an effort to increase literacy, simplified Chinese was introduced. Simplified Chinese is probably easier to learn, because it has fewer strokes per character. Pinyin is the conversion of Chinese characters to a Roman script, based on pronunciation.

The table here shows the Pinyin, Simplified and Traditional characters for three nouns and three verbs.

English	Pinyin	Simplified character(s)	Traditional character(s)
Mathematics	shù xué	数学	數學
To count	shù	数	數
To learn	xué	学	學
Book	shū	书	書
Horse	mǎ	马	馬
To thank	xiè	谢	謝

D Can approximations ever be exact? Do more representations make understanding easier?

Representation is the manner in which something is presented.

Representation in symbols

Maps contain symbols that represent features of the landscape or terrain. Which of the symbols below do you recognize? Are they ones that are used in places other than maps?

Global context: Globalization and sustainability

Exploration: Explore different ways of measuring human-made systems

🗂️ Launch additional digital resources for this unit.

1.1 Problem solving

Global context: Globalization and sustainability

Related concept: Simplification

FORM

Objectives

- Applying Pólya's problem-solving steps to solve any type of problem
- Selecting and applying appropriate mathematical strategies to solve problems
- Checking if a solution makes sense in the context of the problem

Inquiry questions

F
- What are Pólya's steps in solving a problem?

C
- Which problem-solving strategies are most useful in solving real-life problems?

D
- How can you represent and simplify given information in order to solve real-life problems?
- How useful is it to approximate?

ATL Organization

Use appropriate strategies for organizing complex information

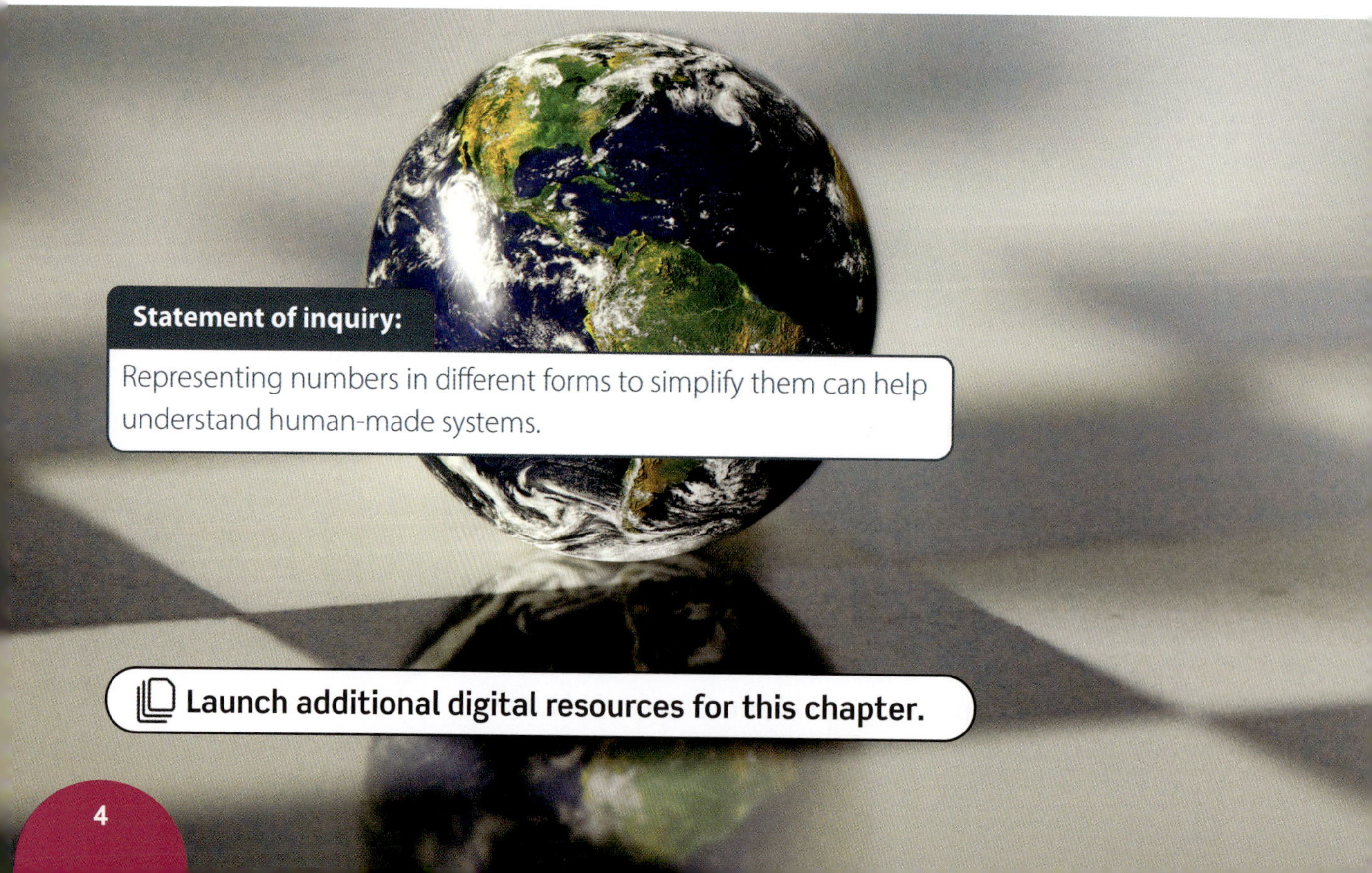

Statement of inquiry:

Representing numbers in different forms to simplify them can help understand human-made systems.

📖 Launch additional digital resources for this chapter.

4

You should already know how to:

• use the Pythagorean Theorem	**1** Find the length of side *x*. 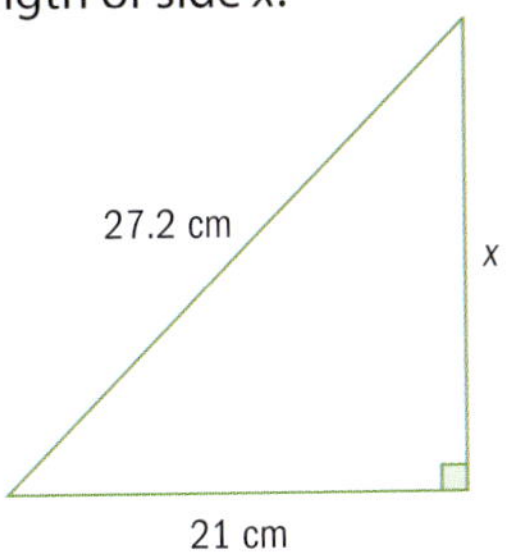 27.2 cm *x* 21 cm
• find the perimeter and area of basic shapes	**2** Find the perimeter and area of each shape. **a** 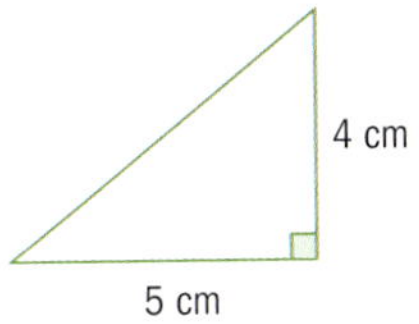 **b** 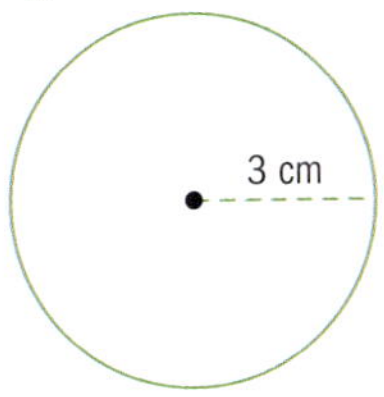 4 cm 3 cm 5 cm
• find the volume of cuboids, prisms and cylinders	**3** Find the volume of each solid: **a** 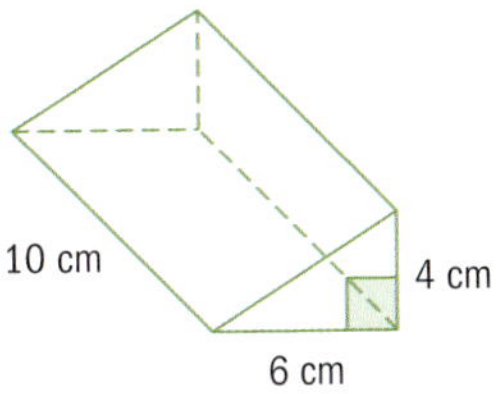 **b** 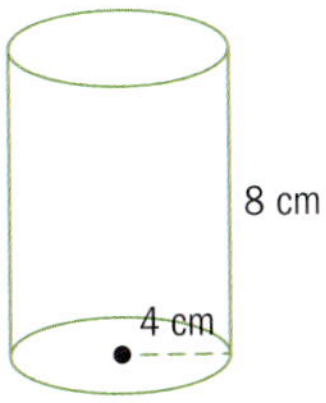 10 cm 8 cm 4 cm 4 cm 6 cm
• write and solve equations	**4** Write an equation for the angles in this triangle. Solve it to find *x*. 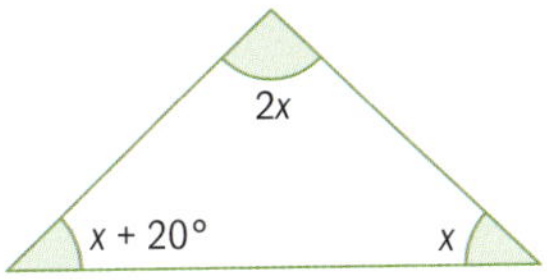 2*x* *x* + 20° *x*

 Pólya's problem-solving steps

- What are Pólya's steps for solving a problem?

Sometimes, the method to solve a problem isn't immediately obvious. Some problems may involve a lot of complex mathematics, but others may be very simple. The same question could be considered easy for some people but challenging for others.

Reflect and discuss 1

Are the following questions easy or challenging? Does everyone agree?

- For $x^2 + 4x = 100$, what is the value of x?

- One liter per minute of water flows into a cylindrical tank of height 1.5 m and radius 30 cm. How long will it take to fill the tank?

- What is the highest common factor of 1752 and 356?

- How many triangles are there in the diagram at the right?

George Pólya (1887–1985) was a Hungarian professor of mathematics. He described the following problem-solving steps to use for all problems in mathematics and in other subjects.

Pólya's problem-solving steps[1]

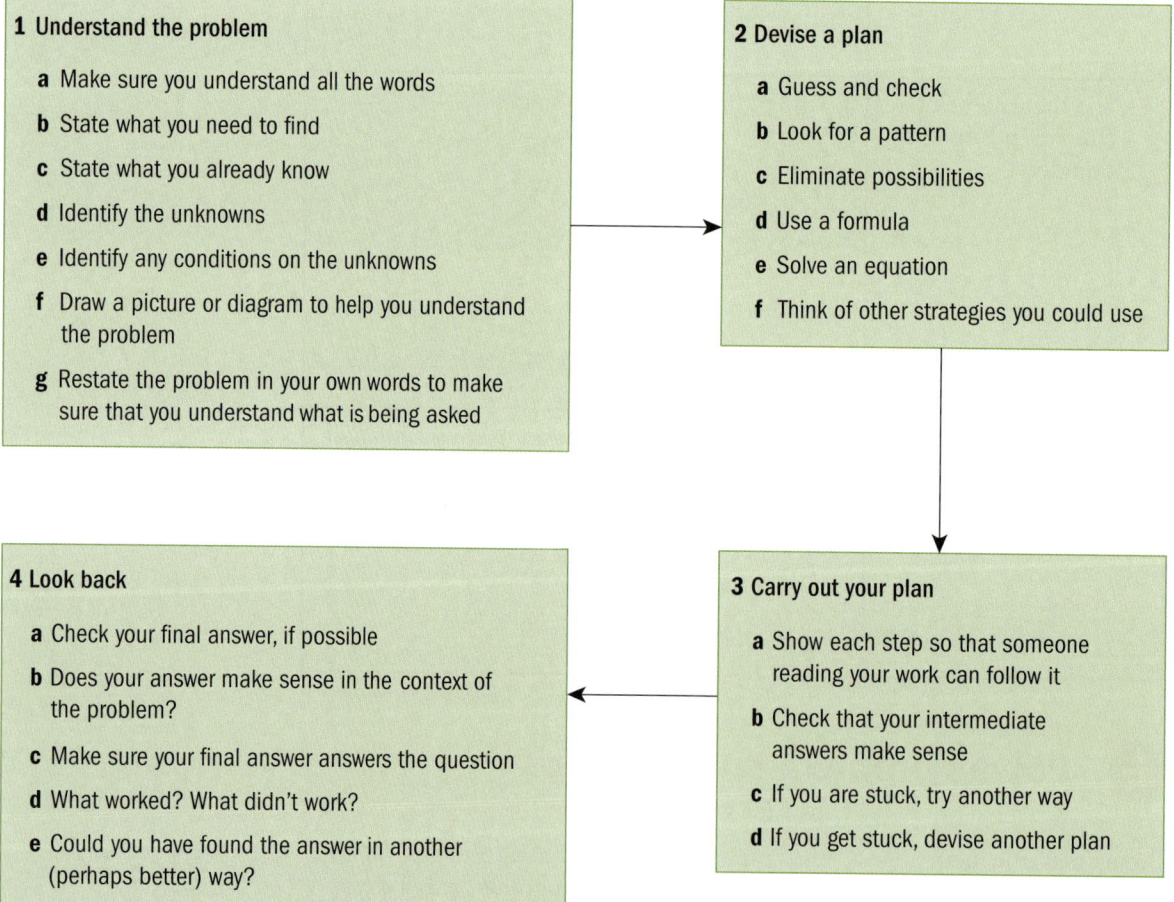

1 Understand the problem

 a Make sure you understand all the words

 b State what you need to find

 c State what you already know

 d Identify the unknowns

 e Identify any conditions on the unknowns

 f Draw a picture or diagram to help you understand the problem

 g Restate the problem in your own words to make sure that you understand what is being asked

2 Devise a plan

 a Guess and check

 b Look for a pattern

 c Eliminate possibilities

 d Use a formula

 e Solve an equation

 f Think of other strategies you could use

4 Look back

 a Check your final answer, if possible

 b Does your answer make sense in the context of the problem?

 c Make sure your final answer answers the question

 d What worked? What didn't work?

 e Could you have found the answer in another (perhaps better) way?

3 Carry out your plan

 a Show each step so that someone reading your work can follow it

 b Check that your intermediate answers make sense

 c If you are stuck, try another way

 d If you get stuck, devise another plan

You already have a range of strategies for solving problems in mathematics. Some you will have been taught, others you may have discovered for yourself.

[1]Pólya, George (1945). *How to Solve It* Princeton University Press.

Exploration 1

Solve these problems using your usual method. For each one, write down the steps you use from Pólya's list.

1 $175 - 123 =$

2 Find the value of x:

a $5x = 35$ **b** $4x - 2 = 30$

c $\dfrac{3x - 2}{7} = 7$ **d** $\dfrac{4}{x - 4} = \dfrac{1}{2}$

3 In the diagram to the right, $\angle KLM = 120°$ and $\angle ULM = 30°$. Find angle KLU.

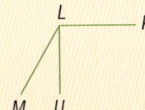

4 Find the unknown angle:

a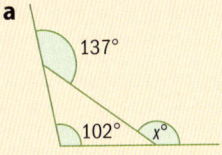

b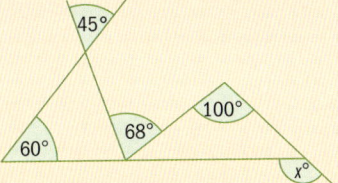

5 Find x:

a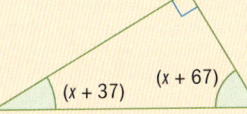

b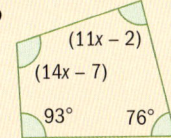

6 Find the area of each triangle. Where necessary, round your final answer to the nearest tenth.

a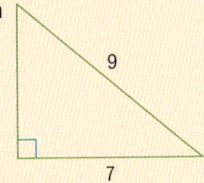

b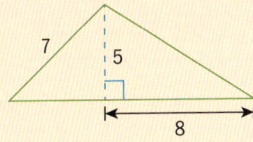

7 Find the volume of each solid. Give your answers to 1 decimal place.

a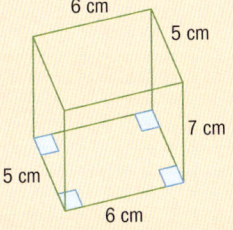

b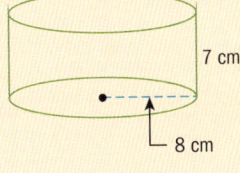

8 Find the volume of a cube that has surface area 384 m^2.

9 In Canada, how many ways can you make a dollar with coins? The Canadian coins are nickels (5 cents), dimes (10 cents), quarters (25 cents) and dollars (or loonies). One dollar is 100 cents.

Currency is a human-made system.

Reflect and discuss 2

- When you were solving the problems in Exploration 1, which of Pólya's steps did you use most often? Were there any you didn't use? Did everyone use the same steps?

- Look back at the four problem-solving steps. Are they equally important? Explain. Would it matter if you missed one?

> 'If you can't solve a problem, then there is an easier problem you can solve. Find it.'
>
> *George Pólya*

ATL

Example 1

It takes Anna 20 minutes to wash a car, and Bianka 30 minutes to wash a similar car. How long will they take to wash a car together?

t = time to wash one car together

$t_A = 20$ min

$t_B = 30$ min

1 Understand the problem
  b State what you need to find
  c State what you already know
  d Identify the unknowns

r = rate of washing a car together, 1 car every t minutes.

r_A = Anna's rate

r_B = Bianka's rate

$r = r_A + r_B$

Use $r = \dfrac{1\,\text{car}}{t}$ to find t.

2 Devise a plan
  The time to wash one car depends on the rate of washing – how many cars they wash in a given time.
  Their rate of washing together is the sum of their individual rates.

$r_A = \dfrac{1\,\text{car}}{20\,\text{min}}$ $r_B = \dfrac{1\,\text{car}}{30\,\text{min}}$

3 Carry out the plan
  a Show each step

$r = r_A + r_B = \dfrac{1\,\text{car}}{20\,\text{min}} + \dfrac{1\,\text{car}}{30\,\text{min}}$

$= \dfrac{3\,\text{cars}}{1\,\text{hour}} + \dfrac{2\,\text{cars}}{1\,\text{hour}}$

Change to fractions with common denominator 1 hour.

$= \dfrac{5\,\text{cars}}{1\,\text{hour}}$

Together they wash 5 cars per hour,

which is $\dfrac{1\,\text{hour}}{5} = 12$ minutes per car.

$t = 12$ minutes

b Check that your intermediate answers make sense. They wash more cars together than they do on their own.

If it takes each girl 20 minutes to wash a car, then together they could wash a car in 10 minutes. If they each took 30 minutes, then together they could wash a car in 15 minutes.

4 Look back
  a Check your answer

Since they take 20 and 30 minutes respectively to wash a car, the answer should be somewhere in between 10 and 15 minutes.

Anna is the quickest and takes 20 min. Together they should be quicker than that.

b Does your answer make sense in the context of the problem?

They will take 12 minutes to wash one car together.

c Make sure your final answer answers the question

In Example 1, most of the work is in step **2**: Devise a plan. The main causes of incorrect solutions are:

- rushing to step **3** and starting to do calculations without a clear plan
- leaving out step **4**, and not checking answers in the context of the problem.

Practice 1

Solve these problems using Pólya's steps. Show your plan and your working clearly. Remember to check that your answers make sense in the context of the problem.

1 Light travels six trillion miles in one year. If the radius of the Earth is approximately 4000 miles, find how many times around the Earth light could travel in one year.

2 Under ideal conditions, algae can double in area every day and cover an entire pond in 1 month and 2 days. Determine how many days it will take for the algae to cover just half of the pond.

3 A team can row 40 km in 2 hours when rowing with the current, but only 16 km in 2 hours when rowing against the current. Determine the team's rowing speed when there is no current.

4 Sidney has two different acid solutions: A is a 50% acid solution, and B is an 80% acid solution. Determine how much of each solution he needs to create 200 ml of a 68% solution.

5 Corinne and Justine sold jewelry at a bazaar. They sold some for $9.50 a piece, and then dropped the price to $7.50 a piece. In total they sold 90 pieces for $721. Find how many they sold at $9.50.

6 Ilhan began her triathlon at 7:22 am. She crossed the finish line at 8:07 pm, after swimming 2.4 miles, cycling 112 miles and running 26.2 miles. Find her average speed for the race.

- -

C Problem-solving strategies

- Which problem-solving strategies are most useful in solving real-life problems?

The next examples show some strategies you can use in problem solving. They may help you get started when you are stuck.

> **Strategy: Take 1**
>
> Sometimes you can simplify a problem by replacing one of the numbers with 1. For example, how much does 1 item cost? Or how many hours does it take 1 person to complete a task?

If your answer is: a pencil weighs 50 kg or a plane travels at 20 km/h, common sense should tell you something must be wrong in your solution.

One definition of problem solving is 'knowing what to do when you don't know what to do'.

Example 2

Three painters can paint a house in 8 hours. How many painters are needed to paint the house in 6 hours?

n = number of painters to paint the house in 6 hours

3 painters take 8 hours

$n > 3$

1 Understand the problem
   b State what you need to find
   c State what you already know
   e Identify any conditions on the unknowns.
   Assume all painters paint at the same rate.
   To paint in less time, you need more painters.

1 painter takes t hours

n painters take 6 hours

2 Devise a plan
   Strategy: Take 1
   Find out how long it takes one painter to paint the house.
   Work out how many painters you need to paint it in 6 hours.

3 painters $\rightarrow$ 8 hours

1 painter $\rightarrow$ 24 hours

4 painters $\rightarrow$ 6 hours

$n = 4$

3 Carry out the plan
   One painter takes 3 times as long as 3 painters.
   4 painters take $\frac{1}{4}$ the time of 1 painter.

4 painters are needed to paint the house in 6 hours.

4 Look back
   The final answer satisfies $n > 3$, which fits with expectations.

Strategy 2: Use easy numbers

Replacing numbers in the problem with 'easy numbers' can help you see the method to use in the original problem.

Example 3

Potatoes cost $1.56 per kilogram. Shona spent $1.95 on potatoes. How many kilograms of potatoes did she buy?

x = mass of potatoes

$x > 1$

1 Understand the problem
   Shona paid more than $1.56, so she bought more than 1 kg.

Assume potatoes cost $2 per kg, and a customer bought $10 worth.

That means the customer bought 5 kg of potatoes.

$\frac{10}{2} = 5$

2 Devise a plan
   Strategy: Use easy numbers
   Rewrite with numbers that are easier to work with, to see what operations to use to solve the problem.

▶ Continued on next page

$$\frac{\text{Amount paid}}{\text{price per kg}} = \text{mass in kg}$$

$$\frac{\text{Amount paid}}{\text{price per kg}} = \frac{1.95}{1.56} = 1.25 \text{ kg}$$ ——————————————————————— **3** Carry out the plan

4 Look back
    a Check your answer
    b Does it make sense?
1.25 kg satisfies $x > 1$.
$1.95 is less than $3.12 for 2 kg,
so 1.25 kg is a reasonable answer.

Shona bought 1.25 kg of potatoes. ——————————————

Reflect and discuss 3

- In Example 3, how did substituting easier numbers help solve the problem?
- How are the 'Take one' and 'Use easy numbers' strategies related?

ATL

Practice 2

Solve these problems using Pólya's steps. Use one of the two strategies seen so far. Remember to check that your answers make sense in the context of the problem.

1 It takes 6 students 2 hours to stuff envelopes for Back to School Night. Determine how many students would be needed to finish the job in a quarter of an hour.

2 Jordan has an average of 82% on her first four tests.

  a Find the score she needs on the next test for her average to be 84%.

  b Find the average score she needs on the next two tests for her overall average to be 85%.

  c Determine the minimum number of tests that could be left to take if Jordan wanted to have an average of 90%, and assuming that she could score as high as possible on all remaining tests.

3 Two painters work for a painting company. One of them can paint a 200 m^2 area in 5 minutes while the other one takes 8 minutes to paint the same area. Find how long it would take them to paint an area of 1300 m^2 if they painted it together.

4 Light travels 3 000 000 km in ten seconds. If Earth is 150 million kilometers from the Sun, find how many minutes it takes for light from the Sun to reach our planet.

5 After installing a new pool, Kedrick's family is going to use two pumps to fill it. Pump 1 can fill a pool in 8 hours while pump 2 can fill it in 12 hours.

  a Determine how fast the pool can be filled using both pumps.

  b If both pumps start at the same time, but pump 1 breaks down after an hour, find how long it will take to fill the pool (in total).

6 Thien lives on the 11th floor of a building. He has to climb 48 steps just to get to the third floor. Determine how many steps he needs to take to get to his floor.

7 There were enough provisions at a space station to feed 20 people for 80 days. After 20 days into the mission, 10 astronauts returned to Earth. Assuming the rate of food consumption doesn't change, determine how many more days the food will last.

8 Diagonals in polygons are line segments that connect the vertices of the polygon, excluding its sides.

   a Find how many diagonals there are in a 20-sided polygon.

   b Find how many diagonals there are in an *n*-sided polygon.

Strategy 3: Draw it!

It often helps to draw a diagram, especially if the problem involves geometry.

Example 4

A water sprinkler is placed in the middle of a rectangular lawn 6 m long and 5 m wide. The sprinkler sprays water to a distance of 2 m. What proportion of the lawn is watered by the sprinkler?

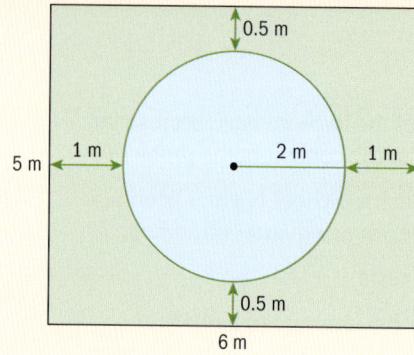

1 Understand the problem

   f Draw a diagram to help you understand the problem. A fairly accurate drawing can help you see whether your answer makes sense.

p = proportion of lawn watered by sprinkler.

$p = $ close to $\frac{1}{2}$

   b State what you need to find

   e Identify any conditions on the unknowns. Based on this fairly accurate diagram, $p = $ close to $\frac{1}{2}$

$p = \dfrac{\text{area of the watered circle}}{\text{area of the whole lawn}} = \dfrac{A_c}{A_l}$

2 Devise a plan

$A_c = \pi r^2$ where $r = 2$ m

$A_l = l \times w$ where $l = 6$ m and $w = 5$ m

To find the proportion, you first need to find the area of the circle and the area of the rectangle.

$A_c = \pi r^2 = \pi \times 2^2 = 4\pi$

$A_l = l \times w = 6 \times 5 = 30$

$p = \dfrac{A_c}{A_l} = \dfrac{4\pi}{30} = \dfrac{2\pi}{15}$

3 Carry out your plan

Always use exact values until the final answer. Do not use 3.14 for π.

$p = 0.4188790205$

$p = 0.42 = 42\%$

4 Look back

In this situation, it is reasonable to round the final answer to the nearest percent. Final answer satisfies $p = $ close to $\frac{1}{2}$

42% of the lawn is watered by the sprinkler.

   c Answer the question

Practice 3

1 A 6 cm long prism has a base that is a right-angled triangle with two sides of length 5 cm. Find its volume.

2 The square base of the Great pyramid at Giza measures 230.4 m on each side. Its slant height is 186.4 m.

   a Determine the ratio of the height of the pyramid to the perimeter of its base.

   b Explain how this ratio is related to the number π.

   c Discuss whether you think this is a coincidence.

> **Strategy 4: Work backwards**
>
> Some problems give you an answer and ask you to find a part of the question. For example, you are given the total price of oranges and are asked how much one orange costs, or you are given the area of a square and asked to find its side length.

Example 5

The diagonal of one side of a cube is 11.3 cm to 3 s.f. Find the cube's volume.

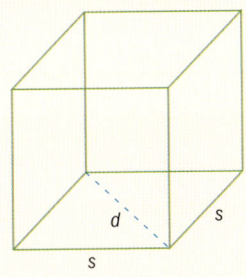

1 Understand the problem
  f Draw a diagram

$d = 11.3$ cm

  c State what you know
  b State what you need to find

Volume of cube $= s^3$

Need to find s.

$s^2 + s^2 = d^2$

$2s^2 = d^2$

2 Devise a plan
  Use the Pythagorean Theorem with d and s to find s.
  Use s to find the volume of the cube.

$2s^2 = 11.3^2$

$2s^2 = 127.69$

$s^2 = 63.845$

$s = 7.990$ cm

Volume $= s^3 = 7.990^3 = 510.1$ cm^3

3 Carry out the plan
  The final answer should be rounded to 3 s.f. only at the end. All previous answers must be rounded to *at least* one more place as needed.
  b Check your answers make sense.
  The side s is shorter than the diagonal.

The volume of the cube is 510 cm^3.

4 Look back
  c Answer the question

Practice 4

1 The height of a cylinder is twice as long as its diameter. Its volume is $500\,\pi\,cm^3$. Find the area of its base.

2 The diagonal of a cube (that passes through the middle of the cube, as shown in the diagram at right) measures 17.32 cm. Find the volume of the cube.

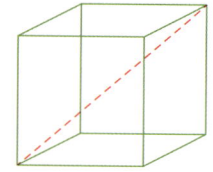

3 A box with no top has a height that is six times its length and a width that is $\frac{2}{3}$ of its height. If the surface area is $576\,cm^2$, find the dimensions of the box.

4 When milk freezes, its volume increases by one-fifteenth. Find the fraction by which its volume will decrease when it melts back into a liquid state.

5 It takes Nathan twice as long to mow the lawn with the pushmower than with the electric mower. One day, he used the electric mower for 30 minutes. Then it broke down. He took 20 minutes to finish mowing the lawn with the pushmower.

Find how long it takes Nathan to mow the whole lawn using only the electric mower.

6 The surface area of a cube-shaped box without a top is $252\,cm^2$. Find the volume of the box.

7 Suppose you have a 4L container and a 9L container. If you had access to a source of running water, explain how you could measure out exactly 6L of water.

L = liter

Reflect and discuss 4

- Compare the methods you and others used to solve problems so far. Which ones were used most often?

- How can different methods lead to the same solution?

- Is the best strategy always the simplest?

D When is an estimated solution 'good enough'?

- How can you represent and simplify given information in order to solve real-life problems?
- How useful is it to approximate?

In the practice problems you have solved so far, all the information you need to solve the problem was given in the question. In real-life situations, sometimes there is a lot of information and you have to choose what you need. Sometimes there is not enough information and you have to find extra information, or make estimates. Then your answer will also be an approximation.

Exploration 2

A square room has four walls, each 3 m long and 2.2 m tall. Paint comes in 10-liter or 5-liter pots. One liter of paint covers an area of 1.5 m². The room's one door measures 1.8 m by 0.8 m and its one window is 1.5 m by 1 m.

Pedro calculates the area of the walls and ignores the door and window.

Mia calculates the area of four walls, and subtracts the areas of the door and window.

Work out the number and sizes of tins of paint needed using Mia's and Pedro's areas. Justify whether it is better to calculate accurately or to approximate the amount of paint used in this situation.

Reflect and discuss 5

In which situations is it better to approximate than to make exact calculations? When is it important to be as exact as possible?

When is it better to over-estimate than to under-estimate?

Practice 5

ATL

Some of these problems have too much information and some do not have enough. For each problem, state which information is irrelevant, and write down which information is missing in order for you to solve it.

1 Find the area of this parallelogram.

2 Amy's five friends come to visit her by bus. Each pays $4 for a ticket. For supper, Amy buys four pizzas at $5.75 each, 500 g of strawberries at $2.75 per kilogram, and a tub of ice cream for $4.75. Find how much change she gets.

3 Elizabeth would like to buy a television for her apartment. She knows that a 42-inch television has a diagonal that measures 42 inches. The cabinet where she wants to put the television measures 30 inches wide, 30 inches tall and 24 inches deep.

Determine whether or not the television could fit.

4 Jack gets up at 7:00 am and needs to catch the bus to school at 7:53 am. The bus stop is 400 m from his house. Determine at what time he needs to leave the house.

5 Josip just bought a lightweight cylindrical water bottle where the radius of the bottle is half of its height. When full, it weighs 450 grams and holds a volume of 770 cm³. Find the dimensions of the water bottle.

6 On her way home, Natalee's plane took off at 8:10 am and flew at an angle of 30° with the ground. If the plane's speed was 285 km/h and it rose to an altitude of 8000 meters, what horizontal distance did it cover during that time?

Summary

Pólya's problem-solving steps

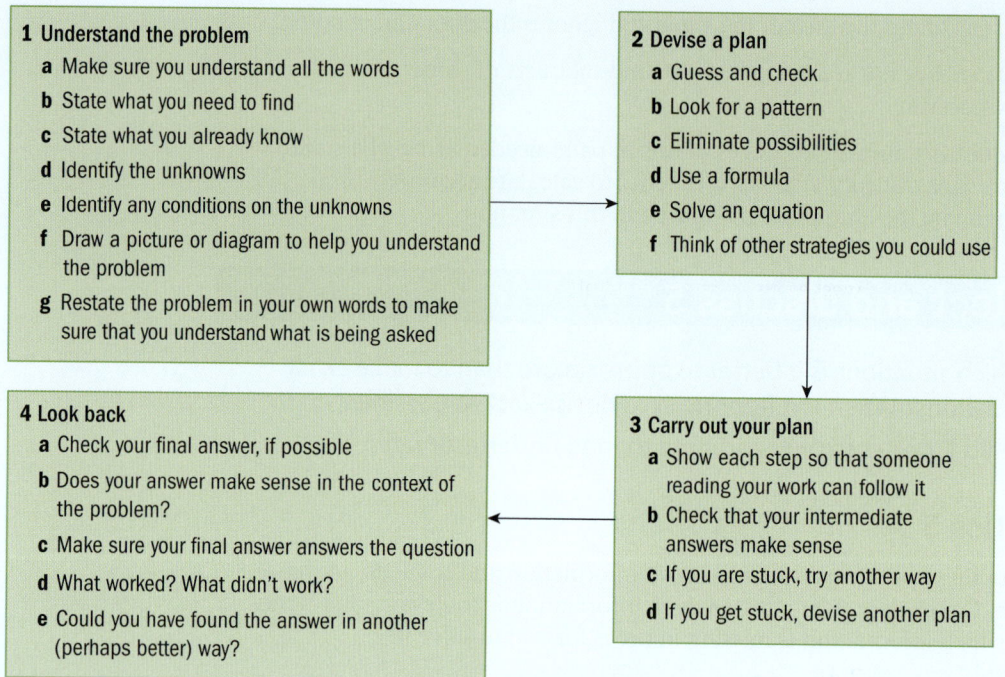

1 Understand the problem
- **a** Make sure you understand all the words
- **b** State what you need to find
- **c** State what you already know
- **d** Identify the unknowns
- **e** Identify any conditions on the unknowns
- **f** Draw a picture or diagram to help you understand the problem
- **g** Restate the problem in your own words to make sure that you understand what is being asked

2 Devise a plan
- **a** Guess and check
- **b** Look for a pattern
- **c** Eliminate possibilities
- **d** Use a formula
- **e** Solve an equation
- **f** Think of other strategies you could use

4 Look back
- **a** Check your final answer, if possible
- **b** Does your answer make sense in the context of the problem?
- **c** Make sure your final answer answers the question
- **d** What worked? What didn't work?
- **e** Could you have found the answer in another (perhaps better) way?

3 Carry out your plan
- **a** Show each step so that someone reading your work can follow it
- **b** Check that your intermediate answers make sense
- **c** If you are stuck, try another way
- **d** If you get stuck, devise another plan

Strategy 1: Take 1

Sometimes you can simplify a problem by replacing one of the numbers with 1. For example, how much does 1 item cost? Or how many hours does it take 1 person to complete a task?

Strategy 2: Use easy numbers

Replacing numbers in the problem with 'easy numbers' can help you see the method to use in the original problem.

Strategy 3: Draw it!

It often helps to draw a diagram, especially if the problem involves geometry.

Strategy 4: Work backwards

Some problems give you an answer and ask you to find a part of the question. For example, you are given the total price of oranges and are asked how much one orange costs, or you are given the area of a square and asked to find its side length.

Mixed practice

1 Three times the reciprocal of a number equals nine times the reciprocal of 6. **Find** the number.

2 Angles x and $\frac{3}{4}x$ are complementary. **Find** x.

3 The denominator of a fraction is 1 less than twice the numerator. When 7 is added to both the numerator and denominator, the resulting fraction is equivalent to $\frac{7}{10}$. **Find** the original fraction.

4 Sophie leaves school and travels east at an average speed of 40 km/h. Jenny leaves school one hour later, and travels west at an average speed of 50 km/h. **Determine** how many hours after Jenny leaves school they will be 400 km apart.

5 Kim and Tom both cycle to work from their homes, at the same speed. Kim lives 20 km away from work, and Tom lives only 15 km away from work. It takes Kim 1 hour more to cycle to work than Tom. **Determine** how long Tom takes to get to work.

6 **Determine** how many milligrams of a metal containing 45% nickel must be combined with 6 milligrams of pure nickel to form an alloy containing 78% nickel.

7 Two different fruit juices are mixed together. 7 liters of the first fruit juice contains 60% apple juice, and 5 liters of the second fruit juice contains 30% apple juice. **Find** the percentage of the new mix that is apple juice.

8 Chloe can type a story in 6 hours. If Molly helps her, they finish typing the story in 4 hours. **Find** how long it would take Molly to type the story on her own.

9 Mary takes 8 days to do a full check of the library's online catalog. Her assistant takes 12 days. If they work together, **determine** the fraction of the catalog that is checked after 4 days.

10 The number of hamsters in a pet store doubles each month. Today, there are 20 hamsters.

   a Supposing that no hamster dies and no hamster gets sold, **determine** in how many months the store will have 640 hamsters.

   b If 10 hamsters are sold at the end of each month, after the number of hamsters double, **find** how many hamsters are left after 5 months.

11 Sacha picked some apples from a tree in her garden. She then gave some to her friends. To her first friend, she gave half the apples she had, plus 2 more. To her second friend, she gave half the apples she had left, plus 2 more. And she did the same thing for her third friend. After giving away all these apples, she had 1 apple left. **Find** how many apples she originally pick from the tree.

12 A house and a piece of land are sold for €850 000. The house is sold for one and a half times as much as the land. **Find** how much the house sold for.

Review in context

Globalization and sustainability

Hungarian Paul Erdős (1913–96) was a highly productive, yet highly eccentric mathematician who enjoyed solving and posing mathematical problems, even offering cash prizes for solutions. There are thought to be around 1000 problems still unsolved, with prizes from $25 upward.

Erdős collaborated on academic papers with over 480 co-authors, more than any other mathematician in history.

Many people enjoy mathematical puzzles, not just mathematicians. Some puzzles have led to interesting discoveries in mathematical theory, or other fields entirely. Use problem-solving strategies to solve these famous historical puzzles.

1 Rice on a chessboard

Sissa ben Dahir, Grand Vizier to the Indian King Shirham, invented the game of chess. Shirham liked the game so much, that he asked Sissa what he wanted as a reward. Sissa replied: 'I would like to cover the chessboard with 1 grain of rice on the first square, 2 grains on the second, 4 grains on the third, 8 grains on the fourth, and so on.' The King accepted immediately, thinking he had himself a bargain.

How much rice would there be on the chessboard?

Answer these questions to help work it out.

a **Find** the number of grains of rice on:

i the 8th square

ii the 16th square

iii the 64th square.

> How does it help to know that each square has double the grains of rice as the previous square?

b About 50 grains of rice fit in 1 cm². Leaving your answer correct to 2 d.p., **find** how many cm² of rice are on:

i the 8th square

ii the 16th square

iii the 24th square.

c 10 000 cm² = 1 m².

Find how many m² of rice are on the 24th square.

d 1 000 000 m² = 1 km².

Find how many km² of rice are on the 64th square. Leave your answer correct to 2 d.p.

e Challenge: **Find** the total number of grains of rice in:

i the first row

ii the first two rows

iii the first three rows

iv the entire chessboard.

2 The Tower of Hanoi

French mathematician Édouard Lucas invented this puzzle in 1883.

This stack of disks in order from the largest to the smallest is called a tower. The aim of the puzzle is to move a tower from one rod to another, obeying the following rules:

Rule 1 Only one disk can be moved at a time.

Rule 2 One move consists of taking the top disk from one stack and placing it on top of a stack on another rod.

Rule 3 A disk can be placed only on top of a larger disk. No disk can be placed on top of a smaller disk.

The minimum number of disks in a tower is 3. The original problem had 64 disks.

a **Find** the minimum number of moves needed to move a tower of:

i 3 disks

ii 4 disks

iii 5 disks.

> You could use different sized coins or counters to model the tower.

b Suppose each move takes 1 second. **Find** the minimum time it would take to move a tower of:

i 3 disks

ii 5 disks

iii 6 disks.

c The minimum number of moves for a tower of n disks is $2^n - 1$. **Find** the minimum time it would take to move a tower of:

i 10 disks

ii 20 disks.

3 Rope around the Earth

> The English philosopher and mathematician William Whiston first posed this in 1702.

Part 1: Wrap a rope around the equator of a basketball. What length of rope would need to be added to make the rope hover 1 inch away from the basketball's equator at all points?

Part 2: Wrap a very, very long rope around the equator of the Earth. What length of rope would need to be added to make the rope hover 1 inch above the Earth's equator at all points?

You may find this information useful.

- the diameter of a basketball is about 24 cm.

- the radius of the Earth at the equator is 6378 km.

a Before calculating the amount of rope to be added in each part of the problem, **suggest** an amount that seems reasonable to you.

b **Write down** an expression to represent the circumference of a sphere with radius r.

c **Write down** an expression to represent the circumference of a sphere with radius $(r + 1\text{ in})$. Simplify this expression.

d Hence, **find** how much string needs to be added to the circumference when adding 1 in to the radius of a sphere.

e **Determine** whether the size of the sphere matters in part **d**. Justify your answer. Now you can answer the riddle. Are you surprised?

The Columbus Problem Puzzle

In 1882, chess enthusiast and recreational mathematician Sam Loyd (1841–1911) offered a $1000 prize for the answer that best showed how to arrange the seven figures and the eight 'dots' below which would add up to 82.

$$.4 \ .5 \ .6 \ .7 \ .8 \ .9 \ .0 \ .$$

Of the several million answers submitted, only two were found to be correct. One is shown here; can you find another solution?

$$
\begin{array}{r}
80 \\
.\dot{5} \\
.\dot{9}\dot{7} \\
+ \quad .\dot{4}\dot{6} \\
\hline
82
\end{array}
\equiv 80 + \frac{55}{99} + \frac{97}{99} + \frac{46}{99} = 82
$$

---

4 24 Game

In 1988, inventor Robert Sun created the 24 Game to make mathematics appealing and accessible to children. The rules of the game are:

Rule 1 Choose four numbers between 1 and 13 at random.

Rule 2 Use all four numbers with mathematical operations and brackets, to make a total of 24.

Use problem-solving strategies to make 24 from each set:

a 7, 2, 1, 1

b 2, 3, 2, 4

c 2, 3, 4, 6

d 2, 2, 7, 12

Reflect and discuss 6

How have you explored the statement of inquiry? Give specific examples.

Statement of inquiry:

Representing numbers in different forms to simplify them can help understand human-made systems.

1.2 The number system

Global context: Globalization and sustainability

Related concept: Representation

FORM

Objectives

- Classifying the different kinds of real numbers
- Representing the different kinds of real numbers
- Knowing basic properties of real numbers and their operations

Inquiry questions

F
- What is a set?
- What kinds of sets are there?
- How are numbers classified?

C
- What are the different forms of representing numbers?
- What are properties of number sets?
- How do you round to a certain degree of accuracy?

D
- How are numbers used?
- What does it mean to be exact?
- Are some numbers more beautiful than others?

ATL Communication

Organize and depict information logically

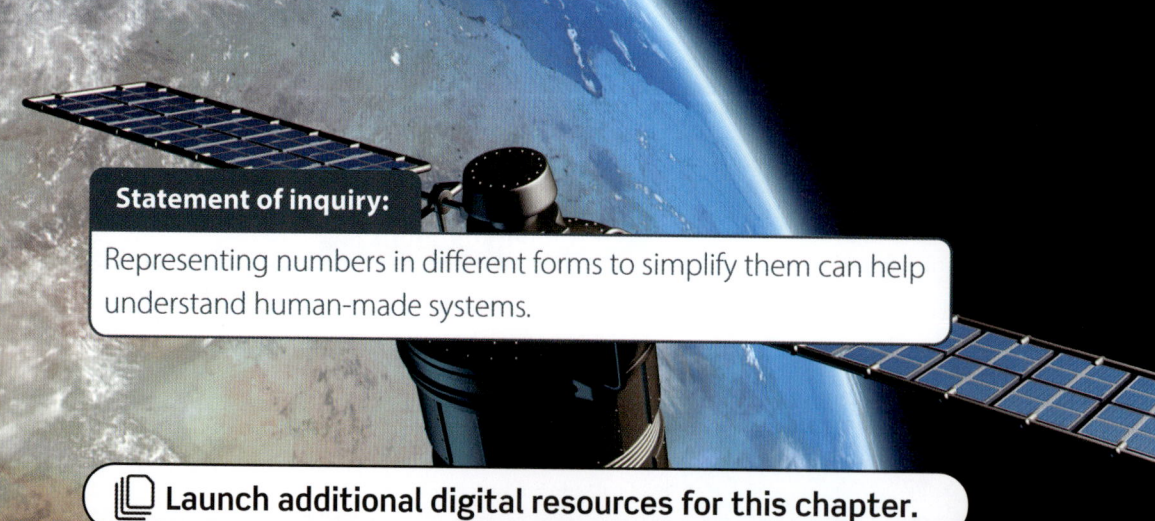

Statement of inquiry:

Representing numbers in different forms to simplify them can help understand human-made systems.

📖 **Launch additional digital resources for this chapter.**

You should already know how to:

• Describe the different types of real numbers	**1** For each number, state which number set(s) it is a member of (e.g. natural numbers, irrational numbers, etc.). **a** 7 **b** −7 **c** 0 **d** 1.5 **e** π **f** −0.1 **g** $\sqrt{14}$ **h** $\sqrt{121}$ **i** $\frac{1}{2}$ **j** $\frac{2}{3}$ **k** $1\frac{3}{4}$ **l** $-\frac{4}{3}$

 F   ## Sets

- What is a set?
- What kinds of sets are there?
- How are numbers classified?

Some examples of sets are: the set of students in your class, the set of all your subject teachers this year, the set of your favorite books, the set of parking spaces at your local supermarket.

> A **set** is a collection of objects. Each member of a set is called an **element** of the set.

You use capital letters to denote a set, and put the members of the set in curly brackets. You can describe a set using words, or by writing a list of its elements.

Sets described in words:	**Sets described by listing their elements:**
A = {my three favorite colors}	A = {blue, orange, green}
B = {vowels in the English alphabet}	B = {a, e, i, o, u}
C = {seven largest moons in the solar system}	C = {Ganymede, Titan, Callisto, Io, Earth's Moon, Europa, Triton}
D = {integers between 1 and 21}	D = {2, 3, 4, …, 20}

> The symbol $\in$ means 'is an element of'.
>
> The symbol $\notin$ means 'is not an element of'.

For example, if the set A = {16, 25, 36, 49, 64}, then $49 \in A$ but $81 \notin A$.

The order in which you write the elements of a set is not important.

B = {a, e, i, o, u} is the same as B = {e, o, u, i, a}.

In a class there are ten students aged 16, and four students aged 15.

The set of *students* in the class has 14 elements (the students' names). The set of their *ages* has only two elements: {15, 16}, not 16 written ten times and 15 written four times.

> The number of elements in a set A is written $n(A)$. It is called the **cardinality** of the set.

…

The three ellipsis dots mean 'and so on' or 'continue the pattern'. It was first used by the ancient Greeks. With sets, the ellipsis is used when writing out all the elements of a set is impractical.

For example if the set $A = \{$knife, fork, spoon$\}$ then $n(A) = 3$. If $n(A)$ is a real number, then the set A is a finite set.

You can write common number sets using set notation.

Natural numbers $\mathbb{N} = \{0, 1, 2, 3, \ldots\}$

Integers $\mathbb{Z} = \{\ldots, -3, -2, -1, 0, 1, 2, 3, \ldots\}$

Positive integers $\mathbb{Z}^+ = \{1, 2, 3, \ldots\}$

These are infinite sets, as they contain an infinite number of elements.

> Even though zero is not considered to have a positive or negative value, it is still a natural number and an integer.

Practice 1

1 List the elements of these sets, and find the number of elements in each set.

  a A is the set of the days of the week.

  b B is the set of months of the year not containing the letter r.

  c C is the set of factors of 12.

  d D is the set of positive integers less than 30 that are multiples of 4.

2 Describe each set in words.

  a $J = \{1, 3, 5, 7, 9\}$

  b $K = \{$isosceles, equilateral, right-angled, scalene$\}$

  c $L = \{$right angle, obtuse, acute, reflex$\}$

  d $M = \{4, 8, 12, 16, \ldots, 40\}$

> The symbols for numbers sets are often referred to as 'double struck' because they could be produced by double-striking a character on a typewriter, or 'blackboard bold' as they were written with the edge of the chalk on a blackboard instead of the point, to differentiate them from other bold characters.

ATL

3 Given the sets $A = \{4, 6, 8, 10\}$, $B = \{1, 8, 27, 64\}$, $C = \{1, 3, 4, 7, 11\}$ and $D = \{0, \pm1, \pm2, \pm3, \pm4\}$, state whether each statement is true or false. If the statement is false, write the correct statement.

  a $4 \in A$ **b** $7 \notin C$

  c $1 \in A$ **d** $27 \in A$

  e $8 \in D$ **f** $n(C) = n(D)$

- -

Set builder notation

In addition to describing a set in words or by listing its elements, a set can also be described using set builder notation. This uses curly brackets enclosing a variable, a vertical line, and any restrictions on the variable. It can be used for finite or infinite sets. For example, the set $A = \{1, 2, 3, \ldots 9\}$ can be written in set builder notation, which would look and read like this:

A	$=$	$\{x$	$\mid$	$x \in \mathbb{N}$	$,$	$1 \leq x \leq 9\}$
A	is the set of	all values of x	such that	x is a natural number	and	x is between 1 and 9 inclusive.

> For natural numbers, $1 \leq x \leq 9$ is equivalent to $0 < x < 10$.

Using set builder notation you can define another number set that you need to know: the rational numbers

Rational numbers: $\mathbb{Q} = \left\{ \frac{p}{q} \,\middle|\, p, q \in \mathbb{Z}, q \neq 0 \right\}$

In words, $\mathbb{Q}$ is the set of rational numbers (numbers of the form $\frac{p}{q}$) such that both p and q are integers, and q does not equal 0.

All of the integers, rational numbers and irrational numbers together form the set of real numbers, $\mathbb{R}$. The real numbers can be represented on the real number line.

> We don't have a symbol for irrational numbers. They are numbers that cannot be expressed as a fraction, for example: π or $\sqrt{2}$.

Example 1

Write these sets in set builder notation.

a S is the set of real numbers between 0 and 1

b $P = \{2, 3, 5, 7, \ldots, 37\}$

c $M = \{2, 4, 6, 8, \ldots\}$

a $S = \{x \mid x \in \mathbb{R}, 0 < x < 1\}$ ——————— Use the 'less than' symbol because 0 and 1 are not included.

b $P = \{x \mid x \in \text{primes}, 2 \leq x \leq 37\}$ ——————— There is no special symbol for prime numbers.

c $M = \{x \mid x = 2n, n \in \mathbb{Z}^+\}$ ——————— Even numbers are multiples of 2, so they can be written as $2n$.

Example 2

Write out the elements of each set in list form.

a $E = \{x \mid x \in \mathbb{Z}, -3 < x < 2\}$

b $F = \left\{ \frac{1}{n} \,\middle|\, n \in \mathbb{Z}^+ \right\}$

Describe set G in words.

c $G = \{x \mid x \in \mathbb{R}, 0 < x < 1\}$

a $E = \{-2, -1, 0, 1\}$ ——————— -3 and 2 are not included.

b $F = \left\{ 1, \frac{1}{2}, \frac{1}{3}, \frac{1}{4} \ldots \right\}$

c G is the set of real numbers greater than 0 and less than 1. —— There is no first real number greater than 0, or last real number less than 1, so you cannot list the elements of this set.

Practice 2

1 Write out the elements of each set in list form. State whether each set is finite or infinite. If the set is finite, state its cardinality.

a $\{x \,|\, x \in \mathbb{Z}, -2 < x < 5\}$

b $\{y \,|\, y \in \mathbb{Z}, y > 0\}$

c $\{a \,|\, a \in \mathbb{N}, a \text{ is a multiple of } 5\}$

d $\{b \,|\, b \in \mathbb{R}, b \text{ is a factor of } 28\}$

e $\{c \,|\, c \in \mathbb{N}, c + 3 < 8\}$

f $\{p \,|\, p \in \text{primary colors}\}$

2 Write each set using set builder notation.

a $S = \{1, 9, 25, 49, 81, \ldots\}$

b $T = \{\ldots, -10, 0, 10, 20, \ldots\}$

c U is the set of real numbers between 1 and 2, including 2.

d V is the set of rational numbers between 0 and 1.

Problem solving

3 Write in set builder notation:

a The set of odd numbers.

b The set of multiples of 3.

c $W = \{1, 2, 4, 8, 16, 32\}$

The **universal set**, U, is the set that contains all elements being considered.

The **empty set**, $\{ \}$ or $\varnothing$, is the set with no elements, so $n(\varnothing) = 0$.

For example, for the set W of winter months and set S of summer months, the universal set U is the set of months of the year.

From the universal set $U = \{\text{yellow, red, blue}\}$ you can make these sets:

$J = \varnothing$ $P = \{\text{yellow, red}\}$

$K = \{\text{yellow}\}$ $S = \{\text{yellow, blue}\}$

$L = \{\text{red}\}$ $T = \{\text{red, blue}\}$

$M = \{\text{blue}\}$ $U = \{\text{yellow, red, blue}\}$

In examinations, the universal set will be given to you in the question, when necessary.

All these sets, which can be made from the elements of U, including the empty set and U itself, are called subsets of U.

The set A is a **subset** of a set B if every element in A is also in B. The symbol for subset is $\subseteq$. Written in mathematical form: if for all $x \in A \Rightarrow x \in B$, then $A \subseteq B$.

The **empty set** is a subset of any set. So, for any set A, $\varnothing \in A$.

Every set is a subset of itself.

'$x \in A \Rightarrow x \in B$, then $A \subseteq B$' can be read as 'If for all elements in A the elements are also in B, then A is a subset of B.'

Two sets are equal if they contain exactly the same elements.

Some further examples of subsets are:

- If $A = \{1, 5\}$ and $B = \{1, 2, 3, 4, 5\}$, then $A \subseteq B$.
- If $C = \{3^n \mid n \in \mathbb{N}\}$ and $D = \{1, 3, 9, 27\}$, then $D \subseteq C$, because $D = \{3^0, 3^1, 3^2, 3^3\}$
- If $E = \{x \mid x^2 = 1\}$ and $F = \{-1, 1\}$, then $E \subseteq F$ and $F \subseteq E$ are both true. In other words, $E = F$.

You can always use the symbol $\subseteq$ to denote subset. If two sets are not equal, (when there is at least one element of A that is not in B) then you can use the symbol $\subset$ without a line underneath it. $A \subset B$ means A is a **proper subset** of B.

If $A = B$, then A is an improper subset of B, or B is an improper subset of A, and in this case you use the symbol $\subseteq$.

The symbols $\subseteq$ and $\subset$ are similar in the way they work to $\leq$ and $<$. If in doubt use $\subseteq$ as it can be used for an improper or proper subset.

Exploration 1

1 Consider a set containing two elements, for example $A = \{1, 2\}$. Write down all of its subsets.

2 Now consider a set containing three elements, for example $B = \{1, 2, 3\}$. Write down all of its subsets.

3 Do the same again for a set containing four elements.

4 Based on your findings, suggest a rule for determining the number of subsets of a set with n elements.

5 Test your rule on a set containing five elements.

> The set itself and the empty set are subsets of any given set.

The **complement** of a set A is denoted by A', and described in set notation as $A' = \{x \mid x \in U, x \notin A\}$.

For the universal set $U = \{1, 2, 3, 4, 5, 6\}$, and set $E = \{4, 6\}$, the complement of the set E is made up of the elements in the universal set that are *not* in set E. So $E' = \{1, 2, 3, 5\}$.

Reflect and discuss 1

- For the set $A = \{1, 2\}$, is every element of $\emptyset$ a member of A?

  Is there any element of $\emptyset$ that is not in A?

  Use your answers to explain why $\emptyset$ is a subset of A, and of any set.

- A generalization or general rule is 'a general statement made on the basis of specific examples'.

- What specific examples did you use in Exploration 1?

- Compare the rule you found in Exploration 1 with others in your class. Did you all get the same result? Is that enough to say that this rule is always true for any number of elements in the original set?

- Why should you be cautious when generalizing?

> Justification proves, explains or supports claims.
>
> Validity is the process of using well-founded, logical mathematics to come to a true and accurate conclusion or a reasonable interpretation of results. A valid claim can be trusted or believed.

Practice 3

1 Determine whether or not these pairs of sets are equal.

  a $\{1, 2, 3\}$; $\{2, 3, 1\}$

  b $\{1, 2, 3, 5\}$; {prime numbers less than 6}

  c $\{16, 17, 18, 19, ...\}$; {rational numbers greater than 15}

2 Determine whether these statements are true or false. If the statement is false, give a reason why.

  a $2 \in \{2, 3, 4\}$

  b $\{2\} \subseteq \{2, 3, 4\}$

  c $\{3\} \in \{2, 3, 4\}$

  d $4 \subseteq \{2, 3, 4\}$

  e Given $A = \{x \mid x \in \mathbb{Z}, 1 < x < 5\}$ and $B = \{2, 3, 4\}$, then $A = B$.

  f $1 \in \{2, 3, 4\}'$

  g $\{1, 4\} \subseteq \{2, 3, 4\}'$

Problem solving

3 Determine if the statements **a** to **d** below are true or false. For those that are false, give a counter-example (find an example that makes the statement false). You may find drawing a diagram helpful.

  a If $A \subseteq B$ and $B \subseteq C$, then $A \subseteq C$.

  b If $R \subseteq S$ then $S \subseteq R$.

  c If $p \in P$ and $P \subseteq Q$, then $p \in Q$.

  d If $A = B$, then $B \subseteq A$.

  e If $A \in B'$ and $a \in A$, then $a \in B$.

4 Write a set that has 32 subsets.

5 Determine whether or not a set can have exactly 24 subsets.

C Number sets

- What are the different forms of representing numbers?
- What are properties of number sets?
- How do you round to a certain degree of accuracy?

You are now familiar with the symbols and meanings of:

- Natural numbers (commonly known as counting numbers):
  $\mathbb{N} = \{0, 1, 2, 3,...\}$
- Integers (positive and negative counting numbers, and 0):
  $\mathbb{Z} = \{0, \pm 1, \pm 2, \pm 3,...\}$
- Rational numbers: $\mathbb{Q} = \{\frac{p}{q} \mid p, q \in z, q \neq 0\}$
- Real numbers: $\mathbb{R}$ is the universal set that contains all the numbers above and all the irrational numbers.

Exploration 2

1 Consider the numbers -3, π, $\frac{1}{5}$, $\sqrt{2}$, 0 and 35 and the sets $\mathbb{N}$, $\mathbb{Z}$, $\mathbb{Q}$, $\mathbb{R}$.

Complete the table below by placing a tick in the appropriate box if the number is an element of the set, and a cross if it is not.

	$\mathbb{N}$	$\mathbb{Z}$	$\mathbb{Q}$	$\mathbb{R}$
−3				
π				
$\frac{1}{5}$				
$\sqrt{2}$				
0				
35				

2 The Venn diagram shows the number sets $\mathbb{N}$, $\mathbb{Z}$, $\mathbb{Q}$, $\mathbb{R}$.

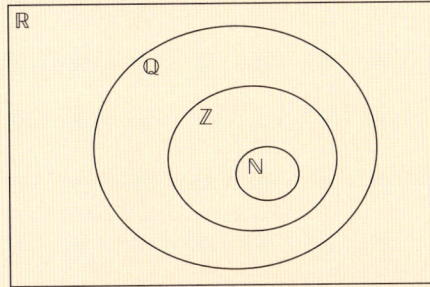

Place each of the following numbers in the appropriate region of the Venn diagram.

-3, π, $\frac{1}{5}$, $\sqrt{2}$, 0 and 35

3 Given that A' is the complement of set A, define a set for π and $\sqrt{2}$.

4 Given the set of integers, $\mathbb{Z}$, the set of rational numbers, $\mathbb{Q}$, and the set of real numbers, $\mathbb{R}$:

   a write down an element that belongs to sets $\mathbb{R}$ and $\mathbb{Z}$

   b write down an element that belongs to sets $\mathbb{Q}$ and $\mathbb{Z}'$

   c write down an element that belongs to set $\mathbb{Q}'$.

Reflect and discuss 2

- Give your own definitions of each of the number sets.

- Which numbers are the hardest to place in the sets? Give reasons for your answers.

- Can you think of any numbers that do not fit into the Venn diagram?

- Number systems are human-made systems. Discuss whether it is easy to categorize numbers using these number systems.

Looking at different representations of the classification of numbers helps us to understand the characteristics of each set of numbers. The set builder notation helps us to understand that a rational number is a number that can be written as a fraction.

Exploration 3

The following tree diagram is another way to represent the classification of real numbers.

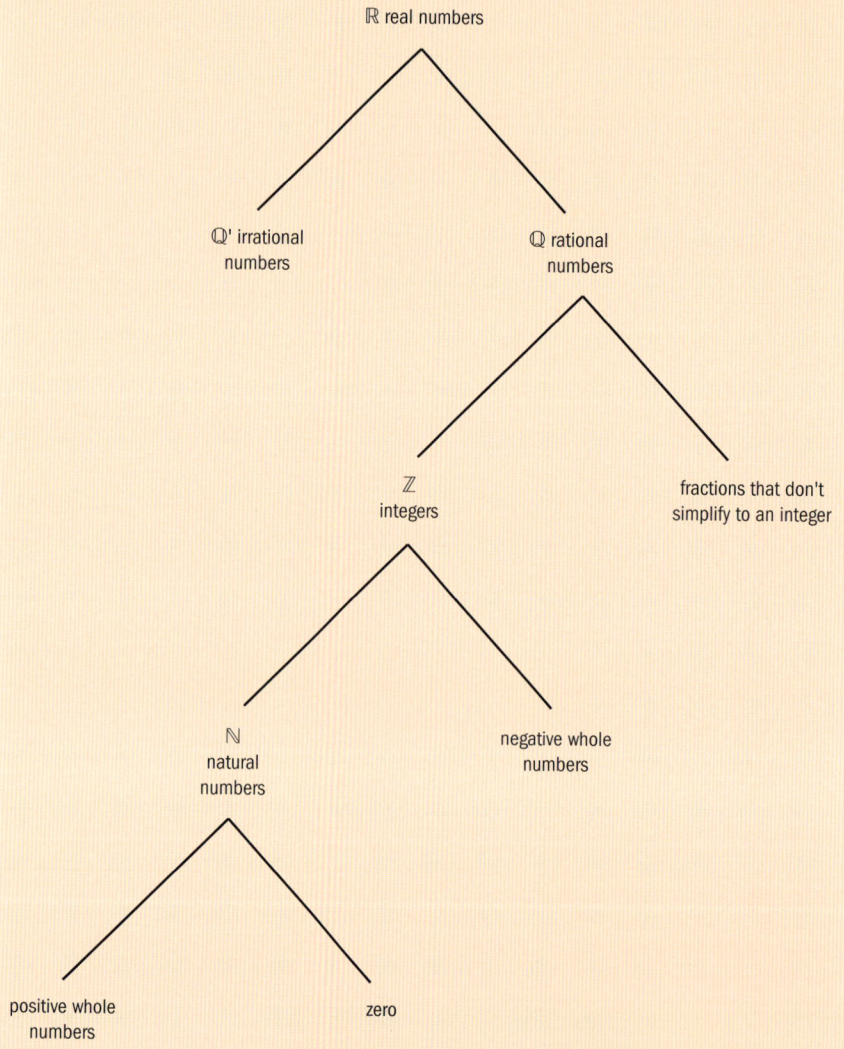

1 Justify whether each statement is always true, sometimes true, or never true:

a $0 \in \mathbb{Z}$

b $0 \in \mathbb{Q}$

c $\mathbb{N} \subset \mathbb{Q}$

d $\mathbb{Q} \subset \mathbb{N}$

e $\mathbb{Q} \subset \mathbb{Q}'$

f $\{\frac{a}{b} \mid, a \in \mathbb{Q}', b \in \mathbb{Z}, b \neq 0\} \subset \mathbb{Z}$

g $\mathbb{Q} \subset \mathbb{Z}$

h $\{a \mid \sqrt{a}, a \in \mathbb{R}\} \subset \mathbb{Q}'$

▶ Continued on next page

The oldest traces of numbers are in the form of piles of bones, or tally marks, most probably used to count.

The number zero is one of the newest numbers, appearing very late in the history of numbers. It appeared much later than counting numbers, rational and even irrational numbers. It is difficult to determine exactly when zero was first used, as it had a different significance at different times. Zero has been used to signify 'nothingness', to indicate the absence of a number, or as a placeholder in place value number systems. Only recently was it considered to be an actual number.

Negative numbers first appeared in China around 200BC for commercial and tax calculations. Red rods and black rods cancelled each other out. More red rods meant the total amount was positive, whereas more black rods meant the amount was negative.

Number lines are also used to represent the set of real numbers.

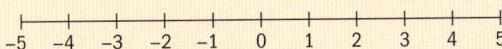

$$-5 \quad -4 \quad -3 \quad -2 \quad -1 \quad 0 \quad 1 \quad 2 \quad 3 \quad 4 \quad 5$$

2 Place the following numbers on your own number line (use your calculator to help you):

a 0   **b** 1   **c** -4

d 5   **e** $\dfrac{1}{2}$ **f** $\dfrac{15}{4}$

g $\dfrac{24}{6}$ **h** $-\dfrac{2}{3}$ **i** $-\dfrac{12}{5}$

j π **k** $\sqrt{2}$ **l** $-\sqrt{4}$

m $-\sqrt{20}$

3 Use your number line to review (and adapt) your answers to question **1**.

A common way of representing the number sets is using a Venn diagram (you will learn more about Venn diagrams in Unit 4).

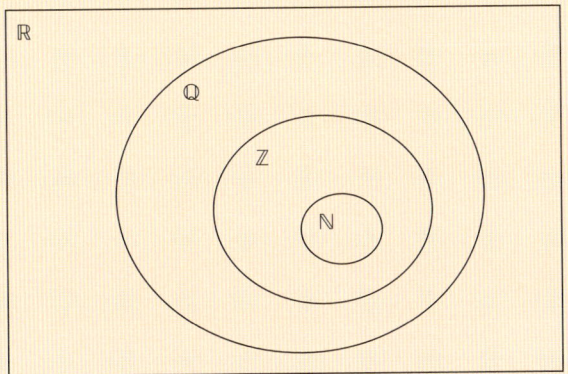

4 Use the Venn diagram to review (and adapt) your answers to question **1**.

5 Write two more statements to add to question **1**, and justify whether your statements are always true, sometimes true or never true.

Reflect and discuss 3

- Why are the symbols $\mathbb{R}$, $\mathbb{Z}$, $\mathbb{Q}$, and $\mathbb{N}$ used for the corresponding sets they represent?

- Why do we call $\mathbb{R}$ the set of real numbers?

- Do numbers exist that are not real numbers? If so, which ones?

Any number that can be placed on a number line is a real number. Real numbers can thus be ordered and compared. Real numbers also behave in certain characteristic ways when performing the operations of addition or multiplication. We call these characteristic behaviors the *properties* of real numbers.

> When drawing a number line, equal amounts must be represented by the same interval. The distance between each whole number must be equal. So for example, the number 3.5 should be placed exactly halfway between 3 and 4.

Properties of real numbers

For all real numbers a, b, and c, and the operations + and x:

- Commutative property:
  - $a + b = b + a$
  - $a \times b = b \times a$
- Associative property:
  - $a + (b + c) = (a + b) + c$
  - $a \times (b \times c) = (a \times b) \times c$
- Identity:
  - 0 is identity for the set of real numbers under addition because $a + 0 = 0 + a = a$.
  - 1 is the identity for the set of real numbers under multiplication because $a \times 1 = 1 \times a = a$.
- Inverse:
  - For any $a \in \mathbb{R}$, $-a$ is the inverse element for addition because $a + (-a) = (-a) + a = 0$, where 0 is the identity element for addition.
  - For any $a \in \mathbb{R}$, $\frac{1}{a} \in \mathbb{R}$, $a \neq 0$ is the inverse element for multiplication because $a \times \frac{1}{a} = \frac{1}{a} \times a = 1$ where 1 is the identity element for multiplication.
- Distributive property:
  - $a(b + c) = ab + ac$ or $(a + b)c = ac + bc$
  - Multiplication distributes over addition.

Practice 4

1 Complete the following table by giving an example for each property. Use different real numbers each time.

Property name	Addition	Multiplication
Commutative		
Associative		
Identity		
Inverse		

2 Justify why subtraction of real numbers is neither commutative nor associative.

3 Justify why division of real numbers is neither commutative nor associative.

4 Name the property that corresponds to each statement.

a $14 + (-12) = (-12) + 14$

b $\pi \times 1 = 1 \times \pi$

c $0 + \sqrt{2} = \sqrt{2}$

d $4\left(\frac{2}{3} + \frac{1}{2}\right) = \frac{8}{3} + 2$

e $6.8 \times 1 = 6.8$

f $\frac{1}{2} + \left(\frac{1}{3} + \frac{1}{6}\right) = \left(\frac{1}{2} + \frac{1}{3}\right) + \frac{1}{6}$

g $0 + (-\sqrt{4}) = (-\sqrt{4}) + 0$

h $(2 \times 3) \times 4 = 2 \times (3 \times 4)$

5 Justify each step in the following equalities using the properties of real numbers:

$(x + 4)(x + 5)$

a $\qquad = x(x + 5) + 4(x + 5)$

b $\qquad = (x^2 + 5x) + (4x + 20)$

c $\qquad = x^2 + (5x + 4x) + 20$

d $\qquad = x^2 + 9x + 20$

Properties of real numbers are used to justify solutions by creating equivalent expressions when solving problems involving equations. These properties are true for all real numbers.

Approximating numbers

Some real numbers, such as integers, can easily be written as exact amounts. However, rational and irrational numbers are often approximated to simplify calculations.

There are two ways of approximating numbers:

1 Rounding to a specific place value (often a power of ten)

2 Rounding to a certain number of significant figures.

In either method, rounding a number to a certain degree of accuracy means that we are going to choose the closest one of two numbers that the original number is between. This is what it would look like visually:

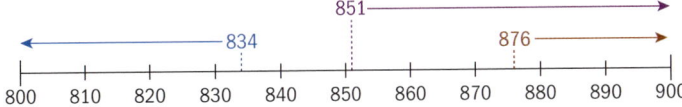

To the nearest hundred, any number between 800 and 900 will be rounded to the closest one of the two. Any number smaller than 850 is rounded to 800, whereas 850 and any number larger than 850 will be rounded up.

> The convention is that we round up when a number is exactly in the middle of two rounding numbers.

Exploration 4

1 Round 34 642 to the nearest 1000, by plotting the following amounts on a number line:

a The nearest thousand below 34 642

b The nearest thousand above 34 642

c 34 642

2 Describe how you could round the same amount to the nearest 100 without using a number line. Then round 34 642 to the nearest 100.

▶ Continued on next page

3 During the Football World Cup in Brazil 2014, one match had a spectator attendance of 53 492. This number can be represented to varying degrees of accuracy. Using your method from the previous step, round the following numbers:

a Round 53 492 to the nearest 10 000.

b Round 53 492 to the nearest 1000.

c Round 53 492 to the nearest 100.

d Round 53 492 to the nearest 10.

4 Use the same method to round π to the following number of decimal places. (Hint: $\pi = 3.14159265358979323846264338327950288419716 9 3993751...$ As an irrational number, the number of digits following the decimal place goes on forever.)

a Round π to the nearest unit.

b Round π to the nearest tenth.

c Round π to the nearest hundredth.

d Round π to the nearest thousandth.

e Round π to the nearest hundred-thousandth.

5 Back to the football game in Brazil with 53 492 spectators.

a List the digits that make up the number 53 492.

b If all the digits were replaced by 0 except one, determine which digit you would keep in order to be as close as possible to 53 492.

c If all the digits were replaced by 0 except two, determine which two digits you would keep in order to be as close as possible to 53 492.

d If all the digits were replaced by 0 except three, determine which three digits you would keep in order to be as close as possible to 53 492.

In the number 53 492, 5 is the most significant figure, as 53 492 is closer to 50 000 than to 3000, 400, 90 or 2. The next significant figure is 3, 4 is the third most significant figure, and so on.

6 Write down the number 53 492 with only three significant figures and zeros. (Hint: Writing a number with only its first few digits followed by trailing zeros is called *truncating*.)

7 This time, round 53 492 to a number that has three significant figures. (Hint: You should not obtain the same result as for the previous question. Justify why not.)

8 Determine which of your two previous answers 53 492 is closest to.

9 Explain the importance of using 0's when rounding a five-digit number to three significant figures.

10 Determine the three most significant figures of 0.00034695.

11 Truncate and then round 0.00034695 to three significant figures. Determine whether you obtain the same number.

For example:

- 5400 has 2 significant figures
- 5040 has 3 significant figures
- 504 has 3 significant figures
- 504.0 has 4 significant figures

- 50.4 has 3 significant figures
- 5.04 has 3 significant figures
- 0.504 has 3 significant figures
- 0.5040 has 4 significant figures

Practice 5

1 Round the following numbers to the nearest 10 000:

   a 36 753   **b** 689 064

   c 9 999 999   **d** 63 893

2 Round the following numbers to the nearest 100:

   a 2984   **b** 14 099

   c 850   **d** 6757

3 Round the following numbers to the nearest 1000:

   a 65 487   **b** 689 064

   c 9 999 999   **d** 63 893

4 Write the following numbers correct to one decimal place:

   a 12.076   **b** 324.567   **c** 23.608

   d 34.657   **e** 1.399 99

5 Write the following numbers correct to two decimal places:

   a 12.076   **b** 324.567   **c** 23.608

   d 34.657   **e** 1.399 99

6 Write down the following rounded to three significant figures:

   a 23 908   **b** 34 565   **c** 421 235

   d 2314   **e** 26 678   **f** 0.034 64

   g 0.000 324

7 Write down the following rounded to two significant figures:

a 23 908

b 34 565

c 421 235

d 2314

e 26 678

f 0.034 64

g 0.000 324

8 Find the correct approximations:

	2 decimal places	3 decimal places	3 significant figures
3.141 592 5			
2.718 28			
234.5678			
3.1782			
51.235			
0.001 235 6			
0.040 022 3			

9 Calculate the following, giving your answers to three significant figures:

a 2.345×3.432

b $\dfrac{2.432}{2.678}$

c 2.54^2

d $\dfrac{2.43 \times 2.64}{8.9523}$

e $5.6 \div 2.567$

f $3.43^3 \times 0.23^2$

Estimations

Even though many calculations can be done with a calculator, it is often useful to estimate the answer using approximations. This helps to have a ball-park figure for an answer, to know if our calculations are correct or not.

Example 3

A rectangular box has dimensions length 34 cm, width 24 cm and height 67 cm.

Estimate the volume.

$30 \times 20 \times 70$	In this case you may choose to round each quantity to one significant figure (or to the nearest 10).
42 000 cm³	This is an *estimate* of the volume of the box.

Reflect and discuss 4

- The actual answer is 54 672 cm³. Why do you think your estimate was quite far away from this?

- How could you improve the estimate?

Practice 6

1 Estimate the answers to the following questions:

a 23×49

b $\dfrac{504}{28}$

c 0.199×7.023

d $78 + 49 + 22 + 34 + 64$

e $\dfrac{233}{19}$

f $\dfrac{23 \times 49}{105}$

2 Estimate the area of each shape.

a

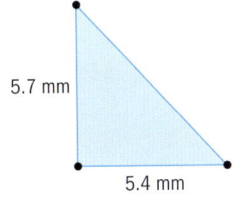

b

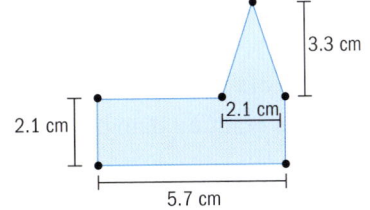

c

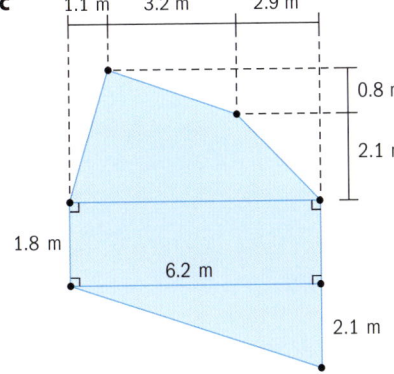

d

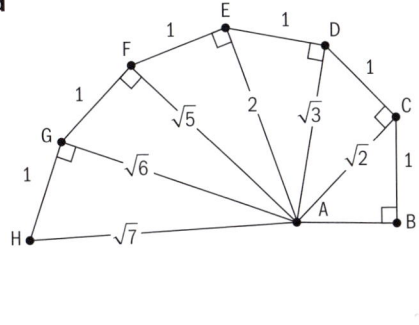

$$\sqrt{1} = 1$$
$$\sqrt{2} = 1.414$$
$$\sqrt{3} = 1.732$$
$$\sqrt{4} = 2$$
$$\sqrt{4} = 2.236$$
$$\sqrt{6} = 2.449$$
$$\sqrt{7} = 2.646$$

3 You have $50. Without doing an exact calculation, determine whether you can afford all the items below.

Shopping list	
Three boxes of cereal	$4.95 per box
Six liters of milk	$1.25 per liter
One loaf of bread	$3.50 per loaf
2 kg of potatoes	$3.00 per kg
6 bottles of water	$1.20 per bottle
500 g of broccoli	$5.00 per kg
6 apples	$0.75 each

Reflect and discuss 5

- When is it better to use an exact amount, and when is it better to use an estimate?

- Give examples of situations in your daily life when getting a precise answer is impossible, inconvenient or unnecessary.

D Approximations and accuracy

- How are numbers used?
- What does it mean to be exact?
- Are some numbers more beautiful than others?

Different representations for the classification of real numbers help us understand how they behave. Real numbers can be used in different ways. One way to classify numbers is by purpose. For example, numbers can be used for counting, measuring, ranking, or labeling.

Reflect and discuss 6

- Can you think of other ways that numbers are used?

- How would you represent the classification of real numbers referring to their purpose?

- Which numbers are suitable or unsuitable for each purpose? For example, can $\sqrt{2}$ be used to count something.

- Which numbers are often approximated?

Exploration 5

1 Complete the following table in this order:

   a Write down the square roots that are integers in both the second and third column.

   b Without resorting to a calculator, and using what you notice about the distribution of the integers in the table, complete the second column with your estimates for the values of the rest of the square roots.

   c Finally, use a calculator to give the actual values for each square root in the third column.

▶ Continued on next page

Square root	Estimate	Calculator value
$\sqrt{1}$		
$\sqrt{2}$		
$\sqrt{3}$		
$\sqrt{4}$		
...		
...		
$\sqrt{25}$		

2 Discuss how this procedure could help you estimate values for any square root, such as $\sqrt{50}$, $\sqrt{75}$, $\sqrt{17}$, or $\sqrt{33}$.

3 Discuss whether or not it would be appropriate to use the estimations for square roots in the second column of the following table.

Square root	Estimate	Calculator value
$\sqrt{4}$	2	2
$\sqrt{5}$	2.2	2.236 068
$\sqrt{6}$	2.4	2.449 489 7
$\sqrt{7}$	2.6	2.645 751 3
$\sqrt{8}$	2.8	2.828 427 1
$\sqrt{9}$	3	3

4 Different calculators sometimes give different values for irrational numbers. These are the values for $\sqrt{3}$ given on three different calculators: 1.732 05, 1.732 050 8, 1.732 050 807 57

a Explain why different calculators give different values for $\sqrt{3}$.

b Discuss why no calculator value for $\sqrt{3}$ is exact.

All irrational numbers, such as $\sqrt{5}$ or π, have an infinite number of decimal places – that is often a sign that they are irrational. Yet, not all infinite decimal numbers are irrational. Some can be written as a fraction, and are therefore rational numbers. Some can even be written as whole numbers.

Exploration 6

1 If $x = 0.024\,242\,424\ldots$, write down the following amounts as decimal numbers.

a $1000x$ b $10x$ c $990x$ (Hint: $1000x - 10x = 990x$)

2 Hence, state which fraction is equal to the infinite decimal number $0.024\,242\,424\ldots$

▶ Continued on next page

3 If $x = 0.999\,999\,999\ldots$, write down the following amounts as decimal numbers.

   a $10x$ **b** x **c** $9x$ (Hint: $10x - x = 9x$)

4 Hence, state which whole number is equal to the infinite decimal number $0.999\,999\,999\ldots$

5 Just like calculators can give different values for irrational numbers (as seen in the previous exploration), they can also give different values for rational numbers. For example, the same calculators as the previous exploration gave these decimal numbers for $\frac{2}{3}$: $0.666\,67$, $0.666\,666\,7$, $0.666\,666\,666\,67$

   a Explain how these decimal numbers are only approximations of the fraction $\frac{2}{3}$

   b Determine whether it is possible to write $\frac{2}{3}$ exactly as a decimal.

   c State how many decimal places would be needed in order to write $\frac{2}{3}$ as a decimal without approximating it.

When represented in decimal notation, some numbers cannot be written exactly, as they would require an infinite number of decimal places. However, represented in a different way, these numbers can be understood as an exact amount.

- π is *exactly* the number of times the diameter fits into the circumference.
- $\sqrt{2}$ is the *exact* length of the hypotenuse of an isosceles right-angled triangle where the legs both have length 1.
- $\frac{2}{3}$ is the *exact* amount of cake you have left if you divide it into three equal shares and eat one of them.

> When an answer is asked to be given in an 'exact' form, it should always be given as an integer, a fraction or an irrational number where appropriate.

Reflect and discuss 7

- If no calculator can give an exact value for $\sqrt{3}$, does its exact value even exist?

- If an infinite number of decimal places are needed to represent the exact value for $\frac{2}{3}$ as a decimal number, does its exact value exist?

- Why are some numbers represented by an infinite number of digits in one human-made numbering system, when they can also be represented differently using a finite number of digits?

- What sort of answers will you give when you are asked to give exact answers?

- Are exact numbers or approximations more useful in real-world situations?

- Why do mathematicians think of numbers such as π, $\sqrt{2}$ or $\frac{2}{3}$ as 'beautiful' numbers?

Summary

A **set** is a collection of objects. Each member of a set is called an **element** of the set.

The **cardinality** of a set, **n(A)**, is the number of elements in a set A.

The **universal set**, U, is the set that contains all elements being considered.

The **empty set**, { } or $\varnothing$, is the set with no elements, so $n(\varnothing) = 0$.

The symbol $\in$ means 'is an element of'.

The symbol $\notin$ means 'is not an element of'.

The **complement** of set A, **A′**, is described as $A' = \{x \mid x \in U, x \notin A\}$.

The set A is a **subset** of a set B if every element in A is also in B. This is written as $A \subseteq B$.

The empty set is a subset of any set. So, for any set A, $\varnothing \subseteq A$.

Every set is a subset of itself.

Two sets are equal if they contain exactly the same elements.

Number sets:

- **Natural numbers** $\mathbb{N} = \{0, 1, 2, 3 \ldots\}$
- **Integers** $\mathbb{Z} = \{\ldots, -3, -2, -1, 0, 1, 2, 3 \ldots\}$
- **Positive integers** $\mathbb{Z}^+ = \{1, 2, 3 \ldots\}$
- **Rational numbers:** $\mathbb{Q} = \left\{ \frac{p}{q} \mid p, q \in \mathbb{Z}, q \neq 0 \right\}$
- **Real numbers** $\mathbb{R}$ represents the set of all real numbers

Rounding a number to a certain degree of accuracy means choosing the closest one of two numbers that the original number is in between.

The convention is that when a number is exactly in the middle of two rounding numbers, then we round up.

Exact numbers are represented in the following ways:

- As a decimal number with a finite number of decimal places
- As a fraction (if its decimal equivalent has an infinite number of recurring decimals)
- As a square root (irrational number)
- As a letter of its own, such as π or e (special irrational numbers)

Rules for determining the number of significant figures

These figures ARE significant:

- all non-zero figures
- all zeros between the significant figures
- all zeros that are the last digit after the decimal point

These figures are NOT significant:

- all zeros before the first non-zero figure
- all zeros after the last significant figure but before the decimal point

Mixed practice

1 Let D = {a deck of 52 playing cards}, R = {red cards}, B = {black cards}, H = {cards that are hearts}, Q = {cards that are queens} and N = {cards that have a number on them}.

   a State the cardinality of each set D, R, B, H, Q, N.

   b Determine whether the following statements are true or false. For each one justify your answer.

     i   the queen of hearts $\in R$

     ii   the queen of hearts $\in N$

     iii   the king of hearts $\in H$

    iv   10 of hearts $\notin Q$

    v $R \subseteq Q$

    vi $Q \subseteq R$

    vii $H \subseteq R$

    viii $N = Q'$

    ix $B = R'$

2 **Determine** whether the following statements are true or false. For each one justify your answer.

   a $1.25 \in \mathbb{Q}$ **b** $\pi \in \mathbb{Q}$

   c {prime numbers} $\subseteq \mathbb{N}$ **d** $\dfrac{17}{10} \in \mathbb{N}$

   e {prime numbers} $\subseteq \mathbb{Z}'$ **f** $\sqrt{196} \in \mathbb{Q}$

3 **Find** the correct approximations

	1 decimal place	3 decimal places	3 significant figures
0.1825			
4.253 83			
15.3682			
0.003 823 6			
236 468			
0.076 027			

4 **Estimate** the value of square roots

   a Without using a calculator, which whole numbers is $\sqrt{32}$ between?

b Use a calculator to complete the following table.

n	n²
5	
5.1	
5.2	
5.3	
5.4	
5.5	
5.6	
5.7	
5.8	
5.9	
6	

   c Use the results in the previous table to **approximate** the value of $\sqrt{32}$ to the nearest tenth. Justify your choice.

   d Use a calculator to give the value of $\sqrt{32}$ to 5 significant figures. **Discuss** whether your approximation in the previous answer is acceptable.

   e Use the results in the previous table to **approximate** the value of $\sqrt{26}$ to the nearest tenth. Justify your choice.

   f Use a calculator to give the value of $\sqrt{26}$ to 5 significant figures. **Discuss** whether your approximation in the previous answer is acceptable.

Reflect and discuss 8

How have you explored the statement of inquiry? Give specific examples.

Statement of inquiry:

Representing numbers in different forms to simplify them can help understand human-made systems.

1.3 Laws of exponents and scientific notation

Global context: Globalization and sustainability

Related concept: Quantity

Objectives

- Review the laws of exponents
- Understanding the meaning of zero and negative exponents
- Perform calculations using scientific notation
- Deciding when to use scientific notation for calculations

Inquiry questions

F
- What are the laws of exponents?
- What does a negative exponent mean?
- What does exponent 0 mean?

C
- How do different forms represent quantities?
- How do different forms simplify calculations?

D
- How big is huge? How small is tiny?
- Do we really understand the very large or very small quantities that we are able to represent and use in calculations?

FORM

ATL Communication

Use and interpret a range of discipline-specific terms and symbols

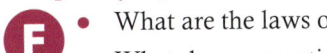

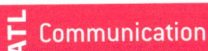

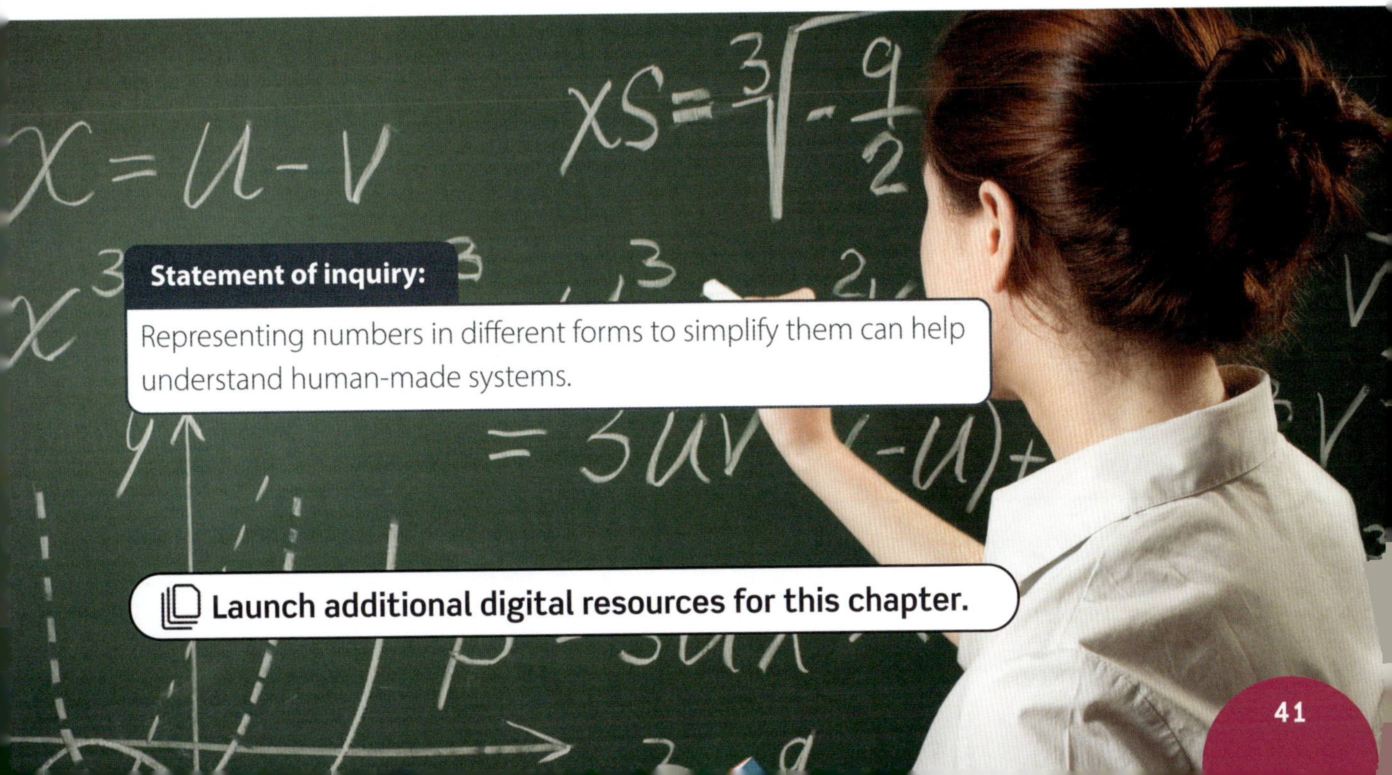

Statement of inquiry:

Representing numbers in different forms to simplify them can help understand human-made systems.

Launch additional digital resources for this chapter.

You should already know how to:

• evaluate exponents	**1** Evaluate the following amounts: **a** 5^3 **b** $(-2)^5$ **c** $(-7)^2$
• simplify expressions with exponents	**2** Use the laws of exponents to simplify the following expressions: **a** $4^3 \times 4^8$ **b** $3^5 \times (-2)^5$ **c** $12^{15} \div 12^2$ **d** $(-48)^7 \div 4^7$ **e** $(2^4)^3$
• use scientific notation to write and interpret numbers	**3** Write the following numbers in decimal form: **a** 3.739×10^7 **b** 9.2102×10^{-3}
• perform operations on numbers using scientific notation	**4** Evaluate each of the following. Leave your final answers in scientific notation. **a** $(3.5 \times 10^8) \times 21\,000$ **b** $0.000\,15 \div (50 \times 10^{-5})$ **c** $(7.1 \times 10^3) + (4.6 \times 10^2)$ **5** Write the following numbers in scientific notation: **a** $0.000\,1199$ **b** $10\,006$ **c** 735.7756

F Laws of exponents

- What are the laws of exponents?
- What does a negative exponent mean?
- What does exponent 0 mean?

Laws of exponents: for $a, b \in \mathbb{R}$, $m, n \in \mathbb{N}$

- Product rules:
  - $a^m \times a^n = a^{m+n}$
  - $a^n \times b^n = (ab)^n$ (power of products)
- Quotient rules:
  - $\dfrac{a^m}{a^n} = a^{m-n}$
  - $\dfrac{a^n}{b^n} = \left(\dfrac{a}{b}\right)^n$ (power of quotients)
- Power rule: $(a^m)^n = a^{mn}$

Laws of exponents are used to simplify expressions with exponents. Numbers can have a negative base or a negative exponent (or both), but a negative base and a negative exponent behave differently and don't have the same impact on the final number.

- -

Exploration 1

1 Use the laws of exponents to simplify the following expressions as much as possible (if necessary, leave your final answer as a power).

  a $(-1)^2$

  b $(-1)^7$

  c $(-9)^3 \times (-9)^4$

  d $(-3)^5 \times (-3)^7$

  e $(-5)^2 \times (-9)^4$

2 Based on your results, explain how the exponent affects a number with a negative base. Determine for which exponents a number with a negative base is positive or negative.

3 Use the laws of exponents to simplify the following expressions. Leave your answer as a power.

  a $2^5 \times 2^0$

  b $(-7)^0 \times (-7)^3$

  c $3^3 \div 3^0$

  d $14^6 \div 14^6$

4 Based on your results, explain why, for $a \neq 0$, a^0 is always equal to 1.

5 Use the laws of exponents to simplify the following expressions. Leave your answer as a power.

  a $2^3 \div 2^5$

  b $3 \div 3^{10}$

  c $20^0 \div 20^2$

  d $(-5)^0 \div (-5)^3$

6 Based on your results, explain what a^{-n} means for $a \neq 0$ and $n \in \mathbb{N}$.

7 Evaluate the following powers of 0:

  a 0^5

  b 0^2

  c 0^{-4}

8 Based on your previous answers, determine the value of 0^a if $a \in \mathbb{Z}$, $a \neq 0$.

9 Evaluate the following powers with exponent 0:

  a 5^0

  b 2^0

  c $(-4)^0$

10 Based on your previous answers, determine the value of b^0 if $b \in \mathbb{R}$, $b \neq 0$.

11 Using you answers from the previous four questions, justify why it would be impossible to give a value to 0^0, hence why it is undetermined.

12 Using a similar reasoning, justify why it would be impossible to have a negative exponent when the base is 0.

Reflect and discuss 1

1 Determine whether each statement is always true, sometimes true or never true. Justify using examples or counterexamples.

a If $a < 0$, then $a^b < 0$, $b \in \mathbb{Z}$.

b If $a > 0$, then $a^b < 0$, $b \in \mathbb{Z}$.

c If $b < 0$, $b \in \mathbb{Z}$ then $a^b < 0$.

d If $b > 0$, $b \in \mathbb{Z}$ then $a^b < 0$.

2 Determine which values for a and b make $a^b < 0$ and which values make $a^b > 0$. Write these conditions with as few statements as possible.

For any number $a \in \mathbb{R}$, $a \neq 0$ and $n \in \mathbb{N}$, the following rules apply:

• Zero power rule: $a^0 = 1$

• Negative power rule: $a^{-n} = \dfrac{1}{a^n}$

Practice 1

1 Evaluate the following expressions. Write down your answers as simplified fractions without exponents.

a $\left(\dfrac{3}{5}\right)^{-3}$

b $(2^3 4^2)$

c $\dfrac{1}{2}\left(\dfrac{128}{2^5}\right)^{-3}$

d $3\left(\dfrac{3^6}{243}\right)$

e $\left(\dfrac{6}{9}\right)^{-2}$

f $\left(-\dfrac{(-6)^4}{4^2}\right)^{-1}$

g $\left(\dfrac{12^5}{4^3}\right)\left(\dfrac{3^0}{9}\right)(2^0 3^{-3})$

h $-\left(-\left(\dfrac{6^3}{4^2}\right)^0\right)\left(\dfrac{6^3}{4^2}\right)^{-1}$

2 Simplify the following expressions. Write down the answers with only positive exponents.

a $(3a^3 b^2)^3$

b $-(2c^3 d^{-1})^0$

c $(e^{-5} f^2 g)^3 (efg)$

d $\dfrac{5h^3 i^{-2}}{hi}$

e $\left(\dfrac{-16jkl^2}{2j^2 k^{-2}l}\right)^{-2}$

f $\left(\dfrac{6m^5 n^{-2} o}{m^{-5} n o^{-3}}\right)^{-1}\left(\dfrac{-36mo}{n}\right)$

g $\left(\dfrac{9p^{11} q^4}{q^0 p^7}\right)\left(\dfrac{pq}{3}\right)^{-1}$

h $\left(\dfrac{s^2 t^{-3} u}{s^3 tu^{-4}}\right)\left(\dfrac{st^{-1}u}{s^2 t^3}\right)$

C Standard form (scientific notation)

- How do different forms represent quantities?
- How do different forms simplify calculations?

We can write amounts using different representations. We can represent numbers in decimal form, or we can represent them using scientific notation.

Standard form (scientific notation)

$a \times 10^n$ where $1 \le a < 10$, $a \in \mathbb{R}$ and $n \in \mathbb{Z}$

ATL

Exploration 2

1 State whether each of the following numbers is written in scientific notation. Then write each one in decimal form.

   a $a = 13.14 \times 10^6$ **b** $b = 9.99 \times 10^{-5}$

   c $c = 7.24 \times 10^0$ **d** $d = 62.05 \times 10^{-2}$

   e $e = 7.93 \times 10^{-1}$ **f** $f = 2.01 \times 10^4$

   g $g = 0.37 \times 10^3$

2 Evaluate each of the following expressions using the previous values. Choose which representation (decimal form or standard form) is more suitable to perform each operation.

   a $b \times e$ **b** $b + e$

   c $a \div f$ **d** $a - f$

   e $9d \times 8e$ **f** $9d - 8e$

   g $3c \times 2g$ **h** $3c + 2g$

   i $a \div 100b$ **j** $a + 100b$

   k $(a \times 150g)^2$ **l** $(a - 150g)^2$

Reflect and discuss 2

- When is it more useful to use the scientific form than the decimal form to represent numbers?

- When is it more useful to use the decimal form than the scientific form to represent numbers?

- Why do you think standard form is also called 'scientific' form? In which areas of science is scientific notation useful?

Scientific notation is used mostly in scientific domains that deal with very large or very small amounts. For example, galactic distances are very large, whereas molecular biology or atomic physics use numbers that are very small.

The standard units of measurement, the **SI base units**, are mostly metric units that are defined by the International System of Units (SI). The table below shows some of the base units of measurement used on Earth.

Type of measurement	Standard unit	References
Time	Second	60 seconds in a minute, 60 minutes in an hour, 24 hours in a day.
Mass	Kilogram	1 kg is the mass of 1L (or 1 dm³ of water). 1 kg = 1000 g. Grams are used for cooking. Kilograms are used to weigh people and larger objects.
Length or distance	Meter	$1 \text{ cm} = \frac{1}{100}$ m. Centimeters are used to measure lengths of objects we can hold. 1 km = 1000 m. Kilometers are used to measure distances between places.

In astronomy, measurements require huge amounts of earthly units of measurements, which would involve calculations with extremely large numbers. This can prove to be highly impractical. Therefore, in astronomy, a different set of reference units are used, called the **astronomical system of units**. In the table below are some of the base units of measurement in the astronomical system.

Type of measurement	Standard unit	References
Time	Day	1 day = 86 400 seconds. There are 365.25 days in one year on Earth.
Mass	Solar mass	The solar mass is equal to the mass of the Sun, which is equivalent to 1.982×10^{30} kg.
Distance	Astronomical unit of length	The astronomical unit of length is the average distance between the Sun and the Earth, which is equivalent to 149 597 870.7 km. It is mostly used to measure distances between planets within our solar system.
	Light year	A light year is the distance light travels in one year, which is equivalent to 9 460 730 472 580.8 km. Light years are commonly used to measure distances between stars outside of the solar system.
	Parsec	A parsec is about 3.1×10^{13} km. A parsec is preferred by astronomers to measure distances on a galactic scale.

Practice 2

1 Based on the information in the tables on the previous page, calculate the following. Leave your answers in scientific notation and correct to three significant figures where applicable.

   a Find the number of grams in a solar mass.

   b Find the number of seconds in a year. (There are 365.25 days in one year on Earth).

   c Find the number of astronomical units in a light year.

   d Find the number of light years in a parsec.

   e Find the number of astronomical units in a parsec.

2 Planetary distances. The closest planet to the Sun, Mercury, is 66 177 000 km from the Sun. The farthest planet, Pluto, is 5 906 380 000 km from the Sun. Earth is 151 870 000 km from the Sun. Calculate the following, rounding your answers to three significant figures.

   a Calculate how many times farther Pluto is from the Sun than Mercury.

   b Calculate how many times farther Earth is from the Sun than Mercury.

   c Calculate how many times farther Pluto is from the Sun than Earth.

D Going to extremes

- How big is huge? How small is tiny?
- Do we really understand the very large or very small quantities that we are able to represent and use in calculations?

It is sometimes difficult to grasp the size of very large or very small quantities when the numbers are written in different forms. Scientific notation makes it easy to perform calculations using such numbers, but does it help us grasp the actual size of the amounts that are being dealt with?

Exploration 3

Are millionaires and billionaires equally rich? Can we put them in the same category of richness? To compare large amounts, it is often helpful to represent them in different ways.

1 Write down 1 million and 1 billion in both decimal form and scientific notation.

2 Calculate these same amounts using different types of measurement.

- The amount of time in 1 million seconds and the amount of time in 1 billion seconds.
- The distance in 1 million millimeters and the distance in 1 billion millimeters.

A good way to understand extreme amounts or sizes is by representing them in a different way that is easier to grasp or visualize. Quantities can be represented using different forms (such as decimal or scientific form). Quantities can also be represented and compared using different types of measurement (such as currency, time, distance) for a better understanding of their actual size.

Reflect and discuss 3

- How does scientific notation help you grasp extremely large or extremely small numbers?

- How does scientific notation help you to compare different quantities in order to help you grasp extremely large or extremely small numbers?

- What other ways can you think of to compare extreme quantities in order to really grasp their size?

Summary

Laws of exponents: for $a, b \in \mathbb{R}$, $m, n \in \mathbb{N}$

- Product rules:

  - $a^m \times a^n = a^{m+n}$

  - $a^n \times b^n = (ab)^n$ (power of products)

- Quotient rules:

  - $\dfrac{a^m}{a^n} = a^{m-n}$

  - $\dfrac{a^n}{b^n} = \left(\dfrac{a}{b}\right)^n$ (power of quotients)

- Power rule: $(a^m)^n = a^{mn}$

For any number $a \in \mathbb{R}$, $a \neq 0$ and $n \in \mathbb{N}$, we have the following rules:

  - Zero power rule: $a^0 = 1$

  - Negative power rule: $a^{-n} = \dfrac{1}{a^n}$

Scientific notation

$a \times 10^n$ where $1 \leq a < 10$, $a \in \mathbb{R}$ and $n \in \mathbb{Z}$

ATL

Mixed practice

1 **Evaluate** the following expressions. Write down your answers as simplified fractions without exponents.

 a $(5^3 2^4)$

 b $\left(\dfrac{7}{3}\right)^{-2}$

 c $\dfrac{2}{27}\left(\dfrac{9^3}{6^2}\right)$

 d $\dfrac{1}{4}\left(\dfrac{2^{12}}{64}\right)^2$

 e $\left(\dfrac{15^4}{3^3}\right)\left(\dfrac{3^{-2}}{25}\right)(5^{-1} \cdot 6^2)$

 f $-\left(\left(\dfrac{-2^3}{(-3)^2}\right)^2\right)(8^3 \cdot 3^{-6})^{-1}$

2 **Simplify** the following expressions. Write down the answers with only positive exponents.

 a $(2x^5 y^{-2})^5$

 b $-(-x^2 y^{-1})^{-4}$

 c $(x^{-5} yz^{-2})^{-1}(xy^2 z^3)$

 d $\dfrac{(-3x^{-1})^2 y^4}{x^{-3} y^{-1}}$

 e $\left(\dfrac{81 y^2 z^{-3}}{3^3 x^{-2} y^{-2} z^{-3}}\right)^{-1}$

 f $\left(\dfrac{10x^2 y^{-2} z^2}{(3x^5 y^3 z^{-1})^{-1}}\right)^2 \left(\dfrac{-xy}{30z}\right)$

3 The number 793 800 can be written in the following way as the product of its prime factors: $2^a \times 3^b \times 5^c \times 7^d \times 11^e$ where $a, b, c, d, e \in \mathbb{N}$. **Find** the values of a, b, c, d and e.

4 There are approximately 86 billion neurons in the human brain. The size of a neuron varies between 10 and 50 microns. (Hint: there are 1000 microns in 1 mm.)

   a Assume that all the neurons are on average 25 microns wide. If all the neurons in the human brain were laid down side-by-side in a straight line, use scientific notation to **calculate** the length of that line.

   b Repeat the calculation in part **a**, assuming that the neurons are all 10 microns wide.

   c Repeat the calculation in part **a**, assuming that the neurons are all 50 microns wide.

   Information travels between neurons at different speeds, varying from 5×10^{-1} m/s to 1.2×10^{2} m/s

   d **Write** these transmission speeds in decimal form.

   e **Convert** these speeds to km/h.

5 In chemistry, the unit of mass used to study atoms is called a **unified atomic mass unit** (u). One u is $\frac{1}{12}$ the mass of a carbon-12 atom, and is approximately equal to 1.6605×10^{-27} kilograms.

   a **Find** the mass, in g, of a carbon-12 atom.

   b **Find** the mass, in g, of a hydrogen-1 atom (a hydrogen-1 atom has a mass of 1.0078u).

   c An oxygen atom has a mass of 15.999u. **Find** the mass, in g, of a water molecule (a water molecule, H_2O, is composed of 2 hydrogen atoms and one oxygen atom).

Reflect and discuss 4

How have you explored the statement of inquiry? Give specific examples.

Statement of inquiry:

Representing numbers in different forms to simplify them can help understand human-made systems.

1.4 Units and measurement

Global context: Globalization and sustainability

Related concept: Approximation

FORM

Objectives

- Converting between metric units, including metric units of area and volume
- Converting between metric and imperial units
- Using units correctly in problem solving
- Solving problems involving compound measures
- Deciding if the answer to a problem is reasonable

Inquiry questions

F
- What are the different systems of measurement?

C
- How do we convert measures of area and volume into different units?
- Are some units more approximate than others?

D
- Should we adopt a single global system of measurement?
- How do human-made systems influence communities?

ATL Communication

Use intercultural understanding to interpret communication

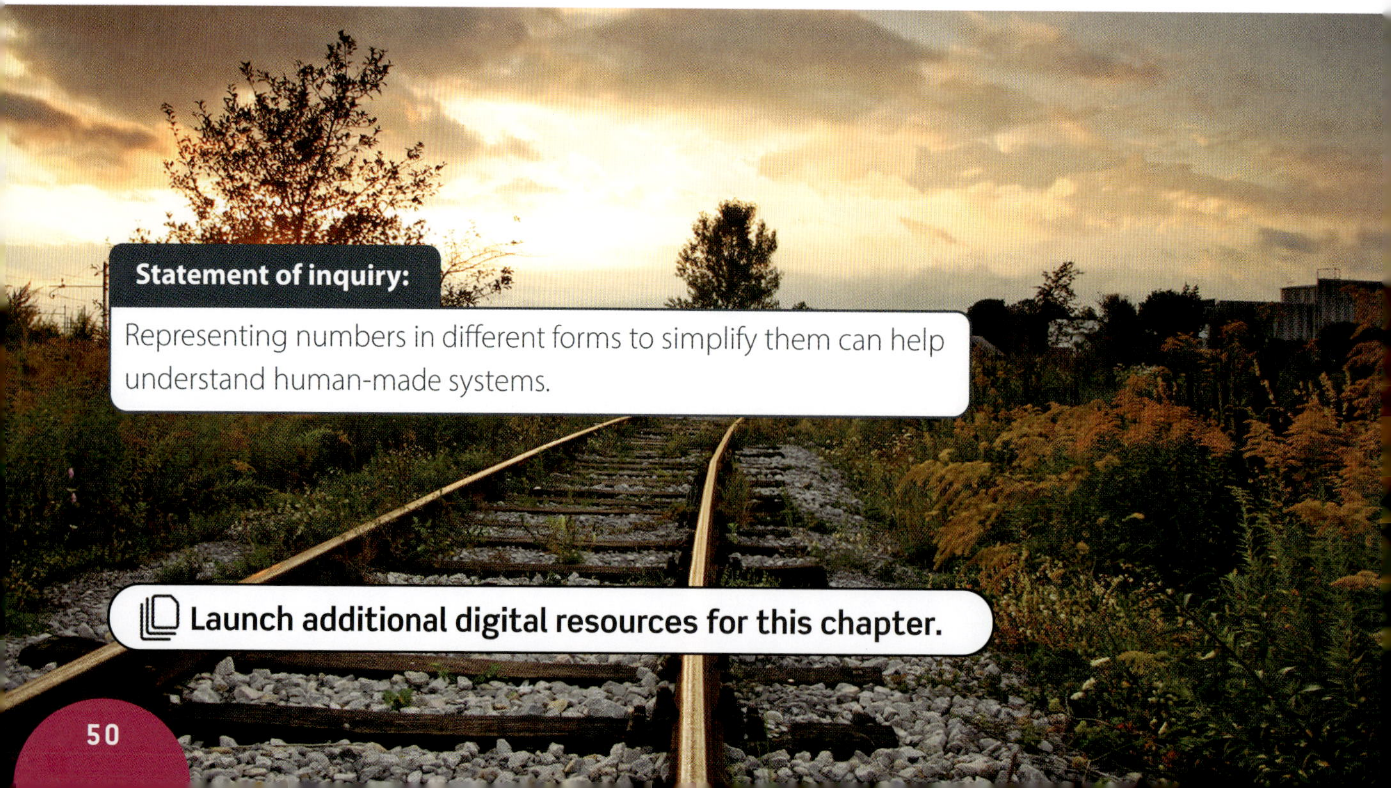

Statement of inquiry:

Representing numbers in different forms to simplify them can help understand human-made systems.

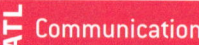

Launch additional digital resources for this chapter.

You should already know how to:

• recognize units for length, mass and volume	**1** Group these measurements into lengths, masses and volumes. Which is the odd one out? 2 kg 34 mm 15 g 24 s 5 ml 9 km 13 miles 6 liters 8.4 cm^3
• write powers of ten in full	**2** Write down these powers of ten in full. **a** 10^3 **b** 10^6 **c** 10^{-2}
• multiply and divide by powers of ten	**3** Calculate: **a** 280×0.001 **b** $34\,500 \div 10^2$
• find the area of a square	**4** Calculate the area of a square with side length 12 cm.
• find the surface area and volume of a cuboid	**5** A cuboid measures $3\,m \times 4\,m \times 5\,m$. Calculate its surface area and volume.

 ## Units for measurement

• What are the different systems of measurement?

Exploration 1

1 Add to this list by writing down all the units of measurement you can think of. Group similar units together.

- kilograms (kg)
- kilometers per hour (km/h)
- minutes (min)
- degrees (°)

Compare your list with others. Did anyone group units differently?

2 Add to this list all the types of measurement you can think of.

- length
- volume
- mass

Are length and distance the same measurement? What about volume and capacity?

3 Compare your two lists. Match each unit to the type of measurement it is used for. Are there any types of measurement that have only one unit?

> Think of the units you use in mathematics and science, which are also used in cooking, when traveling etc.

> Think about how the words *volume* and *capacity* are used. To what space (1D, 2D, 3D) does each refer?

Reflect and discuss 1

- Does every measurement have units? Explain why this is the case.
- Why are there often different units for a single type of measurement?
- Can units measure more than one type of measurement? Explain fully.
- Are measurements human-made systems?

Practice 1

1 Suggest sensible units for these specific measurements.

   a A matchbox measures $40 \times 25 \times 12$

   b The length of an A4 sheet of paper is 297

   c The length of an A4 sheet of paper is 29.7

   d A shoebox has a capacity of 6307

   e A shipping container measures $6.06 \times 2.44 \times 2.59$

   f The floor area of a house is 250

   g The length of a swimming pool is 50

2 Select appropriate units for these.

   a The mass of a farm tractor

   b The dimensions of a tennis court

   c The area of a wall in a house

   d The speed of an ambulance

   e The height of a giraffe

   f The dimensions of a piece of land

   g The speed of a javelin, when thrown by an athlete

- -

Systems of measurement

The two most widely used systems of measurement are the metric system and the imperial system.

> A **system of measurement** is a system of measures based on a set of base units. All other units in the system are derived from the base units.

The metric system

The metric system is used widely in Europe and most of the rest of the world.

The International System of Units (or SI) defines seven base units:

- meter (m) for measuring length
- kilogram (kg) for measuring mass
- second (s) for measuring time
- ampere (A) for measuring electric current
- Kelvin (K) for measuring thermodynamic temperature
- mole (mol) for measuring amounts of a substance
- candela (cd) for measuring the intensity of light.

The 'A' series of paper sizes is used worldwide. Only the US and Canada do not currently conform to the ISO standard although, in practice, Mexico, Venezuela, Colombia, Chile and the Philippines favour the US letter format.

The International System of Units (abbreviated SI from the French 'Le Système International d'Unités') officially came into being at the 11th General Conference on Weights and Measures in Paris in October 1960.

The French brought in the metric system after the French Revolution. In 1793 they even tried to decimalize time with 10 days in a week, 10 hours in a day, 100 minutes in an hour and 100 seconds in a minute. They returned to traditional timekeeping in 1806.

All other units are derived from these and are called *derived units*. For example, the unit of speed, in terms of the base units, is m/s.

In some books, m/s is written ms^{-1}.

The SI (or metric system) allows other units to be created by using prefixes which act as multipliers. The unit prefixes specify a power of ten:

- a *kilo*meter is 10^3 times larger than a meter (standard unit),
  $1 \text{ km} = 1 \times 10^3 \text{ m} = 1000 \text{ m}$

- a *nano*second is 10^{-9} times smaller than a second (standard unit),
  $5 \text{ nanoseconds} = 5 \times 10^{-9} \text{ seconds} = 0.000\,000\,005 \text{ seconds}$.

Dividing by the factor allows you to convert a standard unit into another unit:

- a gram (standard unit) is smaller than a *kilo*gram,
  $500 \text{ g} = 500 \text{ g} \div 10^3 = 0.5 \text{ kg}$

- a meter (standard unit) is larger than a *micro*meter,
  $1 \text{ m} = 1 \text{ m} \div 10^{-6} = 1\,000\,000 \text{ m}$

Prefix	Letter	Power
tera-	T	10^{12}
giga-	G	10^9
mega-	M	10^6
kilo-	k	10^3
deci-	d	10^{-1}
centi-	c	10^{-2}
milli-	m	10^{-3}
micro-	μ	10^{-6}
nano-	n	10^{-9}

Some derived units are named after a person closely associated with them. For example, the Newton (N) is a measure of force. $1 \text{ N} = 1 \text{ kg m/s}^2$.

Practice 2

1 Find these conversions.

    a 3.5 megatonnes to tonnes   **b** 8 gigabytes to bytes

    c 257 mm to meters   **d** 6.5 dl to liters

2 How many:

    a nanoseconds are in a second   **b** micrometers are in a meter

    c watts are in a kilowatt   **d** centiliters are in a liter?

'How many millimeters are in a meter' is the same as 'Convert meters to millimeters'.

3 Find these conversions.

    a 2 m to μm   **b** 3.2 g to mg

    c 2500 watts to microwatts   **d** 0.5 seconds to nanoseconds

4 Find these conversions.

a 285 cm = _____ m

b 923.5 mg = _____ g

c 4358 m = _____ km

d 4358 m = _____ mm

e 7.263 kg = _____ cg

f 12.45 l = _____ cl

g 18 655 ml = _____ l

h 560 mm = _____ cm

i 0.05 km = _____ cm

j 380 506 mg = _____ kg

> Check that your answer makes sense. Should the converted unit be smaller or larger than the original unit?

Problem solving

5 A human ovum has diameter 0.1 mm. The head of a human sperm is roughly 5 μm across. Calculate how many times larger the ovum is compared to the sperm.

6 The cells of the bacterium *Staphylococcus aureus* are spheres with diameter 1 μm. How many of these cells could fit on a rectangular 75 mm by 25 mm microscope slide?

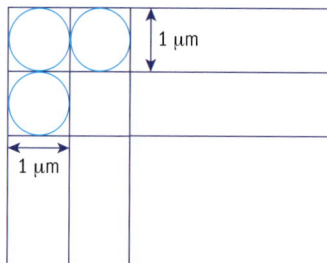

> On the slide, each cell takes up the same area as a square with side length 1 μm.

The imperial system

The imperial system is now chiefly used in the US (US customary units).

Originally, many systems of measurement had their own standard on which the other measures were based. Small distances were counted in number of feet and paces (yards) and larger distances in miles (1000 paces). Capacity was measured using kitchen items, such as cups, because it was mainly used in cooking. Eventually a standard was set so that all measurements were the same for everyone.

> There are differences between imperial and US customary units, but they both are derived from the same system.

Reflect and discuss 2

- What difficulties might have arisen in measuring with units such as paces and cups?

- What types of problems might have occurred from the use of non-standardized units?

The SI (or metric) standards are now accepted worldwide and all other measures are defined in terms of that standard.

For example, 1 yard ≡ 0.9144 meters, where ≡ means 'is equivalent to'.

Some conversions for metric and imperial units are shown in the tables. Those marked * are exact; all others are defined to be exact by the International Yard and Pound Agreement.

Metric	Imperial
1 km	0.625 mile
1 m	39.4 inches
1 kg	2.205 pounds (lbs)
1 liter	1.76 pints (UK)
1 liter	2.113 pints (US)

Imperial	Metric
1 mile	1.609 km
1 foot	30.48 cm (*)
1 inch	2.54 cm (*)
1 ounce (oz)	28.35 g
1 gallon (UK)	4.546 liters
1 gallon (US)	3.785 liters

In 1999, the Mars Climate Orbiter was lost because the NASA team used metric units while a contractor used imperial units. Failing to convert the measurements for such crucial calculations caused the probe to come too close to Mars, where it is thought to have been destroyed by the planet's atmosphere.

Example 1

Find these conversions.

a 8 UK gallons to liters

b 13 liters to UK gallons

a 1 UK gallon $\simeq$ 4.5 liters

$8 \times 4.5 = 36$ liters

$\times 4.5$

1 UK gallon $\simeq$ 4.5 liters
To convert UK gallons to liters, multiply by 4.5.

b $13 \div 4.5 = 2.888\ldots$

$\simeq 2.9$ UK gallons (1 d.p.)

1 UK gallon $\simeq$ 4.5 liters

$\div 4.5$
Use the inverse operation.
To convert liters to UK gallons, divide by 4.5.
Round to a sensible degree of accuracy.

Objective: D. Applying mathematics in real-life contexts
iv. justify the degree of accuracy of a solution

In Practice 3, justify the degree of accuracy of each of your solutions.

Practice 3

1 Find these conversions.

a 1 inch $\simeq$ ___ m

b 1 g $\simeq$ ____ ounces

c 1 pound $\simeq$ ____ kg

d 1 liter $\simeq$ ____ gallons (UK)

e 1 UK pint $\simeq$ ____ liters

f 1 cm = ___ feet

2 Find how many:

   a kilometers is 50 miles

   b miles is 50 kilometers

   c pounds is 70 kilograms

   d centimeters is 6 inches

   e centimeters is 3 feet

   f liters is 5 UK pints

   g UK pints is 2 gallons

   h centimeters is 1 mile

> For **2h**, first convert miles to kilometers.

Problem solving

3 Determine which measurement is largest for each pair.

   a 58 miles or 72 km

   b 25 kg or 60 lbs

   c 50 cl or 1 UK pint

   d 4 oz or 100 g

   e 6 in or 20 cm

   f 6 ft or 180 cm

4 In *This is Spinal Tap*, members of a fictional rock group asked for an 18-inch model of a Stonehenge megalith (large standing stone). The model was intended for their stage show.

   a By converting the height to an appropriate metric measure, determine whether the model would have been effective.

   b Decide what imperial measure of length the band members should have asked for, given that they intended to use the model on a live stage.

Problem solving

5 In 1983, an Air Canada flight ran out of fuel halfway through its journey due to a mix-up between pounds and kilograms. The plane needed 22 300 kg of fuel for the journey. There were 7682 liters of fuel already in the tanks.

   a One liter of jet fuel has a mass of 0.803 kg. Calculate how much fuel should have been loaded. Give your answer in liters.

   b Instead of 0.803 kg per liter, a conversion of 1.77 was used. (One liter of jet fuel has a mass of 1.77 pounds.) Calculate how much fuel was actually loaded. Give your answer in liters.

   c Find how many liters short of fuel the plane was.

C ## What units tell us

- How do we convert measures of area and volume into different units?
- Are some units more approximate than others?

Exploration 2

1 The diagram shows a square with side length 1 m and a square with side length 100 cm.

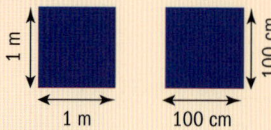

   a Explain why these two squares have the same area.

▶ Continued on next page

b Calculate the area of each square.

c Copy and complete:

$1 \text{ m}^2 = \underline{\hspace{1cm}} \text{ cm}^2$

d Sketch a square with side length 1 cm and a square with side length 10 mm. How do you convert from cm^2 to mm^2? How do you convert from mm^2 to cm^2?

2 Sketch a cube with side length 1 m and a cube with side length 100 cm.

a Calculate the volume of each cube.

b Copy and complete:

$1 \text{ m}^3 = \underline{\hspace{1cm}} \text{ cm}^3$

c Work out the volume of a cube with side length 1 cm and a cube with side length 10 mm.

d How do you convert from cm^3 to mm^3? How do you convert from mm^3 to cm^3?

> **Capacity** refers to the amount of space available to hold something.
> **Volume** refers to the amount of space actually occupied.

> Volume is generally measured in cm^3, and capacity in liters.
>
> $1 \text{ cm}^3 = 1 \text{ ml}$
>
> $1000 \text{ cm}^3 = 1 \text{ liters}$

Practice 4

1 Find these conversions.

a 20 cm^2 to mm^2

b 600 mm^2 to cm^2

c 5000 cm^2 to m^2

d 4.5 m^2 to cm^2

e 2.9 cm^2 to mm^2

f 0.7 m^2 to mm^2

> For question **1f**, convert m^2 to cm^2 then to mm^2.

2 Find these conversions.

a 40 m^3 to cm^3

b 5000 mm^3 to cm^3

c $2\,400\,000 \text{ cm}^3$ to m^3

d 3 cm^3 to ml

e 2.5 liters to cm^3

f 10 m^3 to liters

> For question **2f**, first convert m^3 to cm^3.

3 A piece of foam has volume 500 cm^3. Find its volume in m^3.

4 **a** 1 decimeter (dm) = 10 cm

Copy and complete:

$1 \text{ dm}^3 = \underline{\hspace{1cm}} \text{ cm}^3$

b Find the number of dm^3 in 1 m^3.

c A removal truck has a capacity of 6 m^3. Find its capacity in dm^3.

5 Find the capacity in liters of a swimming pool that measures $33 \text{ m} \times 16 \text{ m}$, with an average depth of 2.15 m.

Problem solving

6 Suggest suitable dimensions for a cuboid-shaped carton designed to hold 1 liter of juice.

Exploration 3

A cuboid is 30 cm tall, 50 cm long and 1 m wide.

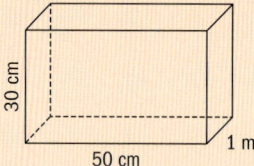

1 **a** Use the lengths in cm to calculate the volume of the cuboid in cm^3.

   b Use the lengths in m to calculate the volume of the cuboid in m^3.

   c Show that your two results are equal.

2 **a** Calculate the surface area of the cuboid in cm^2.

   b Use step **a** to find the surface area of the cuboid in m^2.

3 A box in the shape of a cuboid is 250 cm tall, 472 cm long and 545 cm wide. Calculate the volume of this cuboid in m^3.

Reflect and discuss 3

In Exploration 3:

- Which units would you use to calculate the surface area and volume of the first cuboid? Which units would you use to give the final answers?

- Which units give a more exact measurement for the surface area and for the volume? Which units give a more approximate measure?

- Option 1: Find the volume in cm^3, and convert to m^3.
  Option 2: Convert the dimensions to meters, then find the volume.
  Which is the easiest way to find the volume of the box in m^3?

ATL

Practice 5

1 The dimensions of a tennis court are 2377 cm × 8.23 m. Find its area in m^2.

2 A soccer field measures 0.110 km × 73 m. Find its area in m^2 and in km^2. Which measure is easier to visualize?

3 A container has length 9750 mm, width 6400 mm and height 5640 mm.

   a Find its floor area in m^2.

   b Find its volume in m^3.

Problem solving

4 1 hectare (ha) is the area of a square $10\,000\ m^2$.

   A square field has an area of $0.36\ km^2$.

   Find the area of the field in hectares.

You can use the imperial-to-metric conversion factors for lengths to convert units of area and volume.

Example 2

Find the number of cubic meters (m^3) in 10 cubic yards.

Use the conversions: 1 inch = 2.54 cm, 1 yard = 36 inches

1 inch = 2.54 cm $\qquad$ Write down the conversions.

1 yard = 36 inches

10 yards = 36 inches × 10 = 360 inches

360 inches = 2.54 cm × 360 = 914.4 cm $\qquad$ Convert 10 yards to inches, then centimeters.

10 yards = 9.144 m $\qquad$ Convert 10 yards to meters.

10 cubic yards = (10 yards)^3 = (9.144 m)^3

$\qquad\qquad$ = 764.554...

10 cubic yards = 764.55 m^3 (to 2 d.p.) $\qquad$ Check that the answer makes sense: 10 yards is *shorter* than 10 m (10 yards = 9.144 m) so 10 cubic yards should be *smaller* than 10 m^3.

ATL Practice 6

1 A rectangular piece of land is 2 km long and 3 km wide.

   a Find the dimensions of the piece of land in miles.

   b Find the area of the land in square miles.

2 a A box measures 4 in × 5 in × 6 in. Find **i** its volume in cm^3, and **ii** its surface area in cm^2.

   b Another box measures 3 in × 5 in × 8 in. Find **i** its volume in cm^3, and **ii** its surface area in cm^2.

   Write down what you notice about your answers to parts **a** and **b**.

3 Find the number of cubic centimeters (cm^3) in 5 cubic inches.

4 Find the number of square meters (m^2) in 10 square yards.

5 A truck has a capacity of 25 m^3. Find the capacity of the truck in cubic feet.

6 A cube has volume 64 in^3.

   a Find the side length of the cube in inches.

   b Find the side length in cm.

1 yard = 0.9144 m

Problem solving

7 A dressage arena for horse riding is a rectangle twice as long as it is wide. Its area is 8611.13 ft^2. Find its length in meters.

Converting compound measures

Compound measures involve more than one unit. For example, speed can be measured in meters per second and density in grams per cubic centimeter. When compound measures are involved, you may need to convert both units.

> **Density** is the mass of substance contained in a certain volume. The density of solids and liquids is measured in g/cm^3, and the density of gases is measured in g/l.

Example 3

The density of iron is 7.87 g/cm^3. Find the density of iron in kg/m^3.

$1 \text{ kg} = 1000 \text{ g}$

$1 \text{ m}^3 = 1\,000\,000 \text{ cm}^3$

Write down the conversions you will need.

Method 1:

$7.87 \text{ g/cm}^3 \times 1\,000\,000 = 7\,870\,000 \text{ g/m}^3$

First convert g/cm^3 to g/m^3.

$7\,870\,000 \text{ g/m}^3 \div 1000 = 7870 \text{ kg/m}^3$

Now convert g/m^3 to kg/m^3.

Method 2:

$7.87 \dfrac{g}{cm^3} \times \dfrac{1\,000\,000 \text{ cm}^3}{1\,m^3} = 7\,870\,000 \dfrac{g}{m^3}$

Write the conversion factor for volume as a fraction and multiply.
Multiplying by $\dfrac{1\,000\,000 \text{ cm}^3}{1\,m^3}$ is equivalent to multiplying by 1, since $1\,000\,000 \text{ cm}^3 = 1 \text{ m}^3$. The cm^3 units cancel.

$7\,870\,000 \dfrac{g}{m^3} \times \dfrac{1\,kg}{1000\,g} = 7870 \dfrac{kg}{m^3}$

Write the conversion factor for mass as a fraction and multiply.
Multiplying by $\dfrac{1\,kg}{1000\,g}$ is equivalent to multiplying by 1, since $1 \text{ kg} = 1000 \text{ g}$. This time, the grams cancel.

Example 4

The speed limit on motorways in the UK is 70 miles per hour (mph). In some parts of Europe, the speed limit is 110 kilometers per hour (km/h). Which is faster?

$1 \text{ mile} = 1.609 \text{ km}$

Write down the conversion you will need.

$70 \text{ mph} \times 1.609 = 112.63 \text{ km/h}$

Convert 70 miles per hour to kilometers per hour.

70 mph is faster than 110 km/h.

Practice 7

1 Convert these speeds from kilometers per hour (km/h) to meters per hour (m/h).

 a 10 km/h   **b** 54 km/h   **c** 4.8 km/h   **d** 280 km/h

2 Convert these speeds from meters per hour (m/h) to meters per second (m/s).

 a 3600 m/h   **b** 43 200 m/h   **c** 9000 m/h   **d** 2160 m/h

3 Oliver is driving at 65 km/h. Find his speed in m/s.

4 A sea turtle can swim at a speed of 2 m/s. Find its speed in km/h.

5 Aluminium has density 2.70 g/cm^3. Find its density in kg/m^3.

6 Oxygen has a density of 1.43 g/l. Find its density in mg/cl.

For question **2**, first convert meters per *hour* to meters per *minute*, then to meters per *second*.

Problem solving

7 Lead has density 11.34 g/cm^3. Find the mass of 1 m^3 of lead.

8 Gold has density 19.32 g/cm^3. Find the mass of 0.5 m^3 of gold.

9 The speed limit in urban areas is 30 mph in the US, and 50 km/h in most of Europe. Are these speeds the same? Explain your answer.

Problem solving

10 A domestic cat can reach a top speed of 48 km/h. The sprinter Usain Bolt has reached a top speed of 12.27 m/s. Determine which is faster.

11 Oxygen has a density of 1.43 g/l. Enzo says that 120 cl of oxygen has a mass of 17.16 grams. Justify whether or not he is correct.

12 Timeo is traveling at a speed of 25 m/s. He claims that it will take him 1 hour to travel 110 km. Justify whether or not he is correct.

Units of a compound measure can tell you what to do: $\frac{meters}{seconds}$ will mean distance divided by time.

Problem solving

13 In 1997, a world land-speed record of 763.035 miles per hour was set by the car *Thrust SSC*. The sound barrier is reached when an object moves at a speed of about 340 meters per second. Determine if *Thrust SSC* broke the sound barrier. Explain your answer.

D More conversions and units

- Should we adopt a single global system of measurement?
- How do systems influence communities?

Conversions

Activity

1 Euro (EUR) = 1.18 US Dollar (USD)

1 USD = 0.91 Swiss Franc (CHF)

1 Convert 650 EUR into USD.

2 Convert 1800 CHF into USD.

3 Calculate an approximate value of 900 CHF in EUR.

Reflect and discuss 4

- How is the process of converting from one unit to another similar to converting from one currency to another? Are both the unit conversions and currency conversions standardized? Explain fully.

- Since most currencies are divided into 100 cents (or equivalent), are currency conversions approximated?

- Quantity is defined as an amount or number. Measurement is defined as a method of determining quantity, capacity or dimension using a defined unit. Is currency conversion more to do with quantity, and unit conversion more to do with measurement? Explain fully.

ATL

Exploration 4

1 Research natural units and answer these questions.
   a Determine what natural units are.
   b Which systems of natural units are used?
   c What are the advantages of the natural system of units? Are there any disadvantages?

2 Systems of man-made units need a prototype, that is, an object that defines a unit. Other measurements are compared to the prototype.
   a Determine what the prototype is for the kilogram.
   b Decide whether a natural unit needs a prototype.

Reflect and discuss 5

- Is the day a human-made unit or natural unit?

- Why is there no single global system of measurement?

- What would be the advantages and disadvantages of having a single system of measurement?

- If a single system of measurement was to be adopted, which should be chosen? Explain fully.

Some unusual units of measurement include:

- The Hand (= 4 inches) for measuring the height of a horse

- The Board foot (= 1 inch × 1 foot × 1 foot) for measuring lumber

- The Shake (= 10 nanoseconds) for referring to very short periods of time

- The Foe (= 10^{44} joules) for measuring the enormous amount of energy produced when a star goes supernova

Summary

A **system of measurement** is a system of measures based on a set of base units. All other units in the system are derived from the base units.

The two most common systems of measurement are the metric system and the imperial system.

The metric system allows other units to be created by using prefixes, which act as multipliers. Each unit prefix specifies a power of ten; for example, the prefix *kilo-* specifies 10^3.

Some common conversions:

To convert from m^2 to cm^2, multiply by 10 000.
To convert from mm^2 to cm^2, divide by 100.
To convert from m^3 to cm^3, multiply by 1 000 000.
To convert from mm^3 to cm^3, divide by 1000.

Capacity refers to the amount of space available to hold something. **Volume** refers to the amount of space actually occupied. Both capacity and volume can be measured in cm^3 and liters: $1\ cm^3 = 1$ ml, $1000\ cm^3 = 1$ liter.

Compound measures such as speed and density combine measures of two quantities.

Density is the mass of substance contained in a certain volume.

$$\text{Density} = \frac{\text{mass}}{\text{volume}}$$

The density of solids and liquids is measured in g/cm^3; the density of gases is measured in g/l.

Mixed practice

1 Determine which unit of measurement you would use to measure:

  a the volume of water in a swimming pool

  b a person's walking speed

  c the capacity of a storage box

  d the mass of a person

  e the amount of flour in a cake

  f the distance from Chicago to Los Angeles

2 Find these conversions.

  a 3 m to cm

  b 4.8 kg to g

  c 760 cm to m

  d 9845 m to km

  e 0.01 km to cm

  f 400 600 mg to kg

3 Find these conversions.

  a 4 ounces ≃ ___ g

  b 15 inches ≃ ___ cm

  c 8 m ≃ ___ feet

  d 6 liters ≃ ___ UK gallons

  e 10 UK pints ≃ ___ gallons

  f 800 g ≃ ___ pounds

4 Find these conversions.

  a 50 cm^2 to mm^2

  b 9500 cm^2 to m^2

  c 0.5 m^2 to mm^2

  d 6400 mm^3 to cm^3

  e 10 cm^3 to ml

  f 100 m^3 to liters

5 Find these conversions.

  a 950 meters per hour (m/h) to km/h

  b 36 km/h to m/h

  c 10 meters per second (m/s) to m/h

  d 7200 m/h to m/s

  e 54 km/h to m/s

Problem solving

6 A bottle contains 240 cl of medicine.

  Calculate the number of 25 ml doses that can be poured from it.

7 The table gives the heights and masses of two people.

	Height	**Mass**
Person A	6 ft 2 in	190 lbs
Person B	1.82 m	90 kg

  a Who is taller?   **b** Who is heavier?

8 An airline's hold baggage allowances are:
SIZE: length + width + height must be less than 275 cm.
WEIGHT: free up to 20 kg. Each extra kg (or part of a kg) is charged at 13 Euros.

   a Jo's suitcase measures 18 in × 22 in × 8 in. **Decide** whether he can take it as hold luggage.

   b Suzanne's bag weighs 48 lbs. **Calculate** how much she would have to pay to take it as hold baggage.

9 A water tank has length 2250 mm, width 5800 mm and height 3860 mm. **Calculate** the capacity of the tank in liters.

10 **Find** the number of cubic inches in 9 cm³.

11 **Find** the number of m² in 6 square yards.

> 1 in = 2.54 cm
> 1 yd = 36 inches

12 A square field has area 2323.24 ft².
   Find the side length of the field in meters.

13 The density of nickel is 8900 kg/m³.
   Find the density of nickel in g/cm³.

Problem solving

14 Platinum has a density of 21 450 kg/m³. Gold has a density of 19.32 g/cm³.

   Determine which metal is denser.

15 A car travels at 20 m/s in a village where the speed limit is 50 km/h. **Determine** if the car is exceeding the speed limit.

16 A top speed of 231.523 mph was set by a Formula 1 racing car in 2005. A Chinook helicopter has a maximum speed of 87.5 m/s.

   Determine which is faster.

Review in context

Globalization and sustainability

1 The Golden Gate Bridge in San Francisco opened for vehicular traffic in 1937.

   a Below are some facts about the bridge. **Find** the equivalent measurements in metric units.

      i The towers are 746 feet tall.

      ii Each of the two main cables is 7650 feet long.

      iii The total length of wire used in both main cables is 80 000 miles.

   b Carbon steel is used for the main cables. 1 cm³ of carbon steel has a mass of about 7.85 g. **Find** the density of carbon steel in kg/m³.

   c When the bridge was built, 389 000 cubic yards of concrete was used.

> 1 yard = 0.9144 m

   After the original concrete roadway deck was replaced, there was 6.4% less concrete. **Calculate** the total quantity of concrete in the refurbished bridge in m³.

   d A bolt of diameter 2.125 inches was used in the construction.

      i **Find** the diameter of the bolt in mm.

      ii Imagine that a bolt of diameter 2.125 cm was mistakenly used. **Calculate** the error in mm.

2 Railway tracks in different countries have different gauges (spacing between the rails).

a Approximately 60% of the world's railways today use the standard gauge, which is 4 ft $8\frac{1}{2}$ in. **Find** this measurement in metric units, correct to the nearest mm.

b Originally, English trains used a 4 ft 8 in gauge for coal transport trains. Half an inch was added to the gauge for passenger trains, as this made the trains run more smoothly on the curves.

   i **Find** the length of the coal-mining gauge in metric units, to the nearest mm.

   ii **Find** the difference between the two gauge sizes, in mm.

   iii **Determine** whether your answer in part **ii** corresponds to $\frac{1}{2}$ in. If not, find the percentage error.

c Some countries use the meter gauge, which is exactly 1000 mm. **Find** this measurement in imperial units, in feet and inches.

d Until 2011, Spain used a 1668 mm gauge, and France used the standard gauge. **Suggest** why Spain modified its railway tracks and engines.

Reflect and discuss 6

How have you explored the statement of inquiry? Give specific examples.

Statement of inquiry:

Representing numbers in different forms to simplify them can help understand human-made systems.

1.5 Surds, roots and radicals

Global context: Globalization and sustainability

Related concept: Simplification

Objectives

- Simplifying irrational numerical expressions
- Approximating radicals
- Applying rules of radicals to simplify them
- Performing operations on radicals to simplify expressions that contain radicals

Inquiry questions

F
- What is the difference between a rational number and an irrational number?
- What is a radical (surd)?
- How do you approximate a radical?

C
- How are the rules of radicals related to the rules for combining terms in algebra?
- How is simplifying radicals similar to simplifying fractions?

D
- Can irrational numbers be combined to form rational numbers?

ATL Critical-thinking

Draw reasonable conclusions and generalizations

Statement of inquiry:

Representing numbers in different forms to simplify them can help understand human-made systems.

📖 **Launch additional digital resources for this chapter.**

You should already know how to:

identify radicals and understand what they represent	**1** Simplify each expression.
•	**a** $\sqrt{64}$ **b** $\sqrt{121}$
	c $\sqrt{9+16}$ **d** $\sqrt{9}+\sqrt{16}$

 Reviewing radicals (surds)

- What is the difference between a rational number and an irrational number?
- What is a radical (surd)?
- How do you approximate a radical?

> A **square root** (also known as a **radical** or **surd**) of a positive number x is a number which, when multiplied by itself, gives the original number x. Any positive number has two square roots: one positive and one negative.

> The **principal square root** of a positive number x is the *positive* square root of x, and is written as $\sqrt{x}$.

In general, 'the square root' means the *positive* square root.

For example, $\sqrt{25} = 5$, but the square root of 25 can also be −5. This is normally written down as $-\sqrt{25} = -5$.

Exploration 1

Here are some examples of what we call 'rational numbers':

$$\frac{1}{2} \quad 1.45 \quad 7.262626\ldots \quad -3 \quad \frac{5}{6} \quad 18.2 \quad \sqrt{9}$$

And here are some examples of what we call 'irrational numbers':

$$\pi \quad 2.39841\ldots \quad 17.41002368\ldots \quad 0.83126674\ldots$$

1 State the differences between a 'rational number' and an 'irrational number'.

2 Define each of them in your own words.

3 How would you classify a number like $\sqrt{5}$? Explain your reasoning.

> A **rational number** is a number that can be written as a fraction $\frac{p}{q}$ where $p, q \in \mathbb{Z}$ and $q \neq 0$. For example: $\frac{1}{2}, \frac{5}{6}, \frac{9}{5}, 4, -\frac{12}{51}, 1.2, -0.\bar{3}$, and 0 are all rational numbers.
>
> An **irrational number** is a number that cannot be written as a fraction. Irrational numbers *cannot* be represented as terminating or repeating decimals. $\sqrt{2}$ and π are examples of irrational numbers.

Muhammad ibn Musa al-Khwarizmi (c. 780 – c. 850 CE) referred to rational numbers as *audible*, and irrational numbers as *inaudible*. This later led to the Arabic word 'أصم' (asamm, meaning 'deaf' or 'dumb') for irrational number, which was then translated into Latin as 'surdus'.

We have given names to only a few special irrationals, like π, ϕ, and Euler's number, e. These numbers are called transcendental numbers.

Here are some important facts about square roots:

- The square roots of positive square numbers are rational numbers because their values are whole numbers. $\sqrt{4} = 2$, $\sqrt{25} = 5$, $\sqrt{100} = 10$, and $\sqrt{2025} = 45$ are rational numbers.

- The square roots of positive non-square numbers are irrational. The numbers $\sqrt{2}$, $\sqrt{24}$, $\sqrt{247}$ and $\sqrt{1000}$ are irrational because their values cannot be written as a fraction. A radical (or a surd) is another word for the square root of a number that has an irrational value.

- Some irrational numbers (such as π, for example) can't be written as a square root, yet they are still irrational numbers.

> The terms 'radical' and 'surd' are both used to refer to an irrational square root. You may see either word (or both) used in mathematics books.

Reflect and discuss 1

- Try to find the value of $\sqrt{-25}$.

- Is it possible to take the square root of a negative number? If not, why not?

ATL

Exploration 2

In Exploration 5 in Unit 1.2, you estimated square roots that are irrational without needing a calculator. In this exploration, you will look more closely at how you could do that.

1 Use your results from Exploration 5 in Unit 1.2 to complete this table.

$\sqrt{1} =$	$\sqrt{2} =$	$\sqrt{3} =$	$\sqrt{4} =$
$\sqrt{5} =$	$\sqrt{6} =$	$\sqrt{7} =$	$\sqrt{8} =$
$\sqrt{9} =$	$\sqrt{10} =$	$\sqrt{11} =$	$\sqrt{12} =$
$\sqrt{13} =$	$\sqrt{14} =$	$\sqrt{15} =$	$\sqrt{16} =$

> 1, 4, 9, and 16 are the first few square numbers.

2 Square your estimated values using a calculator.
Comment on the accuracy of your estimates. Can you find a better estimate to 1 decimal place? If you assume that the square roots are evenly spaced, are the estimates more accurate for small square roots or large square roots?

3 Using similar reasoning, suggest a method for estimating any square root.

Practice 1

1 Without using a calculator, write down or estimate the square roots of each of these numbers.

   a 121   **b** 64   **c** 15

   d 12   **e** 27   **f** 50

2 Without using a calculator, estimate the value of the principal square roots.

   a $\sqrt{24}$ **b** $\sqrt{55}$ **c** $\sqrt{82}$

   d $\sqrt{90}$ **e** $\sqrt{56}$ **f** $\sqrt{99}$

Problem solving

3 By estimating the values of any radicals or otherwise, determine which inequality, less than (<) or greater than (>), should replace the ☐ to complete these statements.

   a $\sqrt{7}$ ☐ $\sqrt{11}$ **b** $3+\sqrt{5}$ ☐ $\sqrt{38}$ **c** $\sqrt{23}$ ☐ $1+\sqrt{10}$

   d $7-\sqrt{15}$ ☐ $\sqrt{8}$ **e** $5\times\sqrt{3}$ ☐ $4\times\sqrt{6}$ **f** $4\times\sqrt{50}$ ☐ $25+\sqrt{15}$

$\sqrt{2}$ is irrational, so it cannot be represented by a terminating decimal or a recurring decimal. A calculator can approximate $\sqrt{2}$ to a decimal, such as 1.41421356. Even if you wrote $\sqrt{2}$ correct to a large number of decimal places, it could only ever be an approximation. The only way to write the *exact* value of the square root of 2 is to write $\sqrt{2}$. Unlike the decimal form of, for example, $\frac{4}{11} = 0.363636...$ which is recurring, the decimal form of $\sqrt{2}$ does not recur.

> Numbers like $\frac{3}{8}$ can be represented as a terminating decimal, in this case 0.375. Other numbers such as $\frac{4}{15}$ can be represented as recurring infinite decimals, in this case $0.26666666…$

Hippasus of Metapontum, a follower of Pythagoras, is said to have discovered irrational numbers. He showed that $\sqrt{2}$ cannot be written as the ratio of two integers (i.e. as a rational number), and that therefore it must be irrational.

This discovery of the irrational numbers upset and terrified Pythagoras so much that he sentenced Hippasus to death by drowning at sea (according to legend).

Exploration 3

Consider the following list of numbers:

   3 $\frac{4}{3}$ $\sqrt{5}$ $\frac{3}{4}$ 1 $\sqrt{4}$ 2 $\frac{5}{2}$ $\sqrt{3}$

1 Without using a calculator, order the numbers from smallest to largest.

2 Use a calculator to check your answer.

3 Suggest a strategy that doesn't involve using a calculator to compare:

   a a fraction to a whole number

   b a radical to a whole number

   c a radical to a fraction.

> Your strategy could involve common denominators and squaring numbers. Does a number always become larger when you square it?

▶ Continued on next page

4 Without using a calculator, use your strategies to compare the following pairs of numbers. Replace the ☐ by <, > or =.

a $\sqrt{5} \ \square \ 5$

b $\sqrt{5} \ \square \ \dfrac{5}{2}$

c $6 \ \square \ \dfrac{18}{3}$

d $\sqrt{6} \ \square \ \dfrac{17}{3}$

e $\sqrt{2} \ \square \ \dfrac{7}{5}$

f $\sqrt{8} \ \square \ \dfrac{141}{50}$

g $\sqrt{3} \ \square \ \dfrac{433}{250}$

h $\sqrt{\dfrac{1}{2}} \ \square \ \dfrac{1}{2}$

i $\sqrt{\dfrac{1}{2}} \ \square \ \dfrac{7}{10}$

Reflect and discuss 2

The only way to write the exact value of a radical number is by using the $\sqrt{}$ sign.

- What are the advantages of using such notation for radicals? Are there any possible disadvantages?

- How does this notation affect the way you perform operations on an expression containing radical numbers? Do radicals behave differently when they are written using the $\sqrt{}$ sign than when they are approximated to a decimal?

> The square root sign, $\sqrt{}$, is called the radical sign. Any number or term underneath it is called the radicand.

C   How radicals behave

- How are the rules of radicals related to the rules for combining terms in algebra?
- How is simplifying radicals similar to simplifying fractions?

Exploration 4

You are going to explore the three basic rules of radicals.

Rule 1

1 Evaluate these amounts.

a $\sqrt{16} \times \sqrt{16}$

b $\sqrt{49} \times \sqrt{49}$

c $\sqrt{12} \times \sqrt{12}$

d $(\sqrt{36})^2$

e $(\sqrt{20})^2$

f $(\sqrt{1001})^2$

2 Deduce a general rule from what you found in step **1**.

Rule 2

3 Use a calculator to evaluate these amounts.

a $\sqrt{4 \times 9}$

b $\sqrt{4} \times \sqrt{9}$

c $\sqrt{5 \times 6}$

d $\sqrt{5} \times \sqrt{6}$

e $\sqrt{22 \times 38}$

f $\sqrt{22} \times \sqrt{38}$

4 Deduce a general rule from what you found in step **3**.

> According to the National Oceanic and Atmospheric Administration, the speed s (in meters per second) at which a **tsunami** moves is determined by the depth d (in meters) of the ocean, using the formula $s = \sqrt{gd}$, where g (the acceleration due to gravity) is 9.8 m/s².

▶ Continued on next page

5 Use a calculator to evaluate these radical expressions.

a $\sqrt{\dfrac{4}{9}}$ **b** $\dfrac{\sqrt{4}}{\sqrt{9}}$ **c** $\sqrt{\dfrac{2}{13}}$

d $\dfrac{\sqrt{2}}{\sqrt{13}}$ **e** $\sqrt{\dfrac{28}{9}}$ **f** $\dfrac{\sqrt{28}}{\sqrt{9}}$

6 Deduce a general rule from what you found in step **5**.

The rules of radicals that you discovered in Exploration 4 relate to multiplying and dividing radicals.

Example 1

a Simplify $3\sqrt{2} \times 5\sqrt{5}$ **b** Simplify $3\sqrt{12} \div 4\sqrt{3}$

a $3\sqrt{2} \times 5\sqrt{5} = 3 \times \sqrt{2} \times 5 \times \sqrt{5}$ $3\sqrt{2} = 3 \times \sqrt{2}$

$\qquad\qquad\quad = 3 \times 5 \times \sqrt{2} \times \sqrt{5}$ When multiplying, the order doesn't matter (associative property).

$\qquad\qquad\quad = 15 \times \sqrt{10}$ $\sqrt{2} \times \sqrt{5} = \sqrt{10}$ (Rule 2)

$\qquad\qquad\quad = 15\sqrt{10}$ Leave the final answer without the $\times$ sign.

b $3\sqrt{12} \div 4\sqrt{3} = \dfrac{3\sqrt{12}}{4\sqrt{3}}$ Rewrite a division as a fraction.

$\qquad\qquad\quad = \dfrac{3}{4} \times \dfrac{\sqrt{12}}{\sqrt{3}}$ Recall the rules of fractions: $\dfrac{a}{b} \times \dfrac{c}{d} = \dfrac{ac}{bd}$

$\qquad\qquad\quad = \dfrac{3}{4} \times \sqrt{\dfrac{12}{3}}$ $\dfrac{\sqrt{12}}{\sqrt{3}} = \sqrt{\dfrac{12}{3}}$ (Rule 3)

$\qquad\qquad\quad = \dfrac{3}{4} \times \sqrt{4}$ $\dfrac{12}{3} = 4$

$\qquad\qquad\quad = \dfrac{3}{4} \times 2$ $\sqrt{4} = 2$

$\qquad\qquad\quad = \dfrac{3}{2}$

Rules of radicals

For any real numbers a, b, $c \geq 0$:

Rule 1 $\sqrt{a^2} = a$ **Rule 2** $\sqrt{a \times b} = \sqrt{a} \times \sqrt{b}$ **Rule 3** $\sqrt{\dfrac{a}{b}} = \dfrac{\sqrt{a}}{\sqrt{b}}$ $b \neq 0$

Practice 2

1 Simplify each expression.

a $\sqrt{26} \times \sqrt{5}$ **b** $3\sqrt{21} \times 21\sqrt{5}$ **c** $\sqrt{7} \times \sqrt{11}$ **d** $\dfrac{\sqrt{18}}{\sqrt{2}}$

e $\dfrac{3\sqrt{5}}{\sqrt{75}}$ **f** $\dfrac{\sqrt{42}}{\sqrt{6}}$ **g** $\dfrac{\sqrt{12} \times \sqrt{35}}{\sqrt{20}}$ **h** $\dfrac{\sqrt{2}}{\sqrt{4} \times \sqrt{8}}$

Problem solving

2 Fill in the blank to make the expressions equal.

$$\frac{\sqrt{18}}{\sqrt{9} \times \sqrt{\square}} = \frac{\sqrt{6}}{3}$$

ATL

Exploration 5

1 Simplify the fraction $\dfrac{\sqrt{18}}{3\sqrt{2}}$.

2 When a fraction is equal to 1, determine what this tells you about the numerator and the denominator.

3 Hence, write down (as an equality) what you can deduce from $\dfrac{\sqrt{18}}{3\sqrt{2}} = 1$.

4 Using the Pythagorean Theorem, find the hypotenuse of this triangle.

5 Suppose you aligned three such triangles along the hypotenuse to make a new, larger right-angled triangle like this:

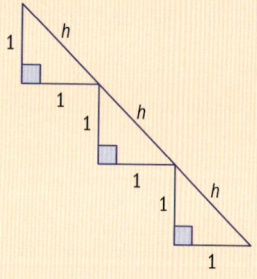 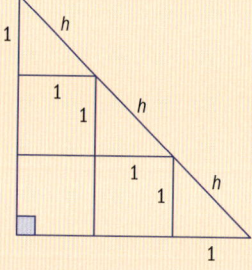 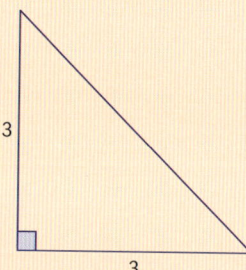

Write down an expression for the length of the hypotenuse of this larger triangle.

6 Now, using the same triangle, use the Pythagorean Theorem to find the length of the hypotenuse.

7 What can you deduce from the previous two steps? Draw a reasonable conclusion or generalization.

Reflect and discuss 3

- Compare your findings in step **3** to your findings in step **7** of Exploration 5. Are they equivalent?

- How does this diagram illustrate your findings?

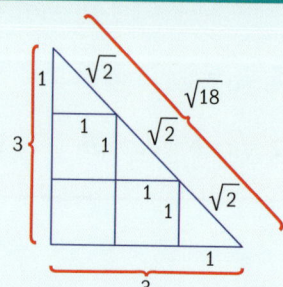

In Exploration 5, you found that $3\sqrt{2} = \sqrt{18}$. A way of saying this is that $\sqrt{18}$ *simplifies* to $3\sqrt{2}$.

Exploration 6

Below are some radicals and their simplified form.

Unsimplified form	Simplified form
$\sqrt{90}$	$3\sqrt{10}$
$\sqrt{12}$	$2\sqrt{3}$
$\sqrt{75}$	$5\sqrt{3}$
$\sqrt{200}$	$10\sqrt{2}$
$\sqrt{28}$	$2\sqrt{7}$
$\sqrt{32}$	$4\sqrt{2}$

1 Explain the process for simplifying a radical.

2 Explain how you would simplify $\sqrt{48}$.

3 Determine in how many ways you can answer question **2**. State which form is the most simplified.

4 Explain how you know when a radical *can* be simplified.

Exploration 6 demonstrated one method of simplifying radicals. Example 2 will illustrate it and a different method.

Example 2

Simplify $\sqrt{18}$.

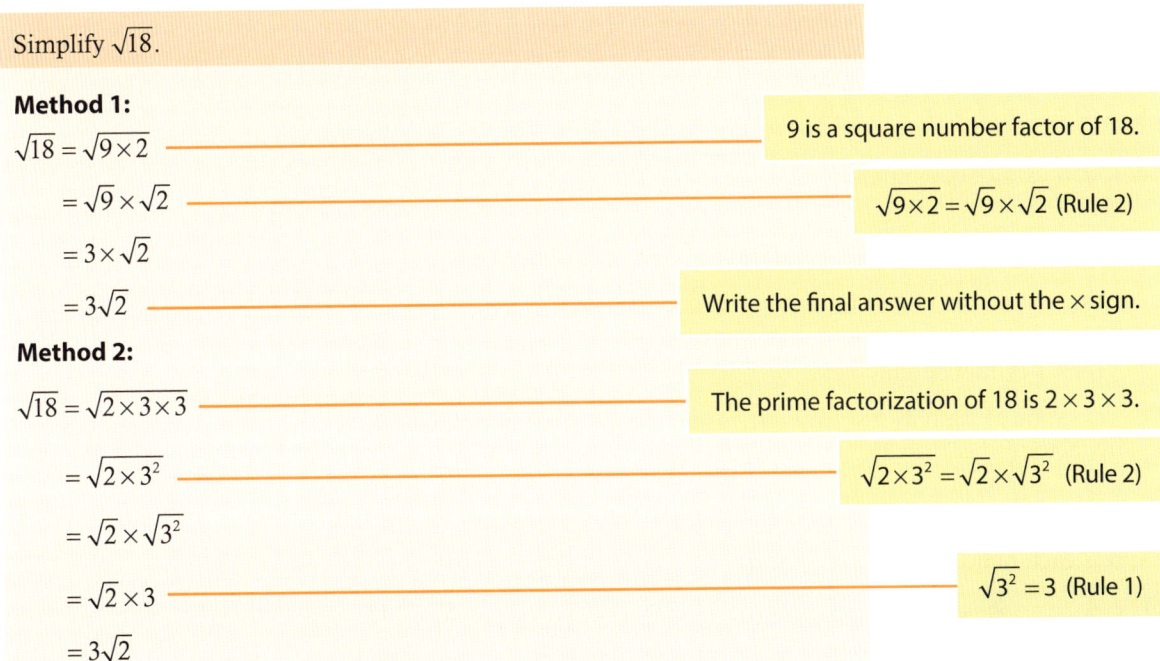

Method 1:

$\sqrt{18} = \sqrt{9 \times 2}$ ——— 9 is a square number factor of 18.

$\quad = \sqrt{9} \times \sqrt{2}$ ——— $\sqrt{9 \times 2} = \sqrt{9} \times \sqrt{2}$ (Rule 2)

$\quad = 3 \times \sqrt{2}$

$\quad = 3\sqrt{2}$ ——— Write the final answer without the × sign.

Method 2:

$\sqrt{18} = \sqrt{2 \times 3 \times 3}$ ——— The prime factorization of 18 is $2 \times 3 \times 3$.

$\quad = \sqrt{2 \times 3^2}$ ——— $\sqrt{2 \times 3^2} = \sqrt{2} \times \sqrt{3^2}$ (Rule 2)

$\quad = \sqrt{2} \times \sqrt{3^2}$

$\quad = \sqrt{2} \times 3$ ——— $\sqrt{3^2} = 3$ (Rule 1)

$\quad = 3\sqrt{2}$

Reflect and discuss 4

- When simplifying a square root using Method 1 from Example 2, why is it important to find factors that are square numbers? Can you simplify a square root by using factors that are *not* square numbers?
- Compare the two methods used in Example 2. Would you say that they are equivalent methods?
- How is simplifying radicals like simplifying fractions?

Sometimes the square root cannot be simplified.

Example 3

Determine whether or not these radicals can be simplified.

a $\sqrt{15}$ **b** $\sqrt{45}$ **c** $\sqrt{30}$

a $\sqrt{15} = \sqrt{1 \times 15}$

$\quad = \sqrt{3 \times 5}$

15 has factors 1, 3, 5, and 15. Only 1 is a square factor.

$\quad = \sqrt{3} \times \sqrt{5}$

You could rewrite 15 as a product of 3 and 5. However, 3 and 5 are not square numbers.

No, $\sqrt{15}$ cannot be simplified.

b $\sqrt{45} = \sqrt{9 \times 5}$

45 has factors 1, 3, 5, 9, 15 and 45. 9 is the largest square factor.

$\quad = \sqrt{3 \times 3 \times 5}$

$\quad = 3 \times \sqrt{5}$

$\quad = 3\sqrt{5}$

Yes, $\sqrt{45}$ can be simplified.

c $\sqrt{30} = \sqrt{1 \times 15}$

30 has factors 1, 2, 3, 5, 6, 10, 15, 30. Only 1 is a square factor.

No, $\sqrt{30}$ cannot be simplified

There are two situations when a square root cannot be simplified:

- the square root of a prime number cannot be simplified
- the square root of a composite number that has no square factors other than 1 cannot be simplified.

The condition to simplify a square root is that the number has at least one square factor (other than 1).

Practice 3

Express each radical in its simplest form.

1 $\sqrt{24}$ **2** $\sqrt{32}$ **3** $\sqrt{72}$ **4** $\sqrt{125}$ **5** $\sqrt{135}$

6 $\sqrt{960}$ **7** $\sqrt{675}$ **8** $\sqrt{864}$ **9** $\sqrt{991}$ **10** $\sqrt{992}$

11 $\sqrt{99a^6}$ **12** $\sqrt{200b^4c^2}$ **13** $\sqrt{288x^8y^3}$

ATL

Exploration 7

When adding and subtracting radicals, the same rules apply as when you are adding or subtracting whole numbers, fractions or variables.

1 Write down each of the following statements in mathematical notation, and then find the answer.

   a Three twos plus four twos makes ☐ twos.

   b Two sixths plus three sixths makes ☐ sixths.

   c Five x's plus six x's makes ☐ x's.

   d Three square roots of two plus five square roots of two makes ☐ square roots of two.

2 Write down each of the following expressions using mathematical notation and determine if they can be further simplified.

   a Three twos plus four fives.

   b One third plus three quarters.

   c Six x's plus five y's.

   d Two square roots of two plus two square roots of three.

3 Based on steps **1** and **2**, deduce a rule for adding and subtracting square roots.

4 Compare and contrast these four expressions. State in what ways are they similar and in what ways are they different.

$$3x + 8x \qquad 3 \times 5 + 8 \times 5$$

$$\frac{3}{10} + \frac{8}{10} \qquad 3\sqrt{2} + 8\sqrt{2}$$

5 Simplify each of these four expressions.

$$\sqrt{5} + \sqrt{5} \qquad 2\sqrt{5}$$

$$\sqrt{10} \qquad \sqrt{20}$$

   a Without using a calculator, determine which of the expressions are equal.

   b Use your calculator to verify your answer.

   c Of the expressions that are equal, suggest which one is written in its simplest form.

6 Each of these expressions has been simplified.

$$2\sqrt{5} + 7\sqrt{5} = 9\sqrt{5} \qquad 6\sqrt{3} - 2\sqrt{3} = 4\sqrt{3}$$

$$2\sqrt{7} - 10\sqrt{7} = -8\sqrt{7} \qquad 7\sqrt{10} + 3\sqrt{10} - 4\sqrt{10} = 6\sqrt{10}$$

Deduce a rule for adding/subtracting radical expressions.

A *vinculum* is a horizontal line used in mathematical notation for grouping things together.

In 1637, René Descartes was the first to combine the German radical sign $\sqrt{}$ with the vinculum to create the radical symbol we use today.

See how it is used to distinguish $\sqrt{288}x^8y^3$ from $\sqrt{288x^8y^3}$.

You can add or subtract two numbers only when you are adding multiples of the same amount. For example:

- $2a + 3a$ can be simplified to $5a$, since a can be factored out to give $(2 + 3)a$ or $5a$.

- $2a + 3b$ cannot be simplified since a and b are not like terms, that is, a and b have no common factors. Thus, $2a + 3b$ is written in its *simplest form*.

The same is true for square roots:

- $2\sqrt{5} + 3\sqrt{5} = 5\sqrt{5}$
- $2\sqrt{5} + 3\sqrt{7}$ cannot be simplified.

Example 4

Where possible, simplify these expressions that involve square roots.

a $4\sqrt{6} + 2\sqrt{6}$ **b** $\sqrt{8} + \sqrt{2}$ **c** $\sqrt{5} + \sqrt{7}$ **d** $\sqrt{48} + \sqrt{32}$

a $4\sqrt{6} + 2\sqrt{6} = 6\sqrt{6}$ ——————— Just like $4x + 2x = 6x$.

b $\sqrt{8} + \sqrt{2}$ ——————— Convert to equivalent square roots.

$\sqrt{8} = \sqrt{4 \times 2} = \sqrt{4} \times \sqrt{2} = 2\sqrt{2}$ ——————— Simplify $\sqrt{8}$.

$\sqrt{8} + \sqrt{2} = 2\sqrt{2} + \sqrt{2}$ ——————— Substitute $2\sqrt{2}$ for $\sqrt{8}$ in the original expression.

$= 3\sqrt{2}$ ——————— Adding terms involving square roots is possible only when they have the same square root.

c $\sqrt{5} + \sqrt{7}$ ——————— There are no like terms, so this is the simplest form.

d $\sqrt{48} + \sqrt{32} = \sqrt{16 \times 3} + \sqrt{16 \times 2}$ ——————— The largest square factor of 48 is 16. The largest square factor of 32 is 16.

$= 4\sqrt{3} + 4\sqrt{2}$ ——————— This cannot be simplified any further.

Reflect and discuss 5

- How does simplification help you add or subtract unlike radicals?

- In part **d** of Example 4, why is it better to simplify $\sqrt{48} + \sqrt{32}$ to $4\sqrt{3} + 4\sqrt{2}$?

- How is adding and subtracting square roots similar to adding and subtracting polynomials?

- How is simplifying square roots similar to simplifying fractions?

<div class="rule-box">

Rule 4 of radicals

For $c \geq 0$:

$a\sqrt{c} + b\sqrt{c} = (a+b)\sqrt{c}$

Similarly, you can also subtract radicals in the same way:

$a\sqrt{c} - b\sqrt{c} = (a-b)\sqrt{c}$

</div>

Practice 4

Simplify these expressions.

1 $7\sqrt{3} - 9\sqrt{3}$

2 $\sqrt{17} + 16\sqrt{17}$

3 $12\sqrt{a+3} - 9\sqrt{a+3}$

4 $2\sqrt{pq} + 4\sqrt{pq}$

5 $\sqrt{27} - \sqrt{12}$

6 $2\sqrt{12} + \sqrt{48}$

7 $2\sqrt{75} - 5\sqrt{27}$

8 $\sqrt{8} + \sqrt{128} + \sqrt{48} + \sqrt{18}$

9 $\sqrt{54} - \sqrt{20} + \sqrt{45} - \sqrt{24}$

10 $\sqrt{12} + \sqrt{32} + \sqrt{75} + \sqrt{162}$

Problem solving

11 $4\sqrt{12x} + 3\sqrt{27x}$

12 $\sqrt{3x^2} - \sqrt{48}$

13 $\sqrt{27x} - \sqrt{3x^3}$

14 $2\sqrt{4x+8y} - 5\sqrt{9x+18y}$

The period T in seconds of a simple pendulum of length L in feet is given by

$T = 2\pi\sqrt{\dfrac{L}{32}}$.

Another way to simplify radicals is to rationalize the denominator.

Reflect and discuss 6

Until now, you have probably dealt with fractions only where the denominator is a whole number, such as $\frac{1}{4}$ or $\frac{10}{3}$.

You can think of $\frac{1}{4}$ as $1 \div 4$ and $\frac{10}{3}$ as $10 \div 3$.

There are two possible types of decimal numbers: those with a finite number of decimal places or an infinite number of decimal places that repeat (rational numbers), and those with an infinite number of decimal places that don't repeat (irrational numbers).

- How difficult is it to divide by rational numbers?

- How difficult would it be to divide by an irrational number?

D How radicals behave

- Can irrational numbers be combined to form rational numbers?

Irrational numbers were discovered around 520 BCE, during the time of Pythagoras. However, it wasn't until around 300 BCE that the Greek mathematician Euclid proved the existence of irrational numbers in his book *The Elements*.

Objective B: Investigating patterns
ii. Describe patterns as general rules consistent with findings

To find a general rule, make sure that the rule applies to all the specific cases which are similar. If the rule applies only to some specific cases but not others, then it is not consistent with your findings.

Exploration 8

Some (but not all) square roots are irrational numbers:

$\sqrt{3}$ is irrational

$\sqrt{4} = 2$ is rational

1 Here is a list of irrational numbers:

$$\sqrt{5} \quad 1+\sqrt{2} \quad \sqrt{27} \quad 3+\sqrt{3} \quad \sqrt{20} \quad 2-\sqrt{2} \quad \sqrt{45}$$

Find pairs such that:

a their sum is rational

b their sum is irrational

c their product is rational

d their product is irrational.

2 Suggest values for the length and width of a rectangle such that:

a its perimeter is rational and its area is irrational

b its perimeter is irrational and its area is rational

c both its perimeter and area are irrational.

Determine if all these combinations are possible. Justify your answer.

3 The simplified form of $\sqrt{20}$ is $2\sqrt{5}$. Explain whether or not you think there are times when $\sqrt{20}$ is better to use than $2\sqrt{5}$.

Some irrational numbers found in nature such as $\pi \, (= 3.14159\ldots)$ and $e \, (= 2.718\ldots)$ cannot be expressed in terms of radicals. They are part of a set of numbers known as transcendental numbers.

The Greek letter phi (ϕ) represents the 'Golden ratio', a geometric relationship. The value of ϕ is given by: $\phi = \frac{1+\sqrt{5}}{2}$.

The Golden ratio appears not just in mathematics, but in architecture, music, painting, nature, design and many other areas.

Summary

- A **square root** (also known as a **radical** or **surd**) of a positive number x is a number which, when multiplied by itself, gives the original number x. Any positive number has two square roots: one positive and one negative.

- The **principal square root** of a positive number x is the *positive* square root of x, and is written as $\sqrt{x}$.

- A **rational number** is a number that can be written as a fraction $\frac{p}{q}$ where $p, q \in \mathbb{Z}$ and $q \neq 0$.

  For example, $\frac{1}{2}, \frac{5}{6}, \frac{9}{5}, 4, -\frac{12}{51}, 1.2, -0.\overline{3}$, and 0 are all rational numbers.

- An **irrational number** is a number that cannot be written as a fraction. Irrational numbers cannot be represented as terminating or repeating decimals. $\sqrt{2}$ and π (pi) are examples of irrational numbers.

Rules of radicals

For any real numbers $a, b, c \geq 0$:

Rule 1 $\quad \sqrt{a^2} = a$

Rule 2 $\quad \sqrt{a \times b} = \sqrt{a} \times \sqrt{b}$

Rule 3 $\quad \sqrt{\dfrac{a}{b}} = \dfrac{\sqrt{a}}{\sqrt{b}} \quad b \neq 0$

Rule 4 $\quad$ For $c \geq 0$:

$a\sqrt{c} + b\sqrt{c} = (a+b)\sqrt{c}$

You can also subtract radicals in the same way:

$a\sqrt{c} - b\sqrt{c} = (a-b)\sqrt{c}$

Mixed practice

Compare the following pairs of values and replace the ☐ by using <, > or =.

1 $\sqrt{84} \ \square \ 2\sqrt{20}$ **2** $\sqrt{20} \ \square \ \dfrac{9}{6}$

3 $\dfrac{\sqrt{6}}{7} \ \square \ \dfrac{\sqrt{7}}{6}$ **4** $\sqrt{15} \ \square \ 3.75$

Without using a calculator, **estimate** the value of the principal square roots correct to 1d.p.

5 $\sqrt{45}$ **6** $\sqrt{17}$

7 $\sqrt{54}$ **8** $\sqrt{12}$

Simplify these expressions completely. Remember to rationalize the denominator when necessary.

9 $\sqrt{12}$ **10** $\sqrt{18}$

11 $\sqrt{125}$ **12** $\sqrt{121x^3}$

13 $\sqrt{10} \times \sqrt{360}$ **14** $\sqrt{3} \times \sqrt{12}$

15 $\sqrt{xy^3} \times \sqrt{x^5 y}$ **16** $\dfrac{\sqrt{98}}{\sqrt{2}}$

17 $\dfrac{\sqrt{15}}{\sqrt{3x}}$ **18** $\dfrac{6}{\sqrt{24}}$

19 $\dfrac{10}{\sqrt{12}}$ **20** $12\sqrt{13} - 2\sqrt{13}$

21 $5\sqrt{8} - 3\sqrt{50}$ **22** $6\sqrt{4x} + 3\sqrt{9x}$

23 $2\sqrt{20t} + 4\sqrt{45t}$ **24** $\sqrt{200a} + \sqrt{128a} - \sqrt{8a}$

Reflect and discuss 7

How have you explored the statement of inquiry? Give specific examples.

Statement of inquiry:

Representing numbers in different forms to simplify them can help understand human-made systems.

1.6 Absolute value

Global context: Globalization and sustainability

Related concept: Approximation

FORM

Objectives

- Knowing different definitions for the absolute value of a number
- Understanding the properties of the absolute value of a number

Inquiry questions

F
- What is an absolute value?

C
- How are the properties of absolute value similar to other properties in mathematics?
- How can error be measured when estimating or approximating?

D
- How can error best be measured?
- Can you ever know the exact value of a measurement?

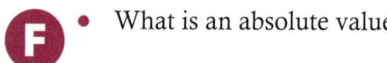

ATL Critical-thinking

Draw reasonable conclusions and generalizations

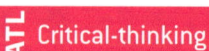

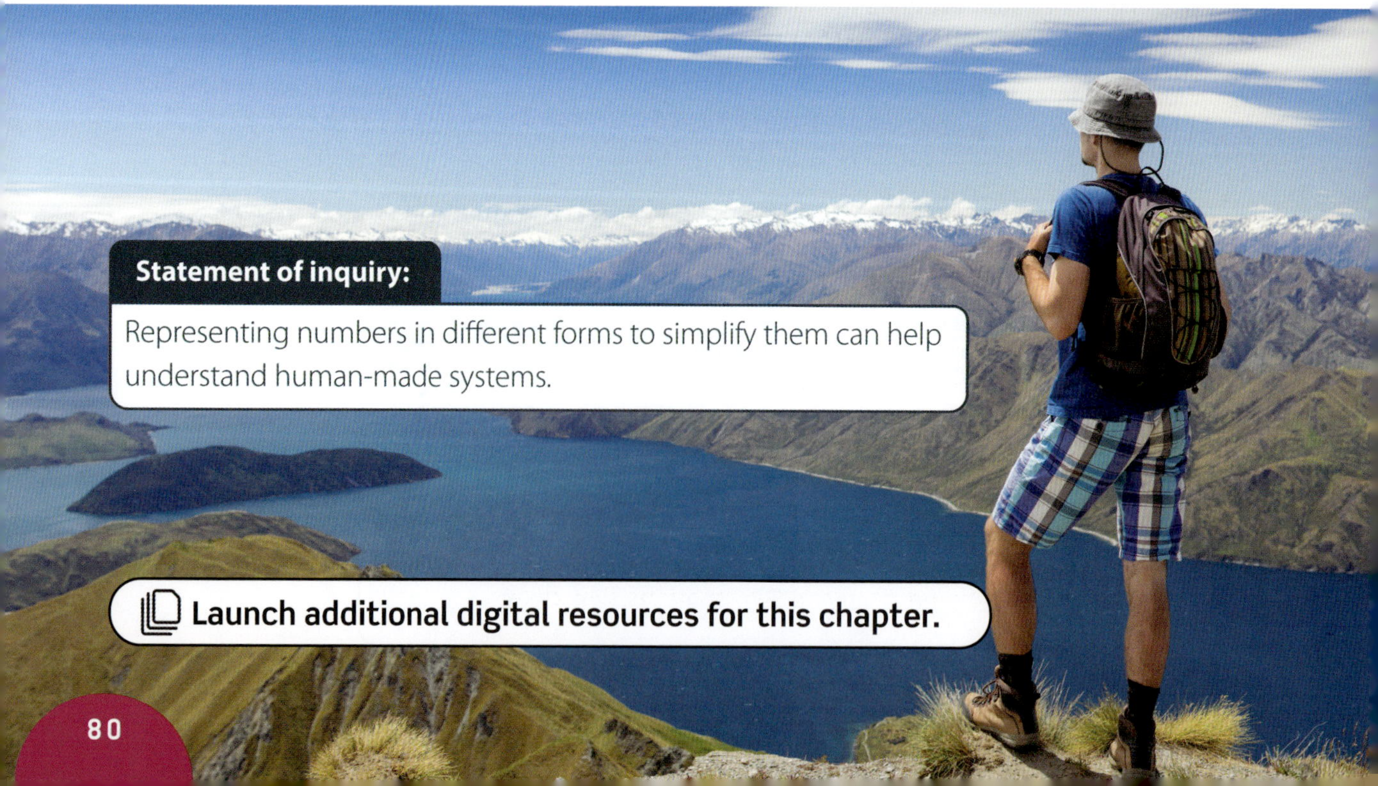

Statement of inquiry:

Representing numbers in different forms to simplify them can help understand human-made systems.

⎘ **Launch additional digital resources for this chapter.**

You should already know how to:

calculate with negative integers	**1** Work out these calculations. **a** $4-6$ **b** $-3+7$ **c** -5×3 **d** $18 \div -2$
find the square root of a number	**2** Work out these expressions. **a** $\sqrt{121}$ **b** $\sqrt{7^2}$ **c** $\sqrt{\dfrac{1}{4}}$ **d** $\sqrt{0.01}$
substitute positive and negative numbers into expressions	**3** When $a = 4$ and $b = -2$, find: **a** $a+b$ **b** $a-b$ **c** a^2 **d** b^2 **e** $\sqrt{a}$ **f** $-ab$

F Introduction to absolute value

- What is an absolute value?

Activity

State the temperature difference between:

1 sunrise and noon

2 sunrise and sunset

3 sunrise and night

4 noon and sunset.

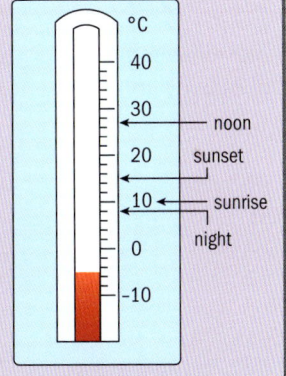

To calculate a difference between two quantities a and b, you subtract one from the other. In this Activity, did you always calculate $a - b$ or $b - a$? Or did you choose the one that gave a positive answer?

Here is one way of calculating the temperature differences:

1 Between sunrise and noon, the temperature *rose* by $17°$, so the difference is $27° - 10° = 17°$.

2 Between sunrise and sunset, the temperature *rose* by $5°$, so the difference is $15° - 10° = 5°$.

3 Between sunrise and night, the temperature *dropped* by $2°$, so the difference is $8° - 10° = -2°$.

4 Between noon and sunset, the temperature *dropped* by $12°$, so the difference is $15° - 27° = -12°$.

Reflect and discuss 1

When we talk about differences in real-life situations, why do we usually use the positive differences?

After playing a game, asking the question 'Who won?' tells you who had the highest score. Asking 'By how much?' gives you the difference between the two scores. The winners may say 'We won by 7 points'. The losers may say 'We lost by 7 points'. It would be highly unusual for someone to say 'We had −7 points'.

The negative difference is implied in the context. When a team loses by 7 points, it has obviously scored 7 points *less* than the other team, and not 7 points *more*. If the temperature dropped by 20°, it obviously went *down* and not *up*. The numbers used are always positive, because we use the absolute value.

The **absolute value** of a number is the distance on the number line between that number and 0. We write $|x|$ to mean 'the absolute value of x'.

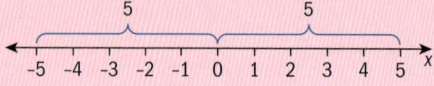

For example, $|5| = 5$, and $|-5| = 5$.

On some calculators the absolute value function button is abs(x).

Using absolute value notation, the temperature differences you calculated in the Activity are:

1 Between sunrise and noon:
$$|27° - 10°| = |17°| = 17°$$

2 Between sunrise and sunset:
$$|15° - 10°| = |5°| = 5°$$

3 Between sunrise and night:
$$|8° - 10°| = |-2°| = 2°$$

4 Between noon and sunset:
$$|15° - 27°| = |-12°| = 12°$$

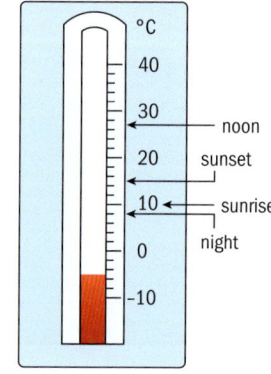

ATL

Exploration 1

1 Let $x = a$ if $a \geq 0$, and $x = -a$ if $a < 0$. Find x for each value of a.

    a $a = 12$ **b** $a = 0$ **c** $a = -5$ **d** $a = \dfrac{3}{5}$

    e $a = -\dfrac{3}{5}$ **f** $a = 3.14159$ **g** $a = -3.14159$ **h** $a = -0.003$

Describe what you notice about your answers.

State your findings as a general rule.

2 Give the positive square root of:

    a $\sqrt{3^2}$ **b** $\sqrt{5^2}$ **c** $\sqrt{(-2)^2}$ **d** $\sqrt{12^2}$

    e $\sqrt{(-12)^2}$ **f** $\sqrt{\left(\dfrac{1}{2}\right)^2}$ **g** $\sqrt{\left(-\dfrac{1}{3}\right)^2}$ **h** $\sqrt{(-a)^2}$

Describe what you notice about your answers.

State your findings as a general rule.

The first definition is an example of a *piecewise function*. The function has a different definition for the different values of x.

Reflect and discuss 2

- Why can't you take the absolute value of the square root of a negative number, for example: $\sqrt{-4}$ or $\sqrt{-9}$?

- Can you take the square root of the absolute value of any real number ($\sqrt{|a|}$, if $a \in \mathbb{R}$)?

- Can you take the absolute value of any real number?

Practice 1

1 Write down the value of the following. Leave your answer as a simplified surd when possible.

a $|35|$ **b** $-|35|$ **c** $|-234|$ **d** $-|-234|$

e $|-5.6|$ **f** $|2.8|$ **g** $|0|$ **h** $\left|\frac{4}{8}\right|$

i $\left|-\frac{2}{5}\right|$ **j** $|10^{-2}|$ **k** $|-4^3|$ **l** $|\sqrt{36}|$

m $-|\sqrt{25}|$ **n** $|-\sqrt{32}|$ **o** $-|-\sqrt{24}|$ **p** $-|(-10)^3|$

2 Find the value of:

a $|4+9|$ **b** $|-2+5|$ **c** $|12-9|$ **d** $|4-9|$

e $|5.1-7.2|$ **f** $|3\times6|$ **g** $|-7.5\times2|$ **h** $\left|-\frac{3}{5}\right|\times10$

i $|-3|+|8|$ **j** $|-3|-|8|$ **k** $|-4|\times|-2|$ **l** $|-4\times-2|$

Problem solving

3 a Write two numbers that have an absolute value of 4.

b Write two calculations whose answers have an absolute value of 6.

4 On a highway, driving too fast or too slow can cause accidents. For safe highway driving, there should be no more than a 20 km/h difference between cars' speeds.

a Gauthier is driving at 97 km/h. Nathan is driving at 113 km/h on the same section of highway. Determine whether or not they are driving safely relative to each other.

b The average speed on a stretch of highway is 110 km/h. If Louis is traveling at the average speed, determine the minimum and maximum speeds for others to be driving safely relatively to Louis on this stretch of highway.

C Properties and applications of absolute value

- How are the properties of absolute value similar to other properties in mathematics?
- How can error be measured when estimating or approximating?

> The absolute value is also called the modulus or the numerical value.

Objective: B. Investigating patterns
ii. describe patterns as general rules consistent with findings

In Exploration 2 you will be looking for patterns. Organizing the information in a table allows you to observe trends.

ATL

Exploration 2

1 Determine which of these real numbers could be an absolute value.

   a 5   **b** -392 **c** -2.625 **d** 1.001

   e -0.005 **f** $\sqrt{25}$ **g** $\sqrt{17}$ **h** $-\sqrt{2}$

   Write down your findings as a general property.

2 Find $|a \times b|$ and $|a| \times |b|$ for each pair of values a and b.

   a $a = 11, b = 7$ **b** $a = -6, b = 4$ **c** $a = 8, b = -\frac{1}{4}$

   d $a = -0.2, b = -15$ **e** $a = -\sqrt{3}, b = -3$ **f** $a = -\frac{1}{6}, b = 6$

   Describe what you notice.

   Write down your findings as a general property.

3 Find $\left|\dfrac{a}{b}\right|$ and $\dfrac{|a|}{|b|}$ for each pair of values of a and b.

   a $a = 3, b = 10$ **b** $a = -2, b = 4$ **c** $a = 1, b = -5$

   d $a = -3, b = -30$ **e** $a = -\sqrt{2}, b = -2$ **f** $a = -0.2, b = -0.8$

   Describe what you notice.

   Write down your findings as a general property.

4 Find $|a^2|$, $|a|^2$ and a^2 for the following values of a:

   a $a = 5$ **b** $a = -3$ **c** $a = \frac{1}{2}$

   d $a = \sqrt{6}$ **e** $a = -\sqrt{11}$

   Describe what you notice.

   Write down a general rule consistent with your findings.

5 Copy and complete this table:

a	$\lvert a^3 \rvert$	$\lvert a \rvert^3$	a^3	$\lvert a^4 \rvert$	$\lvert a \rvert^4$	a^4	$\lvert a^5 \rvert$	$\lvert a \rvert^5$	a^5	$\lvert a^n \rvert$	$\lvert a \rvert^n$	a^n
2												
-2												
-3												

   Describe any generalizations that you notice.

   Write your findings as a general rule using the last three columns to help you.

▶ Continued on next page

6 Copy and complete this table:

a	b	$\lvert a+b \rvert$	$\lvert a \rvert + \lvert b \rvert$	$\lvert a-b \rvert$	$\lvert b-a \rvert$	$\lvert a \rvert - \lvert b \rvert$
8	3					
6	−4					
−1	9					
−5	−7					
$\frac{1}{4}$	$-\frac{1}{2}$					

Draw conclusions from the table.

Use the symbols ≥, ≤ and = to complete these general properties:

a $\lvert a-b \rvert$ ☐ $\lvert b-a \rvert$ **b** $\lvert a+b \rvert$ ☐ $\lvert a \rvert + \lvert b \rvert$

c $\lvert a+b \rvert$ ☐ $\lvert a \rvert - \lvert b \rvert$ **d** $\lvert a-b \rvert$ ☐ $\lvert a \rvert - \lvert b \rvert$

Properties of absolute value

For any numbers $a, b \in \mathbb{R}$:

1 $\lvert a \rvert \geq 0$ **2** $\lvert a \times b \rvert = \lvert a \rvert \times \lvert b \rvert$ **3** $\left\lvert \dfrac{a}{b} \right\rvert = \dfrac{\lvert a \rvert}{\lvert b \rvert}$ **4** $\lvert a \rvert^2 = a^2$

5 $\lvert a^n \rvert = \lvert a \rvert^n$ **6** $\lvert a-b \rvert = \lvert b-a \rvert$ **7** $\lvert a+b \rvert \leq \lvert a \rvert + \lvert b \rvert$ **8** $\lvert a-b \rvert \geq \lvert \lvert a \rvert - \lvert b \rvert \rvert$

Property 7 without the equality is also called the **Triangular Inequality Rule**. If a and b are the lengths of two sides of a triangle, then the length of the 3rd side must be shorter than the sum of the other two sides. Why do you think this is true?

Practice 2

Substitute the values for a and b to find the value of each expression.

1 $a = 7, b = -4$:

    a $\lvert a+2b \rvert$ **b** $\lvert a-2b \rvert$ **c** $\lvert -2a+b \rvert$

    d $\lvert -2a-b \rvert$ **e** $\lvert 3b-3a \rvert$ **f** $\lvert b^3 \rvert$

2 $a = -5, b = 3$:

    a $a + \lvert a+b \rvert$ **b** $-a + \lvert a-b \rvert - b$ **c** $a + \lvert a \rvert + b + \lvert b \rvert$

    d $3a - \lvert a \rvert$ **e** $3b - \lvert b \rvert$ **f** $\lvert a^4 \rvert$

3 $a = 1$, $b = -1$:

a $a + |a| + b + |b|$

b $-b - |b| - a - |a|$

c $\dfrac{a + |b|}{b - |a|}$

d $\left| \dfrac{a + |b|}{b - |a|} \right|$

e $\dfrac{a + |b|}{a - |b|}$

f $\left| a^3 - |b^{11}| \right|$

Problem solving

4 Determine values of b for which $|8 - b| - |b - 3|$ is a positive number.

Any measurement, such as a length, is made to a certain degree of accuracy. For example, you might measure the distance between two cities in kilometers, and the height of a person in meters and centimeters. You choose a degree of accuracy that is 'good enough' to give an idea of the actual distance or height. Would it make sense to calculate the distance between cities to the nearest centimeter? Or a person's height to the nearest kilometer?

Every measurement you make is accurate only to a certain degree, so it is not an exact value. You can weigh an object to the nearest milligram, and this is more accurate than weighing it to the nearest gram or to the nearest centigram, but not as accurate as weighing it to the nearest microgram.

length = 17.4 cm

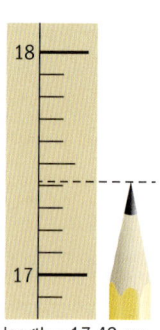

length = 17.42 cm

The **true value** of a measurement is the value that would be obtained by a perfect measurement. This is, by its nature, not really possible to obtain. **Accuracy** describes how close a measurement is to the true value.

In the following exploration, example, and practice we use the most accurate possible measurement as the true value.

Exploration 3

1 Measure your height, the length of a piece of paper, and the width of an eraser to the nearest centimeter. Copy the table and write your measurements in the first column.

2 Now measure your height, the length of a piece of paper, and the width of an eraser as accurately as you can, to the nearest millimeter. Consider these to be the true values for these measurements. Write them in the second column of your table.

	Measurement to the nearest cm	True value – most accurate measurement (to the nearest mm)	Absolute error	Relative error	Percentage error
Your height					
The length of a piece of paper					
The width of an eraser					

> The **absolute error**, Δx, of a measurement is the actual amount of error in a measurement.
>
> $\Delta x = |\text{true value} - \text{measured value}|$

3 Calculate the absolute error for each measurement using this definition:

Write the absolute errors in your table.

4 Compare the absolute errors. Write down what you notice.

> The **relative error** is the error in a measurement compared to the size of the thing being measured.
>
> Relative error $= \dfrac{\Delta x}{x} = \dfrac{\text{absolute error}}{\text{true value}}$

5 Calculate the relative error for each measurement using this definition:

6 Write the relative errors in your table.

7 Calculate the percentage error for each measurement using this definition:

> The **percentage error** is the relative error of a measurement written as a percentage.

8 Write the percentage errors in the table.

9 Compare the percentage errors. Write down what you notice.

Example 1

Frederico measured his height to be 132 cm. His doctor then measures him and says that Frederico has made an error of 5% in his measurement.

a Find Frederico's true height.

b Explain why there are two possible values for his true height.

a An error of 5% means a relative error of 0.05. ——— Write the percentage error as a relative error.

Let x = true value

$|132 - x|$ = absolute error

$\text{Relative error} = \dfrac{\text{absolute error}}{\text{true value}}$ ——— Substitute into the definition.

$0.05 = \dfrac{|132 - x|}{x}$ ——— Solve for x.

$0.05x = |132 - x|$

$0.05x = 132 - x$ or $0.05x = x - 132$

$1.05x = 132$ $-0.95x = -132$

$x = 125.714$ $x = 138.947$

Frederico's true height is either 126 cm or 139 cm. ——— Use the same level of accuracy as in the question.

b Absolute error does not tell us whether Frederico's measurement is above or below his true height – we would need more information to know which.

Practice 3

1 Elias estimated that 20 people would attend an evening lecture. In fact, 23 people attended. Find the percentage error in his estimate.

2 Breanna measured the capacity of a mug five times. Her results were: 240.5 ml, 240.9 ml, 240.2 ml, 239.5 ml, 241.2 ml.

   a Calculate the mean value for the capacity.
   b The true capacity of the mug is 240.1 ml. Calculate the percentage error of the mean result.
   c Do you think this is an acceptable percentage error? Explain.

3 Markéta bought a 250 g pack of butter. She weighed it to find its actual mass was 240 g. Find the percentage error in mass. Take 240 g as the true value.

4 Amelia made an 18% error in a calculation. Her incorrect answer is $27.50. Find two possible correct answers.

5 A factory produces cereal bars with mass 58 g, and percentage error up to 2%. Find the range of possible masses of cereal bars from this factory.

'To err is human; to forgive, divine.'

Alexander Pope, 1711

'To err is human; but to really foul things up you need a computer.'

Paul Ehrlich, 1969

Problem solving

6 Huỳnh tests all the scales in the science lab before an experiment. A scale fails the test if it has a percentage error of 12% or more. Huỳnh uses a 500 g mass to test each scale. Complete this statement: Scales that measure a 500 g mass as less than ___ g or more than ___ g will fail the test.

7 Find the measurement that has the largest absolute error.

- 500 kg measured with a percentage error of 1%

- 30 kg measured with a percentage error of 10%

D When are absolute values useful?

- How can error best be measured?
- How do systems influence communities?

Absolute value measures the error in a measurement. These errors either come from the accuracy of the measuring tool or from your accuracy in reading it.

Reflect and discuss 3

- Which type of error (absolute, relative or percentage) is the best to use? Justify your arguments.

- Absolute error is the absolute value of the difference between the true value and the measured value. Could you measure the absolute error without taking the absolute value?

- Think of situations when it would be better *not* to use the absolute value to describe an error. When is it important to know whether the error has a positive or negative value?

Some websites claim to give the true world population, plus the number of births and deaths so far that year, so naturally this population number is changing constantly. If the population figure varied between 7 379 930 858 and 7 379 930 871 over a one-minute period, what would be a good approximation for the world population? Could anyone ever know the exact value of the world population?

Reflect and discuss 4

- Why do we often use approximations instead of exact amounts? Is it always appropriate to use approximations?

- If you measure a length to the nearest cm and then to the nearest mm, you can still make a more exact measurement to the exact 0.1 mm or 0.01 mm. Can you ever know the *exact* length of something?

- Is it important to know *exact* values, or can you always use approximations? How can knowing the size of the error in a measurement help you decide whether an approximation is acceptable?

The world's population density is 47 people per square kilometer. The most densely populated country is Monaco at 16 205 people per square kilometer; the least populated is Mongolia with 2 per square kilometer.

Summary

The **absolute value** of a number is the distance on the number line between that number and 0. $|x|$ means 'the absolute value of x'.

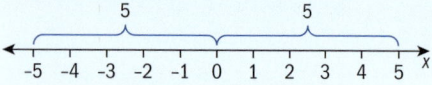

For example, $|5| = 5$, and $|-5| = 5$

Properties of absolute value

For any numbers $a, b \in \mathbb{R}$:

1 $|a| \geq 0$ **2** $|a \times b| = |a| \times |b|$

3 $\left|\dfrac{a}{b}\right| = \dfrac{|a|}{|b|}$ **4** $|a|^2 = a^2$

5 $|a^n| = |a|^n$ **6** $|a - b| = |b - a|$

7 $|a + b| \leq |a| + |b|$ **8** $|a - b| \geq \big||a| - |b|\big|$

The **true value** of a measurement is the value that would be obtained by a perfect measurement. **Accuracy** describes how close a measurement is to the true value.

The **absolute error**, Δx, of a measurement is the actual amount of error in a measurement.
$\Delta x = |\text{true value} - \text{measured value}|$

The **relative error** is the error in a measurement compared to the size of the thing being measured.

Relative error $= \dfrac{\Delta x}{x} = \dfrac{\text{absolute error}}{\text{true value}}$

The **percentage error** is the relative error of a measurement written as a percentage.

Mixed practice

1 **Find** the value of these expressions.

  a $|-33|$ **b** $-|4 - 6.5|$

  c $-|-2.3 + 8.05|$ **d** $|12.3 - 7.8|$

  e $\left|-\dfrac{2}{9}\right|$ **f** $|(-2)^5|$

  g $\left|\sqrt{27}\right|$ **h** $-\left|-\sqrt{81}\right|$

2 **Find** the value of these expressions.

  a $|4| \times |-5|$ **b** $-|-(-6)^2|$

  c $\dfrac{|6|}{-|12|}$ **d** $\left|\dfrac{-27}{-6}\right|$

  e $\left|-\dfrac{2}{5}\right| \times \left|\dfrac{9}{-8}\right|$ **f** $\left|\dfrac{1}{12}\right| \times \left|-\dfrac{144}{5}\right|$

  g $\dfrac{|-56|}{|7.2 - 8|}$ **h** $\dfrac{|15| \times |-3|}{|4 - 6.25| \times |7 - 3|}$

3 The exact length of a bent stick is 22.2 cm. Daniel measured it with a straight ruler and estimated its length to be 21.5 cm. **Find** the percentage error of his estimate.

4 Soraya bought 3 meters of ribbon. When she measured it, she found there were 3.15 meters of ribbon. **Find** the percentage error in the 3 meter measurement.

5 Moa charges €10 to iron 8 shirts. On average, she irons 8 shirts per hour.

  a **Determine** how much she charges to iron 20 shirts.

  b **Determine** her average hourly rate.

  c On Monday, Moa ironed 20 shirts in 2 hours and 15 minutes. She charged the customer €25.

    i **Determine** Moa's hourly rate for these shirts.

    ii **Find** the percentage difference between her average hourly rate (in part **b**) and her hourly rate for these shirts.

  d On Friday, she took 3 hours and 12 minutes to iron 20 shirts. **Find** the percentage difference between her average hourly rate (in part **b**) and her hourly rate for these shirts.

> Which rate is the exact rate?
> Which one is an estimate?

Review in context

Globalization and sustainability

1 The most recent census in China was in July 2015 and the population was reported in official government statistics to be 1 376 048 943.

In two separate articles, this figure was quoted to be 1 376 049 000 and 1.38 billion.

a **Calculate** the absolute error in each of these figures compared to the official figure.

b **Calculate** the percentage errors.

c **Discuss** whether it is better to use absolute or percentage errors.

d Government sources suggest that, due to the reliability of the way it is measured, the official figure may be inaccurate by plus or minus 1.8%.

Calculate what this is as an absolute error.

e **Calculate** the possible range for the population.

f **Discuss** what might be a reliable figure to use to report the population of China.

g Here are the populations of some countries, also given in 2015:

United States	321 442 019
Germany	80 688 545
Malaysia	30 331 007
Australia	23 968 973
Monaco	37 731

If the figures could also be inaccurate by 1.8%, **find** the absolute errors. Use these to give reliable values to quote for these populations, and **justify** why the values are reliable.

2

UK population grows by half a million in a year

Between 2013 and 2014 the UK population rose from 64 106 779 to 64 510 376.

a **Find** the exact change in population.

b **Find** the percentage error in the headline figure of half a million.

c In 2014, 17.7% of the population were aged 65 and over. In 2013 the percentage was 17.4%.

Find the actual change in the number of people aged 65 and over between 2013 and 2014.

d Is this figure an increase or a decrease?

e **Suggest** how these figures could be useful for planning healthcare in the UK.

3 Tobias went grocery shopping for himself and his roommate Felix. They usually split the cost of groceries in half, and since they never have exact change, they usually round the amount paid before splitting it in half. Today, Tobias paid exactly €95.74, and he rounded the amount up to an even €100 before telling Felix that he owed Tobias €50.

a **Calculate** the percentage error between the true amount Tobias paid and the rounded amount.

b **Discuss** whether or not it is reasonable for Felix to pay €50.

c **Calculate** the exact amount Felix should have reimbursed Tobias. Then **calculate** the percentage error between what Felix did pay and what he should have paid.

d **Discuss** what you notice about the two percentage errors. Would it have made sense to just calculate absolute errors in this case?

Reflect and discuss 5

How have you explored the statement of inquiry? Give specific examples.

Statement of inquiry:

Representing numbers in different forms to simplify them can help understand human-made systems.

2 Decisions, decisions

F **Which logical skills enable you to model real life situations effectively?**

Lateral thinking

Three friends have lunch in a bistro and the bill is $25. They each give the waiter $10. The waiter doesn't know how to divide up the $5 in change evenly between three people, so he gives each person $1 back, and keeps $2 for himself as a tip.

Now, each customer contributed $10 and got $1 back, so effectively they each paid $9, which means they paid $27 altogether. So, $27 plus the $2 that the waiter kept adds up to a total of $29.

Where has the remaining $1 gone from the original $30 that they gave the waiter?

The mathematics here seems logical, but the outcome does not. Which do you think is in error?

We make generalizations all the time based on what we observe. How valid are those generalizations? To be valid, a generalization must be supported by facts that use logic and reasoning.

C **How do you validate generalizations?**

A generalization is a general statement made on the basis of specific examples. Validity is the use of well founded, logical mathematics to come to a true and accurate conclusion or a reasonable interpretation of results.

Science generally uses the method of inductive reasoning to validate generalizations, whereas Mathematics generally uses deductive reasoning.

Inductive reasoning involves finding evidence that supports a statement. The more supporting evidence you find, the more you can be sure that the statement is true.

Statement: Every swan I have seen is white, so that means **all** swans are white.

Test: Would you be happy to wager a lot of money that all swans are white? If not, how could you test your hypothesis?

Deductive reasoning involves generating new facts by manipulating existing ones. The transport puzzle below uses deductive reasoning.

Transport puzzle

A farmer is travelling to market with a bag of grain, a chicken, and a wolf. While he is with them, he can prevent the chicken from eating the grain, and the wolf from eating the chicken.

He needs to cross a river in a small boat that has room for him and only one other passenger at a time.

How can the farmer get himself, the grain, the chicken and the wolf safely to the other side of the river? Can you work it out using the fewest number of trips?

Of course, sometimes even logicians overlook sensible questions: Why would the farmer be travelling with a wolf in the first place?

D **To what extent does developing models enable you to understand real life situations effectively?**

A model is a depiction of real-life events using expressions, equations or graphs.

Should you take an umbrella?

How reliable are weather forecasts? Data shows that on the whole they are around seven times more accurate now than they were 20 years ago, because computers are getting faster, and the mathematics more sophisticated. The mathematical models take account of the formation of the atmosphere, equations of motion and thermodynamics and the uncertainty of a chaotic system.

Global context: Scientific and technical innovation

Exploration: Exploring the natural world by developing realistic models

📖 **Launch additional digital resources for this unit.**

2.1 Making generalizations

Global context: Scientific and technical innovation

Related concept: Generalization

LOGIC

Objectives

- Identifying patterns in number problems
- Solving complicated problems by looking at a more general case
- Making generalizations from a given pattern

Inquiry questions

F
- What is a conjecture?
- What is a generalization?

C
- How can generalizations be used to solve specific problems?

D
- What are the risks of making generalizations?

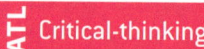

ATL Critical-thinking

Draw reasonable conclusions and generalizations

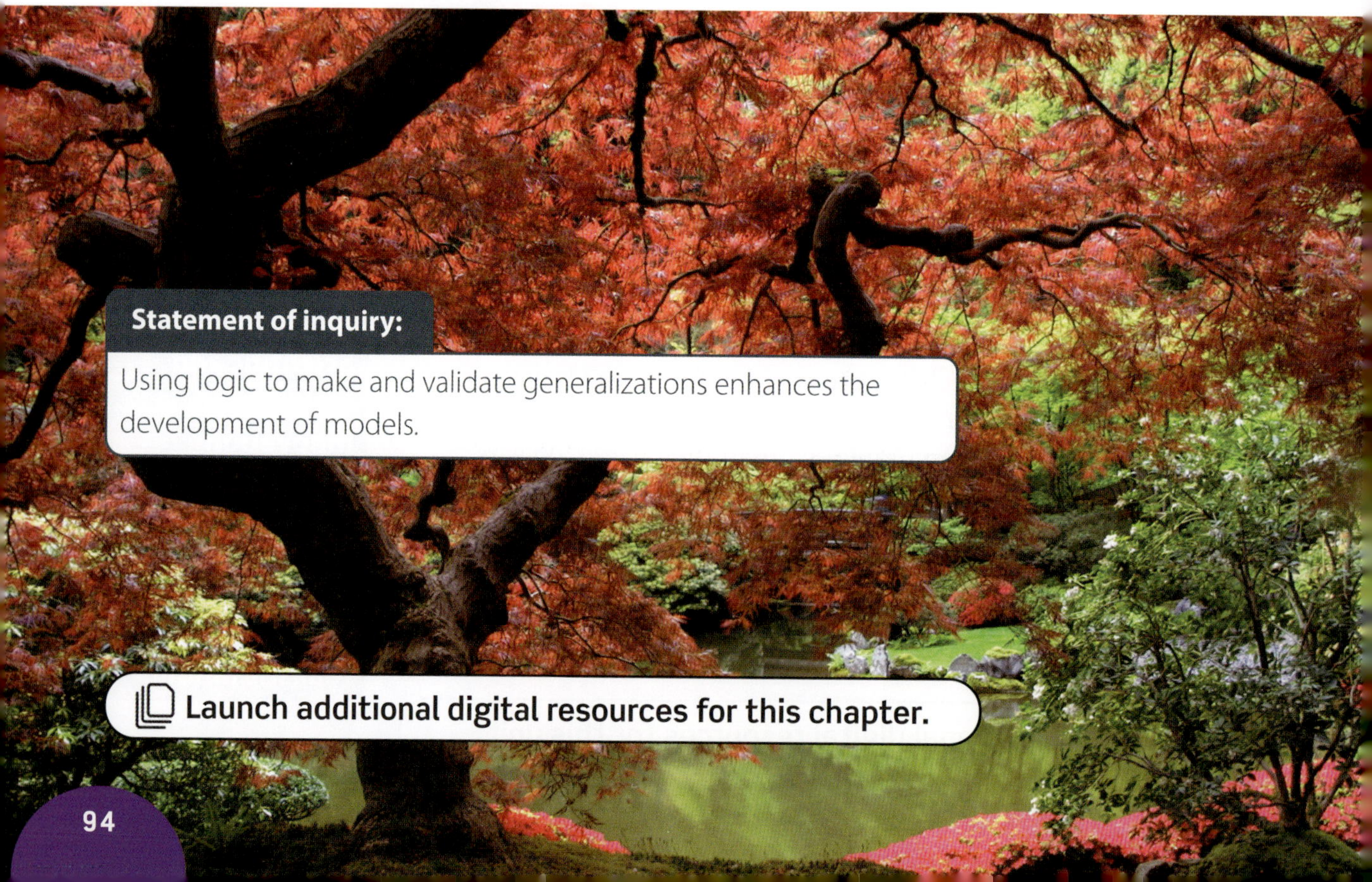

Statement of inquiry:

Using logic to make and validate generalizations enhances the development of models.

Launch additional digital resources for this chapter.

You should already know how to:

• expand brackets and simplify algebraic expressions	**1** Expand the brackets in each expression.
	  a $2x(3-4x)$ **b** $(4+x)(1-3x)$
	
	2 Simplify these expressions.
	  a $\dfrac{6x^3y^2}{2x^2y}$ **b** $\dfrac{12x^3y}{6y}-\dfrac{12x^5}{3x^4}$

• understand the terms LCM (lowest common multiple) and GCD (greatest common divisor) or HCF (highest common factor)	**3** Find the LCM of:
	  a 3 and 8 **b** 6 and 9
	
	4 Find the GCD (HCF) of:
	  a 12 and 54 **b** 10 and 75

 Generalization in mathematics

- What is a conjecture?
- What is a generalization?

In mathematics, one of the meanings of generalization relates to reasoning from the specific to the general. Often, it means looking at a limited amount of information and trying to make a statement (a conjecture) about an underlying trend, rule or pattern.

Reflect and discuss 1

Look at the following powers of 4.

$4^1 = 4$	$4^7 = 16\,384$
$4^2 = 16$	$4^8 = 65\,536$
$4^3 = 64$	$4^9 = 262\,144$
$4^4 = 256$	$4^{10} = 1\,048\,576$
$4^5 = 1024$	$4^{11} = 4\,194\,304$
$4^6 = 4096$	$4^{12} = 16\,777\,216$

Make a general statement about the powers of 4.

> Typically, forming a generalization involves collecting some information and trying to describe any patterns you notice. If you don't find a pattern, try looking at more information.

There are several things you might notice about the powers of 4. For example, they are all even. You might also notice something about the final digits. Suitable generalizations might include:

- Every power of 4 ends with a 4 or a 6.
- Every odd power of 4 ends with a 4.
- Every even power of 4 ends with a 6.

It's important to bear in mind that you don't yet know whether these generalizations will always hold true. Proving that a particular conjecture is *always* true is discussed in the chapter on justification.

A **conjecture** is a mathematical statement which has not yet been proved. Usually it is consistent with some known information. Once a conjecture has been proven to be true, we usually refer to it as a **theorem**.

A conjecture is similar to the idea of a hypothesis in science.

In 1994 Andrew Wiles found the first successful proof to Fermat's conjecture, which stated that no three positive integers a, b and c can satisfy the equation $a^n + b^n = c^n$ for any integer value of n greater than 2, a conjecture that mathematicians had been trying to prove for 358 years.

ATL

Practice 1

1 Write down the first few powers of 5.
Suggest a general statement about the last digits of the powers of 5.

2 For any number, the *digit sum* of the number is found by adding together the values of its digits. For example, the digit sum of 842 is $8 + 4 + 2 = 14$.

Write down some multiples of the number 9. List their digit sums.
Suggest a general statement about the digit sums of multiples of 9.

3 Look at the multiplication square below.

x	1	2	3	4	5	6	7	8	9	10
1	1	2	3	4	5	6	7	8	9	10
2	2	4	6	8	10	12	14	16	18	20
3	3	6	9	12	15	18	21	24	27	30
4	4	8	12	16	20	24	28	32	36	40
5	5	10	15	20	25	30	35	40	45	50
6	6	12	18	24	30	36	42	48	54	60
7	7	14	21	28	35	42	49	56	63	70
8	8	16	24	32	40	48	56	64	72	80
9	9	18	27	36	45	54	63	72	81	90
10	10	20	30	40	50	60	70	80	90	100

From within the square, select any 2×2 square, for example:

35	42
40	48

Find the difference between the sums of the entries in the two diagonal cells, in this case:

$(35 + 48) - (40 + 42)$.

Describe what you notice. Suggest a suitable general statement.

4 The *arithmetic mean* of two numbers a and b is given by $\frac{1}{2}(a + b)$.

The *geometric mean* of two numbers a and b is given by $\sqrt{ab}$.

Choose five pairs of different numbers. For each pair, calculate the arithmetic mean and the geometric mean. Form a general statement about the arithmetic mean and the geometric mean of a pair of numbers.

5 Consecutive integers are whole numbers which differ by one.

For example, 56 and 57 are a pair of consecutive integers.

  a Choose four pairs of consecutive integers.

  b For each pair, double the smaller number and add it to the larger number. Write down the total each time.

  c Divide each total by 3 and describe anything you notice. Suggest a suitable general statement.

Problem solving

6 a Choose a few pairs of numbers (a, b).

  b For each pair, find:

   i their product, ab

   ii their lowest common multiple, $LCM(a, b)$

   iii their greatest common divisor, $GCD(a, b)$.

  c Organize your results.

  d Describe what you notice. Suggest a suitable general statement.

7 Observe that $4 = 2 + 2$, $6 = 3 + 3$, $8 = 5 + 3$, $10 = 7 + 3$ and $12 = 7 + 5$.
All these even numbers have been written as the sum of two prime numbers.

  a Show that 14, 16, 18 and 20 can also be written as the sum of exactly two prime numbers.

  b Determine whether or not the following even numbers can be written as the sum of exactly two primes.

   i 30   **ii** 98

   iii 128   **iv** 2

  c Form a general statement based on your observations.

Conjectures are usually based on a significant amount of evidence that we have collected and studied; the more evidence we have collected, the more likely we are to believe that the conjecture will prove to be true. Whenever we generalize in this way, we take a series of observations, find something that they have in common, and suggest that it will always prove to be true.

> You can use $GCD(a, b)$ to mean greatest common divisor, or $HCF(a, b)$ to mean the highest common factor of a and b. The two terms mean the same thing.

> The general statement formed in question **7** is known as the Goldbach Conjecture, after Christian Goldbach, who first posed it in 1742. Although his claim has been verified for numbers as high as 4×10^{18}, it remains unproven to this day.

> **Objective: B.** Investigating patterns
> **i.** select and apply mathematical problem-solving techniques to discover complex patterns
>
> *In this practice you are not told what constitutes enough information to form a generalization, or even what information you should collect. Choosing how you start the problem is important – maybe some of the techniques you used in Practice 1 will help.*

Practice 2

Problem solving

1 Investigate the value of $7^n - 3^n$ for different values of n, where $n \in \mathbb{N}$. Generalize and suggest a conjecture regarding the value of $7^n - 3^n$.

2 Investigate the value of $n^3 - n + 3$ for different values of n, where $n \in \mathbb{N}$. Generalize and suggest a conjecture regarding the value of $n^3 - n + 3$.

3 Investigate the value of $p^2 - 1$, where p is a prime greater than 3. Generalize and suggest a conjecture regarding the value of $p^2 - 1$.

> Remember that $n \in \mathbb{N}$ means 'n is a natural number'.

Sometimes a general approach can help us to solve numerical problems. For example:

Simplify $2014^2 - 2012^2$.

This is a very specific problem and it has a specific answer. You could solve it by finding 2014^2 and 2012^2 and then finding the difference, but if you were working without a calculator then this would prove challenging.

Look at the approach taken in Example 1.

Example 1

Simplify $2014^2 - 2012^2$.

Let $n = 2013$

Then $2014^2 - 2012^2 = (n+1)^2 - (n-1)^2$ —— Since $n = 2013$, then $2014 = n + 1$, and $2012 = n - 1$.

$= (n^2 + 2n + 1) - (n^2 - 2n + 1)$ —— Expand the brackets.

$= 4n$ —— Simplify.

$= 4 \times 2013 = 8052$ —— Substitute $n = 2013$.

Reflect and discuss 2

In Example 1:

- What was the specific problem?

- What was the general problem that was solved instead?

- How did solving the general problem make it easier to solve the specific problem?

C Generalization in mathematics

- How can generalizations be used to solve specific problems?

Exploration 1

1 Choose any positive integer, and follow these steps:

  a Square your number.

  b Subtract your number from the square of your number.

  c Is the result an odd or even number?

2 Choose another positive integer and follow the same steps as in question **1**. Try this for a few numbers.

3 Make a conjecture about the nature of the resulting number.

4 Below is a visual representation of the above steps. The first row or column is the initial number you choose, in this case 6. The square array represents 6^2. The diagonal represents subtracting 6 from the square. Is the number of dots remaining odd or even? Can you explain your answer using the diagram?

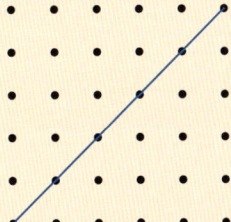

5 Create the same diagram starting with an odd number of dots. Compare your result to starting with 6 dots.

6 Create an algebraic model of your calculation. This means, let n represent your number, and follow the steps **a** to **c** in question **1**.

7 Does this model justify your result is true for any number, not just the ones you chose?

Reflect and discuss 3

- Is there only one way to generalize results?

- Is a representation or diagram just as valid to justify a result as an algebraic proof?

Example 2

Find the smallest number, other than 1, that will *always* divide the difference between the number and the sum of its integers. Prove your result.

n represents the number.

Let $n = 431$. The sum of its digits is $4 + 3 + 1 = 8$.
$431 - 8 = 423$. 3 is the smallest integer other than 1 that divides 423.

▶ Continued on next page

Let $n = 333$. $3 + 3 + 3 = 9$
$333 - 9 = 324$. 2 is the smallest integer other than 1 that divides 324.

Let $n = 561\,324$. $5 + 6 + 1 + 3 + 2 + 4 = 21$.
$561\,324 - 21 = 561\,303$. 3 is the smallest integer other than 1 that divides 561 303.

2 does not divide 423 nor 561 303. 3 does divide all three numbers.

Conjecture: 3 is the smallest number that divides the difference between a number and the sum of its digits.

Let n be the number.

Then $n = a + 10b + 100c + ..., a, b, c \in \mathbb{Z}$

The sum of its digits is $(a + b + c + ...)$.

Then $(a + 10b + 100c + ...) - (a + b + c + ...) = 9b + 99c + ... = 9(b + 11c + ...)$.

The smallest integer to divide 9 is 3, so 3 is the smallest integer that will *always* divide the difference between the number and the sum of its integers.

> Try different numbers with a different number of digits.

> Make a conjecture based on your specific numbers.

> Create an algebraic model and use algebraic techniques to answer the question.

Reflect and discuss 4

- Is it necessary to experiment with certain numbers before trying a general solution?

Although we could have easily evaluated each of the expressions in Exploration 1 with the aid of a calculator, using algebraic expressions in this way can help to generalize and provide better understanding of a problem.

In each of the previous number puzzles we picked a value of n which made it easy to simplify the structure of the problem. To do this for yourself, look for numbers which are similar in value (e.g. 5999 and 6001) or numbers which are close to multiples of one another (e.g. 6000 and 17 999). Then pick n so that the expression simplifies nicely.

For example, if you were attempting a question containing the numbers 999, 1001, 1500 and 1501, you might pick $n = 500$, because 999, 1001, 1500 and 1501 are all close to multiples of 500.

Practice 3

Without using a calculator, find the value of each of these expressions.

1 $500 \times 502 - 501^2$

2 $\dfrac{5002 \times 5006 - 5003 \times 5004}{5}$

3 $\dfrac{2001}{2000} - \dfrac{2000}{2001} + \dfrac{1}{2000 \times 2001}$

4 $1001 \times 2000 - 1000 \times 2001$

5 $\dfrac{3001 + 3002}{3001 \times 3003 - 3000 \times 3002}$

Generalization in mathematics

- What are the risks of making generalizations?

Exploration 2

In these circles, the dots on the circumference are connected by line segments, and this divides the circle into regions.

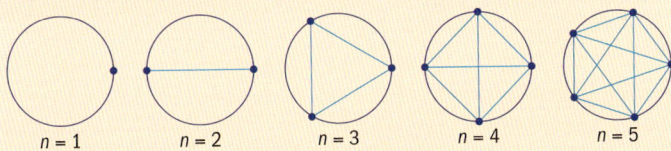

The first diagram has 1 dot, 1 region.

The second diagram has 2 dots, 2 regions.

The third diagram has 3 dots, 4 regions.

1 Write down the number of regions for $n = 4$ and $n = 5$.

2 Predict the number of regions you would expect when $n = 6$. Give reasons for your answer.

3 Here are two sensible ways you could draw the circle for $n = 6$.

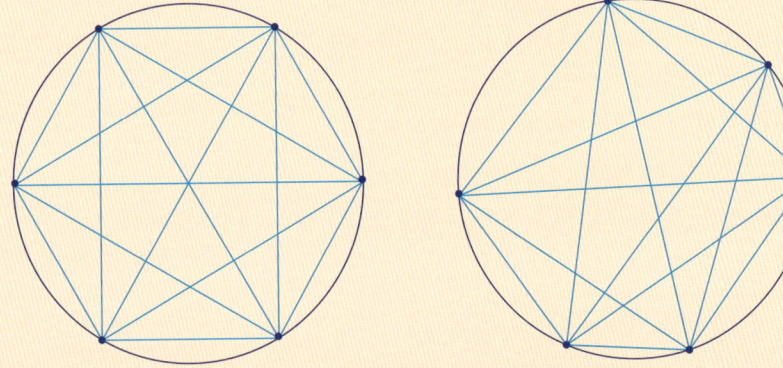

4 Make a table with two columns for n, the number of dots, and r, the number of regions. Fill in your table for $n = 1$ through $n = 5$.

5 Make a conjecture linking n and r based on your table.

6 Test your conjecture for $n = 6$ and $n = 7$.

7 Is your conjecture true?

Reflect and discuss 5

- Is it enough to try some cases to make a valid conjecture that is true for all cases?

You will have seen that you must exercise caution in making a generalization. Once you make your conjecture, test it on further cases to make sure it works. As in Exploration 2, your conjecture might fall apart after trying more cases. For this exploration, there is a general formula connecting the number of dots on a circle and the number of regions created, but it is not at all obvious. It is part of graph theory, and makes use of Euler's formula. Research this famous problem to learn how vertices, edges and regions are related.

The Russian mathematician, V. Ivanov, spent many years factoring the expression $(x^n - 1)$ for $n \in \mathbb{Z}^+$. After many, many examples he conjectured that for any n, the expression would always have coefficients of ± 1. It was only when he factored $(x^{105} - 1)$ that he saw for the first time that one of its factors had a coefficient of 2! The moral of the story is that in mathematics you can never make a generalization based on examples, no matter how many you try.

1	43
2	47
3	53
4	61
5	71
6	83
7	97
8	113
9	131
10	151

Consider the expression $n^2 + n + 41$. It is quite well known among mathematicians as an example of one of the potential pitfalls of careless generalization.

The table here shows the value of $n^2 + n + 41$ for some values of n.

Verify that each of the numbers in the right-hand column is prime. This leads us to wonder whether the expression $n^2 + n + 41$ always generates a prime number. On the evidence here, it seems like a sensible generalization.

Reflect and discuss 6

- Read about RSA encryption to the right. How many examples of $n^2 + n + 41$ being prime would convince you that it could be used for generating primes for use in secure data transmission?

- What is the smallest positive integer n for which the rule fails?

- Investigate the expression $n^2 + n + 11$ in the same way.

- Can you find any other expressions with similar properties?

Prime numbers are very important for a method of cryptography known as RSA encryption.

This type of encryption, which relies on prime factorization of some truly enormous numbers, underpins our modern methods of secure data transmission.

Given that, in this case, generalization has created a false claim, you might wonder whether generalization is a useful skill at all.

Importantly, generalization is usually only one part of a mathematical process. Once you have formed a conjecture, it is important that you then proceed to justify your claim. In this case, you would not be able to justify the claim that '$n^2 + n + 41$ is prime for all n', because it is not true. Forming a conjecture is essential if we are to discover new mathematics, such as an efficient way of generating prime numbers, but you must always bear in mind that a conjecture is not reliable until it has been proved.

Summary

- A **conjecture** is a mathematical statement which has not yet been proved.

- Once a conjecture has been proved to be true, we usually refer to it as a **theorem**.

- Generalization takes two forms:

  ○ the creation of a conjecture based on a collection of pieces of evidence

  ○ the creation of a more general problem in the hope of simplifying a problem

- If you are trying to generalize to form a conjecture, gather your information in a table or other logical layout to help you identify patterns.

- If you are trying to generalize a number problem, look at numbers which are similar, or are close to being factors of other numbers in the problem.

Mixed practice

1 Consider the expression $n(n + 1)(2n +1)$ for different positive integer values of n.

Suggest a suitable general statement about the value of $n(n + 1)(2n +1)$.

2 Consider the expression $4^{n+1} + 3^{2n}$ for different positive integer values of n.

Suggest a suitable general statement about the value of $4^{n+1} + 3^{2n}$.

3 Mersenne numbers are numbers of the form $2^n - 1$ where $n > 2$.

Marin Mersenne, a French mathematician, observed that when $n = 2, 3, 5$ or 7, then $2^n - 1$ is prime.

  a **Verify** this observation.

  b Based on this observation, **explain** why a reasonable generalization might be '$2^n - 1$ is prime whenever n is prime.'

  c **Show** that this generalization does not hold true for all prime values of n.

4 Without the aid of a calculator, **find** the value of:

  a $2002 \times 3001 - 2001 \times 3002$

  b $1000 \times 1003^2 - 3000 (1001 + 1002)$

c $\dfrac{1005 \times 1995 - 995 \times 2005}{1005 + 1995 + 995 + 2005}$

d $\dfrac{542 \times 536 + 8}{540}$

5 A 10×10 grid contains the numbers 1 to 100:

1	2	3	4	5	6	7	8	9	10
11	12	13	14	15	16	17	18	19	20
21	22	23	24	25	26	27	28	29	30
31	32	33	34	35	36	37	38	39	40
41	42	43	44	45	46	47	48	49	50
51	52	53	54	55	56	57	58	59	60
61	62	63	64	65	66	67	68	69	70
71	72	73	74	75	76	77	78	79	80
81	82	83	84	85	86	87	88	89	90
91	92	93	94	95	96	97	98	99	100

Pick any set of five boxes forming a cross shape, for example:

	74	
83	84	85
	94	

Suggest a general rule linking the number in the center of the cross to the total of all five of the boxes added together.

Reflect and discuss 7

How have you explored the statement of inquiry? Give specific examples.

Statement of inquiry:

Using logic to make and validate generalizations enhances the development of models.

Global context: Scientific and technical innovation

Related concept: Validity

Objectives

- Finding the distance between two points
- Finding the midpoint between two points
- Finding the gradient of a straight line
- Finding the gradients of parallel and perpendicular lines
- Finding the equation of a straight line

Inquiry questions

F
- How do you find the distance between two points?
- How do you find the midpoint between two points?

C
- How can the steepness of a line be quantified?
- What is the relationship between the gradients of parallel/perpendicular lines?
- How can you validate the distance and/or midpoint formula?

D
- Are the different forms of a straight line equivalent?
- Are all forms of the equation of a straight line suitable to solve a particular real-life problem?

ATL Critical-thinking

Gather and organize relevant information to formulate an argument

Statement of inquiry:

Using logic to make and validate generalizations enhances the development of models.

📖 **Launch additional digital resources for this chapter.**

You should already know how to:

• plot points on the Cartesian plane	**1** Plot the points $A(2, 4)$, $B(4, -2)$, $C(-5, -2)$, $D(-5, 4)$, and join them up in order. Describe the shape you have drawn.
• apply the Pythagorean Theorem	**2** Find the missing length, h, in this triangle. Give your answer to the nearest millimeter.
• construct a perpendicular from a point to a line with a ruler and compasses	**3** On plain paper, draw a point P, and a line L which does not pass through P. Use a ruler and compasses to construct a line from point P that is perpendicular to line L.

F   Using logic to make generalizations

- How do you find the distance between two points?
- How do you find the midpoint between two points?

Exploration 1

1 A triangular garden house can be represented on grid paper by vertices $(3, -1)$, $(-5, -1)$ and $(-5, 7)$.

  a Sketch the garden house.

  b What kind of triangle is this house?

2 The garden house has square plots of grass on each of its sides. By measuring the sides of the triangle, or otherwise, find the areas of the plots of grass, and describe the relationship between the largest plot and the sum of the two smaller plots of grass.

3 Let a represent the smallest side of the house, b the next largest side of the house, and c the largest side of the house. Write a formula that represents the areas of the two smaller grass plots in relation to the area of the larger one.

As you have probably already learned, the formula you have written down is called the Pythagorean Theorem, and it generalizes the relationship between the three sides of a right-angled triangle. The theorem states that the area of the square on the larger side of the triangle has the same area as the sum of the areas of the squares on the shorter sides.

Pythagorean Theorem: If a, b and c are sides of a right-angled triangle, with c the side opposite the right angle (the hypotenuse) then $a^2 + b^2 = c^2$, or $c = \sqrt{a^2 + b^2}$.

Reflect and discuss 1

- Does the Pythagorean Theorem work with triangles that are not right-angled triangles? Validate your answer.

- What is the relationship between $a^2 + b^2$ and c^2 in **i** an obtuse triangle, and **ii** an acute triangle, where in each case c is the longest side?

- There are many proofs of the Pythagorean Theorem. Do an internet search and write in your own words two of the proofs you found easy to understand.

- Given the lengths of the sides of a triangle, how can you determine if the triangle is a right-angled triangle?

In this last bullet point above you were actually asked whether the converse of the Pythagorean Theorem is true. In other words, we know that in a right-angled triangle of sides a, b, and c, $a^2 + b^2 = c^2$. The converse states that if the sides of a triangle are such that $a^2 + b^2 = c^2$, then the triangle is a right-angled triangle. The converse of the Pythagorean Theorem is indeed true.

> To form the converse of a statement, switch the 'If' part of the statement with the 'then' part of the statement.

> **Converse of the Pythagorean Theorem**: If the three sides of a triangle are related by the equation $a^2 + b^2 = c^2$, then the triangle is a right-angled triangle.

Reflect and discuss 2

- Can you think of mathematical statements whose converse is also true, and mathematical statements whose converse is not true?

- Can you think of everyday statements whose converse is true, and some whose converse is not true?

ATL

Exploration 2

In this exploration, you will find a formula for the distance between two points $P_1(x_1, y_1)$ and $P_2(x_2, y_2)$.

1 In the diagram, point Q is horizontally level with P_1 and is vertically aligned with P_2.

   a What type of triangle is P_1QP_2? Justify your answer.

   b Write down the coordinates of Q.

   c Hence write down the length of P_1Q and P_2Q in terms of x_1, x_2, y_1, and y_2.

   d Use these lengths to find the length d of P_1P_2.

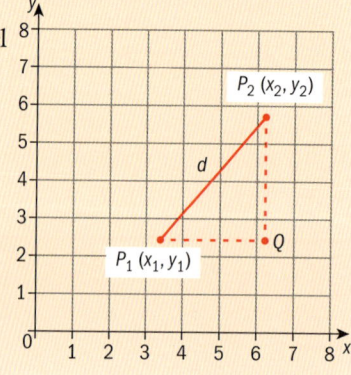

▶ Continued on next page

2 In the first diagram, you assumed that P_2 was above and to the right of P_1. Suppose instead that P_2 was below and to the left of P_1. Show that the distance formula would not change.

3 Suggest other possible positions that P_1 and P_2 could take relative to each other. Explain why, for any positions of P_1 and P_2, the distance formula remains the same.

You could sketch the two other possible arrangements of P_1 and P_2.

The distance formula states that the distance, d, between two points (x_1, y_1) and (x_2, y_2) is given by $d = \sqrt{(x_2 - x_1)^2 + (y_2 - y_1)^2}$.

Reflect and discuss 3

When P_1 and P_2 are on the same horizontal line:

- does the distance formula still work?
- what happens to point Q, and the triangle P_1P_2Q?

Example 1

Plot the points $P(-4, -1)$, $Q(1, 4)$ and $R(-5, 6)$ and prove that they form an isosceles triangle.

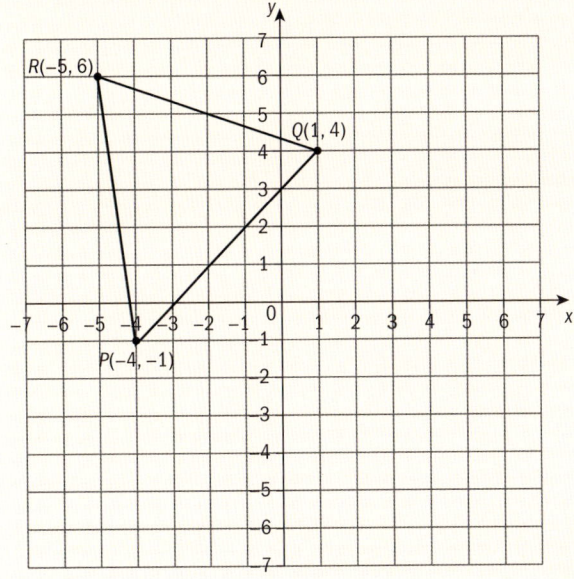

$|PQ| = \sqrt{(4-(-1))^2 + (1-(-4))^2} = \sqrt{50}$

$|PR| = \sqrt{(6-(-1))^2 + (-5-(-4))^2} = \sqrt{50}$

Placing the name of the line segment inside the symbol $||$ means the length of, or the magnitude of, the line segment.

Since two sides of the triangle are equal, the triangle is isosceles.

Reflect and discuss 4

- Do you need to find the length of all three sides in order to prove a triangle is isosceles? Explain.

- Is an equilateral triangle also an isosceles triangle? Is the converse true?

Practice 1

1 Find the distance between each pair of points.

   a (3, 11) and (6, 15)

   b (−3, −8) and (2, −16)

   c (103, 9) and (−17, 208)

Problem solving

2 Show that $P(7, 14)$, $Q(11, 12)$, and $R(13, 8)$ are all the same distance from point $C(6, 7)$.

   Hence find the area of the circle that passes through P, Q, and R.

3 Show that the points $F(−6, 5)$, $G(−4, 5)$, and $H(−5, 9)$ form an isosceles triangle.

4 Find the lengths of the sides of a triangle whose coordinates are $A(1, 6)$, $B(3, 2)$ and $C(9, 5)$. Hence prove that triangle ABC is a right-angled triangle, and state which angle is the right angle.

5 For the points $P(10, 13)$, $Q(17, 37)$, $R(24, 13)$, and $S(17, −11)$:

   a Find the distances PQ, QR, RS and SP.

   b Robin says: 'the lengths PQ, QR, RS and SP are all equal, so the shape $PQRS$ must be a square.' Determine whether Robin is correct.

   c Robin's logical process was:

Premises:	The four lengths are equal.
	If a quadrilateral has four equal sides, then it is a square.
Reasoning process:	Since PQRS has four equal sides, it is a square.
Conclusion:	PQRS is a square.

   Explain the fault in Robin's logic.

ATL

Exploration 3

1 By plotting the points, or using dynamic geometry software, plot the points $A(10, 6)$ and $B(2, 8)$.

2 Find the coordinates of M, the midpoint of AB.

3 Compare the coordinates of M to the coordinates of points A and B. Describe anything you notice.

▶ Continued on next page

4 Create other pairs of points and find the midpoint of each pair. Investigate the relationship between the coordinates of the endpoints and the coordinates of the midpoint. (Hint: construct a table of endpoints and midpoints.)

5 Use your findings in step **4** to predict the coordinates of N, the midpoint of points $C(7, 11)$ and $D(19, 15)$.

6 Verify your answer using the software.

7 Points P and Q have coordinates $P(a, b)$ and $Q(c, d)$.
Suggest a formula for the coordinates of the midpoint of PQ.

8 Verify that your formula gives the correct coordinates for M and N.

Reflect and discuss 5

Generalization means making a general statement on the basis of specific examples.

- Where in Exploration 3 have you generalized?
- How does generalization enable you to predict?
- Why is it important to verify a generalization?

The midpoint of (a, b) and (c, d) is $\left(\frac{a+c}{2}, \frac{b+d}{2} \right)$.

Example 2

Find the midpoint of $A(3, 6)$ and $B(9, 18)$.

Let M be the midpoint of AB.

$M = \left(\frac{3+9}{2}, \frac{6+18}{2} \right)$ ——————— Use the midpoint formula $M = \left(\frac{a+c}{2}, \frac{b+d}{2} \right)$

$\quad = (6, 12)$

Practice 2

1 Find the midpoint of $A(14, 6)$ and $B(18, 20)$.

2 Find the midpoint of $C(5, -13)$ and $D(10, -8)$.

3 a Plot the points $A(2, 7)$, $B(3, 10)$, $C(6, 11)$, and $D(5, 8)$.

   b Find the midpoints of AC and BD.

   c Comment on your answers to part **b**. Explain what this shows about quadrilateral $ABCD$.

Problem solving

4 $M(8, 4)$ is the midpoint of the line joining $A(11, 5)$ to point B. Find the coordinates of B.

5 $Q(5, 1)$ is the midpoint of a line joining $P(p, -3)$ to $R(7, r)$. Find p and r.

6 When archaeologists excavate a site, they mark it off with a coordinate grid so that they can easily identify where artefacts are found and keep a record of the site forever. At the West Kennet Long Barrow in England, a grave site dating back to 3600 BCE, there are three chambers at the coordinates $(7, 9)$, $(17, 33)$, and $(-36, 41)$. It has been said that they form an isosceles triangle with height twice the length of its base.

Determine whether the statement is true. Justify your answer.

 Validating generalizations

- How can the steepness of a line be quantified?
- What is the relationship between the gradients of parallel lines?
- How can you validate the distance and/or midpoint formula?

Exploration 4

1 If the following lines on grid paper represent hills, label them in order from the least difficult to climb to the most difficult.

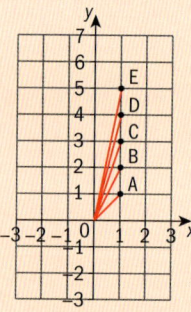

2 Since each hill has a horizontal distance of 1 unit, how can you represent its steepness using the number of vertical units?

3 If we now use a horizontal distance of **i** 2 units and **ii** 0.5 units, how do you think the vertical distance has to change in order for the steepness of the hill to remain the same?

4 How can you quantify the steepness of a hill given that its horizontal distance is called the 'run' and its vertical distance is called the 'rise'?

5 Identify the lines on the grid whose steepness is **i** 1, **ii** 5, **iii** 0.5. How many degrees are in the angle between the hill and the horizontal line in the hill whose steepness is 1? Are the angles greater or smaller than this one for **5ii** and **iii**?

6 How would you quantify the steepness of a **i** horizontal line and **ii** vertical line? Think about the rise and run of these lines.

▶ Continued on next page

7 If you are now at the top of the hill and want to hike down, the steepness of the hill remains the same. How would you distinguish between steepness going uphill and steepness going downhill?

8 Steepness of a hill in mathematics is called the gradient or the slope of a line.

Plot the points $A(2, 4)$, $B(-4, -1)$, $C(8, 1)$ and $D(5, -3)$ on grid paper. Find the gradients of $\overline{AB}$, $\overline{BC}$, $\overline{AD}$, and $\overline{BD}$, making sure you distinguish between lines that slope upward and lines that slope downward.

9 Can you think of a formula for the gradient of the line segment PQ, $P(a,b)$ and $Q(c,d)$, in terms of their coordinates?

While driving in a car you might have seen signs like these on the road. They indicate how steep the road ahead becomes.

10 How are the signs different, and what does the difference mean? How would the gradients of the roads that the signs represent be different?

Steepness is often given as a percentage. As a fraction, 10% is 1/10, which means that the road rises 1 unit for every 10 units in the horizontal direction. This can also be expressed in a ratio as 1:10, meaning that for every 1 unit in the y direction (the rise) there are 10 units in the x-direction (the run).

11 In the USA a warning sign must be placed on some roads if its steepness is more than 8% and the road is longer than 250 m. If a road rises 21 m over a horizontal distance of 280 m, explain if a warning sign should be placed on this road.

The gradient or slope, m, between two points $P(x_1, y_1)$ and $Q(x_2, y_2)$ is given by the formula $m = \frac{y_2 - y_1}{x_2 - x_1}$.

Reflect and discuss 6

- Why would gradients be expressed as percentages on roads?
- Do all countries represent steepness of roads in the same way?
- How can the gradient of a line be represented by the angle between the line and the horizontal distance?

Exploration 5

1 Airplanes flying at different altitudes over an airport are represented by the following lines:

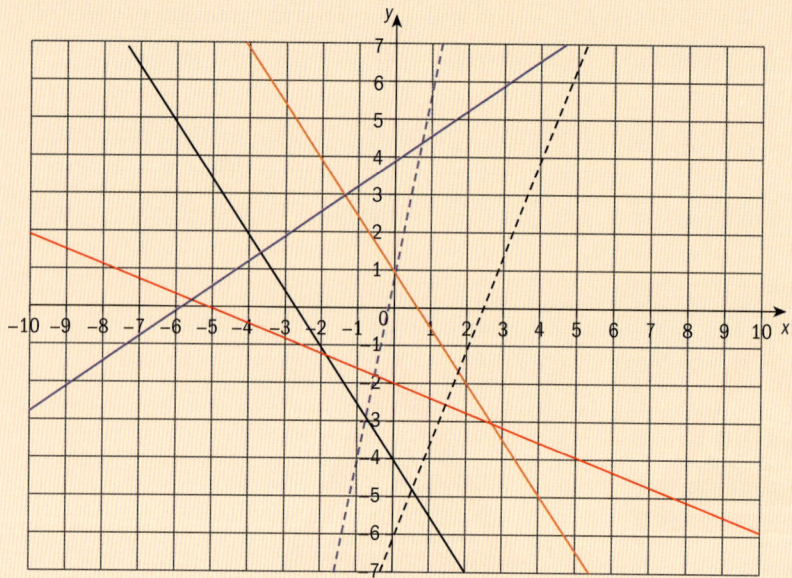

Use two points on each line whose coordinates are easy to identify, and fill in the gradients of the planes' trajectories on the grid.

Line	Gradient	Parallel to:	Perpendicular to:
Blue		None	Orange and black
Orange		Black	Blue
Black		Orange	Blue
Red		None	Dotted black
Dotted black		None	Red
Dotted blue		None	None

2 What do you notice about the gradients of the lines that are parallel? Give a reason for your answer.

3 What do you notice about the signs of the gradients that are perpendicular? Explain why this is so. What do you notice about the numbers, and why do you think this is so?

Parallel lines have equal gradients

The gradients of perpendicular lines are negative reciprocals of each other. In other words, if L_1 and L_2 are perpendicular and have gradients m_1 and m_2 respectively, then $m_2 = \dfrac{1}{m_1}$ or $m_1 \times m_2 = -1$.

Example 3

The points A, B, C, and D have coordinates $A(-3, 4)$, $B(2, 1)$, $C(1, -6)$, $D(3, 8)$, $E(4, -2)$.

a Find the gradients of the lines AB, BC, BD, and CE.

b Use your answers to **a** to state, with reasons, which lines are:

    i parallel

    ii perpendicular.

a Gradient of AB: $m = \dfrac{1-4}{1-(-3)} = \dfrac{-3}{4}$ Use the gradient formula

   Gradient of BC: $m = \dfrac{-6-1}{1-2} = \dfrac{-7}{-1} = 7$

   Gradient of BD: $m = \dfrac{8-1}{3-2} = \dfrac{7}{1} = 7$

   Gradient of CE: $m = \dfrac{-2-(-6)}{4-1} = \dfrac{4}{3}$

b Lines BC and BD are parallel since they have equal gradients.

   Lines AB and CE are perpendicular, since the product of their gradients is -1.

Reflect and discuss 7

- Would the answers to Example 3 change if you switched the positions of the first and second points when using the gradient formula? Justify your result.

Exploration 6

1 Plot the points $(-3, 3)$ and $(1, 3)$. Find the gradient between these points.

2 Describe the relationship of the line to the x-axis.

3 Using the definition of the gradient as the rise divided by the run, justify your answer to **1**.

4 Plot the points $(3, -3)$ and $(3, 1)$. Can you find the gradient between these points?

5 Describe the relationship of the line to the y-axis.

6 Draw conclusions about the gradients of:

    a horizontal lines

    b vertical lines.

A line parallel to the x-axis has a gradient of 0.

A line parallel to the y-axis has no gradient.

Practice 3

1 Find the gradients of the lines passing through the following pairs of points:

   a $(3, -1)$ and $(-2, 5)$ **b** $(2, 3)$ and $(-1, -3)$

   c $(-4, -5)$ and $(0, 0)$ **d** $(-10, 2)$ and $(-10, -2)$

   e $(7, -2)$ and $(-2, 7)$ **f** $(-1, -3)$ and $(2, -3)$

2 By comparing gradients, determine whether PQ is parallel or perpendicular to RS, or neither.

   a $P(1, 0)$, $Q(2, 2)$, $R(0, 4)$, $Q(-2, 0)$

   b $P(4, 4)$, $Q(-2, 2)$, $R(-2, -2)$, $Q(0, -8)$

   c $P(1, 5)$, $Q(-2, -10)$, $R(3, 12)$, $Q(1, 2)$

   d $P(2, -3)$, $Q(-2, -3)$, $R(0, 1)$, $Q(0, -1)$

3 The points $A(2, 6)$, $B(5, 0)$, $C(-1, -3)$ form a triangle. Justify that the triangle is a right-angled triangle and state the letter representing the right angle.

Problem solving

4 If the line joining $A(4, -6)$ to $B(7, b)$ has a gradient of 4, find the value of b.

5 The points $A(a, -2)$, $B(7,0)$ and $C(10, 1)$ all lie on the same straight line. Find the value of a.

6 The coordinates of quadrilateral $ABCD$ are $A(3, -1)$, $B(6, 0)$, $C(7, 3)$ and $D(4, 2)$.

   a Show that the diagonals bisect each other.

   b Show that the diagonals form a right angle.

7 In the constellation of Pegasus, the horse's body is represented by four stars called 'The Great Square'. The stars at the corners of The Great Square can be drawn on a Cartesian plane at $(-1, 5)$, $(3, 2)$, $(-4, 1)$, and $(0, -2)$.

Show that The Great Square of Pegasus has these properties of a square:

   a All sides are the same length.

   b All angles are 90°.

   c Opposite sides are parallel.

8 As you have seen in question **7**, the corners of The Great Square of Pegasus are at $(-1, 5)$, $(3, 2)$, $(-4, 1)$, and $(0, -2)$.

Show that The Great Square of Pegasus has these properties of a square:

   a Diagonals are perpendicular.

   b Diagonals bisect each another.

PEGASUS

The constellation of Pegasus is named after the winged horse in Greek mythology. According to the myth, when Perseus killed the Gorgon Medusa (whose hair was made of snakes), Pegasus was born from her blood.

The proof outline will help you give a complete and coherent proof of the midpoint formula, if you give clear and concise explanations and details in the sections you complete.

ATL

Activity: Proving the midpoint formula

Complete the gaps in this proof that claims the midpoint of points $P(a, b)$ and $Q(c, d)$ is $M\left(\frac{a+c}{2}, \frac{b+d}{2}\right)$.

The proof has two parts: first, to prove that M lies on the line PQ; second, to prove that M is equidistant from P and Q.

Copy and complete the proof outline below.

Theorem:

The midpoint of points $P(a, b)$ and

$Q(c, d)$ is $M\left(\frac{a+c}{2}, \frac{b+d}{2}\right)$.

Proof:
PMQ is a straight line if the gradient of PM and the gradient of MQ are the same.

Since the gradients are equal, PMQ is a straight line.

Therefore M is equidistant from P and Q.

Since _____

and _____,

M is the midpoint of PQ. □

> Draw a diagram to show P and Q on a grid.
>
> The position of P and Q on the graph is not important – just don't put them in the same place!

> Show clearly that PM and MQ have the same gradient.

> Use the distance formula to show that $MP = MQ$.

> Equidistant means having the same distance.

> A square marks the end of a proof.

D **Mathematical models as generalizations**

- Are the different forms of a straight line equivalent?
- Are all forms of the equation of a straight line suitable to solve a particular problem?

Exploration 7

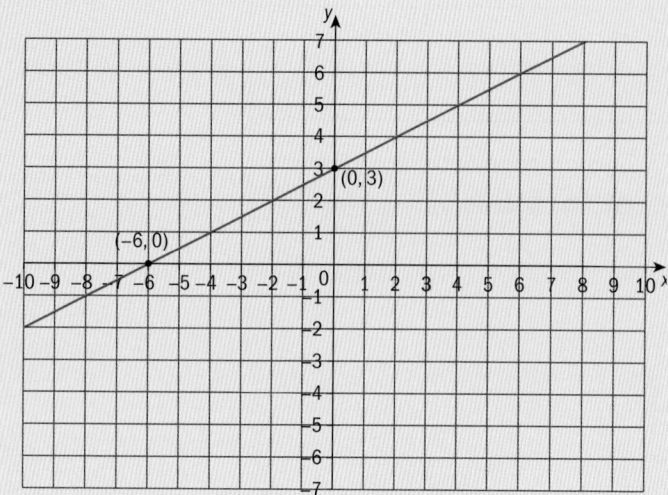

1 The points (0, 3) and (−6, 0) lie on the given line. Find the gradient of this line.

2 The gradient of a line is the same regardless of which two points on the line you use. Let (0, 3) be the first point, and using (x, y) as the 2nd point, put these two points into the formula for the gradient, m, using for m the gradient you found in step **1**.

3 Rearrange the equation in the form $y = mx + c$ where m is the gradient, and $c \in \mathbb{R}$. (Hint: multiply both sides by the denominator, and simplify.)

4 Identify another point on the line and substitute its coordinates into the equation you found in step **3**. Comment on your result.

5 Select a few other points that you can easily identify on the line and do the same as in question **4**. Comment on your result.

6 The equation you found is the equation of the given line, where m is the gradient of the line, and c is the y-intercept, that is, the value of y where the line intersects the y-axis. The form of this equation is called the gradient-intercept form of a straight line.

Why do you think this is so?

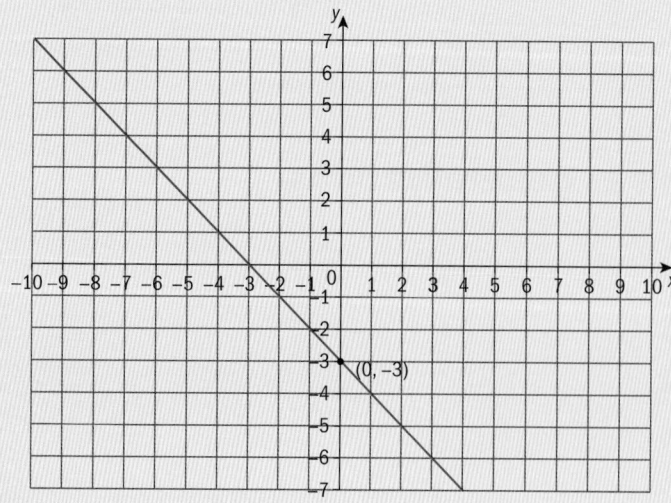

▶ Continued on next page

7 Using the y-intercept, $(0, -3)$ and another point that is easy to identify, find the gradient of the line.

8 Write the equation of the line in the form $y = mx + c$, where m is the gradient and c is the y-intercept.

9 Test other points on the line to see if they satisfy your equation.

> The gradient-intercept form of a straight line is $y = mx + c$ where m is the gradient and c is the y-intercept.

Reflect and discuss 8

- Is the coordinate of x always 0 at the point where a line intersects the y-axis?
- How can you tell if a given point lies on a line if you know the equation of the line?

Example 4

a Write down the equation of a line whose gradient is 2 and passes through the point $(0, -3)$.

b Find the gradients and y-intercepts of the following straight lines.

   i $y = -3x + 2$ **ii** $y = \frac{1}{2}x - 5$

   iii $y = 1 - x$ **iv** $2y = 4x + 3$

   v $x - 3y - 3 = 0$

a $m = 2$ and $(0, -3)$ is the y-intercept, since the x coordinate is 0.

intercept-gradient form is $y = mx + c$, hence the equation of the line is $y = 2x - 3$.

b

   i $m = -3$; $c = 2$, therefore y-intercept is $(0, 2)$

   ii $m = \frac{1}{2}$; $c = -5$, therefore the y-intercept is $(0, 5)$.

   iii $y = -x + 1$, hence $m = -1$ and $c = 1$. The y-intercept is $(0, 1)$.   *Rearrange the equation in the form $y = mx + c$*

   iv $y = 2x + \frac{3}{2}$, hence $m = 2$ and $c = \frac{3}{2}$. The y-intercepts is $(0, \frac{3}{2})$.   *Rearrange the equation in the form $y = mx + c$*

   v $y = \frac{1}{3}x + 1$. $m = \frac{1}{3}$ and $c = 1$, hence y-intercept is $(0, 1)$.   *Rearrange the equation in the form $y = mx + c$*

Practice 4

1 Find the equation of the straight line that:

   a passes through the point $(0, -1)$ and has gradient 3

   b passes through the point $(0, 2)$ and has gradient -1.

2 Find the gradient and y-intercept of the following lines:

a $y = -\dfrac{1}{2}x + 8$

b $y = 4 - 2x$

c $y = \dfrac{2x-6}{3}$

d $2y - x = 5$

e $-2x + 6y - 3 = 0$

3 On graph paper, sketch the straight line passing through the point (0, 1) whose gradient is:

a 2

b −1

c $\dfrac{1}{2}$

d $-\dfrac{2}{3}$

Exploration 8

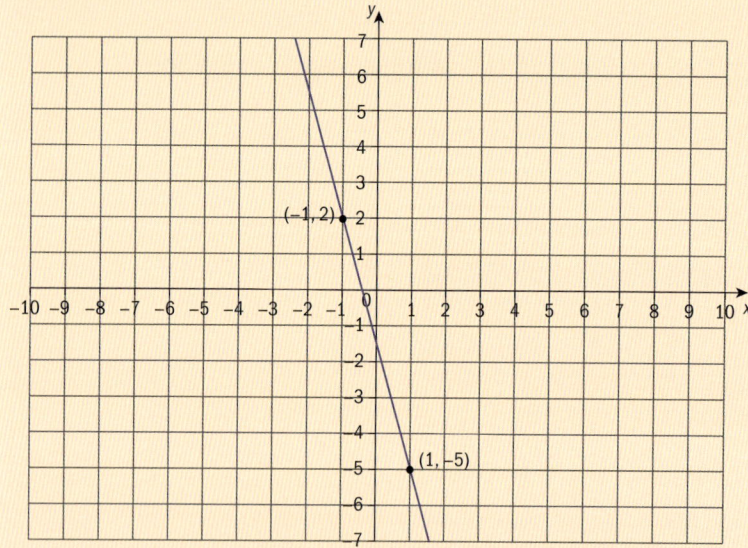

Look at the graph and follow these steps.

1 Find the gradient of the line shown.

2 Now, using (−1, 2) as the first point, and (x, y) as the second point, write out the formula for the gradient, using the value for m from step **1**.

3 Rearrange your result in the form $y = mx + c$.

(Hint: multiply both sides of your equation by the denominator and simplify.)

4 What value do you have for c from your equation in step **3**?

5 Check to make sure that the value you have for c is indeed where the line intersects the y-axis.

6 Repeat steps **2** to **5** using (1, −5) as the first point.

7 Comment on your equations in steps **3** and **6**.

> The point-gradient form for the equation of a straight line is
> $y - y_1 = m(x - x_1)$
> where m is the gradient and (x_1, y_1) is a point on the line.

- What given information would be necessary in order to use the gradient-intercept form of a straight line?

- What given information would be necessary in order to use the gradient–point form of a straight line?

- How are the two forms for finding the equation of a line similar and how are they different?

Another form for the equation of a straight line is standard form. In this form the equation is set equal to 0, and all the coefficients are integers.

Standard form for the equation of a straight line:

$ax + by + c = 0, a, b, c \in \mathbb{Z}$.

Example 5

Find, in standard form, the equation of a straight line that passes through the points $(6, -1)$ and $(12, 1)$.

$m = \frac{1-(-1)}{12-6} = \frac{2}{6} = \frac{1}{3}.$ — Find the gradient.

$y - (-1) = \frac{1}{3}(x - 6)$

$y + 1 = \frac{1}{3}x - 2$ — Use intercept-gradient form and rearrange the equation in standard form, that is, bring everything over to the left hand side.

$\frac{1}{3}x - y - 3 = 0$

Since the standard form requires integers, multiply each term by 3 in order to get rid of the fraction $\frac{1}{3}$.

$x - 3y - 9 = 0$

Practice 5

1 Find the equation of the straight line that passes through the points

  a (0, 4) and (3, 10)   b (0, −1) and (−1, 0)

  c (−2, 0) and (2, 4)   d (5, −1) and (11, 0)

2 Find the equation of the straight line that passes through the point $(-2, 9)$ and has gradient -2.

3 Find in standard form the equation of the line that passes through the points $(6, -2)$ and $(12, 1)$.

4 Find the equation of the straight line that is parallel to the line $y = x - 2$ and goes through the point $(0, 1)$.

5 Find the equation of the straight line that is perpendicular to the line whose gradient is $-\frac{1}{4}$ and which goes through the point $(0, 3)$.

Problem solving

6 Show that the midpoint of points $U(7, 11)$ and $V(-2, 1)$ lies on the line with equation $y = 2x + 1$.

7 The degrees Celsius and equivalent degrees Fahrenheit are shown in the table.

Celsius, C	55	65	80	105	125
Fahrenheit, F	131	149	176	221	257

   a Plot the points (C, F) and show that a relationship of the form $F = pC + q$ exists.

   b Find the values of p and q.

   c Interpret what p and q mean in terms of the problem.

   d The temperature in Dubai is 28°C. Find the temperature in degrees Fahrenheit in Dubai.

   e The temperature in New York is 40°F. Find the temperature in degrees Celsius in New York.

Reflect and discuss 10

- How have you chosen which form of the equation of a straight line to use when answering practice questions?

- When would you choose the intercept-gradient form for the equation of a straight line in solving a given problem?

- When would you choose the point-gradient form for the equation of a straight line in solving a given problem?

- Does it matter which form for the equation of a straight line you use in answering a question?

Summary

The distance formula states that the distance, d, between two points (x_1, y_1) and (x_2, y_2) is given by

$$d = \sqrt{(x_2 - x_1)^2 + (y_2 - y_1)^2}.$$

The midpoint of (a, b) and (c, d) is

$$\left(\frac{a+c}{2}, \frac{b+d}{2}\right).$$

The gradient or slope, m, between two points $P(x_1, y_1)$ and $Q(x_2, y_2)$ is given by the formula

$$m = \frac{y_2 - y_1}{x_2 - x_1}.$$

A line parallel to the x-axis has a gradient of 0. A line parallel to the y-axis has no gradient.

The gradient-intercept form of a straight line is $y = mx + c$ where m is the gradient and c is the y-intercept.

The point-gradient form for the equation of a straight line is $y - y_1 = m(x - x_1)$ where m is the gradient and (x_1, y_1) is a point on the line.

Standard form for the equation of a straight line is $ax + by + c = 0$, $a, b, c \in \mathbb{Z}$

The gradients of perpendicular lines are negative reciprocals of each other. In other words, if L_1 and L_2 are perpendicular and have gradients m_1 and m_2 respectively, then $m_2 = \frac{1}{m_1}$ or $m_1 \times m_2 = -1$.

Mixed practice

1 **Find** the distance between each pair of points.

   a $(0, 0)$ and $(5, 12)$

   b $(1, 4)$ and $(4, 8)$

   c $(5, 7)$ and $(11, 7)$

   d $(-3, -12)$ and $(4, 12)$

2 **Find** the distance between each pair of points, giving your answer correct to 3 significant figures.

   a $(4, 8)$ and $(10, 13)$

   b $(14, 8)$ and $(17, -3)$

   c $(1.5, 4.6)$ and $(2.3, -1.8)$

3 **Find** the distance between each pair of points, giving your answer in the form $\sqrt{n}$, where n is a whole number.

   a $(2, 7)$ and $(6, 15)$

   b $(-3, 9)$ and $(5, -2)$

   c $(-3, -5)$ and $(-9, -14)$

4 **Prove** that the points $(0, 0)$, $(6, 0)$, and $(3, 4)$ form an isosceles triangle.

5 Three points have coordinates $A(-4, -1)$, $B(1, 4)$, and $C(-5, 6)$.

   Show that the points form an isosceles triangle.

6 Point A has coordinates (a, b) and point B has coordinates (c, d).

   M is the midpoint of AB.

   a **Find** the coordinates of M.

   b **Find** the distance AB.

   c **Find** the distance AM.

   d Hence, **prove** that $AM = \frac{1}{2} AB$

7 ABC is a triangle with vertices $A(1, 0)$, $B(5, 9)$ and $C(9, 0)$.

   a **Show** that triangle ABC is isosceles.

   b **Find** the coordinates of the midpoints of the three sides of ABC.

   c **Show** that the midpoints of the three sides of ABC are the vertices of an isosceles triangle.

   d **Show** that the isosceles triangle formed from the midpoints of the sides of ABC has area 9 square units.

8 **Find** where the line $2y - 3x - 7 = 0$ intersects the:

   i y-axis

   ii x-axis.

9 The line $y = px + q$ is parallel to the line $y = 2x - 6$ and passes through the point $(-1, 7)$. **Find** p and q.

10 **Find** in standard form the equation of the line that passes through $(-2, 3)$ and has gradient $\frac{4}{5}$.

Problem solving

11

Costs in Euros C	27	31	37	51	83
Gas units *n*	41	51	66	101	181

   a Plot the points (n, C) on a graph.

   b **Justify** that a linear relationship exists between n and C.

   c **Find** the linear relationship in standard form.

   d Interpret what the gradient means in terms of n and C.

   e Interpret what the y-intercept means in terms of n and C.

Review in context

Scientific and technical innovation

You are lucky enough to have found the only surviving copy of a treasure map left by the notorious pirate Short James Platinum – scourge of the seven seas. He has buried many pieces of treasure on the island – each in a different location. Can you find them all? (On the map, one unit equals one league.)

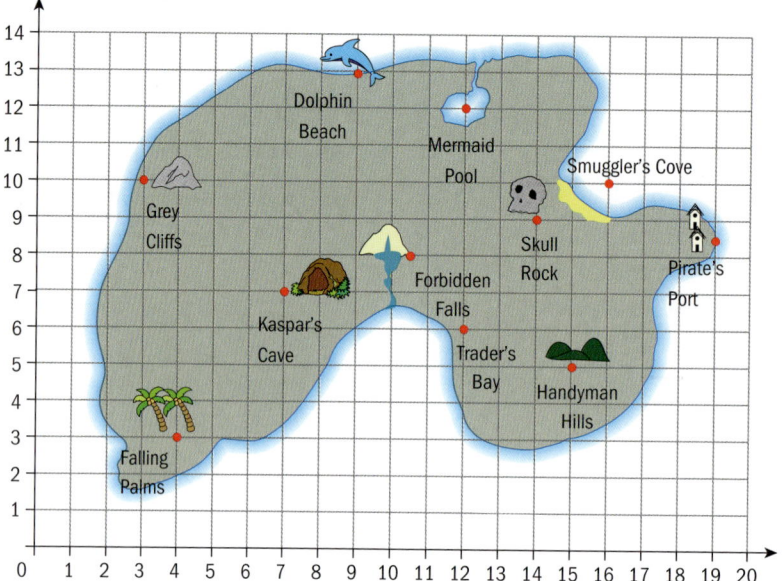

1 The Tsarina's Tiara is buried due west of Skull Rock. It is as far from Skull Rock to the Tiara as it is from Falling Palms to Kaspar's Cave.

   Find the coordinates of the place where the Tsarina's Tiara is buried.

2 The wreck of the Purple Porpoise, a ship that sank carrying 200 gold doubloons, is exactly halfway between Falling Palms and Handyman Hills.

   Find the coordinates of the Purple Porpoise.

3 If Skull Rock is closer to Trader's Bay than Forbidden Falls, then my prized Silver Cutlass is buried two leagues east of Mermaid Pool. If not, it is buried two leagues west of Mermaid Pool.

   Determine the position of the Silver Cutlass.

4 The Emerald Crown, which I looted from an ancient tomb, has been hidden in a ruined building at one of the marked sites on the map. If you can find the correct site, you will find the treasure.

   The true location of the crown is as far away from Kaspar's Cave as the Falling Palms are from the Grey Cliffs. Determine the location of the Emerald Crown.

   Explain how you know this is the only possible correct location.

5 To find the Cursed Medal of Caracas, send your best navigator to the point halfway from Kaspar's Cave to the Grey Cliffs. From there, travel halfway to Pirate's Port, and there the medal is to be found.

   Find the coordinates of the Cursed Medal of Caracas. **Justify** your answer.

6 The Bounty from Belize is buried deep so be sure to pick the right place.

   On the route straight from Falling Palms to the Grey Cliffs, stop at the point that is closest to Kaspar's Cave. Head one league west and dig deep!

   a **Find** the distance from Falling Palms to Kaspar's Cave.

   b **Find** the distance from the Grey Cliffs to Kaspar's Cave.

   c Hence **show** that Grey Cliffs, Kaspar's Cave and Falling Palms form an isosceles triangle.

   d **Explain** how this tells you that the point closest to Kaspar's Cave that lies on the line from Falling Palms to Grey Cliffs is the midpoint of the line.

   e Hence **determine** the location of the Bounty from Belize.

Reflect and discuss 7

How have you explored the statement of inquiry? Give specific examples.

Statement of inquiry:

Using logic to make and validate generalizations enhances the development of models.

2.3 Modelling: Linear equations and systems of linear equations

Global context: Scientific and technical innovation

Related concept: Models

Objectives

- Solving linear equations and systems of linear equations algebraically and graphically
- Using equivalence transformations to solve linear equations and systems of equations
- Creating a mathematical model to solve real-life problems
- Determining if a model solution is equivalent to the real-life solution
- Evaluating and interpreting your solutions in light of the real-life problems

Inquiry questions

F
- What is an equivalence transformation?
- How can you solve linear equations using equivalence transformations?

C
- Are all solution methods for systems of equations equivalent?
- How do the graphs of systems of equations relate to the types of solutions they may have?

D
- Can good decisions be calculated by using a mathematical model?

LOGIC

 **ATL** Transfer

Apply skills and knowledge in unfamiliar situations

Statement of inquiry:

Using logic to make and validate generalizations enhances the development of models.

▢ **Launch additional digital resources for this chapter.**

You should already know how to:

• expand and factorize algebraic expressions to obtain equivalent expressions	**1** Expand:
	  a $4(x+3)$ **b** $5(2x-1)$
	  c $-3(8-6x)$ **d** $4x(7+x-x^2)$
	
	2 Factorize:
	  a $3x+6$ **b** $5x-15$
	  c $14+35x$ **d** $34-85x$

• solve linear equations	**3** Solve these equations.
	  a $\frac{x}{5}=3$ **b** $4x=52$
	  c $5x-7=8$ **d** $\frac{x}{2}+4=32$

• find the equation of a line by finding its gradient and y-intercept	**4** Find the equations of these two lines. 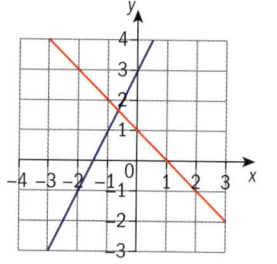

F Linear equations

- What is an equivalence transformation?
- How can you solve linear equations using equivalence transformations?

You know how to solve linear equations, but do you know the mathematical principles that you use to do this?

Exploration 1

1 The examples below show steps that are typically used to solve linear equations. Decide whether you think the example demonstrates 'the addition principle' or 'the multiplication principle'.

a $3x-5=2$
    $3x=7$

b $6x=12$
    $x=2$

c $\frac{1}{4}x=3$
    $x=12$

d $6-2x=11$
    $-2x=5$

e $4n+2=9n$
    $2=5n$

f $7x-1=2x+8$
    $5x=9$

g $\frac{2}{3}x+\frac{1}{6}=1$
    $4x+1=6$

h $16x+4=4x$
    $4x+1=x$

i $5x=2x+9$
    $3x=9$

2 Label the stages in the solution below as either 'the addition principle' or 'the multiplication principle'. If it's neither of these, then state the mathematical property that is being used.

$2(3x-4)=3x+7$
  $6x-8=3x+7$ _____
    $3x=15$ _____
     $x=5$ _____

Reflect and discuss 1

- These principles are called 'equivalence transformations'. Why is this an appropriate name?
- Why don't we need a subtraction principle or a division principle?

When solving linear equations in the past, you may have used very informal language to describe your working steps. In this section, you will learn the formal terms for the mathematical principles used in solving linear equations.

Equivalence transformations

To solve an equation you can use these mathematical principles:

Principle	Example
Addition Principle: Add the same value or variable to both sides of an equation.	Add 3 to both sides of $2x - 3 = 5$ to get the equivalent equation $2x = 8$.
Multiplication Principle: Multiply by the same non-zero value or variable on both sides of an equation.	Multiply both sides of $11 = 5x$ by $\frac{1}{5}$ to get the equivalent equation $\frac{11}{5} = x$.

An **equivalence transformation** uses mathematical principles to transform an equation into an equivalent equation.

Example 1

Solve the equation $\frac{1}{4}(x-2) = \frac{1}{2}(3x+4)$. Show the equivalence transformation used at each step. Remember to check your solution.

$$\frac{1}{4}(x-2) = \frac{1}{2}(3x+4)$$

$$4 \cdot \frac{1}{4}(x-2) = 4 \cdot \frac{1}{2}(3x+4)$$ — Multiply both sides by 4.

$$x - 2 = 2(3x + 4)$$

$$x - 2 = 6x + 8$$

$$x - 2 - 8 = 6x + 8 - 8$$ — Add -8 to both sides (or subtract 8 from both sides).

$$x - 10 = 6x$$

$$-x + x - 10 = -x + 6x$$ — Add $-x$ to both sides (or subtract x from both sides).

$$-10 = 5x$$

$$\frac{1}{5} \cdot -10 = \frac{1}{5} \cdot 5x$$ — Divide both sides by 5.

$$-2 = x$$

Check: LHS: $\frac{1}{4}(-2-2) = -\frac{4}{4} = -1$

RHS: $\frac{1}{2}(3 \times (-2) + 4) = \frac{1}{2}(-2) = -1$

LHS = RHS ✓

Practice 1

1 Solve these equations. Show the equivalence transformation that you use at each step. Remember to check your solutions.

a $2x + 3 = x - 7$

b $5x - 4 = 2x + 6$

c $-(x + 2) - 3x = 2(x + 1)$

d $1 - 3(x + 2) = \frac{1}{2}(2x - 8) + 3$

e $\frac{x}{3} + 2 = \frac{1}{2}x - 4$

f $\frac{x + 2}{5} = \frac{2x - 4}{2}$

g $\frac{1}{3}(6x - 3) = \frac{1}{4}(8 - 4x)$

h $2x = \frac{1}{5}(9 - 8x)$

ATL

Problem solving

2 For the equation $x = 3$, use equivalence transformations to write an equivalent equation with brackets and the variable x on both sides of the equals sign.

3 Apply equivalence transformations to the equation $5(x + 4) - 8 + x = 6(x + 2)$.

Describe what happens, and explain what you think this means.

Reflect and discuss 2

- 'Multiplying both sides of an equation by zero' is not an equivalence transformation. Explain why.

- Can you think of operations that are not equivalence transformations? Explain why these operations do not result in equivalent equations.

C   Systems of linear equations

- Are all solution methods for systems of equations equivalent?
- How do the graphs of systems of equations relate to the types of solutions they may have?

A **system of equations** is two or more equations with the same unknowns. Solving a system of equations means finding values for each unknown that satisfy every equation in the system.

You have seen how you can solve an equation like $3(x + 2) - 6 = 4(2x - 3) + 1$ using an algebraic method (equivalence transformations), but did you know that you can also solve it using a graphical method?

You can consider the two sides of the equation as two separate linear equations, each equal to the variable y. You can then graph each equation on the same set of axes.

Here is a graph of $y = 3(x + 2) - 6$

and $y = 4(2x - 3) + 1$

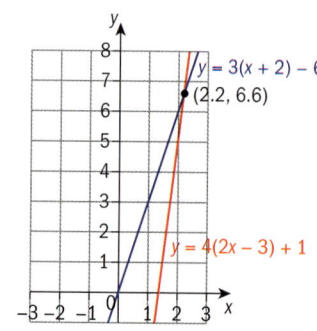

The graph shows that the value of $x = 2.2$ makes both equations equal to the same value, $y = 6.6$. So the solution that satisfies both equations simultaneously is $x = 2.2$.

Reflect and discuss 3

- Why is drawing a graph by hand not the *best* method to solve this equation?

- When is using technology not an appropriate method to finding the solution of an equation? (Hint: Can you always find exact solutions using technology?)

You can solve the two equations $y = 3(x + 2) - 6$ and $y = 4(2x - 3) + 1$ algebraically.

Expanding and simplifying:

$$y = 3(x + 2) - 6 \Rightarrow y = 3x$$
$$y = 4(2x - 3) + 1 \Rightarrow y = 8x - 11$$

So, we have two equations in two unknowns, x and y, to solve.

[1] $y = 3x$

[2] $y = 8x - 11$

There is a third equivalence transformation you can use here:

For example, for the equations $y = 3x$ and $y = 8x - 11$, substitute the value of y from [1] into equation [2] to give $3x = 8x - 11$.

[3] $3x = 8x - 11$

[4] $11 = 5x$

[5] $x = 2.2$

Substituting this value of x into both equations gives $y = 6.6$.

> Substitution Principle: Replace part of an equation by an equivalent expression.

> For a system of two equations in two unknowns the solution is an ordered pair (x, y).

Check the solution pair satisfies both original equations:

[1] $y = 3x$

LHS: 6.6

RHS: $3 \times 2.2 = 6.6$

LHS = RHS ✓

[2] $3x = 8x - 11$

LHS: $3 \times 2.2 = 6.6$

RHS: $8 \times 2.2 - 11 = 17.6 - 11 = 6.6$

LHS = RHS ✓

The *substitution method* reduces two separate equations in two unknowns into one single equation in one unknown.

Example 2

Use the method of substitution to solve the system of equations
$7x + 2y = 19$ and $x - y = 4$, and check your solution.

$x - y = 4 \Rightarrow y = x - 4$ ——————————— Choose one of the equations and solve for y.

$7x + 2(x - 4) = 19$ ——— Substitute the expression for y into the other equation, and solve for x.

$7x + 2x - 8 = 19$
$9x - 8 = 19$
$9x = 27$
$x = 3$

$y = x - 4 \Rightarrow y = 3 - 4 = -1$ ——— Substitute the value for x into one of the equations to find the value of y.

The solution is $(3, -1)$. ——————— Write the solution as an ordered pair (x, y).

$7x + 2y \Rightarrow 7(3) + 2(-1) = 21 - 2 = 19$ ✓ ——— Check algebraically by substituting the x and y values into both original equations.

$x - y \Rightarrow 3 - (-1) = 4$ ✓

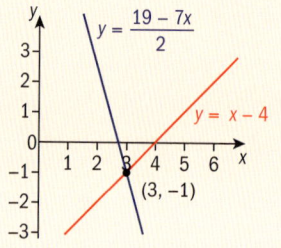

Check graphically by graphing the two equations and finding their intersection.

Practice 2

Solve these systems of equations using the substitution method.

1 $3x - 2y = 0$ and $y = 7 - 2x$ 2 $y = 9 - 2x$ and $3x - 4y = 8$

3 $x = 25 + 9y$ and $6x - 5y = 3$ 4 $3x = 12 - 5y$ and $x + 4y = 11$

5 $2x + 3y = -6$ and $3x + 2y = 25$

Problem solving

6 Rupa and George solve this system of equations: $5x + y = 8$ and $x + 3y = 10$

Rupa	George
[1] $5x + y = 8 \Rightarrow y = 8 - 5x$	[1] $5x + y = 8$
[2] $x + 3y = 10$	[2] $x + 3y = 10 \Rightarrow x = 10 - 3y$
$x + 3(8 - 5x) = 10$	$5(10 - 3y) + y = 8$

Copy and complete their working to find their solutions.

- Does your final solution for the system of equations depend on which variable you choose to solve for and substitute? (Hint: look back at Practice 2, question **6**.)

- When is it easier to substitute:

  i for x

  ii for y?

Exploration 2

In this exploration, you will find a solution for the following system of equations:

$$x + y = 4$$

$$2x - y = 5$$

1 Write the equations one above the other (as above) and then add them together, one term at a time.

2 Explain what happens to the y's in the equation.

3 Find the value of x from this new equation.

4 Starting with the original system,

$$x + y = 4$$

$$2x - y = 5$$

multiply each term in the first equation by -2.

5 Rewrite this new equation and the second equation directly above one another, as you did in step **2**.

6 Add the two equations together term by term. Explain what happens to the x's.

7 Find the value of y from this new equation.

> If the question doesn't tell you which method to use, you can choose either the algebraic or graphical method.

Sometimes the substitution method can be a bit tricky, because it is difficult to solve for either x or y, or because equations with fractions result. There is another method that uses the ideas from Exploration 2. Let's use it to solve the system of equations $3y - x = -3$ and $y - x = 1$:

[1] $3y - x = -3$

[2] $y - x = 1$

Subtracting [2] from [1] eliminates the variable x.

$$\begin{array}{r} 3y - x = -3 \\ \underline{-y + x = -1} \\ 2y = -4 \\ \underline{y = -2} \end{array}$$

> Recall that subtraction is the addition of the opposite.

Substituting $y = -2$ into either [1] or [2] gives $x = -3$. The solution to this system of equations is $(-3, -2)$.

Checking the solution in both original equations:

(1) $y - x = 1$:

$-2 - (-3) = 1$ ✓

(2) $3y - x = -3$

$3(-2) - (-3) = -6 + 3 = -3$ ✓

This method is called the *elimination method* for solving systems of equations. Can you see why?

> To solve systems of equations using the elimination method, add or subtract the equations to eliminate one of the variables. You may need to use an equivalence transformation on one or both equations first.

Practice 3

Solve each system of equations using the elimination method.
Check your solutions algebraically or graphically.

1 [1] $5x + y = 27$

  [2] $2x + y = 12$

3 [1] $2x - 3y = -16$

  [2] $2x + y = 0$

2 [1] $2y - x = 7$

  [2] $4y + x = 11$

4 [1] $3x + 2y = 11$

  [2] $5x - 2y = 13$

- -

Exploration 3

In Practice 2 question **5**, you solved the following system of equations by substitution:

$2x + 3y = -6$

$3x + 2y = 25$

1 Determine if it is possible to eliminate a variable by multiplying just one of the equations by an integer and then adding. Explain.

2 Determine if it is possible to eliminate x by multiplying each equation by a different integer and then adding. Explain.

3 Solve the system by eliminating x.

4 Solve the system by using a similar method to eliminate y instead.

5 Check your answer by substituting it into both of the original equations.

6 Explain how you would decide which variable to eliminate first.

As early as 200 BC the Chinese had invented a method of solving a system of two equations in two unknowns. The method is described in the book *Jiuzhang suanshu* (Nine Chapters in the Mathematical Art), written during the Han Dynasty.

Reflect and discuss 5

- How do you decide which variable to eliminate?

- How do you decide what to multiply one of the equations by in order to eliminate a variable?

Example 3

Solve the system of equations $5x - 7y = 27$ and $3x - 16 = 4y$, using the elimination method. Check your result algebraically or graphically.

[1] $5x - 7y = 27$ ───────────────────── Rearrange the equations to line up like terms.

[2] $3x - 4y = 16$

Multiply both sides of [1] by 4, and both sides of [2] by −7. ─── Choose equivalence transformations that give the same coefficient for one variable.

[3] $20x - 28y = 108$

[4] $-21x + 28y = -112$

$\qquad -x = -4 \Rightarrow x = 4$ ───────────────── Add [3] and [4] to eliminate y.

$5(4) - 7y = 27$ ───────────────────── Substitute into one of the original equations to find the value of the 2nd variable.

$\quad 20 - 7y = 27$

$\qquad -7y = 7$

$\qquad y = -1$

Solution is $(4, -1)$ ───────────────── Write the solution as an ordered pair.

$5(4) - 7(-1) = 20 + 7 = 27 \checkmark$ ───────────── Check algebraically by substituting the solution into both original equations.

$3(4) - 4(-1) = 12 + 4 = 16 \checkmark$

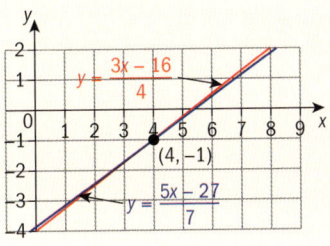

Check graphically to find the point of intersection.

Practice 4

Solve each system of equations using the elimination method.
Check your answers either algebraically or graphically.

1 $2x + 5y = 24$ and $4x + 3y = 20$

2 $2a + 3b = -9$ and $4a + b = 13$

3 $x + 3y - 7 = 0$ and $2y - x = 3$

4 $5r = 23 - 3s$ and $4s = 12 - 2r$

5 $3x = 17 + y$ and $\dfrac{x}{5} + \dfrac{y}{2} = 0$

6 $4x - 0.5y = 12.5$ and $3x = 8.2 - 0.8y$

Reflect and discuss 6

- Would it be more efficient to use the substitution method on any of the systems of equations in Practice 4? If so, explain why.

- When solving a system of linear equations, how do you select the most efficient algebraic method? Write yourself a set of guidelines on how to solve a system of linear equations efficiently.

Practice 5

Use the most efficient algebraic method for solving each system of equations. Explain why you selected your chosen method each time. Check your solutions algebraically or graphically.

1 $3x + y = 9$ and $5x + 4y = 22$ **2** $y = 2x + 4$ and $3x + y = 9$

3 $3y - 2x = 11$ and $y + 2x = 9$ **4** $3x + 2y = 16$ and $7x + y = 19$

5 $4x + 3y = -2$ and $4x - y = 6$ **6** $3x + 2y = 19$ and $x + y = 8$

Exploration 4

1 Draw the systems of equations on separate graphs:

  a $-x + 2y = 16$ **b** $-x + 2y = 16$

     $4x - 8y = -64$ $4x - 8y = 24$

2 Generalize your results from your work so far, and from step **1**. Write down the conditions necessary for a system of two linear equations to have:

- a unique solution (an ordered pair)
- no solution
- a non-unique solution (an infinite number of solutions).

3 Describe how the graphs of systems of equations relate to the number of solutions they may have. Include a sketch for each case.

4 Without actually solving these systems of equations, state, giving reasons, whether or not the system has a solution, and explain why.

  a $2x - y = 5$ **b** $-2x + 3y = 12$

     $x + 2y = 0$ $2x - 3y = 6$

  c $2x - y = 5$

    $-4x + 2y = -10$

5 Explain why it is not possible for a system of two linear equations to have two unique solutions.

6 Explain why you should test your solution in the *original* equations, and not in any of the equivalent equations you get from using equivalence transformations.

D Applications of systems of equations

- Can good decisions be calculated by using a mathematical model?

You are going to take a written driver's license exam that contains 80 questions. The scoring is such that:

- each correct answer scores 1 point
- each incorrect answer is a $\frac{1}{4}$ point deduction.

If you answer all of the questions, how many do you need to get correct in order to earn 70 points (the minimum to pass)?

Step 1: Identify the variables:

Let x represent the number of correct answers.

Let y represent the number of incorrect answers.

Step 2: Identify the constraints:

Both x and y must be positive numbers or zero, since you cannot answer a negative number of questions.

There are 80 questions, so the maximum for x or for y is 80.

Expressed mathematically: $0 \le x \le 80$; $0 \le y \le 80$

> Conditions on the values of the variables are called constraints.

Step 3: Create the model:

Write equations to represent the situation.

The 80 questions are correct or incorrect, so:

number of correct answers + number of incorrect answers = 80 $\Rightarrow x + y = 80$

Total score = (number of correct answers) $-\frac{1}{4} \times$ (number of incorrect answers) = 70

$$\Rightarrow x - \frac{1}{4}y = 70$$

The model is a system of two equations:

[1] $x + y = 80$

[2] $x - \frac{1}{4}y = 70$

Solve your model:

Use an efficient method to solve the system of equations.

Check your solution:

Check your solution algebraically, or by using a graphical display calculator (GDC) or graphing software.

> Finish working out the problem and then fill in the answers in a copy of the last sentence.

Interpret your solution in the context of the problem:

To earn 70 points, you need to answer □ questions correctly, and you can answer □ questions incorrectly.

Example 4

From 1996 to 2012, the total imports and exports from a particular company can be modelled by the following system of equations, where y represents the total exports or imports in millions of dollars, and x represents the time in years. The year 2000 is represented by $x = 0$.

Exports: $y = 1310x + 5165$

Imports: $y = 725x + 7430$

By analysing the system of equations, describe the company's pattern of imports and exports between 1996 and 2012.

$x = 0$ represents the year 2000, so the range of x (from 1996 to 2012) is $-4 \leq x \leq 12$.

> Identify the variables and constraints.

y represents the total exports or imports, thus $y > 0$.

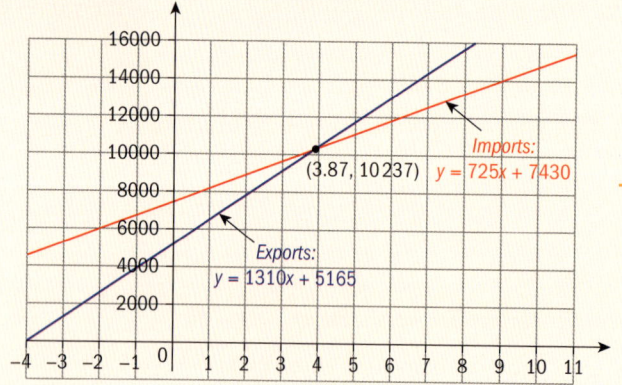

> Graph the system of equations.
>
> The intersection is at $x = 3.87 \approx 4$, which is around the year 2004.

The company had no exports in 1996. Then, until about 2004, it spent more on imports than it made on exports. After 2004 the company's export income exceeded its import expenses.

> Interpret the information from the graph in your own words, and in the context of the problem.

Practice 6

Problem solving

In the following problems, create or use the given mathematical model to answer the question. Choose the most efficient method for solving the system of equations, and check your solution.

1 You open a small business with an initial investment of $90 000. The weekly running costs for the business are $7800. The weekly revenue (income) from your business is $8800. Determine how long will it be before you break even (when your total profit matches the amount you have invested).

2 Between 2000 and 2010, coal and petroleum production from the fuel-producing countries can be modeled by the following system of equations, where $x = 0$ represents the year 2005:

   Coal production: $y = 93.2x + 3100$

   Petroleum production: $y = -29.1x + 2942$

   Calculate the year in which production from both forms of fuel was equal.

3 A phone company has two weekly plans to choose from. Plan A charges an operating fee of $31.45, plus 15.5 cents per minute. Plan B charges an operating fee of $5.20, plus 37 cents per minute. Determine how you would decide on which plan would be best for you, and explain your reasoning.

4 You gave $4500 to an investment broker, who put part of the money in a fund paying 2% annual interest and the rest in a fund paying 5% annual interest. At the end of the year you receive $210 in interest. Determine how much of your initial investment was placed into each fund.

Reflect and discuss 7

- Why would someone want to place their money in two different funds, when one of them offers a lower return than the other one?

- What kind of advantages might the bank offer in the fund with the lower interest rate?

5 Karl wants to lose some weight by burning extra calories each week (2 kg = approx. 3000 calories). He plans to achieve this by riding a bicycle, which burns 350 calories an hour, and by walking, which burns 200 calories an hour. If Karl has 10 hours per week to devote to exercise, determine the combination of walking and cycling that will allow him to achieve his goal of burning exactly 3000 calories.

During the Tour de France race, a cyclist will burn between 4000 and 5000 calories per stage. That is around 123 900 calories for the entire race, equivalent to 252 double cheeseburgers.

ATL

Reflect and discuss 8

- Is it possible to create more than one correct mathematical model to solve a particular problem?

- Are all methods for solving the model equal or equivalent?

- Explain in your own words the similarities and differences between the concepts of equality and equivalence.

Summary

1 An **equivalence transformation** is the application of one or more of the following principles in solving an equation so that all resulting equations are equivalent:

Addition Principle: Adding the same value or values to both sides of an equation.

Multiplication Principle: Multiplying by the same non-zero value or values on both sides of an equation.

Substitution Principle: Replacing part of an equation by an equivalent expression.

2 Methods of solution for systems of two linear equations:

Substitution: Solve one of the equations for one of the variables, and substitute this expression into the other equation, resulting in one equation in one unknown.

Elimination: By applying equivalence transformation(s), reduce the two equations to one equation in one unknown, and solve. Substitute this value into one of the original equations to solve for the other variable.

Graphical: Solve both equations for y and enter the equations into a GDC or graphing software. The point of intersection is the solution of the system.

3 Solution scenarios for a system of two linear equations:

One solution: The algebraic solution to the system of equations is an ordered pair. The graphs of the equations will intersect at one point.

No solution: There is no ordered pair that will satisfy both equations. The graphs of the two equations are parallel lines.

Infinitely many solutions: There is an infinite number of ordered pairs that will satisfy

the system of equations. The graphs of the equations are coincident, which means the two lines are actually the same line.

4 Creating a mathematical model using **systems of equations**:

- Identify the variables and constraints
- Translate the real-life problem into a system of equations
- Solve the system of equations
- Check the solution in the original equations
- Interpret the solution in the context of the real-world problem

Mixed practice

1 Solve these equations by identifying the equivalence transformations you use at each step:

a $3x + 4 = 19$

b $4 - 3x = 5x - 3$

c $3(3x - 1) = 4(2x - 3)$

d $\frac{2}{3}x + 2 = 4 - \frac{1}{2}x$

2 Use either elimination or substitution to solve each system of equations. **Justify** your choice of method. Check your solutions graphically.

a $y = 4x + 3$ and $y = -x - 2$

b $x - 7y = 19$ and $5x - 8y = -13$

c $\frac{1}{4}x + \frac{1}{6}y = 1$ and $x - y = 3$

d $\frac{1}{3}x + \frac{1}{2}y = -\frac{1}{4}$ and $\frac{1}{6}x - \frac{5}{6}y = \frac{11}{16}$

e $3.5x + 2.5y = 17$ and $-1.5x - 7.5y = -33$

Objective: A. Knowing and understanding
iii. solve problems correctly in a variety of contexts

For the mathematical model that describes each real-world problem, select the most efficient solution method for solving systems of equations.

Review in context

Scientific and technical innovation

1 You decide that instead of taking vitamin and mineral supplements you will get your calcium and vitamin A by drinking milk and orange juice. An ounce of milk contains 38 mg of calcium and 56 µg (micrograms) of vitamin A; an ounce of orange juice contains 5 mg of calcium and 60 µg of vitamin A. **Determine** how many ounces of milk and orange juice you would need to drink daily in order to meet your minimum requirement of 550 mg of calcium and

1200 µg of vitamin A. Decide whether or not this a realistic amount for you to drink.

2 A chemist has been asked to make a solution of 8 liters containing 20% acid. The problem is that he has only two acidic solutions, one containing 12% acid and the other containing 32% acid. **Determine** how many liters of each he should use in order to create the solution he has been asked to make.

3 A coffee distributor has two types of coffee. The premium blend sells for $10.50 per kilogram, and the standard blend sells for $8.25 per kilogram. The distributor wishes to create 20 kilograms of a mixture containing these two blends to sell at $9 per kilogram. **Determine** how many kilograms of each blend should be in the mixture.

4 You've decided to buy a printer and have narrowed it down to two choices. The laser printer costs $150 but the average cost of each page is just 1.5 cents. The other option is an inkjet printer, which costs $30, but each page has an average cost of 6 cents. **Determine** the conditions (e.g. the number of pages) where each printer is the better buy.

Coffee is the world's second most valuable traded commodity, surpassed only by petroleum.

Since Brazil produces around 40% of the world's coffee, the single most influential factor in world coffee prices is the weather in Brazil.

In 1991, a group of Cambridge University scientists aimed a fixed camera on their department's coffee pot, streaming the live footage on the web so that they could tell if the pot was empty or not. This made it the world's first live webcam.

Before coffee caught on in the US in the 1700s, the preferred breakfast drink of Americans was beer.

Reflect and discuss 9

How have you explored the statement of inquiry? Give specific examples.

Statement of inquiry:

Using logic to make and validate generalizations enhances the development of models.

3 Back to the beginning

Statement of inquiry:

Discovering relationships in patterns and studying equivalence between representations can lead to better models.

Key concept:

Relationships are the connections between quantities, properties or concepts; these connections may be expressed as models, rules or statements.

F What determines equivalence? What kind of patterns exist?

Equivalence is the state of being identically equal or interchangeable. It can apply to statements, quantities or expressions.

Patterns in language

Patterns play an important role in the learning and understanding of language. Simple sentences follow patterns – and those patterns often vary from language to language. In English, and in other Romance languages, the SVO structure is common: simple sentences are built using a Subject, a Verb and an Object, in that order.

Many languages use the SOV structure. In Turkish, for example, the sentence 'İskender elmayı yedi' would translate in word order as 'İskender the apple ate', but the English translation of the sentence would be 'İskender ate the apple'. The study of patterns in language structure is known as linguistics.

C How can relationships be represented effectively? How does equivalence affect representations?

Representation is the manner in which something is presented.

> The best representation may depend on what you want to show or to find out.

Which representation is best?

Here are four representations of a relationship between variables x and y.

Cartesian coordinate plane

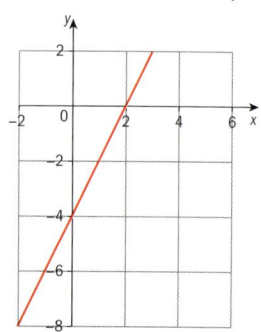

Mapping diagram

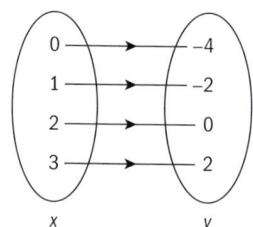

Table of values

x	0	1	2	3	4	5
y	−4	−2	0	2	4	6

Linear equation

$$y = 2x - 4$$

Which representation best shows:

- that the function is linear?
- that $f(1) = -2$?
- that the y-coordinates increase by 2 for every increase in x?

D **To what extent does understanding patterns allow you to understand the natural world?**

Patterns are sets of numbers or objects that follow a specific order or rule.

Patterns in physics

Johannes Kepler (1571–1630) discovered physical laws that explain the motion of the planets around the Sun. His third law tells us that if T is the time it takes a planet to orbit the sun, and r is the radius of its orbit, then $T \propto r^{\frac{3}{2}}$.

What does it mean to have an exponent of $\frac{3}{2}$? By looking for patterns when working with exponents, we can give fractional exponents a sensible definition.

Patterns in finance

When you invest money at a bank, the bank usually awards interest on your savings; many banks compound the interest annually.

What pattern is generated by the amount in the bank account at the end of each year?

Understanding the pattern at the end of each year can help you to work out what would be a fair value for an investment if you needed to withdraw money partway through the year.

Global context: Scientific and technical innovation

Exploration: Explore systems and methods to create models

 Launch additional digital resources for this unit.

3.1 Relations and functions

Global context: Scientific and technical innovation

Related concept: Representation

RELATIONSHIPS

Objectives

- Understanding the difference between a relation and a function
- Understanding mapping diagrams
- Knowing how to find ordered pairs in a relation
- Understanding domain and range
- Manipulating functions using the correct notation

Inquiry questions

F
- What are different ways to represent relationships?
- What is a function?

C
- What are the similarities and differences between relations and functions?
- How are the different ways of determining if a relation is a function related to one another?

D
- What do relations that are not functions look like?
- Can inequality be justified?

ATL Communication

Organize and depict information logically

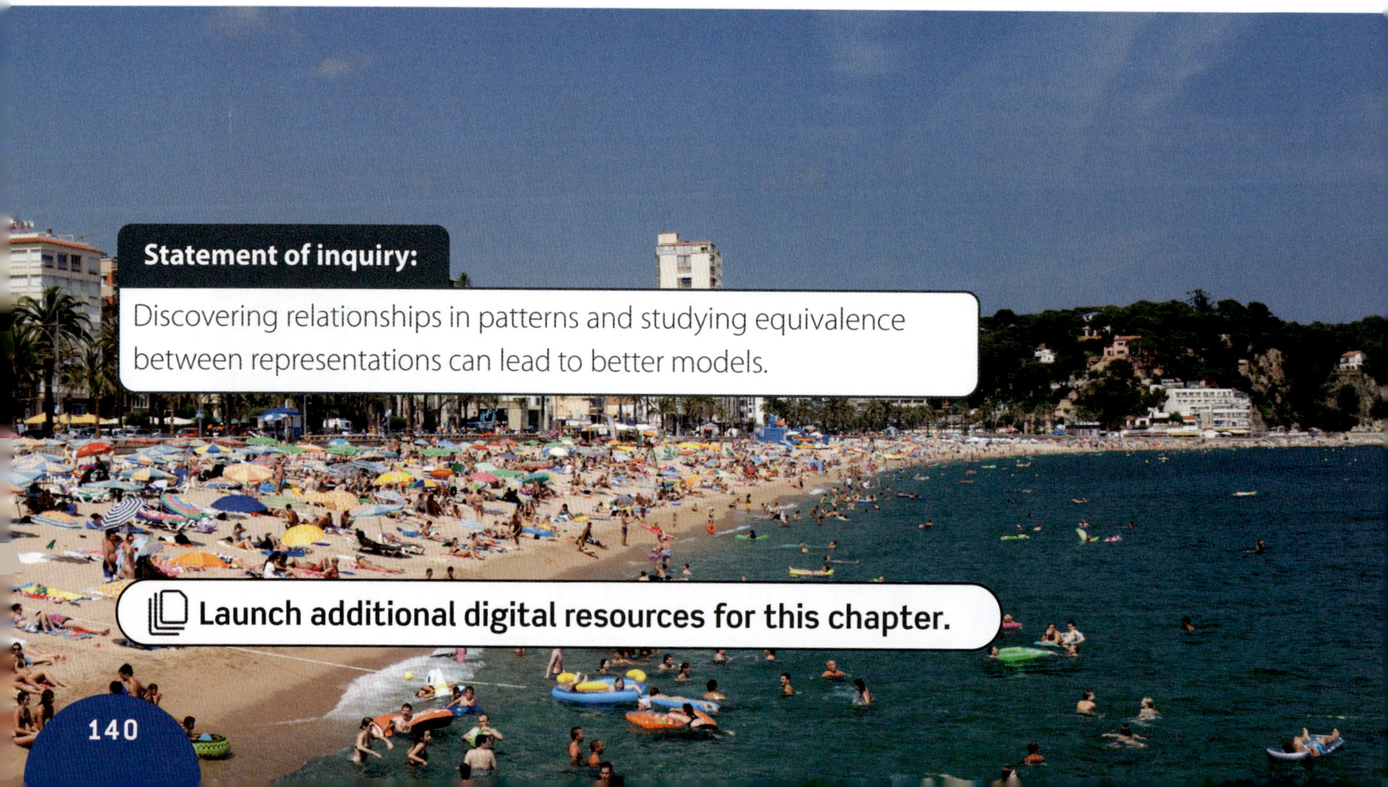

Statement of inquiry:

Discovering relationships in patterns and studying equivalence between representations can lead to better models.

Launch additional digital resources for this chapter.

You should already know how to:

• substitute values into an equation	**1** Find the value of $y = x^3$ when **a** $x = 9$ **b** $x = 0.25$ **2** Find the value of $y = \dfrac{2}{x^2}$ when **a** $x = 6$ **b** $x = \dfrac{1}{3}$
• interpret and use the basic language of sets, including set builder notation	**3** Use set builder notation to write: **a** the set of x's such that x is any real number **b** the set of x's such that x is any integer greater than zero.

Relations, mappings, and functions

- What are different ways to represent relationships?
- What is a function?

There are many situations where you pair objects or things. For example, a cause can be paired with an effect, a piece of art can be paired with the artist, a color can be paired with its HTML color code.

In mathematics, if the first object is x and the second object is y, you can write this pair as (x, y).

> In an **ordered pair** (x, y), the first term represents an object from a first set and the second term represents an object from a second set.

The HTML color code for this shade of blue-gray is 608FB0. The number of possible color codes represented by the HTML system is 16 777 216.

To write an ordered pair, first give the sets that the pairs come from. Examples:

$A = \{$house pets$\}$ and $B = \{$number of legs$\}$, then (dog, 4) is an ordered pair.

$A = \{$person$\}$ and $B = \{$age$\}$, then (Jack, 14) and (Juanita, 15) are ordered

Exploration 1

1 Set A contains all the students in your class. Set B contains the sports available at your school.

a List the members of set A.

b List the members of set B.

c Write down 5 ordered pairs relating set A to set B, describing which sports different students play.

▶ Continued on next page

'Set' has many meanings outside the sphere of mathematics, as do many other terms used in mathematics. In French the word for 'set' is 'ensemble' and in German it is 'Menge', which both have different meanings than 'set' outside the scope of mathematics.

2 Choose other pairs of sets A and B that describe students in your class.

a List the members of each set and list the ordered pairs.

b Compare them to other ordered pairs created by your classmates.

3 Consider these ordered pairs, where $A = \{\text{student}\}$ and $B = \{\text{class}\}$:
(George, Science), (Ann, History), (Enrico, Science), (Matt, Music),
(Donald, History), (Cindy, Science).

a Suggest what these ordered pairs could represent.

b This diagram shows the members of sets A and B. Copy the diagram. For each ordered pair in part **a**, draw a line mapping the element of set A to the element in set B. This is called a mapping diagram.

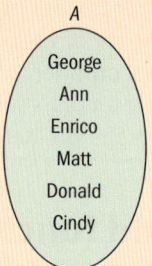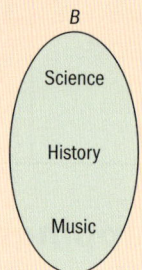

4 Construct a mapping diagram for your ordered pairs in step **1c**.

5 Decide on two sets that you encounter in real life. Draw a mapping diagram for ordered pairs from these sets. Write down 4 ordered pairs.

> A **mapping diagram** shows how the elements in a relation are paired. Each set is represented by an oval, and lines or arrows are drawn from elements in the first set to elements in the second set for each ordered pair in the relation.

These mapping diagrams representing four different types of relations.

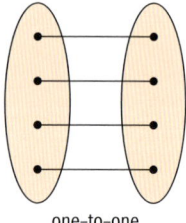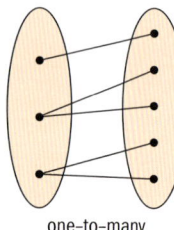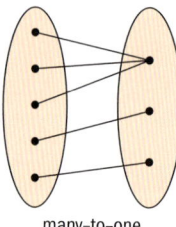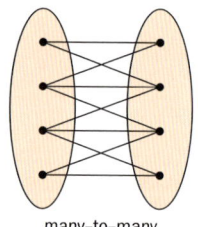

one-to-one   one-to-many   many-to-one   many-to-many

> How do you think each mapping diagram got its name?

So far, you have looked at ordered pairs that describe relationships in real life. However, mathematics is also full of relationships that can be described in the same way.

Exploration 2

1 Consider the equation $y = x + 2$, where x is an element of the set $A = \{0, 1, 2, 3, 4, 5\}$ and y is an element of set B.

a List the elements of set B.

b Draw a mapping diagram to represent the relation between set A and set B.

▶ Continued on next page

c List all the ordered pairs (x, y) that represent this relation.

d Using the ordered pairs as coordinates, plot these points on a coordinate plane.

2 Consider the same equation $y = x + 2$, where x is an element of the set A, where $A = \mathbb{R}$, and y is an element of set B.

  a Define set B.

  b Determine if you can draw a mapping diagram to represent all the ordered pairs in this equation.

    i If possible, draw the mapping diagram.

    ii If not possible, explain why not.

  c Draw the graph of this equation on a coordinate plane, where x is any real number.

3 Consider the equation $x^2 = y^2$, where x is an element of the set $A = \{-2, -1, 0, 1, 2\}$ and y is an element of set B.

  a List all the ordered pairs (x, y) that represent this relation.

  b Hence, list the elements of set B.

  c Draw a mapping diagram to represent the relation between set A and set B.

  d Using these ordered pairs as coordinates, plot these points on a coordinate plane.

4 Consider the same equation $x^2 = y^2$, where x is an element of the set A, where $A = \mathbb{R}$, and y is an element of set B.

  a Use your knowledge of the graph in step **3** to draw the graph of this equation on a coordinate plane, where x is any real number.

  b Define set B.

A relation can be defined either by listing the set of ordered pairs that make a relation (as in Exploration 1) or by giving a specific rule (as in Exploration 2).

Reflect and discuss 1

- What are the advantages and limitations of using a mapping diagram to represent a relation?

- What are the advantages and limitations of using a graph to represent a relation?

- In which situations is a mapping diagram better than a graph?

- In which situations is a graph better than a mapping diagram?

A **relation** is a set of ordered pairs $\{(x, y) \mid x \in A, y \in B\}$.

It has three components:

- a relation or rule that maps x onto y for each ordered pair in the relation
- a set A that contains all the x elements of each ordered pair
- a set B that contains all the y elements.

A relation maps set A onto set B.

Practice 1

1 Determine which type of mapping diagram (one-to-one, one-to-many, many-to-one, or many-to-many) best matches each of these relations:

  a $A = \{$students in your class$\}$, $B = \{$number of siblings$\}$, and the relation maps each student in A to their number of siblings in B.

  b $A = \{$students in your class$\}$, $B = \{$mothers$\}$, and the relation maps each student in A to their mother in B.

  c $A = \{$couples$\}$, $B = \{$grandchildren$\}$, and the relation maps each couple in A to each of their grandchildren in B.

2 Find a real-life situation for each type of mapping diagram.

  a Define the sets A and B as in question **1**.

  b Write down the relation that maps the elements in set A to the elements in set B.

3 For the two equations $y = x + 2$ and $x^2 = y^2$, determine the type of mapping diagram that best describes the relation between set $A = \mathbb{R}$ and set $B = \mathbb{R}$. (Hint: Look back at your answers to Exploration 2.)

- -

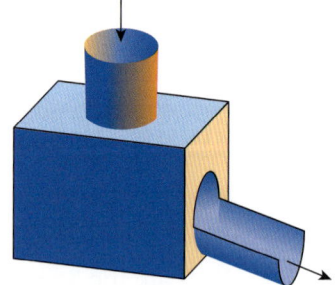

A **function** is a relation where each element in set A maps to one and only one element in set B.

A function can be thought of as a number machine, where for every input value there is only one possible output value. Such a number machine is called a **function machine**.

A function can be written as $f(x) = y$, where:

- x is the input value, $x \in A$
- y is the output value, $x \in B$
- f is the name of the function that maps x to y.

$f(x) = y$ is read 'the function f of x is y' or just 'f of x is y'.

Another way of writing $f(x) = y$ is $f : x \mapsto y$.

> The letter f is most often used to represent a function, but other letters such as g and h are often used in problems involving more than one function.

Linear equations, such as $y = x + 2$, are functions. You can write $f(x) = x + 2$ or $f : x \mapsto x + 2$. Using this notation, you can say that $f(3) = 5$, meaning that when the input x to the function f is 3, the output is 5. You could also write $f(4) = 6$ and $f(-5) = -3$, for example. Function notation uses both elements of an ordered pair in one equation.

If a function maps elements of set A onto elements of set B, then set A is called the domain and set B is called the range.

> The **domain** of a function is the set of input values that the function can take.
>
> The **range** of a function is the set of all output values that the function generates. The range is also called the set of images of the elements in the domain.

In a mapping diagram, all the elements of the domain are in one set, and all the elements of the range are in the other set.

Usually, the domain is specified in the question. If not, it is assumed to be the set of real numbers, $\mathbb{R}$. If a function is defined as a set of ordered pairs $(x, f(x))$, then the domain is simply the set of input values (all the values of x) and the range is the set of output values (all the values of $f(x)$).

Example 1

Consider this mapping diagram.

a Write in words what the relation could represent.

b Justify why the relation is a function.

c State the domain and range of the function.

d Write the function for one of the ordered pairs in this diagram.

In the 18th century, Leonhard Euler, one of the most prolific mathematicians in history, introduced the notation $f(x)$ to represent a function of x.

a This mapping diagram could represent which age group children belong to at a day care center.

b This relation is a function because _____ each child is in only one age group.

In order to be a function, each element from the domain must map to one and only one element in the range.

c Domain: {Alice, Charles, Diego, Gabriel, Pauline, Elsa}
Range: {Baby, Toddler}

g was chosen for the function, since it represents the *group* a child belongs to.

d g(Elsa) = Toddler _____
Elsa is a toddler.

Practice 2

1 Consider this mapping diagram.

a Determine if this relation is a function. Justify your answer.

b Write the domain and range using set notation.

c Find:

   i $f(1)$ **ii** $f(2)$ **iii** $f(5)$

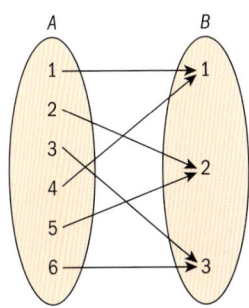

2 For each of the following mapping diagrams:

i Write in words what the relation could represent.

ii Justify why the relation is a function.

iii State the domain and range.

iv Write down one specific ordered pair in the function.

a
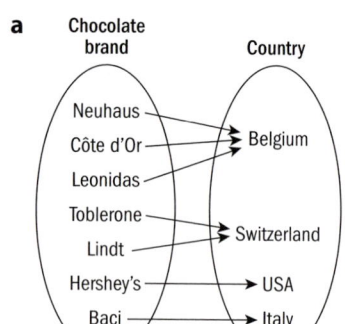

b
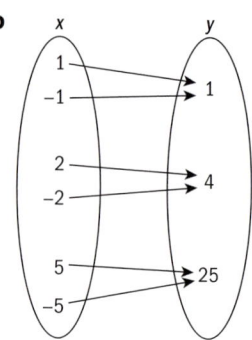

c
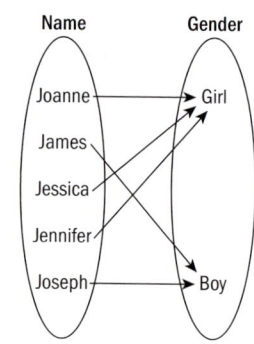

Example 2

State the domain and range of the relation:

$\{(1, 2), (2, 4), (3, 6), (4, 8), (5, 10)\}$

Domain = $\{1, 2, 3, 4, 5\}$ ———————— In a list of ordered pairs, the domain is the list of x-values. The domain is written in set notation.

Range = $\{2, 4, 6, 8, 10\}$ ———————— In a list of ordered pairs, the range is the list of y-values. The range is written in set notation.

Practice 3

1 State the domain and range for each relation.

a $\{(7, 4), (2, 9), (4, 6), (8, 1), (5, 2)\}$

b $\{(6, 2), (8, 8), (3, 7), (4, 4), (4, -4)\}$

c $\{(-3, -1), (5, 1), (-2, -1), (3, 1), (-7, -1), (8, 1)\}$

d $\{(a, g), (t, c), (s, g), (k, w), (j, k), (p, p)\}$

e $\{(a, x), (a, y), (a, z), (b, x), (b, z)\}$

2 Consider the set $A = \{-2, -1, 0, 1, 2\}$. For each relation **a** to **c**:

i List all the ordered pairs (x, y) that represent this relation.

ii Hence, list the elements of the range (set B).

iii Draw a mapping diagram to represent the relation between set A and set B.

iv Use your mapping diagram to determine which type of relation it is.

v Determine whether or not the relation is a function.

    a $y = x$ **b** $y = 3x + 3$ **c** $y = x^2$

Activity

With some functions, it is possible to determine the domain and range by simply thinking about the kinds of values that can be used as input and the kinds of values that are produced as output. Using this method, copy and complete this table.

Function	Domain	Range
$f(x) = 2x$	x can be any value, since you can double any value, so the domain of f is $\mathbb{R}$.	
$g(x) = \sqrt{x}$		By convention, the square root function gives only the positive square root. So the range of g is $\{y \mid y \geq 0, y \in \mathbb{R}\}$.
$h(x) = x^2$	You can square any real number, so the domain of h is $\mathbb{R}$.	
$f(x) = \dfrac{1}{x}$		

The four functions in the Activity show the different possible restrictions you can have on the domain or range for different functions.

> A **natural**, or maximum, domain is the largest possible set of values that a function can take.
>
> A **restricted** domain is a subset of the natural domain of the function.

Practice 4

State the largest possible domain and the corresponding range for each function.

1 $y = 5x - 3$

2 $y = -4x + 9$

3 $y = \dfrac{2}{5}x + 12$

4 $y = 2x^2$

5 $y = x^2 + 5$

6 $y = 3x^2 - 3$

7 $y = \dfrac{32}{x}$

8 $y = \dfrac{15}{2x}$

9 $y = \dfrac{1}{x+1}$

10 $y = \dfrac{1}{x} + 1$

Reflect and discuss 2

Recall the definitions of a relation and a function.

- Are all functions relations?
- Are all relations functions?
- If you answered 'no' to either question above, explain why.

C Using functions to express relationships

- What are the similarities and differences between relations and functions?
- How are the different ways of determining if a relation is a function related to one another?

So far, you have seen that:

- a function is a special type of relation, where for each element of the domain there exists one and only one element in the range. (Each input value generates exactly one output value.)
- a function is a one-to-one or a many-to-one relation.

Exploration 3 investigates further how you can determine whether or not a relation is a function.

Exploration 3

1 For each mapping diagram, draw a set of points on a coordinate plane. Label each graph with its relationship.

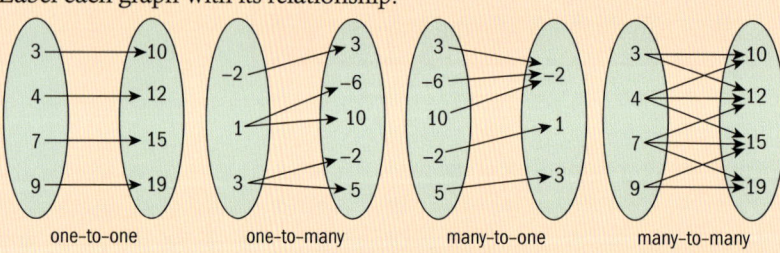

| one-to-one | one-to-many | many-to-one | many-to-many |

> Use a new coordinate plane for each mapping diagram.

If you are stuck, try the following steps to guide you:

a Determine which axis represents the domain, x.

b Determine which axis represents the range, $y = f(x)$.

2 Determine of your graphs show a function. Suggest how you could determine from a graph whether or not a relation is a function.

3 **a** Draw the graph of $y = 4x - 9$.

b Looking at your graph, determine the type of relation this is.

▶ Continued on next page

c Draw a mapping diagram to represent $y = 4x - 9$. Select only a few ordered pairs for your mapping diagram, until you are satisfied with the type of relationship it represents. You do not need to list every possible ordered pair for this mapping diagram.

d Decide whether or not the mapping diagram confirms the type of relationship that your graph represents.

e Hence, decide whether $y = 4x - 9$ is a function.

4 Here is the graph of $y^2 = x$.

a Determine which of the four types of relationship this graph represents.

b Hence, decide whether or not $y^2 = x$ is a function.

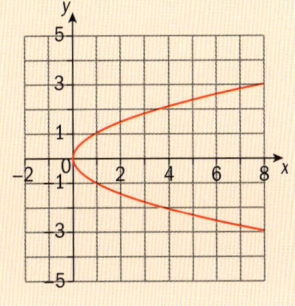

You have used two different methods for deciding whether or not a relation is a function (sometimes called 'a function from x to y'):

- with a mapping diagram: if a mapping diagram is one-to-one or many-to-one, then the relation is a function

- with a graph: if each x-value has only one corresponding y-value, then the relation is a function.

> The **vertical line test**: if no vertical line intersects a graph at more than one point, the relation is a function. If a vertical line intersects the graph at more than one point, then the relation is not a function.

$y = 0.5x - 1.5$ is a function, because no vertical line intersects the graph more than once.

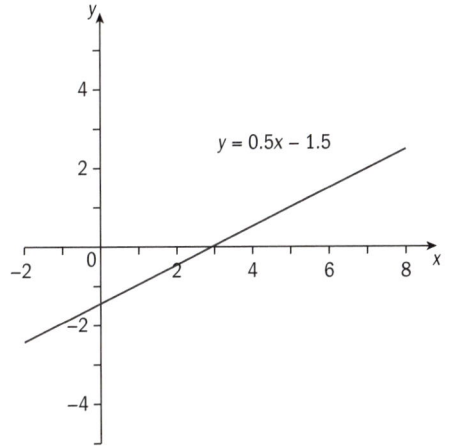

$y^2 = x$ is not a function, because at least one vertical line intersects the graph twice.

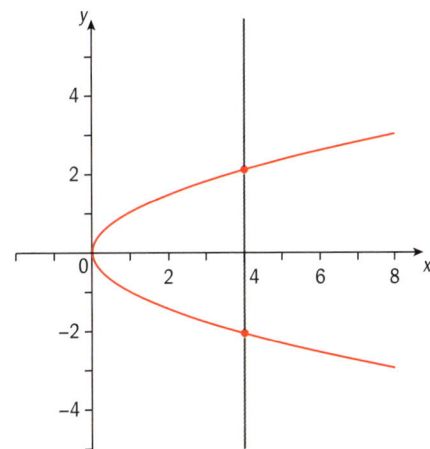

Practice 5

1 Use the vertical line test to determine which of these graphs show functions.

a 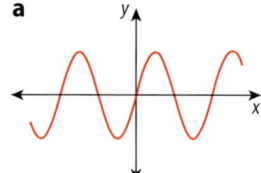 **b** 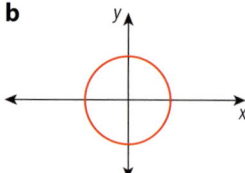 **c** 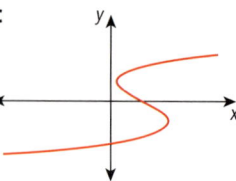 **d**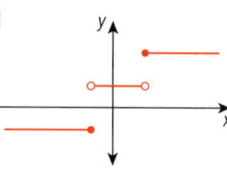

- -

Example 3

Determine whether or not these relations represent a function from x to y.

a $\{(2, 5), (5, 6), (2, -5), (4, -6)\}$ **b** $\{(1, -3), (2, -4), (3, -3), (4, -4)\}$

c $y = x - 3$ **d** $x^2 + y^2 = 4^2$

a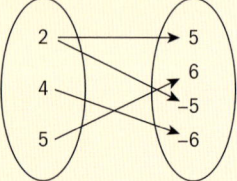

Draw a mapping diagram for the ordered pairs.

This relation is not a function.

2 maps to both 5 and −5.
This is a one-to-many relation.

b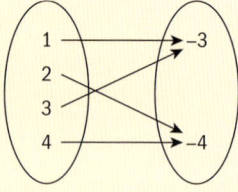

This relation is a function.

This is a many-to-one function.

c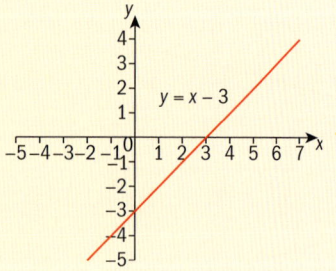

Draw a graph and use the vertical line test.

This relation is a function. Therefore, you use the notation $y = x - 3$ or $f(x) = x - 3$.

No vertical line would cross the graph at more than one point.

▶ Continued on next page

d

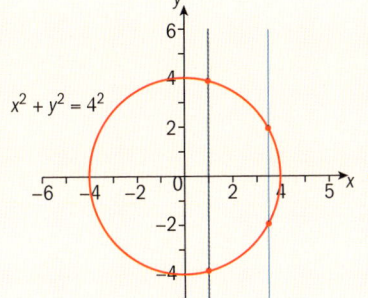

$x^2 + y^2 = 4^2$

Draw a graph and use the vertical line test.

This relation is not a function. ———— You can draw vertical lines that cross the graph of this circle at more than one point.

Reflect and discuss 3

Representation is an MYP related concept. It is defined as 'the manner in which something is presented'.

- How did you represent relations and functions in Example 3?
- How does representation enable you to determine whether or not a relation is a function?
- Why is it important to distinguish between relations and functions?

Practice 6

1 Decide which of the following relations are functions.
Give a reason for your answer.

a

A	1	2	3	4
B	4	2	0	2

b

A	−1	0	−1	1
B	5	5	7	5

c {(3, 12), (−16, 10), (3, 12), (15, 3), (3, 12), (−15, −3)}

d {(9, 9), (8, 7), (7, 5), (5, 9), (9, 5), (6, 12)}

e

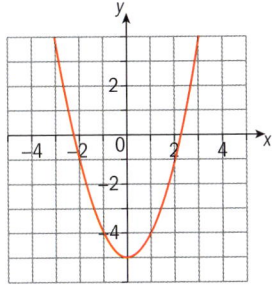

f

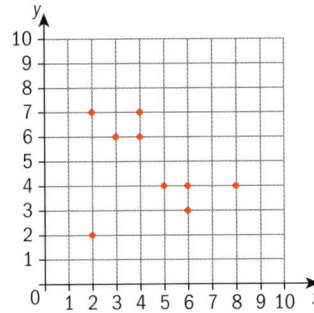

g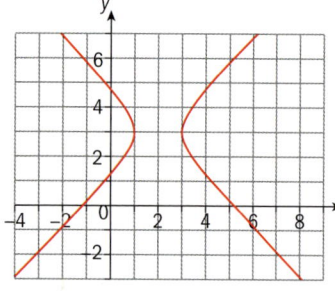

h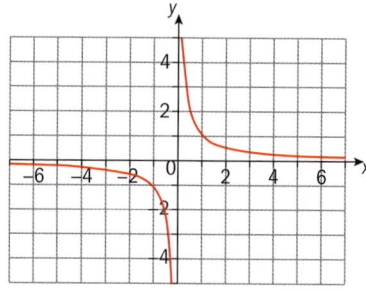

Reflect and discuss 4

Justification is an MYP related concept. It is defined as 'valid reasons or evidence used to support a statement'.

- Where in the previous example and practice problems have you used justification?

- How does justification enable you to support whether or not a relation is a function?

- Is it important to justify whether a relation is a function?

- Can you think of some equations you have worked with that are not functions?

Exploration 4

'I think of a number, double it, add 3 and then square the result.'

1 Explain why this is a function.

2 If x is an element of the domain of this function, write this function mathematically (i.e. $f(x) = $ something).

3 Make up your own 'I think of a number' puzzle. Write the function for your puzzle in mathematical notation. Then share it with others and see if they write the same function definition as you have.

Writing a function mathematically is called defining a specific function.

> A function is **defined** by a mathematical expression that specifies the relationship between a domain (input values) and range (output values).

For example, if a function f is defined as: $f(x) = 3x + 2$, then:

- f is the name of the function
- x is an element of the domain
- $f(x)$ is read as 'f of x'
- '$3x + 2$' tells you what the function does to each element of the domain to get the corresponding element from the range.

This is the definition of this specific function f. When defining a function, the domain is usually specified. If it isn't, it is assumed to be the set of real numbers.

Example 4

A recipe states that chicken needs to be cooked for 15 minutes per kg plus an extra 40 minutes. Express the relationship between mass and cooking time using function notation, and define the domain and range.

x: the mass of the chicken (in kg)

$f(x)$: the cooking time (in minutes)

> Set the input and output variables in the context of the problem.

Domain: $x \geq 0$

Range: $f(x) \geq 40$

> Neither the mass nor the cooking time can be negative. The chicken will take *at least* 40 minutes to cook.

$f(x) = 15x + 40$

> 15 minutes per kg (x) plus 40 more minutes.

Check:

> Check with easy values. Do the results seem sensible?

$f(1) = 15 \times 1 + 40 = 55$

> A 1 kg chicken needs 15 min + 40 min = 55 min.

$f(2) = 15 \times 2 + 40 = 70$

> A 2 kg chicken needs 30 min + 40 min = 70 min.

Reflect and discuss 5

Think what input values are sensible for the function in Example 4. If you had no chicken at all, meaning that $x = 0$, does it make sense that the cooking time is 40 minutes? Yet, $f(0) = 15 \times 0 + 40 = 40$. For what values of x is this function definition intended?

Sometimes input values are mathematically possible, but they do not make sense in a real-life context (as with cooking 0 kg of chicken).

A real-life situation may restrict the elements of the domain in order to make sense of the problem. These restrictions are called *constraints* on the domain.

When setting variables to represent a worded (or real-life) situation, it is important that each variable represents a *number* or an *amount* within the context of the problem. Good variable definition examples are 'x = Tina's height' and 'y = Tina's age'. Why do you think writing "x = Tina" would not be a good variable definition?

> **Objective: C.** Communicating
> **i.** use appropriate mathematical language (notation, symbols and terminology) in both oral and written explanations.
>
> *In these questions you need to use function notation to express the relation, set builder notation for the domain and range, and words such as 'domain', 'range', 'one-to-one' to explain how the relation is a function.*

ATL

Practice 7

For each question **1** to **3**:

- **a** Express the relation using function notation.
- **b** Define the domain and range. Decide what the constraints are on the domain and range based on the real-life context.
- **c** Explain how the relation is a function.

1 A carpenter charges his clients a rate of €30 an hour, plus a single €40 fee for each job. Express the relationship between time spent on a job and the fee charged to the client.

2 A bathtub is filled with 120 liters of water. The drain plug is pulled and the water empties out at a rate of 25 liters per minute. Express the relationship between time elapsed since the plug was pulled, and the amount of water in the bathtub.

3 On a tropical island, the cost of a parcel of land is $200 per square meter. Taxes and fees account for an additional 15%. Express the relationship between the size of a parcel of land, and the final price that the client pays for it.

> The placement of the € symbol is often based on what countries did with their old currency. So it might be €37 in one country, but 37€ in another.

> **Evaluating a function** means finding the element of the range that corresponds to a given element in the domain.

Example 5

If $f(x) = 3x + 2$, find the value of $f(4)$.

$f(x) = 3x + 2$ — Start with the original function definition.

$f(4) = 3 \times 4 + 2$ — Substitute 4 for x.

$f(4) = 12 + 2 = 14$

Practice 8

1 $f(x) = 4x - 2$

- **a** Describe in words what this function does to the input value.
- **b** Draw a table of values that shows at least 5 different input values and the corresponding output values.

2 $g(x) = x^2 + 2$

    a Describe in words what this function does to the input value.

    b Draw a table of values that shows at least 5 different input values and the corresponding output values.

3 $h(x) = \dfrac{2}{x}$

    a Describe in words what this function does to the input value.

    b Draw a table of values that shows at least 5 different input values and the corresponding output values.

4 If $f(x) = 7x - 3$, find:

    a $f(3)$ **b** $f(-1)$ **c** $f(0)$ **d** $f(20)$

5 If $p(3) = $ triangle and $p(5) = $ pentagon, find:

    a $p(4)$ **b** $p(6)$ **c** $p(8)$ **d** $p(10)$

- -

In a function, an input value generates one specific output value. And in certain cases, two or more input values generate the same output value. In Exploration 5, you will see when it is possible to find the input value if you are given only the output value. This is called solving the function.

> **Solving an equation** that is a function means finding the element of the domain that corresponds to a given element in the range.

Exploration 5

Consider the two functions $f(x) = 7x - 12$ and $f(x) = x^2$.

1 For each function, find $f(3)$. This is called *evaluating* the function at $x = 3$.

2 For each function, find the value of x such that $f(x) = 16$. This is called *solving* the equation when $f(x) = 16$.

3 For each function, determine whether there is only one possible input value for each output value.

4 Use your findings to decide if a function is always a one-to-one relationship between an input value and an output value. Justify your answer.

Evaluating a function (finding the value of $f(x)$) only gives one answer.

Solving a function (finding the value of x, given $f(x)$) can give more than one answer.

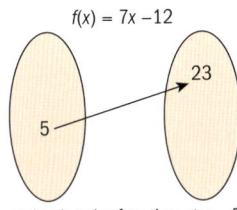

evaluating the function at $x = 5$

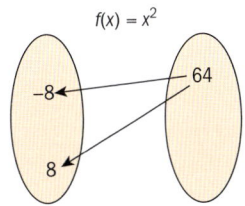

solving the function when $f(x) = 64$

Practice 9

In questions **1** to **7**, evaluate the function at the given values.

1 $h(x) = 2 - 4x$

    a $h(0)$ **b** $h(1)$ **c** $h(-1)$

    d $h(20)$ **e** $h(-a)$ **f** $h(2x)$

> In question **1e**, substitute $-a$ for x in the function.

2 $f(x) = 3x - 5$

    a $f(0)$ **b** $f(4)$ **c** $f(-4)$

    d $f(12)$ **e** $f(3x)$ **f** $f(x+1)$

3 $f(x) = 13$

    a $f(0)$ **b** $f(19)$ **c** $f(20{,}000)$

    d $f(-25)$ **e** $f(-x)$ **f** $f(12x)$

4 $f(x) = x^2 + 1$

    a $f(0)$ **b** $f(5)$ **c** $f(-5)$

    d $f(9)$ **e** $f(x+1)$ **f** $f(4x)$

5 $f(x) = x^2 - 2x + 1$

    a $f(1)$ **b** $f(2)$ **c** $f(0)$

    d $f(7)$ **e** $f(-10)$ **f** $f(3x)$

6 $f(x) = 4x^3 - 2x + 1$

    a $f(2)$ **b** $f(-1)$ **c** $f(0.5)$

    d $f(3)$ **e** $f(-2)$ **f** $f(-x)$

7 $f(x) = 3x + 5$

    a $f(5)$ **b** $f(10)$ **c** $f(2x)$

    d $f(3x)$ **e** $f(x+5)$ **f** $f(3x-2)$

8 If $f(x) = 8x - 4$, find the value of a such that $f(a) = 12$.

9 If $f(x) = x + 12$, find the value of b such that $f(b) = 12$.

10 If $h(x) = 15 - 2x$, find the value of c such that $h(c) = 3$.

11 If $r(x) = x^2$, find the value of d such that $r(d) = 36$.

12 If $f(x) = x^2 + 5$, find the value of e such that $f(e) = 54$.

13 If $k(x) = \dfrac{1}{x+2}$, find the value of p such that $k(p) = \dfrac{1}{4}$.

> In questions **11** and **12** there are two possible values.

14 If $f(x) = \dfrac{1}{x-5}$, find the value of q such that $f(q) = \dfrac{1}{5}$.

Problem solving

15 If $p(135) =$ south-east and $p(180) =$ south, find the value of s such that $p(s) =$ north-west.

16 If child(Olimpia) = Viola and child(Arienne) = William, state the condition(s) that must be satisfied in order for child(x) to be a function. Suggest a value of m such that child(m) = you, and determine if in your family child(m) = you is a function. Explain your reasoning. Share your ideas with others.

> In question **16**, how many children can a parent have if child(x) is a function?

D Recognizing relations that are not functions

- What do relations that are not functions look like?
- Can inequality be justified?

So far, you know that:

- a function is a specific relation between the domain and range
- if an input to a relation generates more than one output, the relation is not a function.

You have already looked at how to decide if a mapping diagram or a graph represents a function. However, is it possible to tell if a relation is a function just by looking at its equation?

Exploration 6

Look at the lists of equations below. For each relation, $x \in \mathbb{R}$ and $y \in \mathbb{R}$.

FUNCTION

$y = 3x - 4$

$2x + 5y = 9$

$y = 2$

$x^2 + 3x - 4y - 5 = 0$

$y = 2(x + 1)^3 - 8$

$y = \sqrt{x - 4}, \, x \geq 4, y \geq 0$

NOT A FUNCTION

$x^2 + y^2 = 16$

$x = 3(y + 1)^2 - 7$

$2x + 3y^2 - 4y = 5$

$x - y^2 = 1$

$\dfrac{(x-1)^2}{4} + \dfrac{(y-2)^2}{25} = 1$

$y = \pm\sqrt{x - 4}, \, x \geq 4$

1 Based on the lists above, make a conjecture about the types of equations that are functions and those that are not.

2 If possible, rewrite each equation to look like $y = f(x)$.

3 Based on your results, suggest which type of equation represents a relation, but is not the equation of a function.

Reflect and discuss 6

- What sort of relations generate more than one output value for a single input value?
- Why do those relations generate more than one output value?
- Are there other relations that have similar properties (and are therefore not functions)?
- How does this relate to the 'vertical line test'?

Summary

In an **ordered pair** (x, y), the first term represents an object from a first set and the second term represents an object from a second set.

A **relation** is a set of ordered pairs:
$\{(x, y) \mid x \in A, y \in B\}$.

It has three components:

- a relation or rule that maps x onto y for each ordered pair in the relation
- a set A that contains all the x elements of each ordered pair
- a set B that contains all the y elements.

A relation maps set A onto set B.

A **mapping diagram** shows how the elements in a relation are paired. Each set is represented by an oval, and lines or arrows are drawn from elements in the first set to elements in the second set for each ordered pair in the relation.

A **function** is a relation where each element in set A maps to one and only one element in set B.

A function can be written as $f(x) = y$, where:

- x is the input value, $x \in A$
- y is the output value, $y \in B$
- f is the name of the function that maps x to y.

$f(x) = y$ is read 'the function f of x is y' or just 'f of x is y'.

Another way of writing $f(x) = y$ is $f : x \mapsto y$.

The **domain** of a function is the set of input values that the function can take.

The **range** of a function is the set of all the output values that the function generates. The range is also called the set of images of the elements in the domain.

A **natural** domain is the largest possible set of values that a function can take.

A **restricted** domain is a subset of the natural domain of the function.

The **vertical line test**: if no vertical line intersects a graph at more than one point, the relation is a function. If a vertical line intersects the graph at more than one point, then the relation is not a function.

A function is **defined** by a mathematical expression that specifies the relationship between a domain (input values) and range (output values).

Evaluating a function means finding the element of the range that corresponds to a given element in the domain.

Solving an equation that is a function means finding the element of the domain that corresponds to a given element in the range.

Mixed practice

1 Determine whether each diagram represents a relation or a function. **Justify** your answer.

a

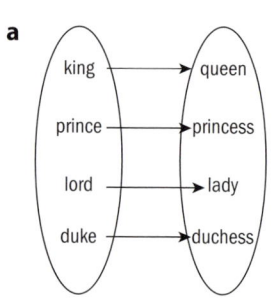

b

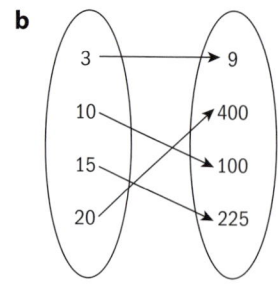

c

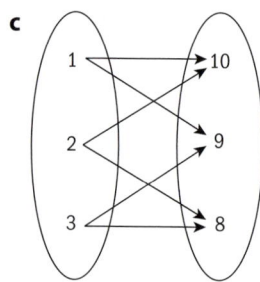

d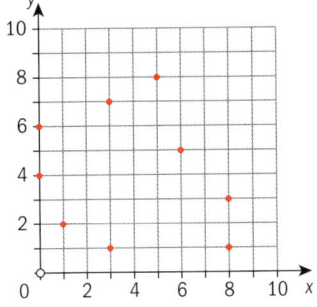

e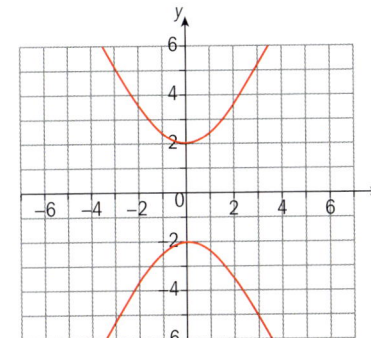

f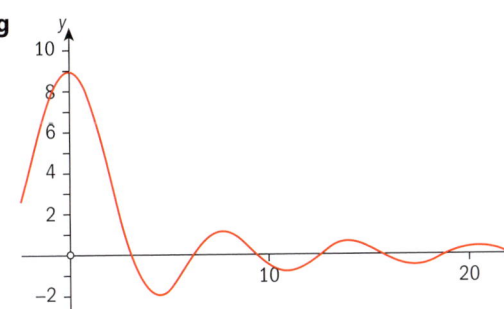

g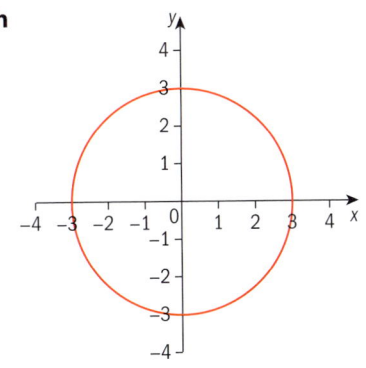

h

i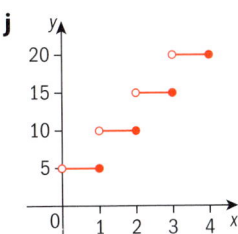

j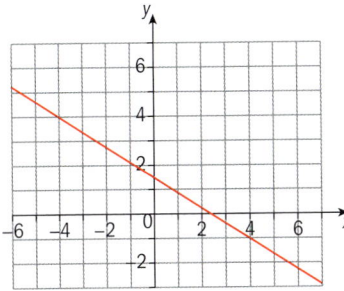

2 State the domain and range:

    a $\{(1, 1), (2, 4), (-2, -4)\}$

    b $\{(3, 5), (4, 5), (5, 6)\}$

    c $\{(-2, -3), (-3, -2), (-2, 5)\}$

    d $\{(1, 1), (2, 3), (5, 8)\}$

3 Find the largest possible domain and range:

    a $f(x) = 3x - 8$ **b** $f(x) = 3\sqrt{x}$

    c $f(x) = \dfrac{x}{4}$ **d** $f(x) = \dfrac{4}{x}$

    e $f(x) = \dfrac{4}{x - 4}$ **f** $f(x) = x^2 - 1$

4 Evaluate each function at the given values:

    a $a(x) = 2 - x^2$

      i $a(2)$ **ii** $a(0)$ **iii** $a(-2)$

    b $b(x) = 8x - 4$

      i $b(4)$ **ii** $b(3)$ **iii** $b(1)$

    c $c(x) = \sqrt{x - 1}$

      i $c(1)$ **ii** $c(5)$ **iii** $c(0)$

    d $d(x) = 2x + 3$

      i $d(4)$ **ii** $d(4x)$ **iii** $d(2 - x)$

5 **Solve** each function at the given values:

a $f(x) = 4x - 2$

   i $f(x) = 18$ **ii** $f(x) = 0$ **iii** $f(x) = 2$

b $f(x) = \dfrac{1}{x}$

   i $f(x) = \dfrac{1}{5}$ **ii** $f(x) = -\dfrac{1}{4}$ **iii** $f(x) = 2$

c $f(x) = \sqrt{x}$

   i $f(x) = 5$ **ii** $f(x) = 1$ **iii** $f(x) = 9$

6 A computer program asks you for any word and returns the number of letters in that word.

a **Justify** why this computer program is a function.

b **Write down** what this computer program does in function notation, where the function is called '*p*' for program.

c **Evaluate**:

   i $p(\text{horse})$ **ii** $p(\text{Mississippi})$ **iii** $p(\text{hi})$

d **Find** x such that

   i $p(x) = 3$ **ii** $p(x) = 8$

e What is $p(\text{three})$?

f For what numbers $0 \leq x \leq 10$ does $p(x) = x$?

7 A hospital has 9 floors above ground (including ground floor) and 3 floors below ground. $T(n)$ gives the average number of times the elevator stops at the nth floor each day.

a **Justify** why $T(n)$ is a function.

b **Find** the largest possible domain of $T(n)$.

c For each floor in the domain, **suggest** the number of times the elevator stops at that floor during 24 hours. Write your answer as a list of ordered pairs.

d Hence, **suggest** a possible range of $T(n)$. **Justify** your choice.

8 The table shows postage rates for letters and parcels.

Letters	
Mass less than	Price
50 g	£0.65
100 g	£0.92
200 g	£1.20
Small parcels	
Mass less than	Price
100 g	£1.90
200 g	£2.35
500 g	£3.40
750 g	£4.50
1 kg	£5.00

a **Draw** a mapping diagram to represent the masses of items and the delivery charge.

b **Decide** whether the mass determines the price or the price determines the mass. Add arrows to your mapping diagram to show this.

c **Determine** whether this relation is a function.

Review in context

Scientific and technical innovation

1 Many universities use a test in their admissions decisions. The results of one such test were paired with family income as reported by test-takers, shown in the table here:

Family income ($)	Total test score (max. 2400)
10 000	1326
30 000	1402
50 000	1461
70 000	1497
90 000	1535
110 000	1569
130 000	1581
150 000	1604
180 000	1625
More than 180 000	1714

a **Draw** a mapping diagram to represent the family income and the total test score.

b **Determine** whether or not this relation is a function.

c **Suggest** reasons why this relationship may exist.

d Should universities use this information in their admission decisions? If so, how?

2 The table shows the percentage of world population in different countries and their use of natural resources.

Country	Percentage of world population	Percentage of world's resources used
Brazil	3	2
China	19	20
India	17	5
Indonesia	4	1
Japan	3	4
Pakistan	3	0.5
Russian Federation	3	6
United States	5	18

a **State** the input variable and the output variable and the domain and range of this relation.

b Is this relation a function? **Explain**.

c **Draw** a mapping diagram of this relation.

d Does this demonstrate an equitable or fair relationship? **Explain** your reasoning.

e What action, if any, do you think should be taken?

3 Car insurance rates vary greatly depending on your age, the kind of car you drive and other factors. For example, male drivers under the age of 22 in one city can calculate their average annual rate by multiplying their age by $1000 and subtracting that from $24 000.

a **Write down** the equation for the average annual cost of insurance (C) for a young male based on his age (a).

b **State** what $C(18)$ represents. Then **find** $C(18)$.

c For males under the age of 22, is the annual average cost of car insurance a function of age?

d Is charging different rates depending on the age of the driver a fair practice? **Explain**.

e **State** what $C(21)$ represents. Then find $C(21)$.

f **Suggest** reasons why this function is only valid for drivers under the age of 24.

Reflect and discuss 7

How have you explored the statement of inquiry? Give specific examples.

Statement of inquiry:

Discovering relationships in patterns and studying equivalence between representations can lead to better models.

3.2 Quadratic expressions

Global context: Scientific and technical innovation

Related concept: Patterns

Objectives

- Factorizing quadratic expressions, where the coefficient of x^2 is 1, including the difference of two squares
- Factorizing quadratic expressions where the coefficient of x^2 is not 1

Inquiry questions

F
- What does 'expanding brackets' mean?
- What does 'factorize a quadratic expression' mean?

C
- How do the patterns in expanding brackets help you factorize quadratic expressions?
- How can patterns help you write quadratic expressions in a form that is easier to factorize?

D
- Can everything be written in a different form?

ATL Critical-thinking

Draw reasonable conclusions and generalizations

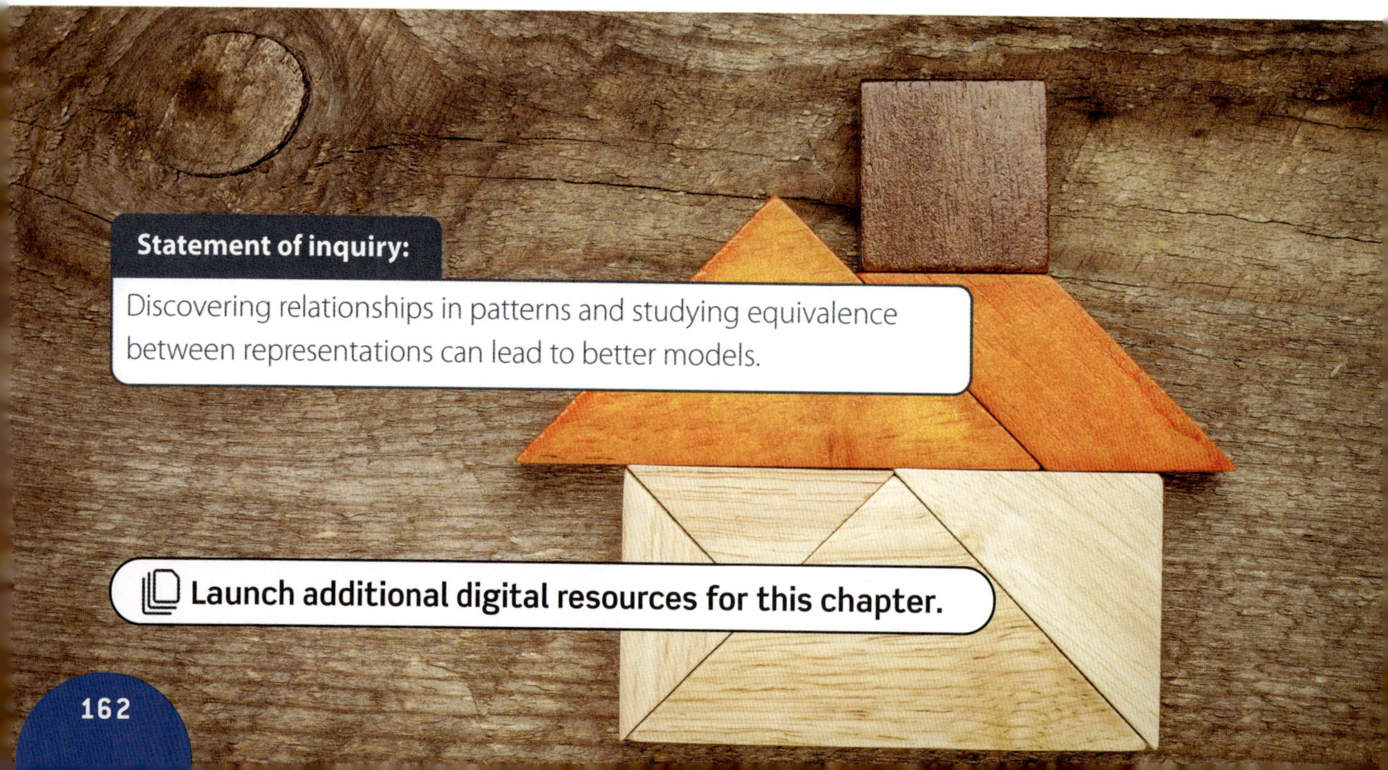

Statement of inquiry:

Discovering relationships in patterns and studying equivalence between representations can lead to better models.

📑 **Launch additional digital resources for this chapter.**

You should already know how to:

• expand brackets	**1** Expand:
	  a $(x + 3)(x + 4)$ **b** $(x - 5)(x + 1)$
	  c $(x - 3)(x - 2)$ **d** $(x + 2)(x - 2)$

• factorize expressions by taking out a common factor	**2** Factorize:
	  a $3x + 12$ **b** $x^2 + 5x$
	  c $6x^2 + 3x + 12$ **d** $4x(3x - 5) + 7(3x - 5)$

F   Expanding and factorizing

- What does 'expanding brackets' mean?
- What does 'factorize a quadratic expression' mean?

To 'expand' an algebraic expression means to multiply out each of the terms and then rewrite the expression without brackets.

For example:

$$(x - 7)(x + 2) \equiv x^2 - 7x + 2x - 14 \equiv x^2 - 5x - 14$$

The symbol $\equiv$ means 'is identically equal to'. It shows that two expressions take the same value for any possible value of the unknown variable (in this case, x).

For example, $3(x - 2) \equiv 3x - 6$, because the statement is always true for any value of x.

$3x + 5 = 17$ is an equation, not an identity, because it is true only when $x = 4$.

Exploration 1

Look at the following expressions:

Quadratic expressions	**NOT quadratic expressions**
$x^2 - 5x - 14$	$x^3 - 5x - 14$
$3x^2 + 2x$	$8t + 12$
$-7w^2 + 21$	$x^2 + 3y - 25$
$\frac{1}{2}m^2 + m + 3$	$z^4 + 3z^2 - 2z + 1$
$2y - 5y^2 + 7$	17^2

1 Based on your observations, suggest what is meant by 'quadratic expression'.

2 Explain why each of the expressions in the right-hand column do not satisfy your description.

3 Explain whether or not you would consider $(x + 3)(x - 5)$ to be a quadratic expression.

$x^2 - 5x - 14$ is a **quadratic expression** because it contains a single variable (x) whose highest exponent is 2.

- $x^2 - 5x - 14$, $x^2 - 4$ and $3x^2$ are all quadratic expressions.
- $x^3 - 5x - 14$ is not quadratic because its highest exponent is greater than 2.
- $5x - 14$ is not quadratic because its highest power is less than 2.

An expression with highest exponent 3, like $x^3 - 5x - 14$, is a cubic expression.

Quadratic expressions can be written in a variety of forms. To 'factorize' means to write as a product of factors. 'Factorize a quadratic' means 'write it as a product of two expressions in brackets'.

ATL

Exploration 2

1 Copy the table. For each row, expand the brackets to help you complete the table.

Factorized expression $(x + p)(x + q)$	p	q	Expanded expression $ax^2 + bx + c$	a	b	c
$(x + 3)(x + 5)$	3	5	$x^2 + 8x + 15$	1	8	15
$(x + 2)(x + 9)$						
$(x - 3)(x - 6)$						
$(x + 3)(x - 4)$						
	−3	4				
$(x + 2)(x - 5)$						
$(x - 8)(x + 4)$						
$(x\ \ \ )(x + 6)$	−1					

2 Look carefully at your table. Describe any patterns you notice in the values and signs of a, b, c, p and q.

3 Copy the table below. Use the patterns you observed in step 2 to predict the values of a, b and c.

Factorized expression $(x + p)(x + q)$	p	q	Expanded expression $ax^2 + bx + c$	a	b	c
$(x + 1)(x + 7)$						
$(x - 3)(x + 8)$						
$(x - 1)(x - 2)$						
$(x + 5)(x - 5)$						

In step 3, you shouldn't need to expand the brackets. If you can't see a pattern yet, go back to step 2 and discuss your results.

4 Verify your predictions by expanding each factorized expression.

5 Copy and complete this table.

Factorized expression $(x + p)(x + q)$	p	q	Expanded expression $ax^2 + bx + c$	a	b	c
$(x + 2)(x + 2)$						
$(x + 4)(x + 4)$						
$(x - 1)(x - 1)$						
$(x - 6)(x - 6)$						

6 Describe any patterns you notice in the values and signs of a, b, c, p and q.

Practice 1

1 Copy and complete this table based on the patterns you observed assuming that $(x + p)(x + q) = ax^2 + bx + c$.

p	q	a	b	c
2	−3	1		
4		1		−8
8		1	0	
	−2	1	−5	
	−7	1		21
9		1	0	
		1	−2	−24

2 Find values such that $a = 1$, $p = q$ and $b = c$.

3 N'nyree has concluded that if $c = 0$, then either p or q is zero. Explain whether you agree or disagree with this statement.

- -

 ## Factorizing expressions

- How do the patterns in expanding brackets help you factorize quadratic expressions?
- How can patterns help you write quadratic expressions in a form that is easier to factorize?

In Exploration 2 you found that in all the expansions of $(x + p)(x + q) = ax^2 + bx + c$, $a = 1$, $c = pq$ and $b = p + q$.

You can use these facts to factorize expressions such as $x^2 + x - 12$.

Suppose $x^2 + x - 12 = (x + p)(x + q)$, where p and q are whole numbers.

Using the fact that $c = pq = -12$ suggests these possible pairs of values for p and q:

   −12 and 1   12 and −1   −6 and 2   6 and −2   −4 and 3   4 and −3

Trying each pair in turn gives:

$(x - 12)(x + 1) \equiv x^2 - 11x - 12$

$(x + 12)(x - 1) \equiv x^2 + 11x - 12$

$(x - 6)(x + 2) \equiv x^2 - 4x - 12$

$(x + 6)(x - 2) \equiv x^2 + 4x - 12$

$(x - 4)(x + 3) \equiv x^2 - x - 12$

$(x + 4)(x - 3) \equiv x^2 + x - 12$ ✔

$(x + 4)(x - 3)$ gives the correct quadratic expression.

Also using the fact that $b = p + q$ makes this process more efficient. Having found pairs of numbers which have product c, you just need to find a pair which has sum b.

In $x^2 + x - 12$, $b = p + q = 1$

$-12 + 1 = -11$

$12 + (-1) = 11$

> Always check your factorization by expanding the brackets.

$-6 + 2 = -4$

$6 + (-2) = 4$

$-4 + 3 = -1$

$4 + (-3) = 1$ ✓

So $x^2 + x - 12 \equiv (x + 4)(x - 3)$.

> To factorize a quadratic $x^2 + bx + c \equiv (x + p)(x + q)$, find two numbers p and q which have product c and sum b.

In Exploration 2 steps **5** and **6** you expanded brackets with $p = q$:

$(x + p)(x + p) = x^2 + 2px + p^2$

You can also write this as:

$(x + p)^2 = x^2 + 2px + p^2$

Recognizing this pattern can help you to factorize special quadratics called perfect squares.

Example 1

Factorize $x^2 + 10x + 25$.

$x^2 + 10x + 25$ $25 = 5^2$ and $10 = 2 \times 5$

$\equiv (x + 5)(x + 5)$

$\equiv (x + 5)^2$ This is a *perfect square*.

If all three terms have a common factor, taking this common factor out first makes the factorization simpler.

Example 2

Factorize $2a^2 + 6a + 4$.

$2a^2 + 6a + 4$

$\equiv 2(a^2 + 3a + 2)$ Take out the common factor 2.

$\equiv 2(a + 1)(a + 2)$

Practice 2

1 Factorize each quadratic.

    a $x^2 + 7x + 12$ **b** $x^2 + 8x + 15$ **c** $x^2 + 3x - 18$

    d $x^2 + 7x - 18$ **e** $x^2 - 7x - 18$ **f** $x^2 + 5x - 14$

    g $x^2 - 13x + 36$ **h** $x^2 - 11x + 24$ **i** $x^2 - 3x$

2 Factorize each quadratic.

    a $x^2 + 14x + 49$ **b** $x^2 + 22x + 121$ **c** $x^2 - 12x + 36$

3 Factorize each quadratic.

    a $3a^2 + 6a + 3$ **b** $4b^2 + 2b$ **c** $5c^2 - 10c - 75$

    d $6d^2 - 3d$ **e** $4e^2 + 20e - 144$ **f** $3f^2 - 24f + 45$

4 Find an expression for the unknown side in these rectangles:

a

$x + 2$ | Area $x^2 + 7x + 10$

?

b

Area $x^2 + 2x - 3$ | ?

$x - 1$

Problem solving

5 Copy and complete, using integer values:

a $x^2 - \square x + 12 \equiv (x - 3)(x - \square)$

b $x^2 \square \square x + 16 \equiv (x - 8)(x \square \square)$

c $x^2 - 5x \square \square \equiv (x + \square)(x - 7)$

d $x^2 \square 9x + 20 \equiv (x + 5)(x \square \square)$

e $x^2 \square 10x \square 16 \equiv (x + \square)(x + \square)$

f $x^2 - 5x \square 24 \equiv (x \square \square)(x \square \square)$

6 A rectangle has area $x^2 - 10x + 21$.

Area $x^2 - 10x + 21$

Its perimeter is $4x - 20$. Find, in terms of x, the lengths of each of its sides.

- -

Exploration 3

1 Copy and complete this table.

Factorized expression $(x + p)(x + q)$	p	q	Expanded expression $ax^2 + bx + c$	a	b	c
$(x + 3)(x - 3)$						
$(x - 9)(x + 9)$						
$(x + 6)(x - 6)$						
$(x + 4)(x - 4)$						

2 Describe any patterns you notice in the values and signs of a, b, c, p and q.

In Exploration 3 you found that expanding brackets in the form $(x + p)(x - p)$ gave a special pattern. When they are expanded, the coefficient of the x term is 0 so there is just an x^2 term and a constant, which is negative.

In general, expanding $(a + b)(a - b) \equiv a^2 - ab + ab - b^2 \equiv a^2 - b^2$.

Any expression of the form $a^2 - b^2$ is the **difference of two squares**, because it is one squared quantity subtracted from another.

$a^2 - b^2 \equiv (a + b)(a - b)$

Reflect and discuss 1

Explain how this diagram illustrates the factorization of $a^2 - b^2$.

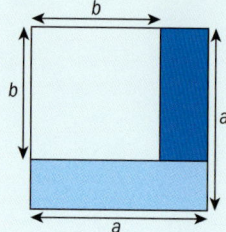 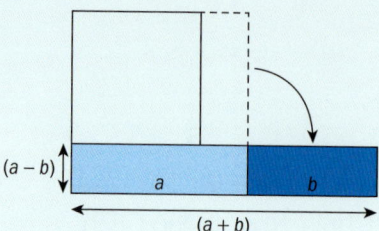

If you recognize an expression as the difference of two squares, you can factorize it easily.

Example 3

Factorize $x^2 - 64$.

$x^2 - 64$ ——————————————————————— Difference of two squares, $x^2 - 8^2$

$\equiv (x - 8)(x + 8)$

'Fully factorize' means write as a product of expressions which cannot be factorized any further.

Example 4

Fully factorize $16x^4 - 81$.

$16x^4 - 81$ ————————————————————————— $(4x^2)^2 - 9^2$

$\equiv (4x^2 - 9)(4x^2 + 9)$ ————————— This is not fully factorized, as $4x^2 - 9$ is the difference of two squares: $(2x)^2 - 3^2$.

$\equiv ((2x)^2 - 3^2)(4x^2 + 9)$

$\equiv (2x - 3)(2x + 3)(4x^2 + 9)$

Practice 3

1 Fully factorize each expression.

    a $x^2 - 25$ **b** $x^2 - 121$ **c** $4x^2 - 9$

    d $x^2 - y^2$ **e** $9x^2 - 1$ **f** $x^4 - 1$

    g $16x^2 - 169$ **h** $81x^2 - 9$ **i** $25u^2 - 16v^2$

    j $16 - 49x^2$ **k** $16 - x^4$ **l** $1 - 81y^4$

2 Copy and complete each identity, using integer values.

a $\Box x^2 - 100 \equiv (3x - \Box)(3x + \Box)$

b $25y^2 - \Box \equiv (\Box y - 4)(\Box y + 4)$

c $16a^2 - \Box b^2 \equiv (\Box a - \Box b)(\Box a + 7b)$

d $\Box u^2 - \Box \equiv (3u + 2)(3u - \Box)$

e $\Box t^2 - \Box \equiv (3t + 5)(\Box t - 20)$

f $\Box x^2 - \Box \equiv (3x + 4)(6x - \Box)$

Reflect and discuss 2

Aishah tried to factorize $3x^2 + 13x + 12$ using the methods you have learned. Here is a sample of her work:

> In the quadratic $3x^2 + 13x + 12$, $a = 3$, $b = 13$ and $c = 12$.
> In the expansion $(x + p)(x + q)$, the product $pq = c$, $\Rightarrow c = 12$.
> The sum $p + q = b$, $\Rightarrow b = 13$, and so $p = 1$ and $q = 12$.
>
> Therefore, $3x^2 + 13x + 12 \equiv (x + 1)(x + 12)$

- Is Aishah's factorization correct? Is it equivalent to the original expression?

- Why doesn't this method work for this expression?

- How is this expression different from the other expressions you have factorized?

> Quadratics where the coefficient of x^2 is 1 are called *monic*. If the coefficient is not 1, the quadratic is *non-monic*.

To have $3x^2$ as the first term of a quadratic expression, the factors need to start with terms that multiply to make $3x^2$.

The factors of 3 are 1 and 3, so the factors need to start $(3x \quad)$ and $(x \quad)$. The second term in each bracket can be found by listing possibilities systematically. Look at the examples below and then attempt Reflect and discuss 3.

Example 5

Factorize $3x^2 + 13x + 12$.

$3x^2 + 13x + 12 \equiv (3x \quad)(x \quad)$ —————— The numbers in the brackets have product 12.

Pairs of values with product 12 are:

1 and 12	2 and 6	3 and 4
12 and 1	6 and 2	4 and 3

$(3x + 1)(x + 12) \equiv 3x^2 + 37x + 12$ ✗

$(3x + 12)(x + 1) \equiv 3x^2 + 15x + 12$ ✗

$(3x + 2)(x + 6) \equiv 3x^2 + 20x + 12$ ✗

$(3x + 6)(x + 2) \equiv 3x^2 + 12x + 12$ ✗

$(3x + 3)(x + 4) \equiv 3x^2 + 15x + 12$ ✗

$(3x + 4)(x + 3) \equiv 3x^2 + 13x + 12$ ✓

Example 6

Fully factorize $6x^2 - 7x - 10$.

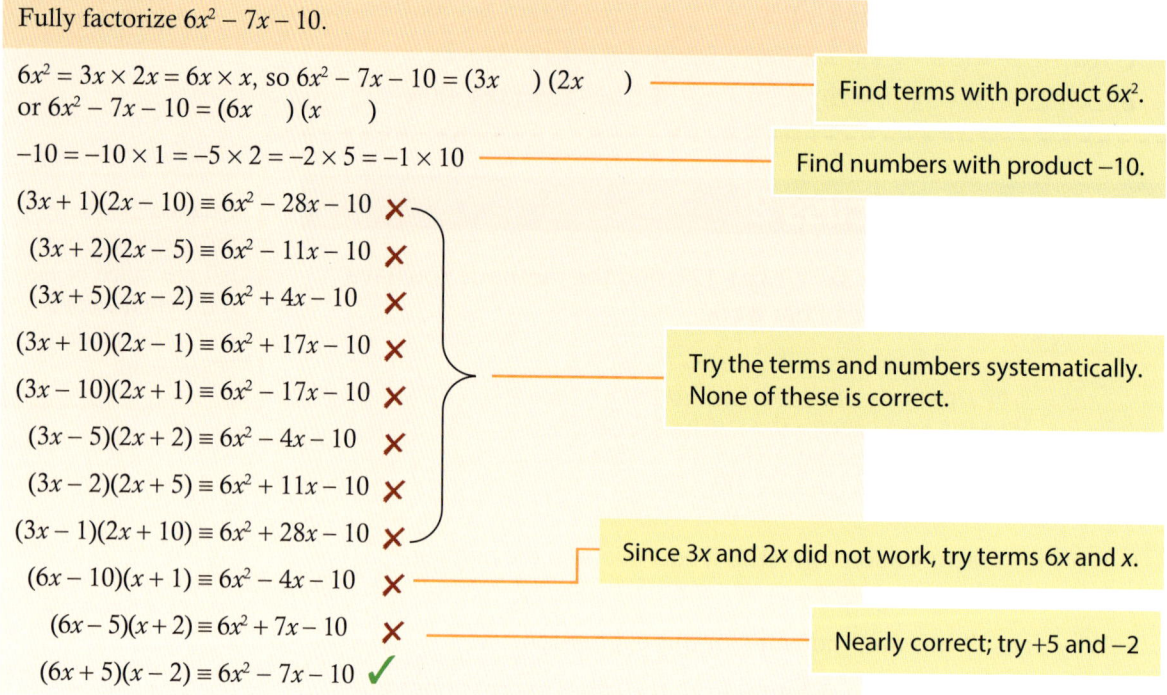

$6x^2 = 3x \times 2x = 6x \times x$, so $6x^2 - 7x - 10 = (3x \quad)(2x \quad)$ ———————— Find terms with product $6x^2$.
or $6x^2 - 7x - 10 = (6x \quad)(x \quad)$

$-10 = -10 \times 1 = -5 \times 2 = -2 \times 5 = -1 \times 10$ ———————— Find numbers with product -10.

$(3x + 1)(2x - 10) \equiv 6x^2 - 28x - 10$ ✗

$(3x + 2)(2x - 5) \equiv 6x^2 - 11x - 10$ ✗

$(3x + 5)(2x - 2) \equiv 6x^2 + 4x - 10$ ✗

$(3x + 10)(2x - 1) \equiv 6x^2 + 17x - 10$ ✗

$(3x - 10)(2x + 1) \equiv 6x^2 - 17x - 10$ ✗   Try the terms and numbers systematically. None of these is correct.

$(3x - 5)(2x + 2) \equiv 6x^2 - 4x - 10$ ✗

$(3x - 2)(2x + 5) \equiv 6x^2 + 11x - 10$ ✗

$(3x - 1)(2x + 10) \equiv 6x^2 + 28x - 10$ ✗

$(6x - 10)(x + 1) \equiv 6x^2 - 4x - 10$ ✗ ———————— Since $3x$ and $2x$ did not work, try terms $6x$ and x.

$(6x - 5)(x + 2) \equiv 6x^2 + 7x - 10$ ✗ ———————— Nearly correct; try $+5$ and -2

$(6x + 5)(x - 2) \equiv 6x^2 - 7x - 10$ ✓

You may not need to write down all the possible factorizations to test them. Each one gives the correct x^2 and constant terms, so you only need to check if expanding gives the correct middle term.

Reflect and discuss 3

- Which factorization was easier: the one in Example 5 or in Example 6?

- What made them easy or difficult?

- A student tries to factorize $3x^2 + 17x + 10$ and gives the answer $(3x + 5)(x + 2)$. Show that the middle term is incorrect.

- Why do you think listing the options systematically might be a time-consuming way to tackle this problem?

Practice 4

Fully factorize each quadratic expression.

1 $2x^2 + 5x + 3$ **2** $3x^2 + 7x + 2$ **3** $3x^2 + 7x - 6$

Write down enough working to be sure you have the correct answer. Look for opportunities to be efficient: it's OK to do some working in your head.

In Example 6 there are two possible pairs of factors for the x^2 term and the constant term, which gives a lot of possible factors to test. You will now explore another way to factorize quadratic expressions where it is not easy to identify the factors straight away.

Exploration 4

To expand a pair of brackets, you use the distributive property of multiplication. You multiply every term in the second bracket by every term in the first bracket.

$$(2x + 3)(x - 4) \equiv 2x(x - 4) + 3(x - 4)$$
$$\equiv 2x^2 - 8x + 3x - 12$$
$$\equiv 2x^2 - 5x - 12$$

> If you use a different method for expanding brackets, check that it gives the same result for $(2x + 3)(x - 4)$.

1 Use the distributive property to show that $(2x - 1)(x + 5) \equiv 2x^2 + 9x - 5$.

2 The table shows five different quadratic expressions, one on each row. Working from left to right, each cell shows one step in expanding the brackets. The top row has been completed. Copy and complete the table.

$(2x + 3)(x - 4)$	$= 2x(x - 4) + 3(x - 4)$	$= 2x^2 - 8x + 3x - 12$	$= 2x^2 - 5x - 12$
$(2x - 3)(x + 7)$	$=$	$=$	$=$
	$= 3x(2x - 1) + 4(2x - 1)$	$=$	$=$
	$=$	$= 4x^2 + 12x - 2x - 6$	$=$
	$=$	$=$	$= 6x^2 + 5x - 4$

3 Explain which you think is easier: completing from left to right or right to left.

4 Comment on which of the steps is most difficult to complete. Explain why it is harder than the others.

5 Two students try to factorize the expression $6x^2 + 25x + 14$.

Carmen	Miranda
$6x^2 + 25x + 14 \equiv 6x^2 + 21x + 4x + 14$	$6x^2 + 25x + 14 \equiv 6x^2 + 20x + 5x + 14$

Explain which student's work helps to factorize the expression.

Exploration 4 shows that you can make a quadratic easier to factorize by splitting the middle term in the correct way. Exploration 5 investigates what happens when you expand some factorized expressions to find a pattern to help you factorize this kind of quadratic.

> **Objective: B.** Investigating patterns
> **iii.** prove, or verify and justify, general rules
>
> *In Exploration 5 you should gather enough information so you can conjecture a general rule. Then you should verify it, by showing that your conjecture holds for a few more examples.*

Exploration 5

Investigate the relationship between the coefficients of the split middle term and the coefficients in $ax^2 + bx + c$.

To work out how to split the middle term of a quadratic by studying some examples, you could make a table like this:

▶ Continued on next page

Factorized expression	Expanded expression	Coefficients of the split middle term		Coefficients in $ax^2 + bx + c$		
				a	b	c
$(2x + 3)(x + 4)$	$2x^2 + 3x + 8x + 12$	3	8	2	11	12
$(2x + 1)(x - 2)$						
...						

Add more rows until you discover the pattern. You may find it useful to find the product and the sum of the coefficients of the split middle term.

You can gather more information by making up your own examples for the left-hand column. You can make new examples by changing the numbers in the examples you have already been given.

This is an important skill when investigating in mathematics.

Reflect and discuss 4

Compare what you found in Exploration 5 with others before moving on.

Example 7

Factorize $15x^2 - 2x - 24$.

$15x^2 - 2x - 24$ ———————————— Find two numbers with product $15 \times -24 = -360$ and sum -2.

$\qquad -360 = 18 \times -20$

$\qquad -2 = 18 + -20$

$15x^2 - 2x - 24 \equiv 15x^2 + 18x - 20x - 24$ ——— Split the middle term into $18x - 20x$.

Take the common factors from each pair of terms.

$\qquad \equiv 3x(5x + 6) - 4(5x + 6)$ ——————————— $(5x + 6)$ is a common factor.

$\qquad \equiv (3x - 4)(5x + 6)$

Does the order of the middle terms matter? Look at these two ways of factorizing the quadratic in Example 7:

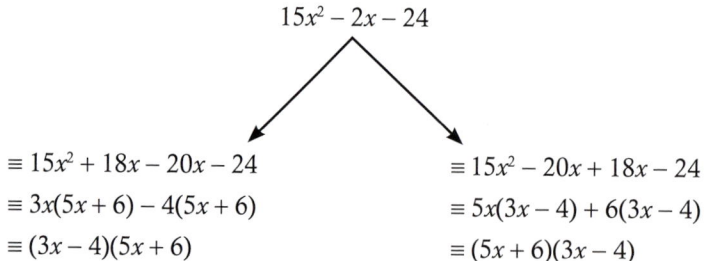

$\equiv 15x^2 + 18x - 20x - 24$ $\qquad$ $\equiv 15x^2 - 20x + 18x - 24$

$\equiv 3x(5x + 6) - 4(5x + 6)$ $\qquad$ $\equiv 5x(3x - 4) + 6(3x - 4)$

$\equiv (3x - 4)(5x + 6)$ $\qquad$ $\equiv (5x + 6)(3x - 4)$

They both give the same factorization.

Quadratics where the coefficient of x^2 is not 1 may be factorized by splitting the middle term. To factorize $ax^2 + bx + c$, look for two numbers whose sum is b and whose product is ac.

Practice 5

Problem solving

1 Find pairs of numbers which have:

    a product 240 and sum 32

    b product −180 and sum 3

    c product 96 and sum −35

    d product −1000 and sum −117

2 Find values to fill these boxes and complete the identities.

    a $\square x^2 + \square x - \square$

$$= \square x^2 + \square x - 4x - 14$$

$$= 5x(2x + 7) - \square(2x + 7)$$

$$= (\square x - \square)(\square x + \square)$$

    b $4x^2 + 27x + \square$

$$= \square x^2 + 3x + \square x + \square$$

$$= x(4x + 3) + \square(4x + 3)$$

$$= (x + \square)(\square x + \square)$$

> Use any of the methods you have learned.

3 Factorize each quadratic.

a $5x^2 - 9x + 4$	**b** $6x^2 + 7x + 2$	**c** $4x^2 + 8x + 3$
d $6x^2 - 11x + 4$	**e** $8x^2 - 14x - 15$	**f** $12x^2 - 17x + 6$
g $6x^2 + 5x + 1$	**h** $6x^2 + x - 2$	**i** $6x^2 - 5x - 1$
j $15x^2 - 7x - 2$	**k** $8x^2 + 10x - 3$	**l** $21x^2 - 23x + 6$
m $2x^2 - 3x + 1$	**n** $2x^2 - 9x + 10$	**o** $15x^2 - 40x - 15$
p $4x^2 + 7x - 15$	**q** $4x^2 + 8x - 21$	**r** $12x^2 + 4x - 5$
s $5x^2 - 2x - 3$	**t** $7x^2 - 16x + 4$	**u** $8x^2 + 24x + 16$
v $5x^2 - 14x - 3$	**w** $9x^2 + 11x + 2$	**x** $10x^2 - x - 21$

Problem solving

4 These expressions can be factorized. Determine the different values that could fill the empty boxes.

    a $3x^2 + \square x + 2$ **b** $\square x^2 + 9x + 2$ **c** $6x^2 + 10x + \square$

- -

D Non-factorizable expressions

- Can everything be written in a different form?

Exploration 6

1 Factorize the following expressions if possible. Verify your solution by expanding.

	factorized form	factorized form expanded
$x^2 - 16$	_____	_____
$49x^2 - 121$	_____	_____
$x^2 + 25$	_____	_____
$25x^2 + 81$	_____	_____
$4x^2 + 9$	_____	_____

▶ Continued on next page

2 Describe anything you notice about the expressions you could not factorize. Explain why they are not factorizable.

3 Factorize the following expressions if possible. Verify your solution by expanding.

	factorized form	factorized form expanded
$x^2 + 6x + 4$	_____	_____
$2x^2 - 3x - 1$	_____	_____
$x^2 - 10x - 24$	_____	_____
$x^2 + 10x + 24$	_____	_____
$4x^2 + x - 10$	_____	_____

4 For those expressions which you could not factorize, explain clearly why the methods you have already learned did not work.

5 Expand these brackets: $(x + 3 + \sqrt{5})(x + 3 - \sqrt{5})$. Describe anything you notice.

> If you have not yet learned how to multiply out brackets like those in step **5**, either use a computer algebra system or complete it as a group with your teacher's assistance.

Reflect and discuss 5

- When we say that a quadratic expression is 'not factorizable', we usually mean that it cannot be factorized using integers. What other types of numbers could you use?

When quadratic expressions cannot be factorized using integers, there are other techniques that will help you work with quadratics.

> **The Fundamental theorem of algebra** says that any quadratic (or higher power polynomial) can be factorized, although it might involve using numbers which are not in the set of real numbers. These numbers are known as complex numbers. You will learn about complex numbers if you take HL Mathematics as part of the Diploma. Proving the Fundamental theorem of algebra is university-level mathematics.

Summary

- The symbol $\equiv$ means 'is identically equal to'. It shows that two expressions take the same value for any possible value of the unknown.

- To factorize a quadratic written in the form $x^2 + bx + c \equiv (x + p)(x + q)$, find two numbers p and q which have product c and sum b.

- Any expression of the form $a^2 - b^2$ is the **difference of two squares**, because it is one squared quantity subtracted from another.

  $a^2 - b^2 \equiv (a + b)(a - b)$

- Where the coefficient of x^2 does not equal 1, one method of factorizing involves listing all the pairs of terms with product ax^2 and all the pairs of numbers with product c. Then try the different combinations until you find pairs which work.

- Alternatively, it is often quicker to look for two numbers whose sum is b and whose product is ac.

Mixed practice

1 Factorize:

a $x^2 + 4x + 4$ **b** $x^2 - 13x + 36$

c $x^2 + 5x - 14$ **d** $x^2 + 18x + 81$

e $x^2 - 7x - 8$ **f** $x^2 - 11x + 24$

g $x^2 - 20x + 100$ **h** $x^2 - 15x - 100$

i $x^2 + 4x + 3$ **j** $x^2 + 11x - 42$

k $x^2 + 4x - 96$ **l** $x^2 + 7x + 6$

m $x^2 - 15x + 56$ **n** $x^2 - 11x - 60$

2 Factorize fully:

a $x^2 - 49$ **b** $x^2 - 169$

c $64 - x^2$ **d** $25x^2 - 4$

e $144x^2 - 81$ **f** $256x^2 - 169$

g $4x^2 - y^2$ **h** $16x^2 - 9y^2$

i $25x^2 - 289y^2$ **j** $x^4 - 16$

k $16x^4 - 1$ **l** $9x^4 - 729y^4$

3 Factorize completely:

a $2x^2 + 8x + 6$ **b** $2x^2 + 14x + 20$

c $2x^2 - 12x + 10$ **d** $3x^2 - 9x + 6$

e $2x^2 + 8x - 24$ **f** $3x^2 + 21x - 24$

g $4x^2 - 8x - 32$ **h** $2x^2 - 2x - 40$

4 Factorize:

a $2x^2 + 5x + 2$ **b** $2x^2 + 13x + 20$

c $2x^2 - 11x + 12$ **d** $3x^2 - 8x - 3$

e $5x^2 - 12x + 4$ **f** $7x^2 + 38x - 24$

g $6x^2 + 31x + 5$ **h** $6x^2 - 17x + 5$

i $8x^2 + 18x + 9$ **j** $8x^2 - 41x + 5$

k $9x^2 + 12x - 32$ **l** $10x^2 - 13x - 30$

5 Factorize:

a $4a^2 - 3a$ **b** $7b^3 - 35b^2 - 168b$

6 Factorize:

a $a^2 - 5a - 36$ **b** $16b^2 - 9$

c $c^2 + 11c + 24$ **d** $4d^2 - 17d - 15$

e $4e^2 - 3e$ **f** $f^2 + 2f - 48$

g $3g^2 - 23g + 14$ **h** $16h^2 - 1$

Problem solving

7 Ornella thinks of a whole number, adds 4 to it, squares the result, and subtracts 9.

     a By letting the original number be n, **write down** an expression for this process.

     b Hence **show** the number that Ornella obtains can always be written as the product of two integers with a difference of 6.

8 Copy and complete:

     a $x^2 - \Box x + 15 \equiv (x - 3)(x - \Box)$

     b $x^2 \Box \Box x + 20 \equiv (x + 4)(x \Box \Box)$

     c $x^2 - 8x \Box \Box \equiv (x + \Box)(x - 11)$

     d $x^2 \Box 11x + \Box \equiv (x \Box 5)(x - \Box)$

9 Dagmar thinks of an even number, squares it, and subtracts 1. By expressing his original number in the form $2n$, or otherwise, **show** that the result of this process can be written as the product of two consecutive odd integers.

10 You have two rectangular grids of $1\,cm^3$ cubes, one measuring $n + 1$ by $n + 6\,cm$, and the other measuring $n + 3$ by $n + 3\,cm$, where n is a positive integer.

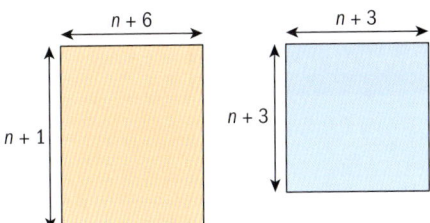

     a **Find** and simplify an expression for the total number of $1\,cm^3$ cubes in the two rectangular grids combined.

     b **Show** that if you take apart the rectangles and recombine the $1\,cm^3$ cubes you will always be able to form a rectangle with no cubes left over (where the rectangle will not simply be a straight line of cubes).

11 A rectangular sports pitch has a border of n meters on each side. The total area occupied by the pitch and its border is $4n^2 + 28n + 45$.

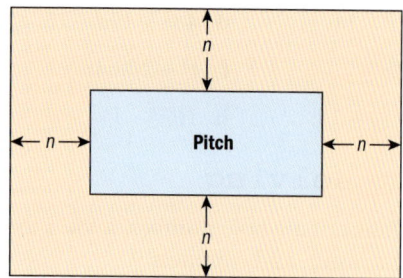

Pitch

Find the dimensions of the pitch.

12 Start with a rectangular grid of 8 cubes:

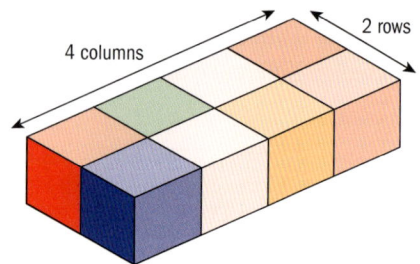

2 rows

4 columns

Somebody else then adds some extra rows and columns to the grid, but doesn't tell you how many they've added. They do tell you that the grid now contains 45 cubes.

They repeat the process, adding the same number of rows as before and the same number of columns as before. Now the grid contains 112 cubes.

They repeat the process a third time, and the resulting grid contains 209 cubes. After a final repetition, there are 336 cubes in the grid.

a **Construct** a difference diagram showing the sequence 8, 45, 112, 209, 336. Analyse the differences and **show** that these numbers follow a quadratic sequence.

b Letting u_n be the number of cubes in the nth grid (so $u_1 = 8$), **find** a formula for u_n in the form $an^2 + bn + c$.

c Factorize your formula for u_n.

d Hence **determine** the number of rows and columns being added each time.

Reflect and discuss 6

How have you explored the statement of inquiry? Give specific examples.

Statement of inquiry:

Discovering relationships in patterns and studying equivalence between representations can lead to better models.

3.3 Representing quadratic functions

Global context: Scientific and technical innovation

Related concept: Representation

Objectives

- Finding the axis of symmetry and vertex of a quadratic function
- Expressing a quadratic function in three different forms: standard, factorized and vertex
- Finding a quadratic function given three distinct points on its graph
- Finding a function to model a real-life parabola
- Understanding how many unique points define an object in a given dimension of space

Inquiry questions

- What shape represents the graph of a quadratic function?
- How do the parameters of a quadratic function affect the shape of its graph?

- How can you represent a quadratic function in three different ways?
- What are the advantages and disadvantages of the different forms of a quadratic function?

D
- What makes one quadratic form better than another?

RELATIONSHIPS

ATL Creative-thinking

Apply existing knowledge to generate new ideas or processes

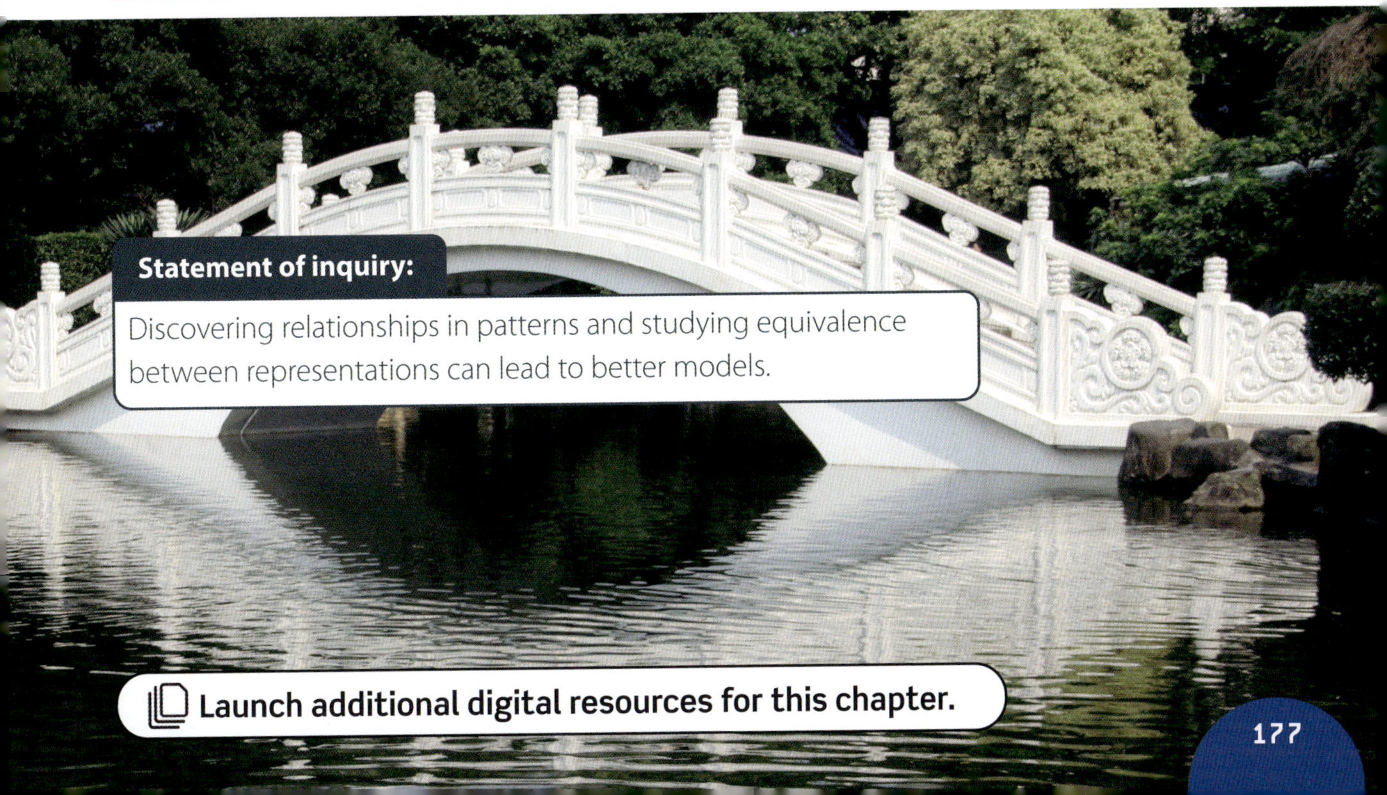

Statement of inquiry:

Discovering relationships in patterns and studying equivalence between representations can lead to better models.

📖 Launch additional digital resources for this chapter.

You should already know how to:

• interpret graphs of linear functions	**1** In the linear function $y = mx + c$, what do m and c represent?
	
	2 From the graph, find:
	   a the x-intercept
	   b the y-intercept.
	
	3 a Determine if the gradient is positive or negative.
	   b Find the equation of this line.

• factorize a quadratic expression	**4** Factorize:
	   a $x^2 + 5x + 6$
	   b $2x^2 - 3x - 2$
	   c $x^2 - 49$
	   d $3 - 2x - x^2$

F Quadratic functions: standard form

- What shape represents the graph of a quadratic function?
- How do the parameters of a quadratic function affect the shape of its graph?

You are surrounded by many different shapes which can be classified according to their mathematical properties. One of the most common shapes is an arch. Arches can be seen everywhere, from the shape of a banana to mouth guards, from water fountains to bridges and buildings, and in trajectories, such as the path of a basketball.

> A **trajectory** is the flight path of a moving object.

Reflect and discuss 1

The photograph shows the trajectory of a basketball. The trajectory is a curve, called a parabola.

If you knew just one of the ball's positions in the air, could you tell whether or not the ball would go in the basket? What if you knew two of its positions, or three?

How many positions do you think you would need to know to be sure that the ball would go in the basket? Make a good guess. You will return to this question later.

Exploration 1

Graph the quadratic function $y = x^2$. The graph is a parabola.

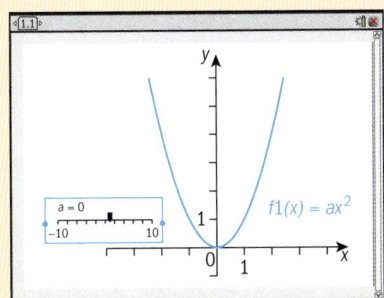

1 Graph $y = ax^2$ for a few values of a between −10 and +10. Include some non-integer values.

2 The parabola in the graph of $y = x^2$ is concave up ∨. The parabola of the basketball's trajectory is concave down ∧.

   a Find the values of a for which the parabola is concave up.

   b Find the values of a for which the parabola is concave down.

   c Find the values of a that make the parabola narrower than the graph of $y = x^2$.

   d Find the values of a that make the parabola wider than the graph of $y = x^2$.

3 Graph $y = x^2 + c$ for different values of c between −10 and +10. Include some non-integer values.

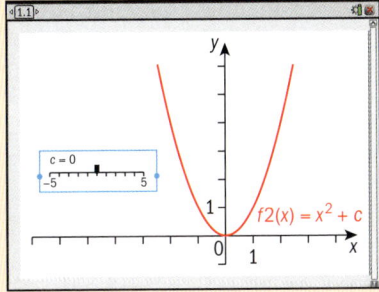

Describe the effect of changing the value of c.

4 Graph $y = ax^2 + bx$ for different values of b between −10 and +10. Include some non-integer values. Describe the effect of changing the value of b. (Leave $a = 1$ for the moment.)

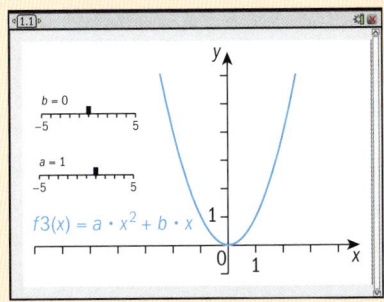

The right sidebar contains:

If your graphing program or GDC has a slider bar function, you can insert a slider to change the values in the functions easily.

A parabola can resemble a smile or a frown; could this help you remember the values of a for which the parabola will be concave down or concave up?

▶ Continued on next page

5 Graph the linear function $y = bx$ for different values of b. Describe how the graph changes for different values of b.

6 Go back to the parabola $y = ax^2 + bx$. Give a any value except 0. Keep a fixed and change b. Describe how the shape of the parabola changes for different values of b.

7 Use your findings to describe the similarities and differences in the shape of the graphs of each pair of quadratic functions.

a $y = 2x^2 + x + 1$; $y = 8x^2 + x + 1$ **b** $y = 3x^2 - 1$; $y = -3x^2 - 1$

c $y = 10x^2$; $y = \dfrac{1}{10}x^2$ **d** $y = x^2 + 3$; $y = x^2 - 1$

e $y = x^2 + x - 1$; $y = x^2 - x + 1$

> Try to answer these questions without drawing the graphs. You can use technology to check your answers.

> The **standard form** of a quadratic function is $y = ax^2 + bx + c$, where a, b and c are real numbers, and $a \neq 0$.

A **parameter** of a function defines the form of its graph.

- The graph of a linear function $y = mx + c$ is always a straight line. The parameter m defines its gradient; the parameter c defines its y-intercept.

- The graph of a quadratic function $y = ax^2 + bx + c$ is always a parabola. The parameters a, b and c define whether the parabola is slim or wide, concave up or concave down, and its y-intercept.

The parameters a, b and c are called the **coefficients** of the quadratic function. Parameter a, the coefficient of x^2, is called the leading coefficient. Parameter c is called the constant.

Quadratic and linear functions belong to the family of functions called **polynomial functions**. These are functions where the variable x has only positive integer exponents.

> A polynomial is a mathematical expression involving a sum of powers of one or more variables multiplied by coefficients, for example, $x^4 - 3x^2 + 1$. The **degree** of a polynomial function is the value of its largest exponent of x. A linear function is a polynomial function of degree 1. A quadratic function is a polynomial function of degree 2.

> A constant polynomial has degree 0. For example, the constant function $y = 2$ can be written $y = 2x^0$, since $x^0 = 1$.

ATL

Reflect and discuss 2

- Why is the parameter a in the quadratic function not allowed to equal 0? What type of function would result if $a = 0$?

- Why do you think parameter c is called the constant?

- One ordered pair of coordinates defines a 0-dimensional space, or point, for example: (2, 7). Two points define a 1-dimensional space, or straight line, for example: (1, 3) and (5, 2).

  How many points do you think are required to define a 2-dimensional space, such as the graph of a quadratic function?

A straight line has a constant gradient. A parabola does not. In fact, **each** point on the parabola has its own gradient. The point where its gradient changes from positive to negative, or vice versa, is called the **vertex** or turning point of the parabola.

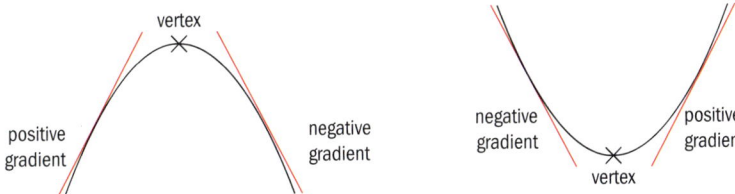

A concave down parabola has a maximum turning point.
$y = ax^2 + bx + c, a < 0$

maximum turning point

A concave up parabola has a minimum turning point.
$y = ax^2 + bx + c, a > 0$

minimum turning point

Exploration 2

Here is the graph of $y = x^2 - 2x - 3$.

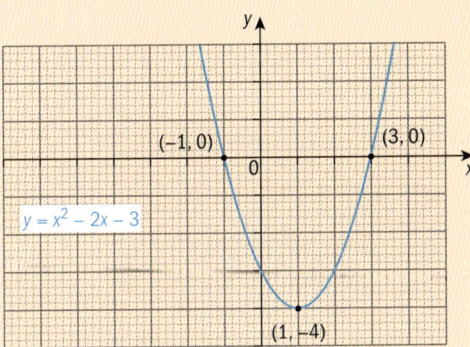

1 Describe the symmetry of the parabola.

2 State the equation of the axis of symmetry.

3 State the coordinates of the vertex.

4 Describe the relationship between the equation of the axis of symmetry and the x-coordinate of the vertex.

▶ Continued on next page

5 State the x-intercepts. Determine the relationship between the x-intercepts x_1 and x_2 of the function and the x-coordinate of the vertex x_v. Write this relationship as a formula: $x_v = $ _____.

6 Graph the following quadratic functions. Test that your formula from step **5** works for these graphs.

   a $y = x^2 - 4x - 5$ **b** $y = x^2 + 6x - 7$ **c** $y = -x^2 + 2x + 10$

7 All the quadratic functions in step **6** have leading coefficient $a = 1$ or -1. Now test your formula from step **5** on the following quadratic functions whose leading coefficient $a \neq \pm 1$.

   a $y = 2x^2 + 4x - 1$ **b** $y = \frac{1}{2}x^2 + 2x - 5$ **c** $2x^2 + 5x - 3$

8 Copy and complete this table with the parameters a and b and the x-coordinate of the vertex for all the quadratic functions in steps **6** and **7**.

Quadratic function	Parameters a and b	x-coordinate of the vertex, x_v
$y = x^2 - 2x - 3$	$a = 1; b = -2$	$x_v = 1$

   Find a pattern relating x_v to a and b. Write this relationship as a formula.

9 Create your own quadratic functions, and test your formula in your examples.

10 Explain how to find the y-coordinate of the vertex, when you know its x-coordinate.

11 Factorize the quadratic expressions in step **6**. Describe the relationship between the x-intercepts and the factors of the quadratic expression. Explain why this relationship holds.

12 Determine how to find the y-intercept of any quadratic equation of the form $y = ax^2 + bx + c$.

> The *x-intercepts* of a function are the x-coordinates of the points where the graph crosses the x-axis. They are also called the *zeros of the function*.

Reflect and discuss 3

- What do you think happens if a quadratic function isn't factorizable? Is it possible for it to still have x-intercepts? If so, how would you find them?

- Do you think it's possible for a quadratic function to have no x-intercepts? What would it look like? When do you think this would happen?

The main characteristics of the graph of a quadratic function are:

- x-intercepts and y-intercepts
- axis of symmetry
- vertex

Properties of quadratic functions

For a quadratic function $f(x) = ax^2 + bx + c$, $a \neq 0$:

- the x-coordinate of the vertex is $-\dfrac{b}{2a}$

- the equation of its axis of symmetry is $x = -\dfrac{b}{2a}$

- the coordinates of its vertex are $\left(-\dfrac{b}{2a}, f\left(-\dfrac{b}{2a}\right)\right)$
- the y-intercept is $(0, c)$.

For a quadratic function $f(x)$ with x-intercepts x_1 and x_2:

- the x-coordinate of the vertex is $x_v = \dfrac{x_1 + x_2}{2}$
- the y-coordinate of the vertex is $f(x_v)$.

Practice 1

For each quadratic function in questions **1** to **6**:

   i find the coordinates of the vertex

   ii find the equation of its axis of symmetry

   iii determine whether the function is concave up or concave down

   iv find the y-intercept

   v if the function is factorizable, find the x-intercepts

   vi draw a sketch of the quadratic function using your results from **i** to **v**.

> Use your GDC to check your results only after you have worked them out.

1 $y = x^2 - x - 6$ **2** $y = -x^2 + 2x - 4$

3 $y = x^2 - 4x - 2$ **4** $y = -8x^2 + 16x - 11$

5 $y = -2x^2 + 20x - 51$ **6** $y = 3x^2 - 6x + 1$

Problem solving

7 Write a concave up quadratic function with x-intercepts -2 and 3.

8 Write a quadratic function with axis of symmetry $x = 4$.

- -

You can use graphs of quadratic functions to solve real-world problems that can be modelled as parabolas. For example, during a baseball match a player hits the ball at a height of 1 m.

The height h (meters) of the ball at time t (seconds) can be modelled by the quadratic function $h = -5t^2 + 14t + 1$. You can graph this function to find the maximum height the ball reaches, and how many seconds it takes before the ball hits the ground.

- Represent time on the x-axis, since time is the independent variable. Time cannot be a negative value, so $t \geq 0$. At $t = 0$, the height of the ball is 1 m.

- Represent height on the y-axis, since height is the dependent variable. The ball will always be above the ground, or on the ground, so $h \geq 0$.

> The time does not depend on the height, so time is the independent variable.

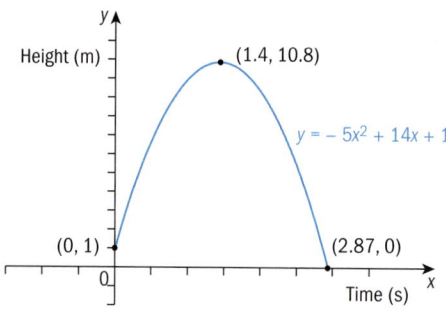

From the graph you can see the maximum height of the ball is 10.8 m and it hits the ground again after 2.87 seconds.

How could you find the times when the ball's height is 8 m? Add to your graph the function $y = 8$. Using a GDC, the points of intersection of the two graphs give the two times: 0.65 seconds and 2.2 seconds, both rounded to 1 d.p.

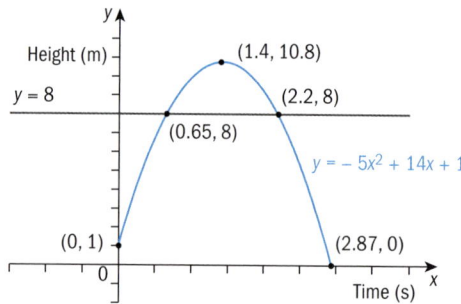

Practice 2

ATL

Graph the functions to answer these questions. When using a GDC, first set up a reasonable viewing window.

Problem solving

1 The US Food and Drug Administration uses this mathematical model for the number of bacteria B in food refrigerated at temperature T (°C):

$$B = 20T^2 - 20T + 120$$

The temperature in a particular refrigerator can be set anywhere between −2°C and 14°C. Determine the temperature where the number of bacteria will be at a minimum.

2 A boy throws a stone into the air while standing on a cliff and after some time sees it fall into the water. The height h (m) of the stone at any time t (s) can be modelled by $h = -4.8t^2 + 16t + 45$. Determine:

   a the height above sea level at which the stone was thrown

   b the time it takes the stone to reach its maximum height, and the maximum height it reaches

   c the time it takes the stone to hit the water.

3 A tennis ball manufacturer estimates its daily costs using the function $C(t) = 200 - 10t + 0.114t^2$ where C is the cost in dollars, and t is the number of tennis balls produced. Determine the number of tennis balls that produce the minimum cost.

4 Sarah's banker tells her that the value of her investment can be modelled by the function $v(t) = 45 + 75t - 4t^2$ where v is the value of her investment in thousands of Euros after t months. Determine:

   a the initial amount that Sarah invested

   b how many months it takes for Sarah's investment to reach maximum value.

5 A company's weekly profit P from selling x items can be modelled using the function $P(x) = -0.48x^2 + 38x - 295$. Determine the number of items the company needs to sell for maximum weekly profit.

- -

 C ## Algebraic forms of a quadratic function

- How can you represent a quadratic function in three different ways?
- What are the advantages and disadvantages of the different forms of a quadratic function?

The quadratic function $y = x^2 - x - 2$ factorizes to $y = (x + 1)(x - 2)$. Graphing either of these functions gives the same parabola:

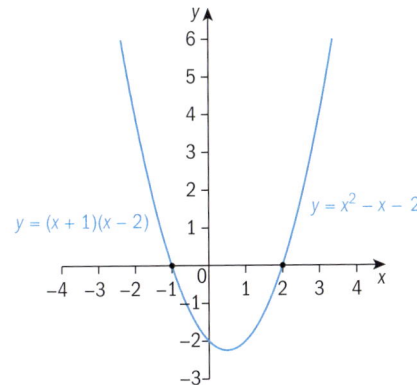

The **factorized form** of a quadratic function is $y = a(x - p)(x - q)$, $a \neq 0$.

Reflect and discuss 4

- The *x*-intercepts of a function are also called its *zeros*. Why is this an appropriate name?

- How do you determine the coordinates of the vertex of a quadratic function when it is in factorized form?

Most of the quadratics you have considered so far have had two distinct zeros. Now consider the quadratic function $y = x^2 + 2x + 1$, which factorizes to $y = (x + 1)(x + 1) = (x + 1)^2$ and has graph:

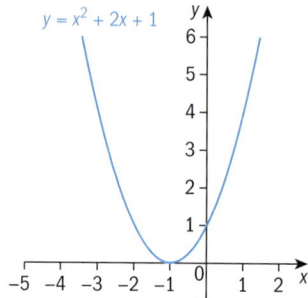

The function $y = x^2 + 2x + 1$ has only one unique factor, $(x + 1)$, and only one unique zero, $x = -1$. Does the formula you developed for the vertex of a quadratic also work when a quadratic function has only one unique factor?

Using the formula for finding the *x*-coordinate of the vertex using the zeros of this function, $x_v = \frac{x_1 + x_2}{2} = \frac{(-1) + (-1)}{2} = -1$

Using the formula $x_v = -\frac{b}{2a} = -\frac{2}{2(1)} = -1$

Both formulae work for this quadratic function.

Exploration 3

1 Graph these quadratic functions separately. For each, state the coordinates of the vertex. Verify that the *x*-coordinate of the vertex is equal to the *x*-intercept.

   a $y = (x - 2)^2$ **b** $y = (x + 3)^2$ **c** $y = -(x - 1)^2$ **d** $y = -(x + 1)^2$

2 Write down the relationship between the *x*-coordinate of the vertex and the unique factor of the quadratic function.

3 Based on your findings in steps **1** and **2**, state the coordinates of the vertex of each function below. Verify your answers by graphing the functions.

   a $y = (x + 2)^2$ **b** $y = (x - 4)^2$ **c** $y = -(x + 4)^2$

▶ Continued on next page

When a quadratic function has only one unique factor, its graph intercepts the
x-axis at one point, the vertex of the graph. The function has a repeated factor
and, therefore, a repeated zero at this point.

Graphing $y = (x - 2)^2$ and $y = (x - 2)^2 + 4$ on the same axes shows that adding 4
to the function translates the graph 4 units in the positive y direction. The
graph of $y = (x - 2)^2 + 4$ has vertex $(2, 4)$ and no x-intercepts.

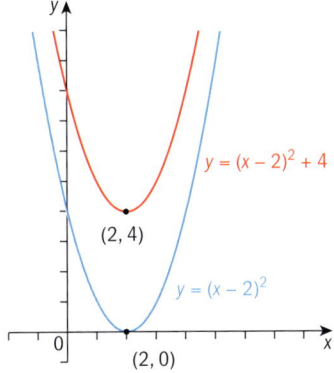

Graphing $y = (x - 2)^2$ and $y = (x - 2)^2 - 3$ on the same axes shows that
subtracting 3 from the function translates the graph 3 units in the negative
y direction. The graph of $y = (x - 2)^2 - 3$ has vertex $(2, -3)$ and two x-intercepts.

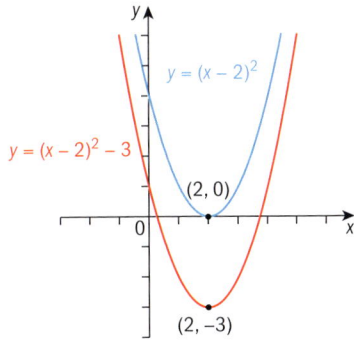

The quadratic functions $y = (x - 2)^2 + 4$ and $y = (x - 2)^2 - 3$ are written in
vertex form.

> The **vertex form** of a quadratic function is $y = a(x - h)^2 + k$, $a \neq 0$, where
> (h, k) is the vertex.

Practice 3

For **1** to **6**, state the coordinates of the vertex of each quadratic function and determine if the quadratic is concave up or concave down.

1 $y = (x - 3)^2 + 1$

2 $y = -(x - 4)^2 - 3$

3 $y = 2(x + 1)^2 - 1$

4 $y = -3(x + 2)^2 + 1$

5 $y = -x^2 + 2$

6 $y = 3x^2 - 1$

Problem solving

7 A quadratic function with leading coefficient 2 has a repeated zero at $x = -3$. Write the function in vertex form.

- -

Converting quadratic forms

To convert from factorized form to standard form, expand the brackets:

$$y = (x + 3)(x - 2) \;\rightarrow\; y = x^2 + x - 6$$

If you can factorize a quadratic function, you can convert it from standard form to factorized form:

$$y = x^2 - x - 2 \;\rightarrow\; y = (x + 1)(x - 2)$$

To convert from vertex form to standard form, expand and simplify:

$$y = (x - 1)^2 + 2$$
$$= (x - 1)(x - 1) + 2$$
$$= x^2 - 2x + 1 + 2$$
$$\Rightarrow \quad y = x^2 - 2x + 3$$

How do you convert from standard form to vertex form? (The next Exploration will help you answer this question.)

Exploration 4

1 Expand these expressions:

   a $(x + 2)^2$ **b** $(x - 3)^2$ **c** $(x + 1)^2$

   d $(x - 1)^2$ **e** $(x + 3)^2$ **f** $(x - 2)^2$

2 Look at your results in step **1**. In $(x + p)^2 = x^2 + bx + c$, find the relationships between p and b, and between p and c.

3 For these quadratic functions, choose values of c so that they factorize into two identical factors $(x + p)(x + p)$, in other words: the square of a linear factor. Write down the factorization for each one.

   a $x^2 - 4x + c$ **b** $x^2 + 4x + c$

   c $x^2 + x + c$ **d** $x^2 - x + c$

4 Write a general rule for what you did in step **3**. For a quadratic function $x^2 + bx + c$, express c in terms of b for the quadratic to be the square of a linear factor.

In steps **3** and **4** of Exploration 4 you were **completing the square**. Given the first two terms of a quadratic expression, you found c so that the quadratic factorizes into the square of a linear factor. For this, $c = \left(\dfrac{b}{2}\right)^2$, where b is the coefficient of the x term.

You can use completing the square to convert a quadratic function from standard form to vertex form.

Example 1

Write $y = x^2 + 2x - 2$ in vertex form.

$y = x^2 + bx + c$

$\left(\dfrac{b}{2}\right)^2 = \left(\dfrac{2}{2}\right)^2 = 1^2 = 1$ ——— Use $\left(\dfrac{b}{2}\right)^2$ to complete the square for the x^2 and x terms.

$x^2 + 2x + 1 = (x + 1)^2$

$y = x^2 + 2x - 2$ ——— Write the completed square in the right hand side. As this adds 1, subtract 1 at the end.

$\quad = (x^2 + 2x + 1) - 2 - 1$

$y = (x + 1)^2 - 3$ ——— You could check by expanding and simplifying.

Example 2

Sketch the graph of $y = (x + 1)^2 - 3$.

Vertex is $(-1, -3)$ ——— For $y = a(x - h)^2 + k$ the vertex is (h, k).

Axis of symmetry is $x = -1$

$y = (x + 1)^2 - 3 = x^2 + 2x - 2$

y-intercept $= -2$ ——— In standard form, y-intercept $= c$.

Graph is concave up. ——— Positive coefficient of x^2.

When $x = 1$, $y = 2^2 - 3 = 1$ ——— Find some other points on the curve by substituting a few values for x.
When $x = -3$, $y = (-2)^2 - 3 = 1$

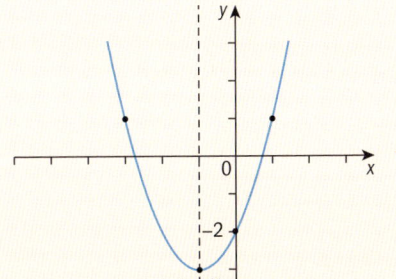

Connect the points with a smooth parabolic curve.

Reflect and discuss 5

Consider the two equivalent quadratic functions:

$y = x^2 + 2x - 2$ in standard form and $y = (x + 1)^2 - 3$ in vertex form.

- Which form of the quadratic function gives you more immediate information to use in sketching its graph?

- In Example 2, the y-intercept was found by expanding the original function. What is another way of finding the y-intercept? Which way is easier?

- How many points are necessary to determine a unique quadratic function or draw its graph? Explain.

Practice 4

1 The quadratic functions below are given in standard form.

  i Convert each function into vertex form.

  ii Sketch the graph of the quadratic by using the vertex and two other points on the quadratic.

> Find the y-intercept, and substitute an 'easy' value of x to find a third point.

  a $y = x^2 + 2x + 1$ **b** $y = x^2 - 4x - 2$ **c** $y = 3 + 6x + x^2$

  d $y = -x^2 - 6x + 1$ **e** $y = x^2 - 2x + 3$ **f** $y = 1 - 2x + x^2$

  g $y = x^2 + x + 2$ **h** $y = x^2 - x - 1$ **i** $y = 1 - 3x - x^2$

2 For the quadratics below:

  i find the vertex using the formula for the x-coordinate of the vertex

  ii find two other points on the quadratic

  iii sketch the graph of the quadratic using the points you have found.

  a $y = 1 - 4x - x^2$ **b** $y = 2x^2 - 4x + 1$ **c** $y = 1 - 6x - 3x^2$

Problem solving

3 Match each quadratic function with its graph.

  a $y = (x + 1)^2 - 3$ **b** $y = x^2 + 2$ **c** $y = (x - 2)^2 + 1$

  d $y = -x^2 + 2$ **e** $y = x^2 - 3x - 1$ **f** $y = 2 - x - x^2$

A

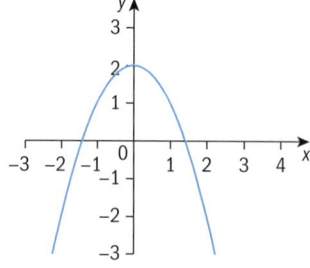

B

C

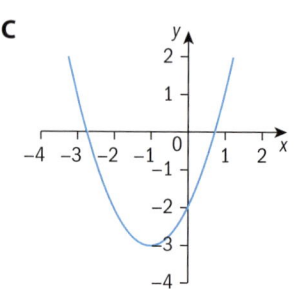

D 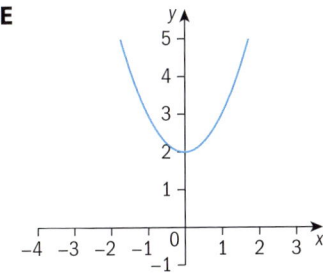 **E** **F**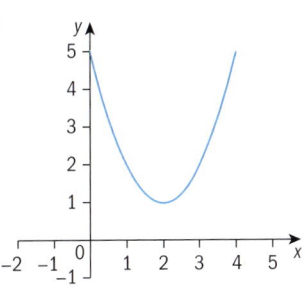

Reflect and discuss 6

- Find a quadratic function that goes through the point (0, 1).

- Find a quadratic function whose zeros are $x = 0$ and $x = 4$.

- Find a quadratic function with vertex (1, 2) and one of its zeros (−1, 3).

- Compare your answers with others. Did you all find the same functions? Explain.

Solving real-life problems

To solve real-life problems, you may have to derive the quadratic function from the given information, and then decide on the best form of the quadratic to use to answer the question.

Example 3

You have 100 meters of fencing to enclose a rectangular plot.

a Find the plot's maximum possible area.

b Determine the dimensions dimensions give the maximum area.

a $P = 2(l + w) = 100$ [1]   Write equations for the perimeter and area of a rectangle.

$A = lw$ [2]

From [1]:

$2(l + w) = 100$ Write l in terms of w.

$l + w = 50$

$l = 50 - w$

$A = (50 - w)w = 50w - w^2$ Substitute into [2], to get an equation linking A and w.

Area is given by the quadratic function $50w - w^2$, which has a maximum value at its vertex.

▶ Continued on next page

Method 1: finding the vertex using the factorized form

$50w - w^2 = w(50 - w) = 0$ ———————— Find the zeros of the function.

$w = 0, \; w = 50$

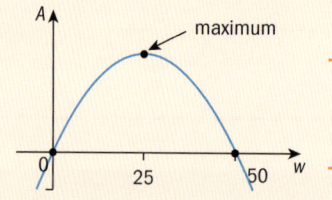

Sketch the graph of the function and identify its maximum point.

The maximum area of the rectangular plot occurs when $w = 25$.

When $w = 25$:

$A = 25(50 - 25) = 625$ ———————— Calculate the maximum area.

Maximum area = 625 m²

Method 2: finding the vertex using the standard form

$A = w(50 - w) = 50w - w^2$

$x_v = -\dfrac{b}{2a} = -\dfrac{50}{2(-1)} = 25$ ———————— Find the x-coordinate of the vertex.

When $w = 25$:

$A = 25(50 - 25) = 625$

Maximum area = 625 m²

Method 3: finding the vertex using vertex form

$w^2 - 50w = (w - 25)^2 - 625$ ———————— Complete the square for $w^2 - 50w$.

Hence $A = -(w^2 + 50w) = -(w - 25)^2 + 625$

Vertex = (25, 625)

Maximum area = 625 m²

b When $w = 25$, $l = 50 - w = 25$. The dimensions that produce the maximum area are width = length = 25 m (a square).

Reflect and discuss 7

When sketching graphs of quadratic functions, what are the advantages and disadvantages of:

- standard form
- factorized form
- vertex form?

Practice 5

In these questions, derive the quadratic function that best fits the situation and use the most efficient method for answering the question.

Problem solving

1 You have 300 m of fencing to enclose a rectangular plot along the side of a river, as shown.

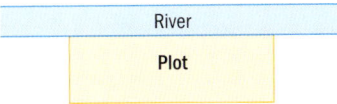

Determine the maximum area that you can enclose and the dimensions of the plot.

2 You have a total of 200 m of fencing to make two equal, adjacent, rectangular plots. Determine the dimensions of each plot, such that the total area enclosed is as big as possible.

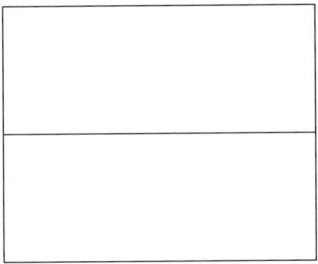

3 Xixi wants to fence off a rectangular exercise area for her dog, using the house as one side of the area. She has 10 m of fencing. Find the maximum possible exercise area.

4 The perimeter of an athletics track is 0.4 km. The track has two parallel sides and a semicircle at each end. Determine the exact values of x and r that would maximize the area of the rectangular part of the track field, and use these dimensions to find the area of the entire track field to the nearest square meter.

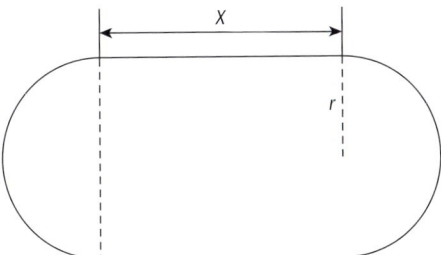

D Form and function

- What makes one quadratic form better than another?

Given a quadratic equation, you can sketch its graph by finding its x- and y-intercepts and vertex. If you start with a parabola, how can you find its quadratic function?

This photograph of water fountains is superimposed upon coordinate axes. Consider the parabolic shape of the 2nd fountain stream from left.

The x-intercepts and y-intercept, which is also the vertex, are labelled. Is this enough information to find the quadratic function modelling the parabolic fountain stream?

The general form of a quadratic function with vertex is (h, k) is $y = a(x - h)^2 + k$.

Substituting the coordinates of the vertex $(0, 7)$ for h and k gives $y = a(x - 0)^2 + 7$ or $y = ax^2 + 7$.

How can you find the leading coefficient a? It must have a negative value since the parabola is concave down. You can use one of the two other points given: $(-4.4, 0)$ or $(4.4, 0)$. Substituting the x- and y-values at point $(4.4, 0)$ gives $a \times 4.4^2 + 7 = 0$. Solving for a gives:

$$a = \frac{-7}{4.4^2} = -0.361 \ (3 \ \text{d.p.})$$

The quadratic function that models the fountain stream is $y = -0.361x^2 + 7$. You can graph this quadratic on the same coordinate axes to check:

Reflect and discuss 8

- Again, find the general form of the quadratic that models the fountain stream, but this time use the other x-intercept to find the leading coefficient a. Is it the same function?

- Does your quadratic function exactly model the parabolic fountain, or is it an approximate model? Explain.

- What minimum information do you need to determine the equation of a unique quadratic function?

- When finding the equation of a quadratic function, under what circumstances would you use:

  i standard form

  ii vertex form

  iii factorized form?

Reflect and discuss 1 asked: How many positions do you think you would need to know to be sure that the ball would go into the basket? The correct answer is 'three'.

A point in space has no dimension, and needs one point to determine it.

A line has one dimension and needs two points to determine it.

A curve has two dimensions and needs three points to determine it.

Can you guess how many points determine a unique object in three-dimensional space? How many points would you need to uniquely define an object in a four-dimensional universe?

You can project 3D objects onto a 2D space, such as with television transmission. In the same way, 4D objects can be projected onto a 3D space.

Exploration 5

The Golden Gate Bridge in San Francisco, USA is a suspension bridge spanning the channel between San Francisco Bay and the Pacific Ocean. The diagram shows the central section of the bridge. The suspension cable is a parabola.

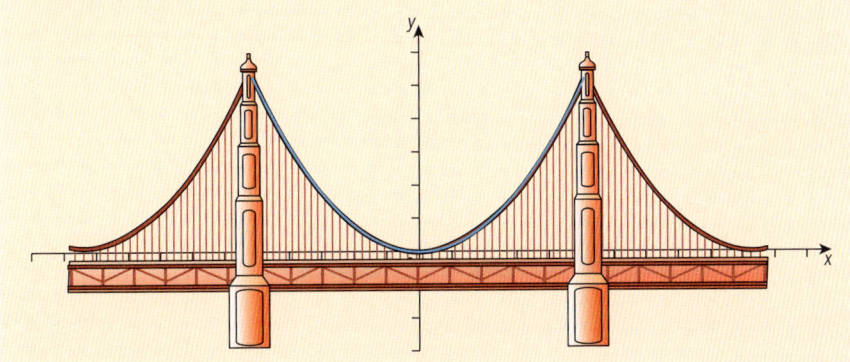

▶ Continued on next page

1 Research the heights of the towers and the length of the central section.

2 Trace the parabola. Draw a pair of coordinate axes, with the y-axis as the axis of symmetry of the parabola.

3 Use the dimensions you found from step **1** to determine a suitable scale for the x- and y-axes.

4 Using your scale, find the coordinates of the vertex, and the x- and y-intercepts.

5 Using your quadratic function and another point on the curve, find the parameter a.

6 Compare your model with others. Discuss any similarities and differences.

Practice 6

1 Trace each parabola. Draw coordinate axes and decide on a suitable scale. Find a quadratic function to model the parabola.

a

b

c

d

Exploration 6

Take photos of parabolic objects you encounter in your everyday life. Use technology to find the quadratic function that defines your object, or use tracing paper over the photo.

Reflect and discuss 9

Why might it be that so many natural and built structures are parabolic?

Objective: D. Applying mathematics in real-life contexts
v. Justify whether a solution makes sense in the context of the authentic real-life situation.
In this activity you will write quadratic models that describe the given situation. You will then decide which one is better in describing the given scenarios, and explain your choice.

Activity

For a free throw shot in basketball (in US standard units):

- the free throw line is 15 ft away from the foot of the basket

- the basket is 10 ft above the ground

- the player releases the ball from an approximate height of 8 ft.

1 Find **two different functions** that could model the shot into the basket. Make sure that each function satisfies the specifications.

2 Decide on the form of the quadratic function that is most appropriate for your models, and give reasons for your choice of form.

3 From your two models, select the one that you think best models a real-life shot. Explain why.

4 Your model does not take into account some factors that affect the path of the ball, or whether the shot goes into the basket. Suggest what some of these factors might be.

5 A player from the opposing team could intercept the ball on its way to the basket. Assume that an opposing player is 5 ft away from the free thrower and can jump to reach a maximum of 10 ft. Could this player intercept the ball in your model? If so, modify your function so that it models the ball reaching the basket.

Massachusetts physical education teacher James Naismith invented basketball in the late 1800s to keep his class occupied indoors in bad weather. He used a peach basket and a ball like a soccer ball.

Summary

- The **standard form** of a quadratic function is $y = ax^2 + bx + c$ where a, b and c are real numbers, and $a \neq 0$.

- The **factorized form** of a quadratic function is $y = a(x - p)(x - q)$, $a \neq 0$.

- The **vertex form** of a quadratic function is $y = a(x - h)^2 + k$, $a \neq 0$, where (h, k) is the vertex.

- The **degree** of a polynomial function is the value of its largest exponent of x. A linear function is a polynomial function of degree 1. A quadratic function is a polynomial function of degree 2. A constant function has degree 0.

- A concave down parabola has a maximum turning point.
  $y = ax^2 + bx + c$, $a < 0$

maximum turning point

- A concave up parabola has a minimum turning point.
  $y = ax^2 + bx + c$, $a > 0$

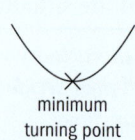

minimum turning point

- For a quadratic function $f(x) = ax^2 + bx + c$, $a \neq 0$:
  - the x-coordinate of the vertex is $-\dfrac{b}{2a}$
  - the equation of its axis of symmetry is $x = -\dfrac{b}{2a}$
  - the coordinates of its vertex are $\left(-\dfrac{b}{2a},\ f\left(-\dfrac{b}{2a}\right)\right)$
  - the y-intercept is c

- For a quadratic function $f(x)$ with x-intercepts x_1 and x_2:
  - the x-coordinate of the vertex is $x_v = \dfrac{x_2 + x_2}{2}$
  - the y-coordinate of the vertex is $f(x_v)$

Mixed practice

1 For each quadratic function:

   i **find** the vertex, x-intercepts and y-intercept

   ii **state** the axis of symmetry, and whether it is concave up or concave down

   iii **sketch** the graph.

   a $y = x^2 + x - 12$ **b** $y = x^2 + 7x + 12$

   c $y = 2x^2 - x - 3$ **d** $y = 2 - x - 3x^2$

   e $y = -6x^2 + 5x - 1$ **f** $y = 2x^2 - 9x - 5$

2 These quadratic functions are in standard form. Change each one to vertex form, and **state** the coordinates of the vertex.

   a $y = x^2 - 4x + 6$ **b** $y = x^2 + 6x + 8$

   c $y = x^2 + 2x - 9$ **d** $y = x^2 - 2x + 7$

   e $y = x^2 + x - 5$ **f** $y = x^2 - x + 7$

Problem solving

3 Kanye has 600 m of fencing to make five adjacent pens like this:

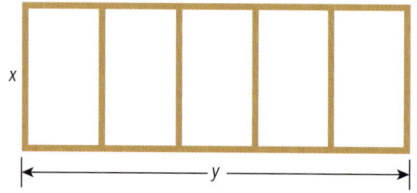

a Express the total area of the pens in terms of x.

b **Determine** the value of x that will maximize the total area.

c **Find** the maximum area.

4 Soraya has 40 m of fencing to make a rectangular play area. **Find** the dimensions for the maximum play area.

5 The population P of an animal species is modelled by the function $P(t) = -0.38t^2 + 134t + 1100$, where t is the time in months since the population was first observed. **Determine**:

a the number of months until the population is at its maximum

b the maximum population

c the number of months before the species disappears.

6 A ball is thrown up into the air, from 5 m above the ground. After 2 seconds, the ball reaches a maximum height of 9 m. It lands on the ground 5 seconds after it was thrown. **Find** a quadratic function that models this situation. Write it in standard and vertex form.

Review in context
Scientific and technical innovation

> The area of a region formed by a parabola is $A = \frac{2}{3}bh$, where b is the length of the base of the parabola, and h is its height, that is, the distance from its vertex to the base.

1 This rollercoaster is in Münich, Germany.

   a **Trace** the outline of the parabolic section of the foreground section of track.

   b **Draw** axes and use the map to determine a suitable scale.

   c **Find** a suitable function to model the shape of section of track.

   d **Use** the function to estimate the area under this section.

2 To the right is the tunnel entrance that runs through Castle Hill in Budapest, Hungary.

   a If the maximum height of the tunnel is the same as its maximum width, 9.8 meters, **determine** a quadratic model to represent the tunnel.

   b **State** a geometric model that could be used to represent a truck passing through the tunnel.

   c If a typical truck has a width of 2.62 m, determine the height limitation that should be put on these trucks if they are going to travel through the tunnel safely. **State** any assumptions that you made and be sure to show all of the steps in your solution.

   d Because its length is almost 350 meters, a truck stopped in the tunnel would need enough room for the passenger door to open fully. Suppose a truck with a width of 2.6 m and height of 3.4 m is stuck in the right lane of the tunnel by the center line. The top of the driver's door is 0.2 m below the top of the truck, and the door opens 0.8 m to the side. **Show that** the door can open fully, showing all of your steps.

   e **Determine** how close to the side of the tunnel the truck could be in **d** be and still be able to open the passenger door.

   f **Describe** some issues/concerns that you think architects take into account when modelling a tunnel before its construction.

Reflect and discuss 10

How have you explored the statement of inquiry? Give specific examples.

Statement of inquiry:

Discovering relationships in patterns and studying equivalence between representations can lead to better models.

Global context: Scientific and technical innovation

Related concept: Equivalence

Objectives

- Solving quadratic equations algebraically and graphically
- Solving real-life problems by creating and using quadratic models

Inquiry questions

F
- What is the null factor law?
- How do you solve a quadratic equation in factorized form?

C
- How can you use equivalence transformations to solve quadratic equations?
- How are the three methods for solving quadratic equations equivalent?

D
- How do you determine a 'best method' among equivalent methods?
- Do systems, models and methods solve problems or create them?

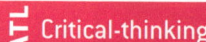

RELATIONSHIPS

ATL Critical-thinking

Propose and evaluate a variety of solutions

Statement of inquiry:

Discovering relationships in patterns and studying equivalence between representations can lead to better models.

📖 **Launch additional digital resources for this chapter.**

You should already know how to:

• convert quadratic expressions into standard form	**1** Rearrange into standard form: **a** $(x + 2)(3x - 1)$ **b** $(x - 1)^2 - 16$
• convert quadratic expressions into factorized form	**2** Factorize: **a** $x^2 + x - 6$ **b** $2x^2 + 5x - 3$ **c** $4x^2 - 81$
• convert quadratic functions into vertex form	**3** Write in the form $y = a(x - h)^2 + k$, where (h, k) is the vertex. **a** $y = x^2 - 6x + 14$ **b** $y = 3x^2 - 6x + 7$
• use equivalence transformations in solving linear equations	**4** Solve $3(x + 2) - 6 = 4(2x - 3) + 1$. State the equivalence transformation you use in each step.

F Quadratic and linear equations

- What is the null factor law?
- How do you solve a quadratic equation in factorized form?

The graph shows the two linear functions $f_1(x) = x + 1$ and $f_2(x) = 2 - x$, and the function which is the product of these two linear functions, $f_3(x) = (x + 1)(2 - x)$.

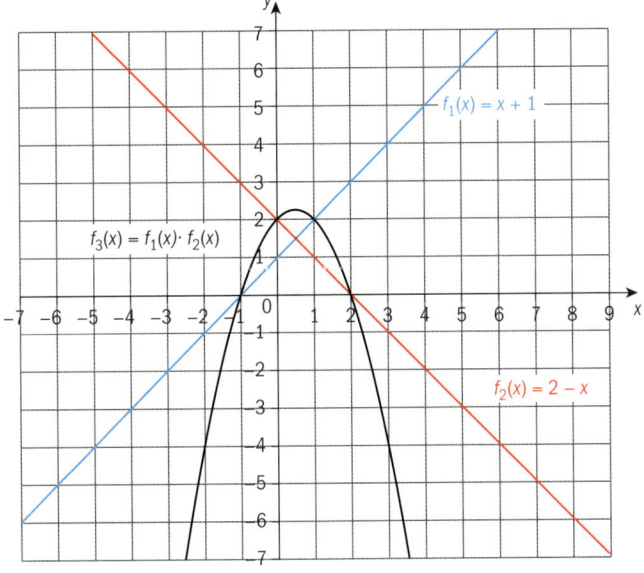

The graph of the product of the two linear functions is a parabola, because $f_3(x) = (x + 1)(2 - x)$ is a quadratic function.

> Expanding $(x + 1)(2 - x)$ gives a quadratic expression.

Exploration 1

1 Write these quadratic functions as the product of two linear functions:

a $f(x) = x^2 + 3x + 2$ **b** $f(x) = -x^2 - x + 2$

c $f(x) = 2x^2 - 5x - 3$ **d** $f(x) = -3x^2 + 4x - 1$

2 Graph each quadratic function with its two related linear functions.

3 Write the function $f(x) = 2x^2 - 4x + 1$ as a product of two linear factors. Graph the quadratic function and its two related linear functions.

Reflect and discuss 1

- What is the relationship between the x-intercepts of the original linear functions and the x-intercepts of the parabola?

- Which parameter of the linear functions is responsible for the parabola being concave up or concave down?

The zeros of a function are the x-coordinates of the points where the graph crosses the x-axis. So, to find the x-intercepts of any function algebraically, you need to find the x-value(s) such that $f(x) = 0$.

Exploration 2

1 a Plot the graph of $f(x) = x^2 + 2x - 3$, and find the zeros of this function.

   b Factorize $x^2 + 2x - 3$ to find two linear functions g and h whose product is $f(x)$.

   c Solve $g(x) = 0$ and $h(x) = 0$.

   d Check your solutions algebraically by substituting them into $f(x)$ and verifying that they satisfy $f(x) = 0$.

2 Plot the graph of $x^2 - 3x - 4 = 0$ and repeat parts **a** to **d** in step **1**.

3 Explain the relationship between the solutions of the linear equations, the zeros of the function and the solutions of the quadratic equation.

You can use the null factor law to solve quadratic equations.

The **null factor law** states that if the product of two or more numbers is zero, then at least one of the numbers must be zero.

For two numbers a and b, if $ab = 0$ then $a = 0$ or $b = 0$, or both.

When $f(x) = g(x) \times h(x)$, where g and h are functions, if $f(x) = 0$ then $g(x) = 0$ or $h(x) = 0$, or both.

Example 1

Solve $2x^2 - 6x = 0$.

$2x^2 - 6x = 0 \Rightarrow 2x(x - 3) = 0$ —————————————————— Factorize the quadratic.

$2x = 0 \Rightarrow x = 0$ —————————————————— Use the null factor law.

$x - 3 = 0 \Rightarrow x = 3$

$x_1 = 0;\ x_2 = 3$

$x_1 = 0$: $2(0) - 6(0) = 0$, LHS = RHS ✓ ————————— Check both solutions in the original equation.

$x_2 = 3$: $2(3)^2 - 6(3) = 0$, LHS = RHS ✓

Example 2

Solve $2x^2 - 5x - 3 = 0$.

$(2x + 1)(x - 3) = 0$ —————————————————— Factorize the quadratic.

$2x + 1 = 0;\ x - 3 = 0$

$x_1 = -\dfrac{1}{2};\ x_2 = 3$ —————————————————— Set both linear functions equal to 0 and solve.

$x_1 = -\dfrac{1}{2}$: $\ 2\left(-\dfrac{1}{2}\right)^2 - 5\left(-\dfrac{1}{2}\right) - 3 = 0$ ✓ ————— Check the solutions in the original quadratic.

$x_2 = 3$: $\quad 2(3)^2 - 5(3) - 3 = 0$ ✓

Practice 1

1 Solve each equation, leaving your answers exact.

a $x^2 - 8x = 0$ **b** $x^2 - 5x + 6 = 0$ **c** $6x^2 + 4x - 16 = 0$

d $x^2 - 9x = 0$ **e** $4x^2 = 1$ **f** $3x^2 - 48 = 0$

g $10 - 3x = x^2$ **h** $x = 6x^2 - 2$ **i** $9x^2 = 10x$

j $3x^2 - 4 = 23$ **k** $13 - 2x^2 = 5$ **l** $18 = 9x + 2x^2$

> To use the null factor law, first rearrange the quadratic so it is equal to zero.

Problem solving

2 Write a quadratic equation in standard form that has solutions:

a -2 and 4 **b** $\dfrac{1}{2}$ and 6 **c** $-\dfrac{2}{5}$ and 3

3 Find a quadratic equation with roots $\dfrac{3}{4}$ and -5:

a whose leading coefficient is 1

b with only integer coefficients.

You have now seen quadratic equations that have two unique solutions. How many solutions can quadratic equations have?

Reflect and discuss 2

- Graph $f(x) = 2x^2 - 6x$ and $g(x) = 4x^2 - 4x + 1$.

- Explain why they have a different number of unique solutions.

- Can a quadratic equation have more than two unique solutions? Explain.

Practice 2

1 Solve each equation, leaving your answers exact, or to 3 s.f.

    a $x^2 + 2x + 1 = 0$ **b** $x^2 - 6x + 9 = 0$ **c** $x^2 - 10x = -25$

    d $9x^2 - 6x + 1 = 0$ **e** $4x^2 + 9 = 12x$ **f** $9x^2 = -4 - 12x$

Problem solving

2 Write a quadratic equation in standard form whose only solution is

    a $x = -2$ **b** $x = \dfrac{1}{5}$ **c** $x = -\dfrac{3}{4}$

- -

Example 3

The length of a rectangle is 4 cm more than its width. Its area is 21 cm².

a Write an equation that represents the area A of the rectangle.

b Solve the equation.

c Write down the dimensions of the rectangle.

a Let $x =$ width. Then length $= x + 4$. ——————— State your variables and write the equation.

    $A = x(x + 4) = 21$

b $x^2 + 4x = 21$ ———————————— Rearrange, factorize, and solve.

    $x^2 + 4x - 21 = 0$

    $(x + 7)(x - 3) = 0$

    $x + 7 = 0 \Rightarrow x_1 = -7$

    $x - 3 = 0 \Rightarrow x_2 = 3$

c width $= 3$ cm, length $=$ width $+ 4$ cm $= 7$ cm ——————— x is a length and cannot be negative hence x_1 is not a solution.

Practice 3

1 The width of a rectangle is 3 cm less than its length. The area of the rectangle is 18 cm². Find the length and width of the rectangle.

2 The length of a rectangle is 1 cm less than 2 times its width. Its area is 45 cm². Find its dimensions.

3 A rectangular shaped garden's length is 2 m less than twice its width. If the area of the garden is 420 m², find the dimensions of the garden.

4 The base of a triangle exceeds its height by 17 cm. If its area is 55 cm², find the base and height of the triangle.

Problem solving

5 A square and a rectangle have the same area. The length of the rectangle is 5 cm more than twice the length of the side of the square. The width of the rectangle is 6 cm less than the side of the square. Find the length of the side of the square.

6 Find the lengths of the sides of this triangle.

7 A pole leans against a vertical wall. The top of the pole touches the wall at a height of 15 m. The length of the pole is 1 m more than twice its distance from the wall. Find the distance from the wall to the bottom of the pole.

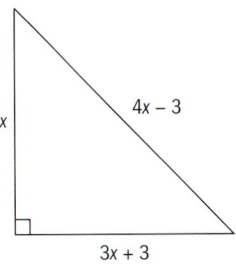

 C **Solving quadratic equations**

- How can you use equivalence transformations to solve quadratic equations?
- How are the three methods for solving quadratic equations equivalent?

Reflect and discuss 3

You have seen that quadratic equations can have one or two solutions. Do you think it is possible for a quadratic equation to have no solutions? What would its graph look like?

Exploration 3

1 Using a GDC or graphing software, graph the function $f(x) = x^2 - 2x - 3$.

   a Find the points where the parabola intersects the x-axis.

   b Construct lines through the intersection points that are parallel to the y-axis.

   c Grab the parabola and move it around the coordinate plane. Describe what happens to the two vertical lines as you move the curve so that its vertex is to the left and the right of the y-axis.

   d The vertex of the original parabola is below the x-axis. Describe what happens to the vertical lines as you move the vertex so that it is above the x-axis, and when it is exactly on the x-axis.

2 Graph the function $f(x) = 3 + 2x - x^2$. Repeat parts **a** to **d** in step **1**.

▶ Continued on next page

3 Based on your answers to steps **1** and **2**, determine:

a whether or not a quadratic function is always the product of two linear functions.

b whether or not a quadratic function has zeros if the function is always above or below the x-axis.

c the number of zeros of the quadratic, if its vertex lies on the x-axis.

Reflect and discuss 4

$f(x) = x^2 - 2$ cannot be factorized using only integers.

- Solve the quadratic equation $x^2 - 2 = 0$ by factorizing using the difference of two squares.

- Solve the quadratic equation $x^2 - 2 = 0$ by first using the addition principle.

- Do your two methods give the same solution?

When a quadratic is of the form $ax^2 - c = 0$, $c > 0$, you can use the addition principle to rearrange to $ax^2 = c$, and the multiplication principle to get $x^2 = \dfrac{c}{a}$. The solution is $x = \pm\sqrt{\dfrac{c}{a}}$.

Taking the square root of both sides of an equation does not always give an equivalent equation. For example $(-1)^2 = 1^2$, but taking the square root of both sides leaves $-1 = 1$, which is obviously false. Therefore 'taking the square root' is not an equivalence transformation.

Reflect and discuss 5

- Discuss the reasons for each step in solving this equation.

$x = \sqrt{2x+3}$

[1] $x^2 = 2x + 3$

[2] $x^2 - 2x - 3 = 0$

[3] $(x - 3)(x + 1) = 0$

[4] $x - 3 = 0$ or $x + 1 = 0$

[5] $x_1 = 3, x_2 = -1$

- Is 'squaring both sides' an equivalence transformation? Explain.

When a quadratic function can be written as the product of linear factors, the quadratic equation has solutions. When quadratics do not have factors with integer coefficients, it may be difficult to express them as the product of linear factors. Instead of factorizing, another method for solving quadratic equations is completing the square.

Example 4

Solve $x^2 - 2x - 4 = 0$.

$x^2 - 2x - 4$ is not factorizable.

$x^2 - 2x - 4 = 0$

$x^2 - 2x = 4$ ────────────────────── 'Complete the square' to write the quadratic in vertex form.

$x^2 - 2x + 1 = 4 + 1$

$(x - 1)^2 = 5$ ────────────────────── Take the square root of both sides. Don't forget the positive and negative square roots.

$x - 1 = \pm\sqrt{5}$

$x = 1 \pm \sqrt{5}$

$x_1 = 1 + \sqrt{5} \; ; \; x_2 = 1 - \sqrt{5}$

Check both solutions in the original equation.

when $x_1 = 1 + \sqrt{5}$: $\quad x^2 - 2x - 4 = \left(1 + \sqrt{5}\right)^2 - 2\left(1 + \sqrt{5}\right) - 4$
$$= (1 + 2\sqrt{5} + 5) - 2 - 2\sqrt{5} - 4$$
$$= 0 \; \checkmark$$

when $x_2 = 1 - \sqrt{5}$: $\quad x^2 - 2x - 4 = \left(1 - \sqrt{5}\right)^2 - 2\left(1 - \sqrt{5}\right) - 4$
$$= (1 - 2\sqrt{5} + 5) - 2 + 2\sqrt{5} - 4$$
$$= 0 \; \checkmark$$

Example 5

Solve the quadratic equation $2x^2 = 4x + 3$. Rationalize the denominator in your answer.

$2x^2 - 4x = 3$ ────────────────────── Rearrange the equation and factorize so that x^2 has coefficient 1.

$2(x^2 - 2x) = 3$

$x^2 - 2x = \dfrac{3}{2}$

$x^2 - 2x + 1 = \dfrac{3}{2} + 1$ ────────────────────── Complete the square.

$(x - 1)^2 = \dfrac{5}{2}$ ────────────────────── Solve for x.

$x - 1 = \pm\sqrt{\dfrac{5}{2}}$

$x = 1 \pm \sqrt{\dfrac{5}{2}} = 1 \pm \dfrac{\sqrt{10}}{2}$

Practice 4

Solve, if possible, by completing the square. Leave your answers exact.

1 $x^2 - 4x = -1$　　　**2** $x^2 + 2x = 1$　　　**3** $x^2 - 2x - 2 = 0$

4 $x^2 - 2x + 2 = 0$　　**5** $x^2 - 4x + 6 = 0$　　**6** $x^2 + 6x + 1 = 0$

7 $x^2 + 20x + 40 = 0$　**8** $2x^2 + 4x = 1$　　　**9** $3x^2 + 6x = 2$

10 $2x^2 + 20x + 3 = 0$　**11** $4x^2 + 4x = 3$　　　**12** $2x^2 + 12x = -9$

- -

When a quadratic equation cannot be factorized, you can use the method of 'completing the square' to solve it. You can also use a method that involves the 'quadratic formula'. Just like with factorized form, the equation should first be set equal to zero before using the formula.

> The quadratic formula to solve $ax^2 + bx + c = 0$, $a \neq 0$, is $x = \dfrac{-b \pm \sqrt{b^2 - 4ac}}{2a}$.

Example 6

Solve $x^2 + 3x - 1 = 0$, giving your solutions to 1 d.p.

$x = \dfrac{-b \pm \sqrt{b^2 - 4ac}}{2a}$　　　　　Write the quadratic formula and the values of a, b and c.

$a = 1$, $b = 3$, $c = -1$

$x = \dfrac{-3 \pm \sqrt{3^2 - 4(1)(-1)}}{2} = \dfrac{-3 \pm \sqrt{9+4}}{2} = \dfrac{-3 \pm \sqrt{13}}{2}$　　Substitute the values into the formula and simplify.

$x_2 = \dfrac{-3 + \sqrt{13}}{2} = 0.3$　　　　　Separate the two solutions.

$x_2 = \dfrac{-3 - \sqrt{13}}{2} = -3.3$

Practice 5

1 Solve for the variable, if possible, using the quadratic formula, leaving your answers exact. Remember to set the equation equal to 0, when necessary.

　a $4p^2 + 8p - 1 = 0$　　**b** $5a^2 + 3a + 1 = 0$　　**c** $-r^2 + 3r - 6 = 0$

　d $-q^2 + 2q = -5$　　　**e** $-3c^2 = -6c + 3$　　　**f** $2m^2 + 23 = 14m$

　g $9x^2 - 11 = 6x$　　　**h** $4b^2 + 4b - 8 = 1$　　**i** $-4t^2 + 8 = -t$

2 Solve, if possible, the quadratic equations giving your answers to 1 d.p. Check your solutions using a GDC or graphing software.

　a $x^2 + x - 3 = 0$　　　**b** $x^2 - 2x - 4 = 0$　　**c** $4p^2 + 8p - 1 = 0$

　d $5a^2 + 3a + 1 = 0$　　**e** $-r^2 + 3r - 6 = 0$　　**f** $-x^2 + 4x + 7 = 0$

3 Solve these quadratic equations giving your answers in radical form.

   a $x^2 = x + 5$ **b** $x^2 + 5x = 1$ **c** $2x - x^2 = 1$

   d $x^2 - 7x = 3$ **e** $-2z^2 + 6z = -95$

4 Solve, giving your answer to 3 s.f.

   a $x^2 + 0.6x - 2.6 = 0$ **b** $0.2x^2 - 3x + 0.3 = 0$ **c** $4 - 2x - 3x^2 = 0$

   d $3.2 + x - 1.2x^2 = 0$ **e** $2.2x^2 = 3x + 1.1$

> For the equations in question **3**, rearrange so that the right hand side is equal to 0.

- -

Exploration 4

1 Create a table with the same column headings as the one below, and give it 8 rows. Copy the first two rows as shown here, then enter the six equations below in the first column. Solve each equation, if possible, using one method from the three equivalent solution methods: factorization (if possible), completing the square, or the quadratic formula. In the fourth column, substitute the parameters a, b and c of the quadratic into $b^2 - 4ac$.

   $2x^2 + 5x - 3 = 0$ $-x^2 + 4x - 4 = 0$ $2x^2 + x + 1 = 0$

   $x^2 + 2x - 2 = 0$ $3x^2 + 4x + 1 = 0$ $2x^2 - 6x + 5 = 0$

Equation	Solutions	Number of distinct solutions	$b^2 - 4ac$	Can the quadratic be factorized?	Sketch of graphical solution (include x-axis, but not y-axis)
$x^2 + 2x + 1 = 0$	$x_1 = -1; x_2 = -1$	1	$2^2 - 4(2)(1) = 1$	Yes	
$x^2 + 1 = 0$	No solutions	0	$0^2 - 4(1)(1) = -4$	No	

2 Use the answers in your table to complete these sentences.

   a When $b^2 - 4ac = 0$, the quadratic equation has _____ distinct solution(s).

   b When $b^2 - 4ac > 0$, the quadratic equation has _____ distinct solution(s).

   c When $b^2 - 4ac < 0$, the quadratic equation has _____ distinct solution(s).

3 State at how many points the quadratic expression intersects the x-axis when:

   a $b^2 - 4ac = 0$ **b** $b^2 - 4ac > 0$ **c** $b^2 - 4ac < 0$

> You may need to look back at other quadratics that are factorizable in Practice 1 and evaluate $b^2 - 4ac$.

4 Explain how the expression $b^2 - 4ac$ helps you determine whether or not a quadratic expression can be factorized.

The part of the quadratic formula, $b^2 - 4ac$, is called the **discriminant**, and the symbol we use for it is the Greek letter delta Δ. We write $\Delta = b^2 - 4ac$.

In 820 CE, mathematician Muhammad ibn Musa Al-Khwarizmi derived the quadratic formula for positive solutions. His method was brought to Europe by the mathematician Abraham bar Hiyya, who lived in Spain around 1100. In 1545 Girolamo Cardano compiled the existing work on quadratic equations. The quadratic formula first appeared in the form we know today in Rene Descartes' *La Géométrie* in 1637.

Practice 6

1 By considering the discriminant of each quadratic, state:

    i the number of distinct solutions of the quadratic equation

    ii whether or not the quadratic is factorizable.

    a $2x^2 - 3x + 2 = 0$ **b** $x^2 - 7x + 6 = 0$ **c** $-3x^2 + 17x - 2 = 3$

    d $3x + 7 = -5x^2 - 4$ **e** $4x^2 - 28x + 40 = 0$

Problem solving

2 Find the values of k such that the quadratic has the given number of solutions.

    a $x^2 + kx + 16 = 0$ (1 solution)   **b** $3x^2 + kx + 12 = 0$ (1 solution)

    c $-4x^2 + 8x + k = 0$ (2 solutions)   **d** $kx^2 + 3x + 5 = 0$ (no solutions)

D Solutions of quadratic equations

- How do you determine a 'best method' among equivalent methods?
- Do systems, models and methods solve problems or create them?

When solving quadratic equations, particularly for real-life problems, how do you decide which of the three methods of solution (factorizing, completing the square, or the quadratic formula) is the best method?

ATL

Reflect and discuss 6

- Which of the three methods would you try first? Explain why. If this method did not work, which method would you try next?

- How could you find out if the equation is factorable?

- Which method would you try first if the question asked you to give your solutions to 2 decimal places? Explain why.

Example 7

A gardener has 16 m of fencing to section off a rectangular area of 15 m². Determine the constraints on the dimensions of the rectangle, and find the dimensions of the rectangle.

Perimeter = 2(length + width) = 16

$\Rightarrow$ length + width = 8

Let width = x. Then length = $8 - x$.

Constraint 1: $x > 0$ ——————————

> 'Determine the constraints' means 'write an inequality for the values'.

> Length and width can be only positive values. Write inequality statements to reflect this.

Constraint 2: $8 - x > 0$, so $x < 8$

$\Rightarrow 0 < x < 8$

Area = $x(8 - x) = 15$

$8x - x^2 = 15$

$x^2 - 8x + 15 = 0$ ——————————

> Calculate the discriminant to see if the equation is factorizable.

Here, $a = 1$, $b = -8$ and $c = 15$

$\Rightarrow b^2 - 4ac = (-8)^2 - (4 \times 1 \times 15) = 4$ ——————

> The discriminant is positive, so there will be two unique solutions.

$x^2 - 8x + 15 = (x - 3)(x - 5)$

$x_1 = 3; x_2 = 5$ ——————————

> Both values 3 and 5 satisfy $0 < x < 8$.

When $x = 3$: width = 3, length = $8 - 3 = 5$

When $x = 5$: width = 5, length = $8 - 5 = 3$

The dimensions of the rectangle are 3 m by 5 m.

Practice 7

In these problems, create a mathematical model to solve the problem. Select the most efficient method to solve the quadratic equation.

> With geometric models, draw a sketch to help you visualize the problem.

Problem solving

1 A gardener has 40 m of fencing to make three separate equal rectangular plots. The total area of the three plots is 30 m². Determine the constraints on the dimensions of the rectangles, and find the dimensions of each rectangle.

2 50 m of fencing is used to make three sides of a rectangular area, using an existing wall as the fourth side. The area of the rectangle is 150 m². Determine the dimensions of the rectangular area.

3 A rectangular garden measures 24 m by 32 m. A path of uniform width is built all around the outside of the garden. The total area of the path and garden is 1540 m². Find the width of the path.

4 A rectangular swimming pool measures 10 m by 6 m. A paved area on two sides of the pool has width x meters. The total area including the paved area is $\frac{4}{3}$ of the pool area on its own. Find x.

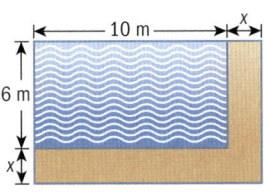

5 The perimeter of a rectangle is 42 cm. Its diagonal is 15 cm. Find the width of the rectangle.

6 A student cycles from home to school, due north for a distance x km, then the same distance plus an additional 7 km due east. If the direct distance from home to school is 17 km, find the distances that the student cycles north and east.

7 A box has a square base of side x cm, height 4 cm, and volume 289 cm³. Find x.

8 A box with an open top is made from a rectangular piece of cardboard by cutting squares of equal size from each corner. The cardboard measures 50 cm by 40 cm. The area of the base is 875 cm².

   a Determine the side length of the squares cut from each corner.

   b Find the volume of the box.

9 Two numbers have a difference of 3 and a product of 88. Find the numbers.

10 The product of two consecutive odd numbers is 143. Find the numbers.

11 The sum of two numbers is 9 and the sum of their squares is 153. Find the two numbers.

12 When the square of a number is decreased by 1, the result is 4 times the original number. Find the number.

Example 8

When the brakes are applied in a certain make of car, the length L of the skid in meters is given by $L = 0.168s^2 - 0.8s + 0.3$, where s is the speed of the car in km/h at the time when the brakes were first applied. A car involved in an accident leaves skid marks measuring 50 m. Determine the car's speed at the time of braking.

$0.168s^2 - 0.8s + 0.3 = 50$ — Write the equation.

$0.168s^2 - 0.8s - 49.7 = 0$

Using the quadratic formula: — a, b and c are decimals, so the quadratic cannot be factorized.

$a = 0.168$, $b = -0.8$, $c = -49.7$

$$s = \frac{-(-0.8) \pm \sqrt{(-0.8)^2 - 4(0.168)(-49.7)}}{2(0.168)}$$

$s_1 = -15.0$; $s_2 = 19.7$ — Only the positive value makes sense in the context of the question.

The car was traveling at approximately 20 km/h.

The distance a car skids depends on several factors, including the speed of the car and weather conditions. Car accident investigators use skid distances to calculate traveling speeds, to help discover the cause of an accident.

Practice 8

Problem solving

1 The amount of money in bank account A is given by the formula
   $A = P(1 + r)^t$ where P is the initial investment, r is the interest rate
   compounded annually and t is the time in years. Your mother wants to
   invest $5000 and would like it to be worth $6500 after two years, to help
   you with your first year of university costs. Determine the interest rate
   she needs.

2 An internet company was listed on a small stock exchange for several
   months before going bankrupt. The price P of the company's stock in
   terms of the number of months x that the stock traded on the exchange
   is given by $P(x) = -2.25x^2 + 40.5x + 42.75$. Determine the number of
   months it took for the company to go bankrupt, in other words
   when $P(x) = 0$.

3 A charity organizes a soccer game to raise money. There are 15 000 seats in
   the stadium. From past experience they know that when the tickets cost $15,
   they sold 9500 tickets. For every $1 decrease in ticket price, the number of
   tickets sold increases by 1000.

   a Copy and complete the table.

Price ($)	Decrease in ticket price	Increase in attendance	Total attendance	Total sales ($)
15	$15 - 15 = 0$	0	9500	$15 \times 9500 = 142\,500$
14	$15 - 14 = 1$	$1000 \times 1 = 1000$	$9500 + 1000 = 10\,500$	$14 \times 10\,500 = 147\,000$
13				
12				
p	$15 - p$			

   b From the last row in the table, find a function for sales generated in terms
     of ticket price p.

   c Write an equation to find the ticket price that would be so expensive that
     nobody would buy a ticket. Solve it using the most efficient method.

   d Determine the ticket price that would maximize sales. How many tickets
     would you sell at that price?

   e Determine the ticket price needed to fill all 15 000 seats.

   f Consider your answers for d and e. Decide what you could do with the
     unsold seats if you sold tickets at the price that gives maximum sales.

4 A swimming team sells t-shirts with their logo to raise money for an international competition. A survey into prices and predicted sales is shown in this table.

Price of t-shirt in Euros (p)	Predicted number of t-shirts sold (s)
5	165
10	150
15	130
20	118
25	97
30	85
35	65
40	56
45	42
50	28

a Find the line of best fit that best describes the relationship between price and number of t-shirts sold. This is the demand function.

b Determine the revenue function.

c Determine the t-shirt price that would maximize revenues.

d Determine the t-shirt price that would guarantee that no t-shirts are sold.

> Lines of best fit are covered in topic 4.3.

5 A ski rental shop charges a rental fee of $50 per pair of skis and averages 36 rentals per day. A ski journal article states that for every $5 increase in rental price, the average ski rental business can expect to lose two rentals per day, and vice versa.

a Determine the revenue function.

b Determine the ski rental price that would maximize revenues.

c Determine the ski rental price that would guarantee the shop could not rent out any skis.

6 You have designed a new kind of exercise bike which you want to sell to retailers. Your advertising and start-up costs will be $800 000. Each exercise bike will cost $120 to make. Sales of such bikes (demand) tend to follow a linear function modeled by $s = 80\,000 - 180p$, where s is the number of bikes sold and p is the price of the bike in dollars.

a Determine how many bikes you could sell at the price of:
i $100   **ii** $300   **iii** $500.

b Use the linear function to write the revenue function for the sale of bikes.

c Write a function for the total costs of producing the bikes.

d Write a function for the profit you would make on producing the bikes.

e Calculate what the price of the bike would be if you were to make no profit on the bikes, and use this to calculate the price that would ensure a maximum profit.

Objective: D. Applying mathematics in real-life contexts
ii. select appropriate mathematical strategies when solving authentic
real-life situations

*Draw and label suitable diagrams, create equations and select the most efficient
method to solve them.*

Activity

Do the open box problem in Practice 7 question **8**, before this activity.

1 Suitcases are made from rectangular sheets of leather 60 cm by 92 cm.

Each sheet is folded in half, squares are cut from the corners and the
sheet is opened up again.

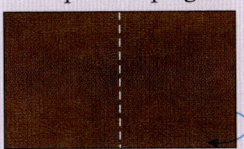  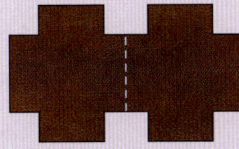

   a Draw a diagram and label the variable for the side of each square cut out.

   b Express all the dimensions in terms of your variable.

   c Express the volume of the case using these dimensions.

   d Define the constraints.

   e Use your GDC or software to determine the maximum volume of the
case and the size of the cut-out squares that give this maximum volume.

2 Determine the size of the squares to cut out to give a case with
volume 18 350 cm^3.

3 Create a mathematical model which enables you to decide on the sizes
of the squares to be cut out from any size rectangle.

Use suitable software to explore the size of the square giving the
maximum volume for several different starting rectangles.

4 Research suitable size cases for a travel set of 3 cases. Use your model
to calculate the size of the rectangle and the size of squares to cut out to
give maximum volume for your set of cases.

Summary

The **null factor law** states that if the product of
two or more numbers is zero, then at least one of
the factors must be zero.

For two factors a and b, if $ab = 0$ then $a = 0$ or
$b = 0$, or both.

When $f(x) = g(x) \times h(x)$, where g and h are functions,
if $f(x) = 0$ then $g(x) = 0$ or $h(x) = 0$, or both.

When a quadratic is of the form $ax^2 - c = 0$, $c > 0$,
you can use the addition principle to rearrange
to $ax^2 - c$, and the multiplication principle to get

$x^2 = \dfrac{c}{a}$. The solution is $x = \pm\sqrt{\dfrac{c}{a}}$.

The quadratic formula to solve $ax^2 + bx + c = 0$,
$a \neq 0$, is $x = \dfrac{-b \pm \sqrt{b^2 - 4ac}}{2a}$.

The part of the quadratic formula, $b^2 - 4ac$, is
called the **discriminant**, and the symbol we use for
it is the Greek letter delta Δ. We write $\Delta = b^2 - 4ac$.

- If $\Delta < 0$, the quadratic has no real roots.

- If $\Delta = 0$, the quadratic has one real root
  (a repeated root).

- If $\Delta > 0$, the quadratic has two real roots.

When the discriminant is a perfect square
(e.g. 1, 4, 9, 16, ...), then the quadratic expression
is factorizable.

Mixed practice

1 **Solve** each quadratic by factorizing, and check your answers graphically. Leave your answers exact.

a $x^2 - 2x - 24 = 0$ **b** $x^2 - 6x = 27$

c $6x^2 = 5x + 4$ **d** $17x - 2x^2 = 21$

e $-5x^2 + 7x = 2$ **f** $2x^2 = 8x - 6$

2 **Solve**, if possible, by completing the square, and check your answers graphically. Leave your answers exact.

a $x^2 + 6x - 59 = 0$ **b** $x^2 + 12x = -23$

c $x^2 - 10x + 26 = 8$ **d** $3x^2 + 6x = 7$

e $2x^2 = 8x - 3$ **f** $2x^2 - 5x - 3 = 0$

3 **Solve**, if possible, using the quadratic formula, giving answers to 2 d.p., and check your answers graphically.

a $x^2 + 10x + 13 = 0$ **b** $x^2 - 5x = 7$

c $3x^2 = 1 + 3x$ **d** $x^2 - \frac{1}{3}x = 2$

e $4x^2 + 8x = 1$ **f** $-3x^2 + 2x = 12$

4 **Solve**, if possible, using the most appropriate method. Leave your answer exact and completely simplified. Check your answers graphically.

a $(x+3)^2 + x^2 - 9x = 8$ **b** $\frac{x^2}{2} + \frac{5}{2} = -x$

c $(x-2)^2 - 11 = 0$ **d** $2x(x-1) - 5 = -x^2$

e $(2x-6)^2 = 12$

f $(2x+5)(x-1) = (x-3)(x+8)$

Solve these next problems using the most efficient method. Round your answers appropriately.

Problem solving

5 The length of a rectangle is 3 cm greater than its width. Its area is 108 cm². **Find** the dimensions of the rectangle.

6 The length of a rectangle is 2 cm more than 3 times its width. Its area is 85 cm². **Find** the dimensions of the rectangle.

7 The length of a rectangle is 1 cm more than its width. If the length of the rectangle is doubled, the area of the rectangle increases by 30 cm². **Find** the dimensions of the original rectangle.

8 A rectangular lawn measures 8 m by 4 m and is surrounded by a border of uniform width. The combined area of the lawn and border is 165 m². **Find** the width of the border.

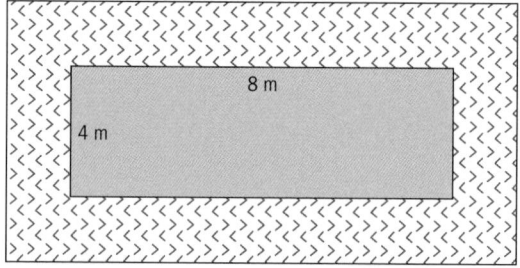

9 The height of a right-angled triangle is 5 cm less than its base. The area of the triangle is 42 cm². **Find** its base and height.

10 One side of a triangle is 2 cm shorter than the hypotenuse and 7 cm longer than the third side. **Find** the side lengths of the triangle.

11 **Find** two consecutive odd integers whose product is 99.

12 The square of a number exceeds the number itself by 72. **Find** the number.

13 **Find** two consecutive positive integers such that the square of the first less 17 equals 4 times the second.

14 The height h in meters of a football kicked into the air can be modelled by the function $h(t) = -4.9t^2 + 24.5t + 1$ where t is in seconds.

  a **Find** how long after being kicked it takes the ball to hit the ground.

  b **Determine** how long it takes the object to reach a height of 20 meters.

  c For how long was it above this height?

15 The profits of an international ticket agency can be modelled by the function $P(t) = -37t^2 + 1258t - 7700$, where t is the number of tickets sold and P is in dollars. **Determine** the ticket price that would leave the agency no profit or loss.

16 A square piece of cardboard is to be formed into a box. After 5 cm squares are cut from each corner and the sides are folded up, the box will have a volume of 400 cm³. **Find** the length of a side of the original piece of cardboard.

Review in context
Scientific and technical innovation

Quadratic equations can model the path of a projectile through space, and its height above the ground at different times. A projectile is any object that is propelled with force through the air, such as kicking a soccer ball, doing the high jump or even launching fireworks.

Quadratic models of projectile motion take into account three factors:

- the initial height off the ground
- the initial velocity with which the object moves
- the acceleration due to gravity that affects all falling objects.

The formula for calculating the height above ground is:

$$h(t) = \frac{1}{2}(-9.8)t^2 + V_i t + h_i$$

where the acceleration due to gravity (on Earth) is -9.8 m/s^2, V_i is the initial velocity, and h_i is the initial height.

Problem solving

1 A model rocket is launched from 2.5 m above the ground with initial velocity 49 m/s **Use** the quadratic model $h(t) = \frac{1}{2}(-9.8)t^2 + 49t + 2.5$ to **determine** how long it takes for it to land.

2 An object is launched directly upward at 24 m/s from a platform 30 m high.

a Write the quadratic model for this object.

b **Determine:**

   i the maximum height the object reaches

   ii how long the object takes to reach this height

   iii how long the object takes to strike the ground again.

3 A projectile is launched from ground level directly upward at 39.2 m/s. **Determine** how long the projectile's altitude is 34.3 m or above.

4 Suppose NASA wants to launch a probe on the surface of the Moon, which has one sixth the gravitational pull of the Earth (and therefore one sixth the acceleration due to gravity). The height of the launcher is 0.5 m.

a On the Moon, how long would it take the probe to reach a height of 60 m if its initial velocity is 15 m/s?

b If the initial velocity is 24.5 m/s, how much longer will it be in the air on the Moon compared to a similar launch on Earth? (It is launched from the surface in both places.)

c **Explain** how you think scientists test their hypotheses about the behavior of objects on the Moon (or Mars) when the force of gravity there is so different than on Earth.

Reflect and discuss 7

How have you explored the statement of inquiry? Give specific examples.

Statement of inquiry:

Discovering relationships in patterns and studying equivalence between representations can lead to better models.

4 Mathematically speaking

Statement of inquiry:

Understanding health and validating lifestyle choices results from using logical representations and systems.

Key concept:

Logic is a method of reasoning and a system of principles used to build arguments and reach conclusions.

F How can representing language with symbols facilitate the operations?

Representation is the manner in which something is presented.

Is a picture worth a thousand words?

$ABCD$ is a quadrilateral. AB is parallel to CD and perpendicular to BC.

Angle $ADC = 70°$. Find angle DAB.

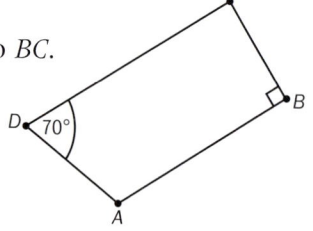

- How does drawing a diagram help you solve this problem?
- Could you solve it without a diagram?

C How do axioms enhance the understanding of logic?

Axiomatic system for number

You have been working with the real number system since you first learned to count. The number system is based on a set of axioms, which are assumed to be true for real numbers.

Verify the axioms below for real numbers x, y and z.

Addition and multiplication are:

Commutative: $x + y = y + x$
$xy = yx$

Associative: $(x + y) + z = x + (y + z)$
$(xy)z = x(yz)$

Distributive: $x(y + z) = xy + xz$

These axioms form the basis for all of your number skills.

D What factors validate our lifestyle decisions?

Validation is the use of well-founded, logical mathematics to come to a true and accurate conclusion or a reasonable interpretation of results.

Validation in medical research

Pharmaceutical companies are continually trying to produce new medicines to treat as-yet incurable conditions, or to treat curable conditions more effectively. Before a new drug can go on sale, the company needs to justify that the drug is safe and effective. To do this, they run clinical trials to test the drugs on humans and collect evidence on positive results as well as negative side effects.

All clinical trials have to be approved by a scientific and ethical committee. The researchers must justify that the volunteers in the trial will not be exposed to unnecessary risk, and that the new drug can reasonably be expected to improve patient care.

Ecosystems

When an ecosystem is in balance, all the living organisms within it are healthy and capable of reproducing themselves. If one part of the ecosystem is damaged – either by natural events or human activity – every other element of the ecosystem is affected.

Forest fires cause widespread destruction, but fire is a natural and vital element in some forest ecosystems. After a fire, more sunlight can reach the forest floor, which is free from dead wood and leaf litter and has increased nutrient levels from the ash. This creates perfect conditions for some trees and plants to thrive. Some species have evolved to withstand fire (or sometimes even rely on it) as part of their life cycle. For example, sand pine cones open to disperse their seeds only in intense heat.

Global context: Identities and relationships

Exploration: Explore personal and physical health and good lifestyle choices

📖 Launch additional digital resources for this unit.

4.1 Set operations and Venn diagrams

Global context: Identities and relationships

Related concepts: Validity

LOGIC

Objectives

- Finding the intersection and union of sets
- Drawing Venn diagrams to represent real-life situations
- Interpreting Venn diagrams to solve real-life problems
- Applying the language of sets to different areas of mathematics
- Using the language of sets to model real-life problems

Inquiry questions

F
- What are set operations?
- How do you represent sets and their operations?

C
- Can diagrams and drawings be used to validate mathematical laws?

D
- How does a Venn diagram help to interpret a real-life situation?
- How useful are sets and Venn diagrams in solving real-life problems?

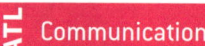

ATL Communication

Organize and depict information logically

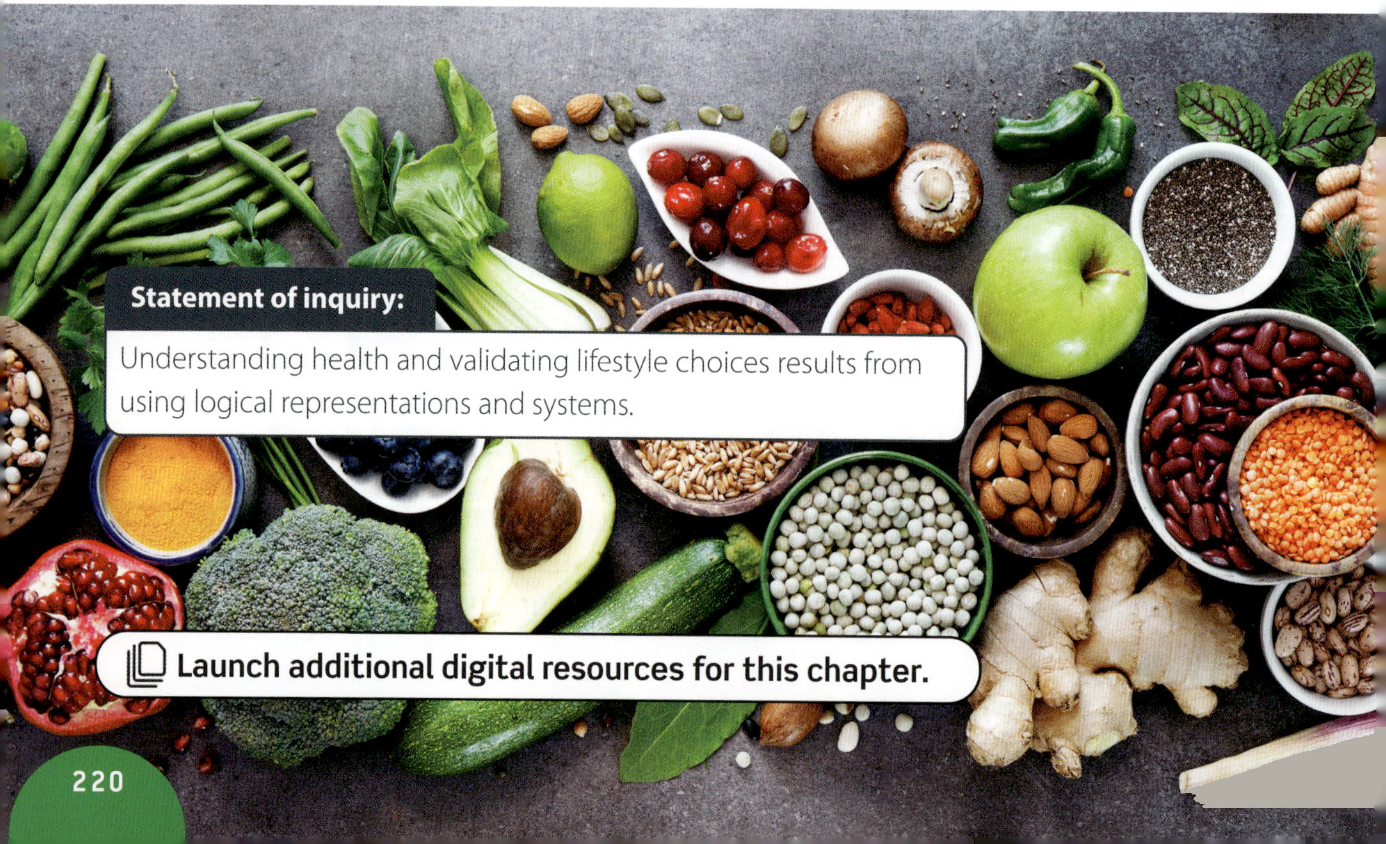

Statement of inquiry:

Understanding health and validating lifestyle choices results from using logical representations and systems.

Launch additional digital resources for this chapter.

You should already know how to:

• list prime numbers between two given numbers	**1** What are the prime numbers between 1 and 30?
• find factors and multiples of integers	**2** What are the factors of 3 between 1 and 31? What are the multiples of 4 between 1 and 31?
• find the complement of a set	**3** If $A = \{$Odd numbers$\}$, what is A'?

F ## Set operations

- What are set operations?
- How do you represent sets and their operations?

You have learned an operation used on sets, namely the complement of a set. Just like arithmetic operations, the branch of mathematics called Set Theory also has its own operations. The complement of a set, A', is defined as the elements in the universal set that are not in set A. There are other set operations that you will learn about in the following exploration.

Exploration 1

1 $U = \{$cats, dogs, monkeys, zebras, kangaroos, horses$\}$

$A = \{$cats, dogs, horses$\}$

$B = \{$cats, monkeys, zebras, horses$\}$

$C = \{$dogs, kangaroos, horses$\}$

Create the following sets, but remember that you use an element only once in a set:

a The set of elements common to both B and C.

b The set of elements in either A or C, or both.

c The set of elements common to all three sets A, B and C.

d The set of elements in either of the sets A, B and C, or all 3 sets.

2 $U = \{x \mid x \in \mathbb{Z}, 0 \leq x \leq 20\}$

$A = \{$factors of 3$\}$

$B = \{$multiples of 4$\}$

$C = \{$prime numbers$\}$.

Create the following sets:

a Write out the elements of sets U, A, B, and C.

b The set of elements common to A and B.

c The set of elements common to both A and C.

d The set of elements in either A or C, or both.

e The set of elements common to A, B, and C.

▶ Continued on next page

f The set of elements in both A and C'.

g The set of elements in either A' or B, or both.

h The set of elements that are not in the set of elements common to both A and C.

i The set of elements that are not in the set of elements common to both B and C.

j The set of elements that are not in the set of elements in either A or C.

Reflect and discuss 1

- Do you think that it would be convenient to have symbols for the operations between sets, 'elements common to' and 'elements in either set'?

- How do symbols in mathematics facilitate doing mathematics?

There are symbols for the sets you have found in the previous exploration. To express the set of elements common to both A and B, mathematicians use the symbol $\cap$ between the sets. So, to find the set of elements common to both A and B, you would write $A \cap B$. This is read as the *intersection* of sets A and B. In the same way, the symbol for the elements that are in either A or B, or both, is $A \cup B$. This is read as the *union* of sets A and B.

Just as you use arithmetic operations to manipulate numbers, sets also have their own operations.

Union and intersection of sets

- Union: $A \cup B = \{x \,|\, x \in A \text{ or } x \in B\}$
- Intersection: $A \cap B = \{x \,|\, x \in A \text{ and } x \in B\}$

If $A = \{1, 2, 3\}$ and $B = \{2, 3, 4, 5\}$, the set that contains all the elements that are in both A and B without repeating any of them is $C = \{1, 2, 3, 4, 5\}$. Set C is the **union** of sets A and B, and is written $A \cup B$.

The set that contains the elements that both sets have in common is $D = \{2, 3\}$. D is the **intersection** of sets A and B, and is written $A \cap B$.

Example 1

If $U = \{1, 2, 3, \ldots, 10\}$, $A = \{2, 4, 6, 8\}$, $B = \{2, 3, 5, 7\}$ and $C = \{1, 5, 9\}$, find:

a $A \cap C$

b $A \cup B'$

c $(A' \cap B)'$

d $(A \cup B \cup C)'$

a $A \cap C = \varnothing$ ——————————————— A and C have no elements in common.

b $B' = \{1, 4, 6, 8, 9, 10\}$ ——————————————— First find B'.

$A \cup B' = \{1, 2, 4, 6, 8, 9, 10\}$

c $A' = \{1, 3, 5, 7, 9, 10\}$

$A' \cap B = \{3, 5, 7\}$ ——————————— First find $A' \cap B$. $(A' \cap B)'$ is made up of the elements in U that are not in $A' \cap B$.

$(A' \cap B)' = \{1, 2, 4, 6, 8, 9, 10\}$

d $A \cup B \cup C = \{1, 2, 3, 4, 5, 6, 7, 8, 9\}$

$(A \cup B \cup C)' = \{10\}$

Practice 1

ATL

1 If $U = \left\{x \mid x \in \mathbb{Z}^+, 1 \leq x \leq 20\right\}$, $A = \{2, 4, 8, \ldots, 20\}$,
$B = \{1, 3, 5, \ldots, 19\}$ and $C = \left\{x \mid x \in \text{primes}, 1 \leq x \leq 20\right\}$, find:

a $A \cap B$　　**b** $A \cup B$　　**c** $A' \cap C$　　**d** $(A \cap C)'$　　**e** $(A' \cup B)'$

2 If $U = \mathbb{Z}$, $R = \left\{x \mid x \in \mathbb{Z}^+, x < 10\right\}$, $S = \{x \mid -5 < x < 5\}$
and $T = \{x \mid x \in \mathbb{N}; x \leq 15\}$, find:

a $R \cap S$　　**b** $R \cup T$　　**c** $R' \cap T$　　**d** $S' \cap T$　　**e** $(R \cap S)' \cap T$

Problem solving

3 The universal set is $U = \{11, 12, 13, 14, 15, 16, 17, 18, 19, 20\}$.
Write three subsets F, G and H such that:

- $n(F \cap G) = 2$
- $F \cap H = \varnothing$
- $G' = \{x \mid x \text{ is odd}, 11 \leq x \leq 19\}$

Reflect and discuss 2

For any two sets, A and B, explain why the intersection $A \cap B$ is a subset of their union $A \cup B$.

Try with any two sets A and B. Can you generalize your result?

C Venn diagrams

- Can diagrams and drawings be used to validate mathematical laws?

Venn diagrams

In a Venn diagram, a rectangle represents the universal set.

Circles represent subsets of the universal set.

It is important that you use the forms of representation correctly – for example, remembering to include the universal set in your Venn diagrams, or using curly brackets when listing the elements of a set.

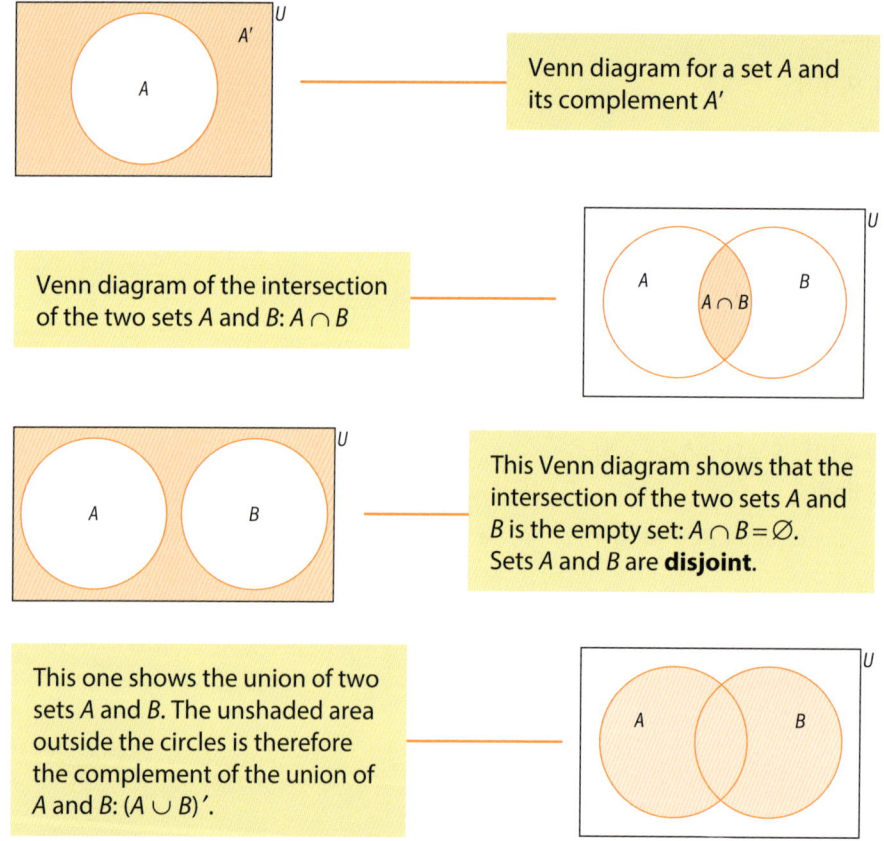

Venn diagram for a set A and its complement A'

Venn diagram of the intersection of the two sets A and B: $A \cap B$

This Venn diagram shows that the intersection of the two sets A and B is the empty set: $A \cap B = \varnothing$. Sets A and B are **disjoint**.

This one shows the union of two sets A and B. The unshaded area outside the circles is therefore the complement of the union of A and B: $(A \cup B)'$.

Exploration 2

1 Draw two Venn diagrams: in the first one shade the region that represents the set $A' \cap B'$; in the second diagram shade the region that represents the set $(A \cup B)'$. Describe the relationship between these two sets mathematically.

2 Draw two Venn diagrams: in the first one shade the region that represents the set $(A \cap B)'$; in the second diagram shade the region that represents the set $A' \cup B'$. Describe the relationship between these two sets mathematically.

3 Draw a Venn diagram to show that for any two sets, A and B, the intersection $A \cap B$ is a subset of their union $A \cup B$. Do you think it was easier to prove this using reasoning in Reflect and discuss 2, or by drawing a diagram?

Reflect and discuss 3

- How many different ways have you represented the set $A' \cup B'$ in Exploration 2?

- What can you say about $A' \cup B'$ and $(A \cap B)'$?

- How has representing sets using a Venn diagram helped you discover new information about sets?

The relationships you have discovered so far by using Venn diagrams are called De Morgan's Laws, named after the British mathematician Augustus De Morgan. They are used extensively in the fields of circuitry and electronics, as well as in the field of logic.

Example 2

Draw Venn diagrams to represent these sets or relationship between sets.

a $B \subseteq A$ **b** $A' \cup B$ **c** $A \cap B'$ **d** $A \cap B \cap C$ **e** $(A \cap B) \cup C$

a $B \subseteq A$

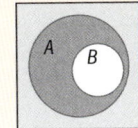

Draw a rectangle representing the universal set. Set B is completely contained in A.

b $A' \cup B$

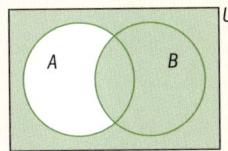

Shade the area that contains everything that is not in A, together with all of B.

c $A \cap B'$

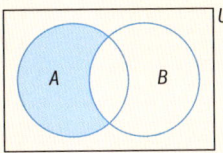

The shaded area represents what A and the complement of B have in common.

d $A \cap B \cap C$

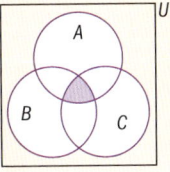

The shaded area shows the intersection of all three sets.

e $(A \cap B) \cup C$

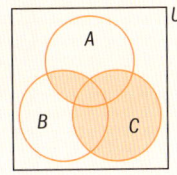

Shade the intersection of A and B first, then shade all of C.

When drawing Venn diagrams it can be useful to shade one set using vertical lines and the other using horizontal lines. The union will be the total area shaded and the intersection of the sets is where the lines cross.

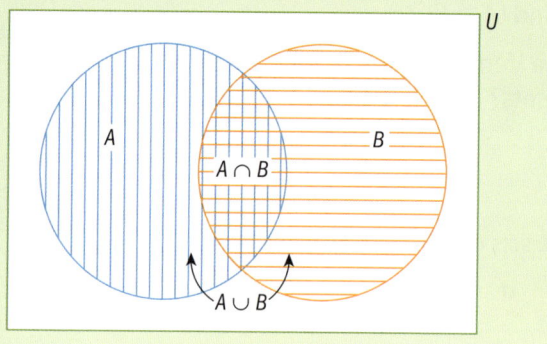

Practice 2

ATL

1 Draw Venn diagrams to represent each set.

a $(A \cap B)'$

b $A \cup (A \cap B)$

c $(A' \cap B)'$

d $(A' \cup B')'$

e $A \cup (B \cap C)$

f $(A \cap B)' \cup C$

g $A \cap (B \cup C)'$

h $(A \cap B) \cup (A \cap C) \cup (B \cap C)$

Problem solving

2 Write the set that the shaded part of each Venn diagram represents.

a
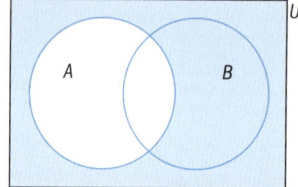

b
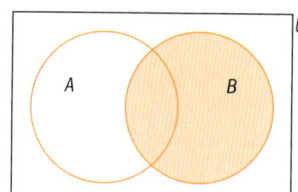

c
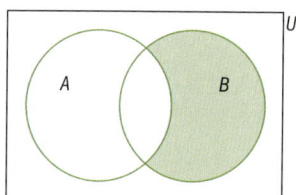

d
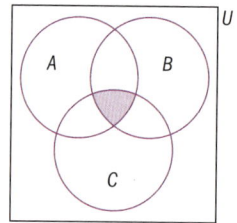

Venn diagrams are named after an English mathematician, John Venn. This stained glass window in Cambridge University commemorates his achievements.

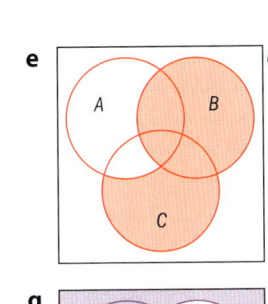

e

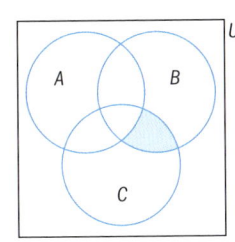

f

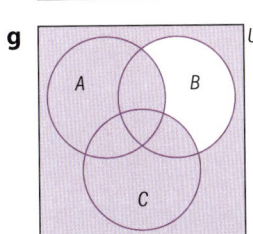

g

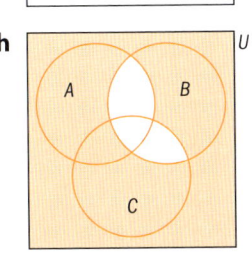

h

You are already familiar with the properties of real numbers under the binary operations of addition and multiplication. In the following exploration you will determine which of these properties are also valid under the set operations of intersection and union.

Exploration 3

1 By drawing a Venn diagram for each side of the equals sign in the statements below, show that the following properties hold for set operations:

a $A \cap B = B \cap A$ **b** $A \cup B = B \cup A$ ——— Commutative laws

c $A \cap (B \cap C) = (A \cap B) \cap C$ **d** $A \cup (B \cup C) = (A \cup B) \cup C$ ——— Associative laws

e $A \cap (B \cup C) = (A \cap B) \cup (A \cap C)$ **f** $A \cup (B \cap C) = (A \cup B) \cap (A \cup C)$ ——— Distributive laws

2 The additive identity of the real numbers is 0 since $n + 0 = 0 + n = n$ and the inverse of n is $-n$ since $n + (-n) = (-n) + n = 0$.

The multiplicative identity of m is 1 since $m \times 1 = 1 \times m = m$ and the inverse of m is $\frac{1}{m}$ since $m \times \frac{1}{m} = \frac{1}{m} \times m = 1$ $(m \neq 0)$.

Determine whether or not there is an identity and inverse for the operations $\cup$ and $\cap$.

Find sets B and C such that $A \cup B = B \cup A = A$ and $A \cap C = C \cap A = A$. B and C are the two identities.

Find if sets E and F exist such that $A \cup E = E \cup A = B$ and $A \cap F = F \cap A = C$. E and F, if they exist, are the inverses.

3 Summarize the properties of the set operations union and intersection.

D Modelling real-life problems using Venn diagrams

- How does a Venn diagram help to interpret a real-life situation?
- How useful are sets and Venn diagrams in solving real-life problems?

Venn diagrams are used to model and solve problems in fields such as market research, biology, and social science, where 'overlapping' information needs to be sorted.

Example 3

A market research company surveys 100 students and learns that 75 of them own a television (T) and 45 own a bicycle (B). 35 students own both a television and a bicycle. Draw a Venn diagram to show this information.

a Find how many students own either a television or a bicycle, or both.

b Find how many own neither a television nor a bicycle.

c Explain how your diagram shows that 50 students own either a television or a bicycle, but not both.

Set theory is used by online shopping search engines. Data on products for sale is split into sets so that your search query will get a response more quickly.

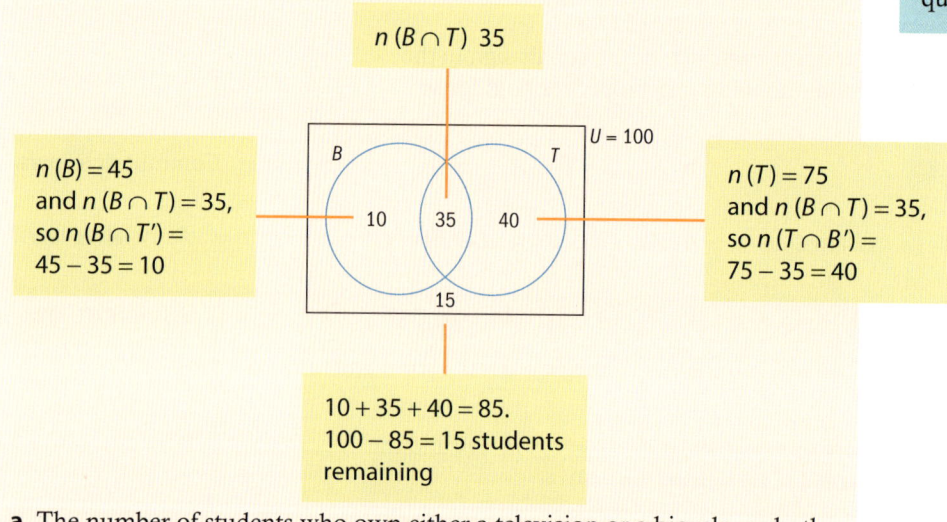

$n(B \cap T)$ 35

$n(B) = 45$
and $n(B \cap T) = 35$,
so $n(B \cap T') =$
$45 - 35 = 10$

$n(T) = 75$
and $n(B \cap T) = 35$,
so $n(T \cap B') =$
$75 - 35 = 40$

$10 + 35 + 40 = 85$.
$100 - 85 = 15$ students
remaining

a The number of students who own either a television or a bicycle, or both is $n(B \cup T) = 85$.

b The number of students who own neither a television nor a bicycle is $n(B \cup T)' = 15$.

c The number of students who own either a television or a bicycle but not both can be seen as the union of the two sets less the intersection, or $10 + 40 = 50$.

Practice 3

Objective: **C.** Communicating
v. organize information using a logical structure

*These questions encourage students to use Venn diagrams (and a table in Question 1)
to organize information logically. The students should be able to draw and interpret
Venn diagrams.*

1 a i For the Venn diagram, describe the
characteristics of only whales, of only fish,
and those of both whales and fish.

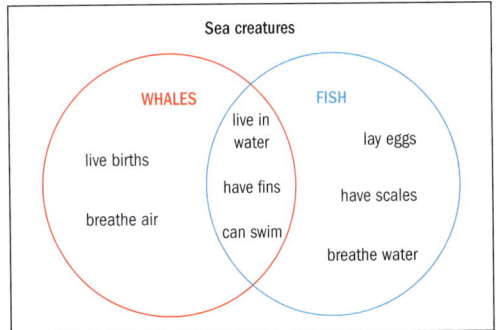

ii Explain how the diagram has helped you with your
descriptions and whether a different form could be
more useful.

b i Below is a table describing some characteristics of
whales, fish, and shrimp. Create a Venn diagram
that illustrates these characteristics. Make sure to
choose an appropriate universal set.

	live births	fins	have scales	lay eggs	live in water	breathe air	breathe water	have legs
whales	✓	✓			✓	✓		
fish		✓	✓	✓	✓		✓	
shrimp				✓	✓		✓	✓

ii Explain whether the table form or the Venn diagram form is best to
illustrate the given information.

2 In a year group of 50 students, 18 are enrolled in Music, 26 in Art, and
2 in both Music and Art. By drawing a Venn diagram, determine how
many students are not enrolled in either Music or Art.

3 In a school of 350 students, 75 are involved in community service
projects, 205 in athletics, and 62 are involved in both. By drawing a
Venn diagram, determine how many students are involved in either one
of these two activities.

4 In a school cafeteria at lunchtime, 93 students chose a soft drink and
47 students chose bottled water. 25 students chose both drinks. If each
student chose one of these drinks, determine the total number of students
in the cafeteria by drawing a Venn diagram.

5 Of 150 new university students, 85 signed up for Mathematics and 70 for
Physics, while 50 signed up for both subjects. By drawing a Venn diagram,
determine how many students signed up for:

a only Mathematics

b only Physics

c neither Mathematics nor Physics.

6 There are 30 students enrolled in three different school clubs: chess, archery
and cookery. Of these, 5 students are in all three clubs, 6 of them are only in
the cookery club, 2 are in chess and cookery but not archery, 15 belong to
cookery in total, 2 are only in chess, and 3 are only in archery. By drawing a
Venn diagram, determine how many students are in:

a the archery and cookery clubs only

b the chess club.

7 In a class of 32 students, 5 live in the school town and travel to school by bus, and they have school lunches. 3 live in the school town and travel to school by bus, but do not have school lunches. 9 students do not live in the school town, do not travel to school by bus, and do not have school lunches. 11 students live in the school town and have school lunches. A total of 16 students live in the school town. 9 students travel to school by bus and have school lunches. 13 students travel to school by bus. By drawing a Venn diagram, determine how many students in total have school lunches.

Problem solving

8 The Venn diagrams below represent participants in an after school sports program. The students can choose to select table tennis (T), basketball (B), or squash (S).

a 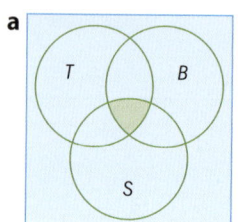 **b** 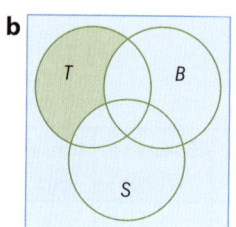 **c**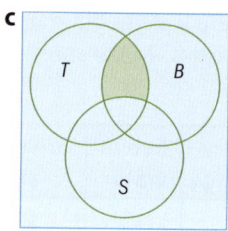

Write in words what each diagram represents.

- -

Exploration 4

1 $n(U) = 105$, $n(A) = 37$, and $n(B) = 84$. All of the elements of U are either in A or B or both.

a Draw a Venn diagram showing A, B and U.

b Find a rule connecting the number of elements in $A \cup B$ with the number of elements in sets A, B, and the intersection of A and B.

c Justify your rule.

2 Apply your rule to the following situation. Your student council held a vote on which charity to support. A mobile library received 47 votes, and a neighborhood watch committee received 36 votes. 24 students voted for both charities. Determine how many students actually voted.

Reflect and discuss 4

In Exploration 4:

- How have you used sets to model the situation in step **2**?

- Why was it easier to consider sets of students rather than considering the students individually?

- What set operation models the fact that some students voted for both charities?

Working with one or more of your classmates, discuss how Venn diagrams can be used to organize and categorize some of the following situations: your school timetable, your household chores, your homework for different subjects, your test schedules. Create two Venn diagrams with at least three circles to illustrate the different situations you have chosen.

Summary

Union and intersection of sets

- Union: $A \cup B = \{x \,|\, x \in A \text{ or } x \in B\}$
- Intersection: $A \cap B = \{x \,|\, x \in A \text{ and } x \in B\}$

Mixed practice

1 $U = \{x \,|\, x \in \mathbb{N}\}$,
$A = \{x \,|\, x \in \mathbb{N}, x \text{ is a multiple of } 7\}$,
$B = \{1, 3, 5, 7, 9, \ldots, 19\}$ and
$C = \{x \,|\, x \in \text{primes } 5 < x \le 20\}$.

Find:

a $A \cap B$

b $A' \cap C$

c $A \cap B'$

d $(A \cap C)'$

2 Create Venn diagrams to represent the sets:

a $A \cap B'$ **b** $A' \cup B$

3 The table shows the facilities at three hotels in a rcsort.

	Hotel A	Hotel B	Hotel C
Pool	✓		✓
Bar	✓	✓	✓
Jacuzzi		✓	
Sauna	✓		
Tennis		✓	✓
Gym			✓

Draw a Venn diagram to represent this information.

4 Create a Venn diagram to illustrate the relationships of the following number sets:
$\mathbb{R} = \{\text{real numbers}\}$, $\mathbb{Z} = \{\text{integers}\}$, $\mathbb{Q} = \{\text{rational numbers}\}$, $I = \{\text{irrational numbers}\}$, $\mathbb{N} = \{\text{natural numbers}\}$, and $P = \{\text{prime numbers}\}$.

5 Create a Venn diagram illustrating the relationships of the following geometric figures:
$U = \{\text{all quadrilaterals}\}$, $P = \{\text{parallelograms}\}$, $R = \{\text{rectangles}\}$, $S = \{\text{squares}\}$, $K = \{\text{kites}\}$, $T = \{\text{trapezoids}\}$.

6 If $U = \{-10, -9, \ldots, 9, 10\}$, $A = \{0, 1, 2, \ldots, 9\}$, $B = \{-9, -8, \ldots, 0\}$ and $C = \{-5, -4, \ldots, 4, 5\}$, **list** the elements of the following sets:

a $A \cap B$ **b** $(B \cup C)'$

c $(A \cup B) \cap C$ **d** $A' \cap (B \cup C)$

e $(A \cap B) \cup (A \cap C)$

7 Determine whether the following statements are true or false. If false, explain why.

a $0 \in \mathbb{Q}$

b $\{\text{primes}\} \subseteq \{\text{odd integers}\}$

c If $U = \mathbb{N}$, then $(\mathbb{Z}^+ \cap \mathbb{N})' = \{0\}$

d $2 \subseteq \{\text{primes}\}$

Problem solving

8 In a school sports day, medals were awarded as follows: 36 in running, 12 in high jump, and 18 in discus. The medals were awarded to a total of 45 students, and only 4 students received medals in all three events. **Determine** how many students received medals in exactly two out of three events.

9 A survey of 39 university students found:

- 10 worked part-time while studying
- 18 received financial help from home
- 19 withdrew money from their savings as needed
- 2 financed themselves from all three sources
- 12 received financial help from home only

- 5 received financial help from home and withdrew money from savings
- 6 financed themselves only by working part-time and withdrawing money from savings.

Determine how many students:

a did not finance themselves using any of the three resources

b worked part-time and received money from home

c received financial help from home and withdrew money from their savings

d financed themselves using only one of the three ways surveyed.

Review in context

Identities and relationships

1 Below is a Venn diagram used by medical researchers showing the genes associated with different brain diseases.

The sets represent the number of genes associated with:

A = {Alzheimer's disease}
M = {multiple sclerosis}
S = {stroke}
G = {brain diseases}

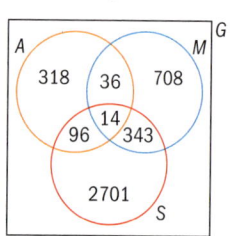

Using this diagram:

a **Calculate** how many genes in total are associated with each of the three diseases: Alzheimer's, multiple sclerosis, and stroke.

b **State** how many genes all three diseases share in common.

c **Explain** how this diagram might be useful to medical researchers.

Problem solving

2 Venn diagrams are widely used to show 'overlapping' concepts. Here are two fields from Sociology and Environmental Science where a Venn diagram can be used to illustrate the interrelation of key concepts.

In each example, **identify** sets and **draw** a Venn diagram to illustrate the information given.

a According to Plato there are many propositions. Some of these are true and some are beliefs (some may be neither). Only true beliefs can be justified and those he defines as knowledge.

b There are three main types of development: environmental, social and economic. Development that is both social and economic is equitable, that which is economic and environmental is viable, and that which is environmental and social is bearable. Development that is all three of these is sustainable.

3 Scientists have studied the genome of a number of organisms. The genome contains all the information used to build and maintain that organism. For medical researchers, knowing that different species share particular genes will enable them to unlock the secrets of countless diseases.

The Venn diagram shows the genes of four species: human, mouse, chicken, and zebrafish.

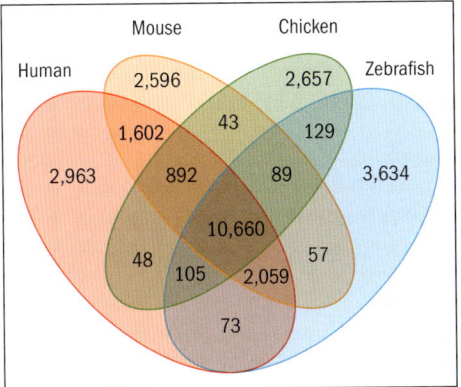

Using the diagram:

a **Determine** how many genes are shared by all four species.

b **Determine** how many genes does a human have in total.

c **Determine** how many genes are shared by human and mouse, by human and chicken, and by human and zebrafish.

d **Determine** the percentage of genes shared by the human and each of these three species.

e If you were a medical scientist and you wanted to conduct research into a species that was genetically closest to the human, which of the three – mouse, chicken or zebrafish – would you choose?

Reflect and discuss 6

How have you explored the statement of inquiry? Give specific examples.

Statement of inquiry:

Understanding health and validating lifestyle choices results from using logical representations and systems.

4.2 Probability of single and combined events

Global context: Identities and relationships

Related concept: Representation

Objectives

- Understanding and using formal probability axioms and notation
- Representing sample spaces in tables, lists and diagrams
- Drawing tree diagrams, Venn diagrams and two-way tables
- Calculating probabilities from Venn diagrams and two-way tables
- Using tree diagrams to calculate probabilities with and without replacement
- Understanding informal ideas of randomness

Inquiry questions

- What are the axioms of probability?
- What are the different ways of representing a sample space?
- How do you calculate the probability of an event?

- How do you calculate the probability of combined events?
- What are the advantages and disadvantages of the different probability representations?

- Does randomness affect the decisions we make?

ATL Communication

Understand and use mathematical notation

Statement of inquiry:

Understanding health and validating lifestyle choices results from using logical representations and systems.

📖 **Launch additional digital resources for this chapter.**

You should already know how to:

• calculate simple probabilities	**1** This spinner is spun once. What is the probability that it lands on
	  a blue
	  b yellow
	  c blue or white
	  d blue or yellow
	  e not yellow?

• use set notation, specifically the complement of a set	**2 a** Using set notation, write the set P of prime numbers less than 10.
	  b Let the universal set $U = \{1, 2, 3, 4, 5, 6, 7, 8, 9, 10\}$. Write down the elements of P'.
	  c Write down $n(P)$ and $n(P')$.

• draw a Venn diagram	**3** In a group of 24 children, 10 of them like bananas, 16 of them like apples and 7 children like both. Draw a Venn diagram to represent this information.

F The axiomatic system for probability

- What are the axioms of probability?
- What are the different ways of representing a sample space?
- How do you calculate the probability of an event?

Probability theory determines the likelihood of an event happening. For an event A, probability assigns a numerical value P(A), called the probability of the event A. P(A) is a measure of the likelihood or chance that A occurs.

Probability is a system which satisfies a set of axioms.

> A *system* is a group of interrelated elements. An axiomatic system is governed by a set of axioms or rules. Everything in the system obeys the rules.

Exploration 1

1 Use these probability terms to describe the probability of each event listed below.

a You will get full marks on your next English test.

    (certain) (very likely)

b You will be given homework tonight.

    (likely) (even chance)

c The last meal you ate was breakfast.

d It will snow tomorrow.

    (unlikely) (very unlikely)

e When you add 2 and 2 you will get 5.

f Brazil will win the next World Cup.

    (impossible)

g The Queen of Denmark will come to your maths class tomorrow.

h The sun will come up in the morning.

> We use probability in many applications, including weather forecasting, science, social science, philosophy and psychology.

▶ Continued on next page

2 Suggest approximate numerical values for the probability of each event in step **1**.

3 In a raffle, a total of 500 tickets are sold. Find the probability that you win the prize if you buy:

a 10 tickets   **b** 50 tickets

c 0 tickets   **d** 500 tickets

4 Describe each event in step **3** with a probability term (like those in step **1**).

Reflect and discuss 1

- Can you think of real-life events where the probability of the event occurring would be 0?

- Can you think of real-life events where the probability of the event occurring would be 1?

In Exploration 1, you should have seen that that the smallest value a probability can ever take is zero (an impossible event). This is the first axiom of probability.

Axiom 1

For any event A, $P(A) \geq 0$. This means that all probabilities have a value greater than or equal to zero.

An axiom is a statement whose truth we assume without proof.

Exploration 2

A new restaurant in town runs a promotion to generate business. Before a person pays their bill, they are given a sealed envelope with a message inside that either says 'Your meal today is free' or 'Sorry, better luck next time'.

The restaurant owners claim that the chance of a winning message is 1 in 6.

During a one-hour period on the first day, eight customers pay their bill, and three of them get a winning message.

To test that the restaurant's claim is correct, you can set up a simulation. Assume that they are correct and a winning message indeed appears in 1 out of every 6 sealed envelopes. The probability of winning is therefore the same as rolling a six on a fair die.

1 Roll a die 8 times to simulate 8 people paying their bills.

2 Record the number of 6s you roll.

The probability of 1 in 6 is true for any number on a standard die; you could record 3s or 4s, as long as you were consistent.

▶ Continued on next page

3 Repeat this process 30 times. Combine the results for others in a spreadsheet.

Based on the combined results of the simulation:

4 Calculate the percentage of outcomes where 8 bills paid resulted in 3 winners.

5 Calculate the percentage of outcomes with no winners.

6 Deduce the most common number of winners in 8 bills paid.

7 Discuss whether the 8 people who had 3 winners were just lucky. Do you think the restaurant printed too many winning messages?

Your GDC or other software can run simulations that perform the experiment thousands or even millions of times.

Reflect and discuss 2

- Aside from rolling a die, what other way(s) could you have used to simulate the probability of 1 winning message in 6?

- What number of winners from 8 people is most likely?

Simulation is a powerful tool to investigate the probabilities of events and predict what might happen in the future. You can also find probabilities by constructing a sample space for the experiment or situation.

When you flip a standard die, it will land on one of six possible numbers, 1, 2, 3, 4, 5, or 6. This forms the sample space, S, where $S = \{1, 2, 3, 4, 5, 6\}$. When you flip a coin, you can either get heads (H) or tails (T), so $S = \{H, T\}$.

> The sample space S, is a representation of the complete set of all possible outcomes from an experiment. It can be a list, a table or a diagram.

An event that is certain to occur has probability 1. The whole sample space S includes all the possible events, so the probability that one of those events occurs is 1. This is the second axiom of probability.

> **Axiom 2**
>
> For a sample space S, $P(S) = 1$. In other words, the probability of all occurrences is equal to 1.

If you ever calculate a probability which is less than 0 or greater than 1, you have made a mistake.

> A natural consequence of axioms 1 and 2 is that the probability of any event happening is a number between 0 and 1, $0 \leq P(A) \leq 1$.

Example 1

Two fair 6-sided dice are rolled. One die is blue and the other is red.

Represent all the possible outcomes as:

a a list

b a table

c a diagram.

a $S = \{(1,1),(2,1),(3,1),(4,1),(5,1),(6,1),(1,2),(2,2),(3,2),$
$(4,2),(5,2),(6,2),(1,3),(2,3),(3,3),(4,3),(5,3),(6,3),$
$(1,4),(2,4),(3,4),(4,4),(5,4),(6,4),(1,5),(2,5),(3,5),$
$(4,5),(5,5),(6,5),(1,6),(2,6),(3,6),(4,6),(5,6),(6,6)\}$

As a set

b

	1	2	3	4	5	6
1	(1,1)	(1,2)	(1,3)	(1,4)	(1,5)	(1,6)
2	(2,1)	(2,2)	(2,3)	(2,4)	(2,5)	(2,6)
3	(3,1)	(3,2)	(3,3)	(3,4)	(3,5)	(3,6)
4	(4,1)	(4,2)	(4,3)	(4,4)	(4,5)	(4,6)
5	(5,1)	(5,2)	(5,3)	(5,4)	(5,5)	(5,6)
6	(6,1)	(6,2)	(6,3)	(6,4)	(6,5)	(6,6)

As a table

The table is the most common representation of a sample space.

c

As a diagram

Practice 1

Objective C: Communicating
iii Move between different forms of mathematical representation

Make sure you list outcomes systematically and include all the possible outcomes in all your representations of sample spaces.

1 The Scandinavian board game Daldøs uses 4-sided (tetrahedral) dice. The roll of one such die results in a score of I, II, III or IV.

Represent the sample space for rolling two of these dice as a list and as a table.

2 A fair coin is flipped three times.

Define the sample space for this experiment.

For question **2**, make a list of the possible outcomes.

3 Copy and complete this sample space table for the sum of the scores from rolling two 4-sided dice, each with faces numbered 1, 2, 3 and 4.

		2nd die			
		1	2	3	4
1st die	1	2			
	2			5	
	3				
	4			7	

4 A street vendor sells two types of sandwich – a South African Gatsby or a Greek Gyro – and three types of fruit – apple, orange or banana. List the sample space for the possible choices of a sandwich and a piece of fruit.

5 A tetrahedral die (4-sided) and a normal die (6-sided) are rolled simultaneously. Construct a sample space to represent the possible outcomes.

6 Each of two boxes contains five cards numbered 1 to 5. A card is drawn from each box. Draw a sample space to represent the possible outcomes.

7 There are two sets of five cards. One contains the numbers 0 to 4 and the other contains the numbers 2 to 6. You draw a card from each set and multiply the numbers together. Draw a sample space to represent this information.

Problem solving

8 The sample space for an experiment is:

$S = \{(1, H), (2, H), (3, H), (4, H), (1, T), (2, T), (3, T), (4, T)\}$

Describe the experiment.

- -

In rolling a die, $S = \{1, 2, 3, 4, 5, 6\}$. If A is the event 'obtaining the number 3', then $A = \{3\}$. The event 'not obtaining the number 3' is $A' = \{1, 2, 4, 5, 6\}$. It therefore follows that $A \cup A' = S$. Since the probability of obtaining the number 3 is $\frac{1}{6}$, $P(A) = \frac{1}{6}$, the probability of not obtaining the number 3 is $\frac{5}{6}$, $P(A') = \frac{5}{6}$. Clearly, $P(A) + P(A') = 1$, and since $A \cup A' = S$, $P(S) = 1$.

An **event** is a subset of the possible outcomes listed in the sample space.

Probability of event $A = \dfrac{\text{number of ways event } A \text{ can occur}}{\text{total number of possible outcomes}}$

$$P(A) = \frac{n(A)}{n(S)}$$

$P(A)$ represents the probability of event A occurring. $P(A')$ is the probability of A not occurring.

$$P(A) + P(A') = 1$$

Use capital letters for events, like A, B, C and define the event. For example, A = getting the same number on both dice.

Example 2

You roll two 6-sided dice. Calculate the probability of getting:

a the same number on both dice

b two different numbers.

a A = getting the same number on both dice. ——————————— Define the event.

	1	2	3	4	5	6
1	(1,1)	(1,2)	(1,3)	(1,4)	(1,5)	(1,6)
2	(2,1)	(2,2)	(2,3)	(2,4)	(2,5)	(2,6)
3	(3,1)	(3,2)	(3,3)	(3,4)	(3,5)	(3,6)
4	(4,1)	(4,2)	(4,3)	(4,4)	(4,5)	(4,6)
5	(5,1)	(5,2)	(5,3)	(5,4)	(5,5)	(5,6)
6	(6,1)	(6,2)	(6,3)	(6,4)	(6,5)	(6,6)

Identify the outcomes with the same number on both dice.

$$P(A) = \frac{6}{36} = \frac{1}{6}$$

b A' = getting different numbers on the two dice. ———————

The outcomes with two different numbers are in the set A', the complement of A.

$$P(A') = \frac{30}{36} = \frac{5}{6}$$

Count all the other outcomes …

$$P(A') = 1 - \frac{1}{6} = \frac{5}{6}$$

… or use $P(A) + P(A') = 1$

Practice 2

Use your sample spaces from Practice 1 to answer these questions.

1 a Calculate the probability of getting two 4s when you roll two 4-sided dice.

   b Calculate the probability of not getting two 4s when you roll two 4-sided dice.

2 Two tetrahedral dice are rolled and their scores are added.

   a Calculate the probability of getting a sum of 5.

   b Calculate the probability of getting a sum not equal to 5.

3 A fair coin is flipped three times. Calculate the probability of getting:

   a three heads

   b two heads in any order

   c no heads.

Non-cubical dice are commonly used in role-playing games and trading card games. The numerals 6 and 9 often have a dot or line below them to indicate what value they represent.

Probability diagrams

- How do you calculate the probability of combined events?
- What are the advantages and disadvantages of different probability representations?
- Do all probability events occur simultaneously?

Exploration 3

1 a Write down the sample space for rolling a 4-sided die and flipping a fair coin.

  b Based on your sample space, calculate the probability of rolling a 1 and flipping tails.

  c How does your answer to **1b** relate to the probability of rolling a 1 and the probability of flipping tails?

2 a Write down the sample space for rolling two 4-sided dice.

  b Based on your sample space, calculate the probability of rolling an even number on the first die and a 3 on the second one.

  c State how your answer to **2b** relates to the probability of rolling an even number and the probability of rolling a 3.

3 Determine whether the probability of either event is affected by the outcome of the other event.

A tree diagram is a representation of a sample space, so you can see all the possible outcomes and calculate the probabilities of more than one event.

Example 3

By drawing a tree diagram, calculate the probability of rolling an odd number on both of two 6-sided dice.

1st event: rolling the 1st die.
2nd event: rolling the 2nd die.

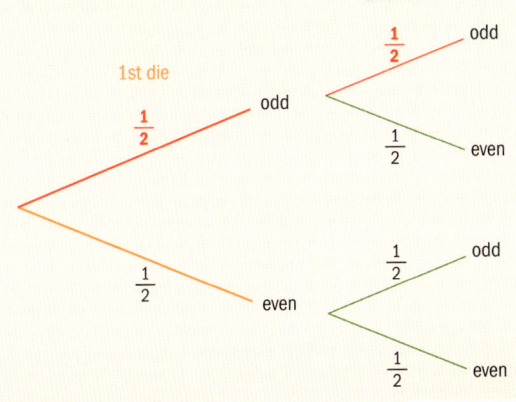

Draw a pair of branches to represent the two outcomes (odd or even) for rolling the 1st die.

For each outcome on the 1st die, draw the two possible outcomes for the 2nd die.

There are three odd numbers (1, 3 and 5) and six possible outcomes.

$P(\text{odd}) = \frac{3}{6} = \frac{1}{2}$

$P(\text{even}) = 1 - \frac{1}{2} = \frac{1}{2}$

$P(\text{odd, odd}) = \frac{1}{2} \times \frac{1}{2} = \frac{1}{4}$

Identify the branches that represent the event P(odd, odd), shown in red in the tree diagram. Multiply the probabilities along those branches.

Reflect and discuss 3

- Would it change the answer in Example 3 if you put the branches for the 2nd die first in the tree diagram?

- What do you notice about the sum of the probabilities on any pair of branches? Explain why this happens.

- Why do we multiply the probabilities on each branch?

> Half of all possible outcomes have an odd number on the 1st die, and half of these have an odd number on the 2nd die as well.

Practice 3

1 A box contains three brand-A batteries and seven brand-B batteries.

The probability that a brand-A battery is faulty is 0.3, and the probability that a brand-B battery is faulty is 0.4.

a Copy and complete the tree diagram to show all the probabilities.

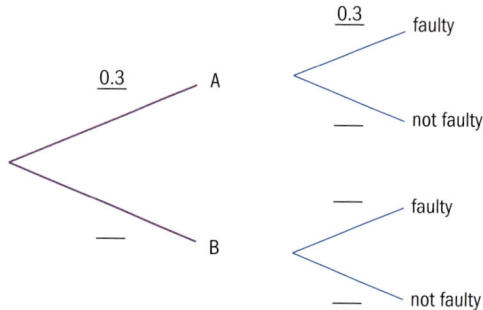

b A battery is selected at random from the box. Calculate the probability that the battery is:

i a faulty brand-A

ii not a faulty brand-A.

2 Two fair coins are flipped.

a Draw a tree diagram to represent the possible outcomes.

b Calculate the probability that both coins show heads.

3 James wants to find the probability of rolling two sixes on two fair dice.

He starts to draw this tree diagram.

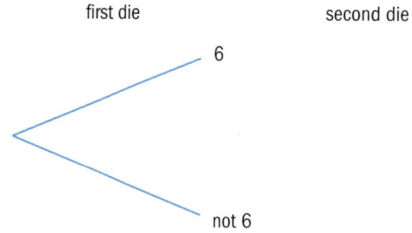

Copy and complete the tree diagram.

Calculate the probability of rolling two sixes.

4 Nienke and Merel both play netball. The probability that Nienke will score a goal on her first attempt is 0.75. The probability that Merel will score a goal on her first attempt is 0.82.

By drawing a tree diagram, calculate the probability that:

a Nienke and Merel will both score a goal on their first attempt

b neither Nienke nor Merel will score a goal on their first attempt.

5 A drawer contains 3 green and 2 yellow candles. G is the event picking a green candle, and Y is the event picking a yellow candle.

a Calculate P(G) and P(Y).

b A candle is picked from the drawer. Its color is noted and it is replaced in the drawer. A second candle is then picked.

Draw a tree diagram to represent the sample space.

> Because the candle is replaced, there are still 5 candles to pick from the second time.

Problem solving

c Verify that picking two green candles is more likely than picking two yellow candles.

Exploration 4

1 Calculate the probability of picking a red card from this set.

2 a If you pick a red card and then replace it, calculate the probability of picking a red card the next time.

b If you pick a blue card and then replace it, calculate the probability of picking a red card the next time.

3 a If you pick a red card but do not replace it, calculate the probability of picking a red card from the remaining cards.

b If you pick a blue card but do not replace it, calculate the probability of picking a red card from the remaining cards.

4 Determine what happens to the probabilities for the second event when you do not replace the card.

Tree diagrams show each outcome and its associated probability clearly. Here are two types of tree diagram:

- With replacement – these represent situations where the probability does not change for the second event.

- Without replacement – these represent situations where the probability changes for the second event.

Situations 'with replacement' produce independent events; 'without replacement' events are dependent.

Example 4

A bag contains 3 lemons and 2 limes. A piece of fruit is picked at random from the bag and not put back. Then a second piece of fruit is picked at random.

a Draw a tree diagram to represent the outcomes and their probabilities.

b Find P(Lemon, Lemon) and P(Lime, Lime).

This is a 'without replacement' situation.

a

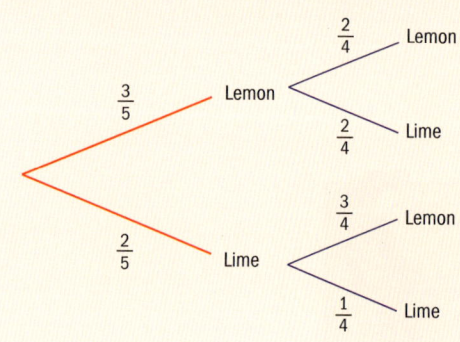

The upper arm of the first branch shows the probability of selecting a lemon; the lower arm represents selecting a lime. Since there is no replacement, the first pick affects the probabilities for the second pick, as you can see in the second set of arms.

b P(Lemon, Lemon) $= \frac{3}{5} \times \frac{2}{4} = \frac{6}{20} = \frac{3}{10}$

P(Lime, Lime) $= \frac{2}{5} \times \frac{1}{4} = \frac{2}{20} = \frac{1}{10}$

ATL

Example 5

In a box are 3 red pens, 4 black pens and 2 green pens. You pick a pen at random and then put it back. Your friend then picks one at random. Calculate the probability that you both select the same color pen.

This is a 'with replacement' situation.

R = choosing a red pen

B = choosing a black pen

G = choosing a green pen

Define the events.

▶ Continued on next page

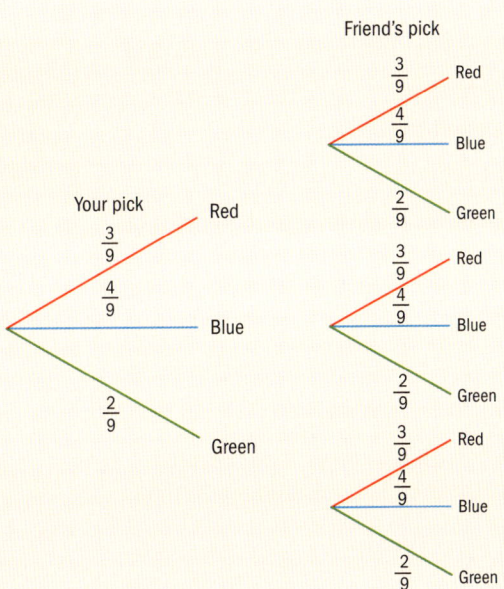

Friend's pick

$$P(R, R) = \frac{3}{9} \times \frac{3}{9} = \frac{9}{81}$$

$$P(B, B) = \frac{4}{9} \times \frac{4}{9} = \frac{16}{81}$$

Find the probability for getting the same color pen, for each of the three colors.

$$P(G, G) = \frac{2}{9} \times \frac{2}{9} = \frac{4}{81}$$

$$P(R, R) + P(B, B) + P(G, G) = \frac{9}{81} + \frac{16}{81} + \frac{4}{81} = \frac{29}{81}$$

Probability of (R, R) **or** (B, B) **or** (G, G) is $P(R, R) + P(B, B) + P(G, G)$

The probability that you both select the same color is $\frac{29}{81}$.

Practice 4

1 A bag contains three red peppers and four green peppers. You take a pepper from the bag and eat it. You then take another pepper.

  a Copy and label the tree diagram below to show all the probabilities.

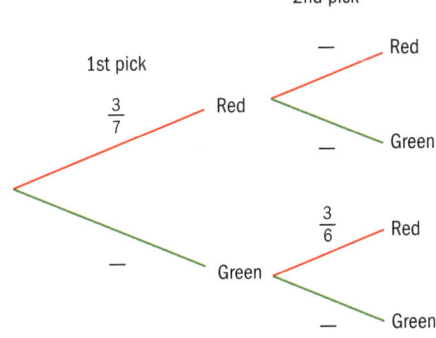

  b Calculate the probability you eat two red peppers.

  c Calculate the probability you do not eat a red pepper.

  d Calculate the probability you eat at least one red pepper.

2 A bag contains 1 white, 4 red and 2 blue counters. Rose picks a counter and does not replace it. She then picks another counter.

    a Draw a tree diagram to show all the probabilities.

    b Calculate the probability that she picks 1 white and 1 red counter.

> In question **2b**, there are two possible outcomes: (white, red) and (red, white).

3 Three coins are rolled. Draw a tree diagram and calculate the probability that:

    a only one head is rolled

    b at least one head is rolled

    c no heads are rolled.

    d Explain the relationship between your answers to **b** and **c**.

4 There are 9 numbered cards on a table, each with a number 1 to 9 printed on one side. The other side is blank. The cards are all blank side up. Serena picks two cards from the set.

    a Copy and complete this tree diagram.

    Find the probability that:

    b both cards are even

    c at least one card is odd.

5 Of a group of five students, two will be selected for a school trip by picking names out of a hat. The five students are Jack, Mary, Rafa, Harry and Pietronella.

> 'Mary and Jack' is the same as 'Jack and Mary'.

    a With the aid of a tree diagram or a table of outcomes, find the number of **different** possible combinations of students that could be selected.

    b Find the probability that Mary and Pietronella will go on the trip.

Problem solving

6 Alix has a box of red, yellow and green marbles. She picks a marble from the box, without looking.

The table shows the probabilities of picking the different colors.

Color	Probability
red	0.40
yellow	0.25
green	

    a What is the probability that Alix picks a green marble?

    b There are 5 yellow marbles in the box. How many red marbles are there?

    c Alix picks a marble, then replaces it in the box and picks another.

    Draw a tree diagram to show the probabilities.

    d What is the probability that at least one of the marbles is red?

Reflect and discuss 4

Compare your tree diagrams for Practice 4, questions **2**, **3**, **5** and **6** with others in your class.

- Did you all get the same answers?
- Did you all draw the same tree diagrams?
- For question **6**, do you need to draw a branch for each color?

Venn diagrams

Example 6

In a group of 30 children, 9 children like only vanilla ice cream, 13 like only strawberry ice cream and 5 children like both. The remaining children do not like either flavor.

a Draw a Venn diagram to represent this information.

b What is the probability that a child picked at random:

i likes strawberry ice cream but not vanilla

ii doesn't like strawberry or vanilla?

> You can use Venn diagrams to represent information and then calculate probabilities from the diagram.

a

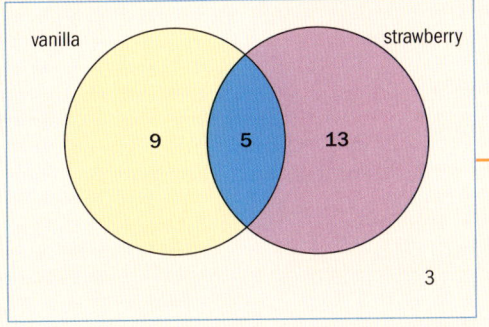

> Draw the Venn diagram. Remember to include the 3 children who like neither flavor.

b i P(likes strawberry but not vanilla) $= \dfrac{13}{30}$

> $\dfrac{n(\text{strawberry but not vanilla})}{n(S)}$

ii P(doesn't like strawberry or vanilla) $= \dfrac{3}{30} = \dfrac{1}{10}$

Practice 5

1 In a group of 40 people, 35 choose a main course, 10 choose a starter and 7 choose both.

a Draw a Venn diagram to represent this information.

b What is the probability that a person picked at random chooses a main course but no starter?

2 A group of 30 children are asked if they play lacrosse (*L*), basketball (*B*), volleyball (*V*) or none of these sports. The results are:

- 3 children do not play any of these sports
- 2 children play all three sports
- 6 play volleyball and basketball
- 3 play lacrosse and basketball
- 6 play lacrosse and volleyball
- 16 play basketball
- 12 play volleyball

a Draw a Venn diagram to display this information.

b Calculate the probability that a child selected at random:

   i plays volleyball and basketball but not lacrosse

   ii plays only lacrosse

   iii plays only volleyball.

3 A group of 90 students filled in a questionnaire about their free-time activities. The three most popular choices were: go to the cinema (*C*), read (*R*) and watch television (*T*). The results were:

- 26 students watch television, read and go to the cinema
- 20 students watch television and go to the cinema only
- 18 students read and go to the cinema only
- 10 students read and watch television only
- 60 students watch television, 60 students read, 70 students go to the cinema.

a Draw a Venn diagram to display this information.

Calculate the probability that a student picked at random:

b only watches television

c only goes to the cinema.

Problem solving

4 Of 150 new university students, 65 of them study Arabic, 80 study Chinese, and 50 students study both languages. Calculate the probability that a student selected at random studies:

a only Arabic

b only Chinese

c neither Arabic or Chinese.

Two-way tables

A two-way table represents information in rows and columns.

This two-way table shows the genders and degree subjects of 150 first-year university students.

	Science	Arts	Linguistics
Male	40	18	33
Female	15	20	24

From the **rows**:

- There are 91 male students (40 + 18 + 33)
- There are 59 female students (15 + 20 + 24)

A total of 150 students (91 + 59)

From the **columns**:

- There are 55 Scientists (40 + 15)
- There are 38 Artists (18 + 20)
- There are 57 Linguists (33 + 24)

A total of 150 students (55 + 38 + 57)

There are two ways of calculating the total number of students – adding row totals or adding column totals.

Example 7

From the two-way table of 150 students and the subjects they study:

	Science	Arts	Linguistics
Male	40	18	33
Female	15	20	24

a Find the probability that a student chosen at random:

i is male

ii is either male or studies Science.

b A female student is picked at random. Find the probability that she studies Arts.

a **i** $P(\text{male}) = \frac{91}{150}$

91 male students. Total 150 students.

ii $P(\text{male or studies Science}) = \frac{106}{150} = \frac{53}{75}$

91 males, plus 15 females studying Science makes 106.

b $P(\text{female, studies Arts}) = \frac{20}{59}$

59 female students in total, of which 20 study Arts. Note that since it is given that a female student is being picked at random, the sample space is now 59, not 150.

Practice 6

1 The table shows customers' menu choices in a restaurant.

	Miso-glazed salmon	Chicken stir-fry	Lamb kibbeh
Male	9	12	8
Female	1	14	6

From this two-way table calculate:

a the number of male diners in the restaurant

b the number of diners who ordered chicken stir-fry

c the probability that a randomly chosen dish was chicken stir-fry for a female diner.

2 a Complete a two-way table to represent this information on snowboarding groups. The students were categorized according to gender (M/F) and ability (advanced/intermediate/beginner).

- There were 60 students in total.

- Half of them were male.

- There were 16 male beginners.

- There were 28 beginners in total.

- There were 12 advanced females.

- There were 10 intermediate students in total.

b A student is selected at random. Calculate the probability that this student is an advanced male snowboarder.

3 The table shows staff preferences for mid-morning drink, grouped by age.

	Tea	Coffee	Water
Under 40	4	13	10
40 or over	12	12	6

Calculate:

a the percentage of staff under 40

b the fraction of staff who drink water

c the probability that a randomly chosen staff member was under 40 and drank tea.

Problem solving

4 A choir has 51 members in three age groups: under 15, 15 to 20, and over 20.

- There are 4 male under-15s.

- $\frac{2}{3}$ of the under-15s are female.

- 26 females are over 15.

- 7 males and 11 females are over 20.

a Calculate the probability that a choir member picked at random is:

   i female

   ii male aged 15 to 20

   iii over 15.

b The conductor chooses a male soloist at random. Calculate the probability that the soloist is under 15.

Exploration 5

1 Listed below are events that could occur when rolling a fair, six-sided die. Select and write down pairs of events that could **not** occur at the same time when rolling the die just once.

rolling a 4	rolling an odd number	rolling a 2
rolling a multiple of 2	rolling a 3	rolling a factor of 6
rolling an even number	rolling a factor of 18	rolling a 5

2 Listed below are some of the possible events that could happen when drawing a card from a standard deck of 52 cards.

drawing a red card	drawing a face card	drawing a factor of 8
drawing a heart	drawing a black 6	drawing an odd-numbered card
drawing a red ace	drawing a multiple of 3	drawing a ten

a Select and write down pairs of events that could **not** occur at the same time.

b Invent a pair of events that could not happen at the same time if you drew a card from the deck.

A shopping bag contains pearl onions and baby creole onions. An onion is taken from the bag. It is either a pearl onion or a baby creole, but it cannot be both. The events 'taking a pearl onion' and 'taking a baby creole onion' are mutually exclusive.

> In probability, two events are **mutually exclusive** if only one can happen in any given experiment.

Formally, two events are mutually exclusive when the sets representing the events are disjoint, in other words: $A \cap B = \varnothing$ (the empty set).

For example, when a die is rolled once:

- the sample space $S = \{1, 2, 3, 4, 5, 6\}$

- Event A = 'odd number' = $\{1, 3, 5\}$

- Event B = 'even number' = $\{2, 4, 6\}$

- $A \cap B = \varnothing$, so A and B are mutually exclusive.

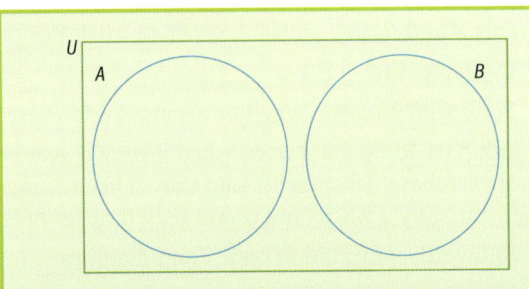

For mutually exclusive events A and B, $A \cap B = \varnothing$.

Probability of event $A = \dfrac{\text{number of ways event } A \text{ can occur}}{\text{total number of possible outcomes}}$

or: $\qquad\qquad P(A) = \dfrac{n(A)}{n(S)}$

So $\qquad\qquad P(A \cap B) = \dfrac{n(A \cap B)}{n(S)}$

For the die example, $P(A \cap B) = \dfrac{0}{6} = 0$. This means the probability that event A and event B both happen is impossible, and therefore equal to zero.

> Two events A and B are mutually exclusive if it is impossible for them to happen together. In mathematical language, if $A \cap B = \varnothing$, then $P(A \cap B) = 0$.

> **Axiom 3**
>
> If $\{A_1, A_2, A_3, \dots\}$ is a set of mutually exclusive events then
> $P(A_1 \cup A_2 \cup A_3 \dots) = P(A_1) + P(A_2) + P(A_3) + \dots$
>
> When the occurrences do not coincide, their associated probabilities can be added together.

Venn diagrams – if the circles are intersecting they are not mutually exclusive.

Two-way tables – sections in two-way tables are mutually exclusive unless you are told otherwise.

Reflect and discuss 5

Why is the term 'mutually exclusive' an appropriate term for events that cannot happen at the same time?

Practice 7

1 A fair, six-sided die is rolled once. State whether or not the following events are mutually exclusive (i.e. they cannot happen together).

   a 'rolling a 6' and 'rolling a 3'

   b 'rolling a multiple of 2' and 'rolling a multiple of 3'

   c 'rolling a 4' and 'rolling a factor of 42'

2 The numbers 1, 2, 3, 4, 5, 6, 7, 8 are written on table tennis balls and placed in a bag. A ball is selected at random. State whether or not the following events are mutually exclusive.

   a 'the number on the ball is even' and 'the number on the ball is a square number'

   b 'the number on the ball is a multiple of 5' and 'the number on the ball is a prime number'

   c 'the number on the ball is a factor of 8' and 'the number on the ball is an odd number'

3 Events A and B have probabilities $P(A) = 0.4$, $P(B) = 0.65$ and $P(A \cup B) = 0.85$.

   a Calculate $P(A \cap B)$.

   b State with a reason whether events A and B are mutually exclusive.

4 A group of 30 students were asked if they'd ever been stung by a bee or a wasp. Of these, 18 students said they'd been stung by a bee, 10 said they'd been stung by a wasp, and 6 said they'd never been stung by either insect.

   a Show this information on a Venn diagram.

   b Find the number of students who had been stung by both insects.

   c Explain why being stung by a bee and being stung by a wasp are not mutually exclusive events.

Write down the possible outcomes for event A and event B. If necessary draw a Venn diagram.

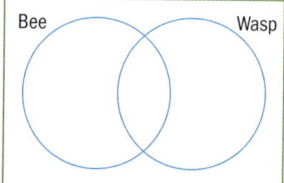

5 Children in a class of 30 students are asked whether they like strawberries (S) or bananas (B).

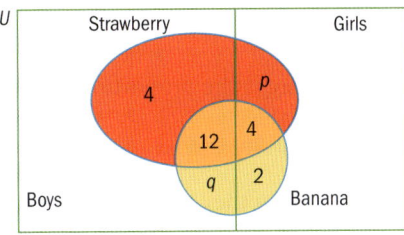

There are 12 girls in the class: 8 girls like strawberries, 6 girls like bananas and 4 girls like both.

16 boys like strawberries, 13 boys like bananas and 12 boys like both.

This information is shown in the Venn diagram. The teacher chooses a student at random.

a Use the information given to find p and q.

b Find P(boy) and P(girl). State whether these events mutually exclusive.

c Find P(S) and P(B). State whether these events mutually exclusive.

Problem solving

6 For the experiment 'Pick a card from a standard, 52 card deck', write:

a two mutually exclusive events

b two events that are not mutually exclusive.

D Randomness

- Does randomness affect the decisions we make?

What do you understand by the word random in the following sentence: 'Choose one piece of fruit at random'? In probability, it means that each piece of fruit has an equal chance of being chosen.

Exploration 6

1 a Pretend that you are flipping a coin. Without actually flipping the coin, imagine the first outcome (H or T) and write it down.

b Now, imagine flipping the coin again and record the result.

c Repeat this until you have recorded 50 outcomes.

2 Next, take a real coin and flip it 50 times recording the results.

3 Simulate the flipping of a coin using technology; let the number of flips, $n = 100, 1000, 10\,000$ and so on.

4 The simulation of flipping a real coin give random results. Determine whether your imaginary results are random.

5 Find the longest run of heads and longest run of tails in each set of data. State whether there is much difference in the lengths of run in random and non-random data.

6 Count the number of heads in each set of data.
For a fair coin P(Head) $= \frac{1}{2}$, so you would expect roughly half the results in each set of data to be a head.
In which set of data is the number of heads closest to half the results?

> The probability of an event happening is the proportion of times the event would occur in a large number of trials.

Probabilities describe what will happen in the long run. Sometimes events may not look random because they do not show the regularity that occurs after many repetitions.

These ideas lead to the differences between experimental and theoretical probability. If you take a fair die and roll it 100 times or 1000 times and record the number of 6s, you can calculate the experimental probability of 'rolling a 6'. As the number of trials increases, this probability gets closer to the theoretical probability value of $\frac{1}{6}$.

Practice 8

1 Amelia wants to pick 5 students at random from her class for a probability experiment. Which of these methods will ensure a truly random selection?

  a Picking the first 5 students to walk into the room.

  b Picking the last 5 students on the register.

  c Putting the names of all the students into a hat, and picking 5 out.

2 Jo, Amy and Sam play a board game where you need to throw a 6 to start. After five rounds, Jo rolled a 6 twice, Amy rolled a 6 three times, and Sam did not roll a 6 at all. Sam thinks Jo and Amy must be cheating. Use the ideas of randomness and probability to explain how these results are due to chance.

3 Max flips a coin 10 times and gets 7 tails.

  a Explain whether or not this shows his coin is biased.

  b He keeps flipping the coin and counting the tails. The table shows his results.

> Biased means unfair.

Number of flips	Number of Tails
50	24
100	52
500	265
1000	580

  Do you think the coin is fair? Justify your answer.

4 a Hadley and Morgan each roll a 6-sided die, then sum their scores. Hadley wins if the sum is even, and Morgan wins if the sum is odd.

    Draw a sample space to represent the outcome. Is the game fair?

  b Hadley and Morgan change the rules. If the sum of the two dice is a multiple of 3, Hadley wins. If it is a multiple of 4 then Morgan wins. If neither multiple, they roll again.

    i Determine if this game is fair.

    ii Suggest what would happen if they both rolled a 6.

5 Peter and Eliott are playing a coin game.

If Peter throws a head he wins; if he throws a tail, it is Eliott's turn. If Eliott throws a head he wins; if he throws a tail it is Peter's turn.

a Draw a tree diagram to represent this game.

b Calculate the probability that:

   i Peter wins on his first turn

   ii Eliott wins on his first turn

   iii Peter wins on this third turn.

c Discuss whether or not you think this is a fair game.

Reflect and discuss 6

Design a game for two players using dice, coins or spinners, so that:

- each player has an equal chance of winning
- one player has a greater chance of winning.

Summary

The sample space S, is a representation of the complete set of all possible outcomes from an experiment. It can be a list, a table or a diagram.

A single **event** is a subset of the possible outcomes listed in the sample space.

Probability of event $A = P(A) =$

$\dfrac{\text{number of ways event } A \text{ can occur}}{\text{total number of possible outcomes}} = \dfrac{n(A)}{n(S)}$

$P(A)$ represents the probability of event A occurring. $P(A')$ is the probability of A not occuring.

$$P(A) + P(A') = 1$$

The probability of an event happening is the proportion of times the event would occur in a large number of trials.

- Two events A and B are mutually exclusive if $A \cap B = \varnothing$. Therefore $P(A \cap B) = 0$.

Axiom 1

For any event A, $P(A) \geq 0$. This means that all probabilities have a value greater than or equal to zero.

Axiom 2

For a sample space S, $P(S) = 1$. In other words, the probability of all occurrences is equal to 1.

In probability, two events are **mutually exclusive** if only one can happen in any given experiment.

Two events A and B are mutually exclusive if it is impossible for them to happen together. In mathematical language, if $A \cap B = \varnothing$, then $P(A \cap B) = 0$.

Axiom 3

If $\{A_1, A_2, A_3, \dots \}$ is a set of mutually exclusive events then
$$P(A_1 \cup A_2 \cup A_3 \dots) = P(A_1) + P(A_2) + P(A_3) + \dots$$

When the occurrences do not coincide, their associated probabilities can be added together.

Mixed practice

1 There are four main blood types: A, B, AB and O. These are paired with something called a Rhesus factor, which is either '+' or '−'. For example, your blood type could be B+.

   a **Write** the sample space for the different blood types that are possible.

   If all blood types are equally likely, what is the probability that you have:

   b type AB− blood

   c type O blood

   d a blood type other than A or B

   e a 'positive' blood type?

2 Olivia rolls two 6-sided dice at the same time. One die has three red sides and three black sides. The other die has the sides numbered from 1 to 6. By means of a tree diagram, table of outcomes or otherwise:

   a **Find** how many different possible combinations she can roll.

   b **Calculate** the probability that she will roll a red and an even number.

   c **Calculate** the probability that she will roll a red or black and a 5.

   d **Calculate** the probability that she will roll a number less than 2.

3 Ann has a bag containing 3 blue whistles, 4 red whistles and 1 green whistle.

   Simon has a bag containing 2 blue whistles and 3 red whistles.

   The whistles are identical except for the color.

   Ann chooses a whistle at random from her bag and Simon chooses a whistle at random from his bag.

   a **Draw** a tree diagram to represent this information and **write down** the probability of each of the events on the branches of the tree diagram.

   b **Calculate** the probability that both Ann and Simon will choose a blue whistle.

   c **Calculate** the probability that the whistle chosen by Ann will be a different color to the one chosen by Simon.

4 A recent study of 24 sodas revealed that 8 have high amounts of caffeine, 12 have high amounts of sugar and 6 have both.

   a **Draw** a Venn diagram to represent this information.

   What is the probability that a soda picked at random from the group in the study:

   b is high in sugar but not in caffeine

   c is high in caffeine only

   d is not high in caffeine or sugar?

5 A bag contains four calculators (C) and six protractors (P). One item is taken from the bag at random and *not replaced*. A second item is then taken at random.

   a **Complete** the tree diagram by writing probabilities in the spaces provided.

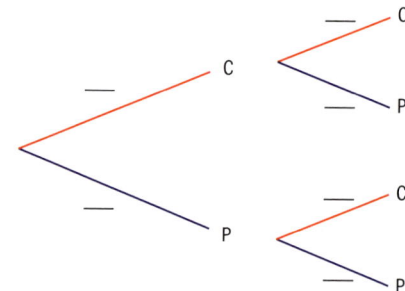

   b **Calculate** the probability that one protractor and one calculator are taken from the bag.

6 Repeat question **5**, but this time the item *is* replaced.

   Calculate how the probabilities change.

7 In a group of 50 people, 10 are healthy and the rest have either high blood pressure, high cholesterol or both; 23 people have high blood pressure and 28 have high cholesterol. **Find** the probability that a person selected at random:

   a has high blood pressure

   b has high blood pressure and high cholesterol

   c has high blood pressure or high cholesterol

   d has high cholesterol only.

8 A group of 30 students were asked about their favorite way of eating eggs.

- 18 liked boiled eggs (B)
- 10 liked fried eggs (F)
- 6 liked neither

a Find
  i $P(B)$ **ii** $P(B \cup F)$
  iii $P(F)$ **iv** $P(B' \cup F')$

b Find $P(B \cap F)$.

c Represent the information on a Venn diagram.

d A student chosen at random likes boiled eggs. **Find** the probability that the student also likes fried eggs.

Problem solving

9 A survey was carried out at an international airport. Travelers were asked their flight destinations and results are shown in the table.

Destination	Geneva	Vienna	Brussels
Number of males	45	62	37
Number of females	35	46	25

a **i** **Determine** whether or not the destinations are mutually exclusive.

  ii **Determine** whether or not gender is mutually exclusive.

b One traveler is chosen at random. **Find** the probability that this traveler is going to Vienna.

c One female traveler is chosen at random. **Find** the probability that she is going to Geneva.

d One traveler is chosen at random from those **not** going to Vienna. **Find** the probability that the chosen traveler is female.

For the above data, test whether or not destination and gender are independent.

10 100 students were asked if they liked various toast toppings.

- 56 like avocado
- 38 like marmalade
- 22 like soft cheese
- 16 like avocado and marmalade, but not soft cheese
- 8 like soft cheese and marmalade, but not avocado
- 3 like avocado and soft cheese, but not marmalade
- 4 like all three toppings

a **Draw** a Venn diagram to represent this information.

b **Find** the number of students who didn't like any topping.

c **Determine** if the toppings are mutually exclusive.

d A student is chosen at random from the group who like soft cheese. **Find** the probability that they also like marmalade.

11 Events A and B have probabilities $P(A) = 0.4$, $P(B) = 0.65$, and $P(A \cup B) = 0.85$.

a **Calculate** $P(A \cap B)$.

b **Determine** whether or not events A and B are mutually exclusive.

12 Stefan rolls two 6-sided dice at the same time. One die has three green sides and three black sides. The other die has sides numbered from 1 to 6.

a **Draw** a tree diagram to represent this sequence of events.

b **Find** the probability that Stefan rolls a 5.

c **Find** the probability that he rolls a number less than 3.

d **Find** the probability that he gets green on the one die and an even number on the other.

e **Determine** if the events 'rolling green' and 'rolling an even number' are independent, and explain your answer.

13 The table below shows the number of left- and right-handed golf players in a sample of 50 males and females.

	Left-handed	Right-handed	Total
Male	3	29	32
Female	2	16	18
Total	5	45	50

A golf player is selected at random.

a **Find** the probability that the player is:
  i male and left-handed
  ii right-handed
  iii right-handed, given that the player selected is female.

b **Determine** whether the events 'male' and 'left-handed' are are mutually exclusive.

Review in context
Identities and relationships

Problem solving

1 The chart shows the risk of developing Type 2 diabetes for different body mass index (BMI) values. BMI is a way of measuring the amount of fat in the body. For adults, a healthy BMI is between 18.5 and 25.

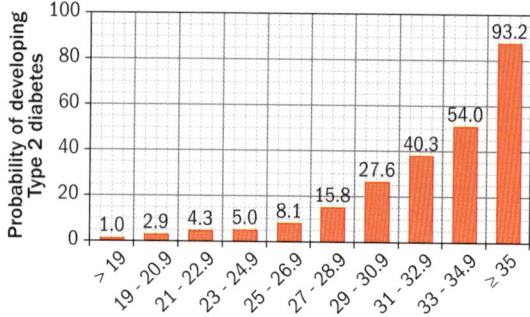

a An adult has BMI 28. What is their risk of developing Type 2 diabetes?

b **Describe** how the risk of developing diabetes changes as BMI increases.

c An adult has BMI 31. He loses mass and has BMI 26. How many times smaller is his risk of Type 2 diabetes now?

d **Write** some advice for reducing the risk of developing Type 2 diabetes. **Use** probabilities to justify your comments.

2 Probability can be used in genetics to predict the likelihood of children inheriting a condition from their parents. Suppose the gene for normal sight is represented by 'M' while that of short sightedness (myopia) is represented by 'm'. A child inherits one allele (gene) from each parent. For instance, if the parents are MM and Mm, then the child would receive an 'M' from the first parent and an 'M' or 'm' from the second.

    a Copy and complete the sample space for the different outcomes.

			Mother					
			MM		Mm		mm	
			M	M	M	m	m	m
Father	MM	M						
		M						
	Mm	M						
		m						
	mm	m						
		m						

b If a child inherits myopia only when they inherit 'mm', **calculate** the probability that a child born will have myopia.

c **Calculate** the probability that the child will carry the myopia gene (m).

Suppose two parents, both of whom are Mm, have two children.

d **Calculate** the probability that the first child will have myopia (mm).

e **Calculate** the probability that only one child will have myopia.

f **Calculate** the probability that neither child will have myopia.

g **Determine** which genes the parents would have to have in order for the probability that their first child has myopia to be $\frac{1}{2}$.

3 The table shows 60 students' choices of yoghurt.

Sugar levels	Yoghurt			
	Strawberry	Chocolate	Vanilla	Total
Low sugar	3	8	14	25
High sugar	8	9	18	35
Total	11	17	32	60

a One student is selected at random.

    i **Find** the probability that the student chose vanilla yoghurt.

    ii **Find** the probability that the student chose a yoghurt that was not vanilla.

iii The student chose chocolate yoghurt.
   Find the probability that the student chose the low sugar one.

   iv **Find** the probability that the student chose a high sugar or vanilla yoghurt.

   v The student chose a low sugar yoghurt. **Find** the probability that the student chose strawberry.

b The 60 yoghurts were then classified according to fat content type: 15 of the yoghurts had high fat, 37 had medium fat and 8 had low fat content. Two yoghurts were randomly selected.
   Find the probability that:

   i both yoghurts had low fat content

   ii neither of the yoghurts had medium fat content.

4 All human blood can be categorized into one of four types: A, B, AB or O. The distribution of the blood groups varies between races and genders. The table shows the distribution of the blood types for the US population.

Blood type	O	A	B	AB
Probability	0.42	0.43	0.11	x

a **Find** the probability that a person chosen at random:
   i has blood type AB
   ii does **not** have blood type AB.

b **Determine** if the two events 'have blood type AB' and 'do not have blood type AB' are mutually exclusive.

c **Find** the probability that a randomly selected person in the US has blood type A or B.

d Damon has blood type B, so he can safely receive blood from people with blood types O and B. **Find** the probability that a randomly chosen person can donate blood to Damon.

e Given that Damon received blood, **find** the probability that it was type O.

5 This table shows the distribution of blood type in the US by gender.

Blood type	Probability		
	Male	Female	Total
O	0.21	0.21	0.42
A	0.215	0.215	0.43
B	0.055	0.055	0.11
AB	0.02	0.02	0.04
Total	0.50	0.50	1.0

a **Determine** if the events 'gender' and 'blood type' are mutually exclusive.

   Let M be the event 'selecting a male'.

   Let F be the event 'selecting a female'.

b **Find:**

   i P(M)

   ii P(F)

Reflect and discuss 7

How have you explored the statement of inquiry? Give specific examples.

Statement of inquiry:

Understanding health and validating lifestyle choices results from using logical representations and systems.

5 Spacious interiors

Statement of inquiry:

Representing transformed objects and studying their form helps us enjoy their creativity in space.

Key concept:

Form is the understanding that the underlying structure and shape of an entity is distinguished by its properties.

F What is space?

Space is the frame of geometrical dimensions describing an entity.

Dimensions

We live in a three-dimensional world, meaning that everything in our world can be located using three aspects: latitude, longitude and altitude. Letting time be the 4th dimension, people and objects can be located at a particular place and moment in time.

We can imagine what a two-dimensional universe would be like if we simply look into a mirror or observe shadows on the ground. These images possess no thickness. You are familiar with using the 2D coordinate plane to create graphs. This representation of 2D space is called the Cartesian plane, named after the French philosopher, scientist and mathematician, René Descartes.

In order to locate three-dimensional objects, we need to add a third axis to the Cartesian plane. A point in 3D would therefore have three coordinates instead of two.

There is a wonderful book written over a hundred years ago by Edwin Abbott called *Flatland, a Romance of Many Dimensions*, about a two-dimensional world where one of its inhabitants encounters a mysterious visitor from the third dimension and struggles to comprehend how such a being could exist and what it might look like.

C How can you create different representations of space?

Representation is the manner in which something is presented.

As big as a whale

Media reports use comparisons such as 'an area the size of two football pitches' or 'an area twice the size of Belgium.'

A blue whale can be up to 30 m long and weigh as much as 200 tonnes.

- Which of these two comparisons gives you the best idea of the size of a blue whale?

A blue whale can be as long as 7 family cars and weigh as much as 33 elephants.

D To what extent does expressing shapes in different forms allow creativity?

Form and function

In design, form is the shape and appearance of an object. Function is the purpose of the object; does it do the job it was designed for? One definition of a good design is one that balances form and function – it does the job it was designed to do and is also attractive.

- Which do you think is the best chair design?

- Which do you think is the best logo design?

Global context: Personal and cultural expression

Exploration: Exploring the ways in which we reflect on, extend and enjoy our creativity

📖 Launch additional digital resources for this unit.

5.1 Surface area and volume

Global context: Personal and cultural expression

Related concept: Representation

FORM

Objectives

- Finding the surface area of any 3D shape (including pyramids, cones and spheres)
- Finding the volume of any 3D shape (including pyramids, cones and spheres)

Inquiry questions

F
- What is the difference between area and surface area?
- What are some properties of prisms, cylinders, pyramids and cones?

C
- How are the surface areas of pyramids, cones and spheres related?

D
- Is there a best method for finding volume?

ATL Creative-thinking

Apply existing knowledge to generate new ideas, products or processes

Statement of inquiry:

Representing transformed objects and studying their form helps us enjoy their creativity in space.

▢ **Launch additional digital resources for this chapter.**

You should already know how to:

• use the Pythagorean Theorem	In each triangle, find the length of the missing side. If necessary, give your answer as a radical. **1** 5 m, a, 5 m **2** 9 cm, 41 cm, b
• find the volume and surface area of cuboids, prisms and cylinders	Find the volume and surface area of each solid. If necessary, round your answer to 3 significant figures. **3** 6 cm, 4 cm, 5 cm, 3 cm **4** 12 m, 8 m **5** 4 mm, 6 mm, 3.5 mm, 4 mm, 2 mm
• find the area of a sector and length of an arc	**6** Find the area of the shaded sector and the length of its arc. 8 cm, 110°

Area of a trapezium:
$$A = \frac{(a+b)h}{2}$$

F Properties of 3D solids

- What is the difference between area and surface area?
- What are some properties of prisms, cylinders, pyramids and cones?

Exploration 1

1 Make a list of shapes that have an area that you can calculate.

2 Make another list of shapes that have a surface area that you can calculate.

3 Next to each shape in step **2**, state the number of its faces.

4 Compare and contrast the shapes in each list. Identify similarities and differences between the ways of calculating area and surface area.

A **polyhedron** is a 3D solid that has only plane (flat) faces.

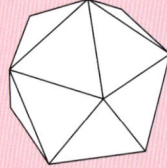

A **pyramid** is a 3D solid with a polygon base. The other faces are triangles that meet at a point called the **apex**. A pyramid is a polyhedron.

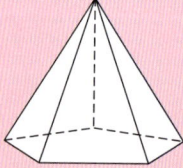

A **cone** is a 3D solid with a circular base and an apex or vertex. A cone is not a polyhedron.

A **sphere** is a 3D solid with one curved face. All the points on the sphere's surface are equidistant (the same distance) from the center. A sphere is not a polyhedron.

You already know how to find the surface area and volume of cuboids, cylinders and prisms. Now you will look at finding the surface area and volume of pyramids, cones and spheres.

The **surface area** is the total area of all the faces of a 3-dimensional solid.

The **volume** of a 3-dimensional solid is the amount of space it occupies.

Exploration 2

Copy and complete this table with your observations about the different 3D solids.

	Prism	Cylinder	Pyramid	Cone
Base	• any shape, often a regular polygon • rectangular based prisms are called cuboids • two opposite faces could each be the base			
Cross-section parallel to the base		• always a circle • the same radius as the base all along the cylinder		
Sides			• triangles • if the base is a regular polygon, the triangles are all congruent • the triangles all meet at the apex	

Reflect and discuss 1

- How is a sphere similar to the 3D solids in the table in Exploration 2? How is it different?

- How do you think the volume and surface area of a sphere is found, given its differences compared to other 3D solids?

C Finding surface area

● How are the surface areas of pyramids, cones and spheres related?

Surface area

Pyramids, cones and spheres each require a different method for finding surface area.

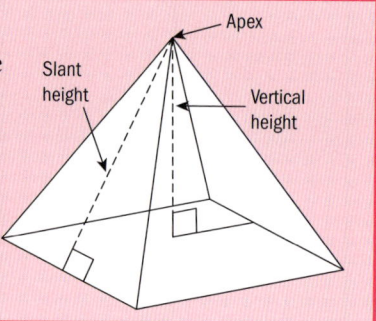

The **slant height** of a pyramid is the distance from the center of one edge of the base to the apex of the pyramid.

The **vertical height** is the perpendicular distance from the apex to the base.

ATL

Exploration 3

1 a Determine which 2D (flat) shapes make up the different faces of this square-based pyramid.

b Identify the information you need to find the surface area of square-based pyramids.

2 a Use the information given in the diagram to find the area of the base of pyramid A.

b Justify whether the information in the diagram is enough to find the area of one of the triangles on the side of the pyramid.

c Calculate the surface area of pyramid A.

3 a In pyramid B, the side of the square base and the vertical height of the pyramid are given. Suggest how you could calculate the slant height of the pyramid using this information.

b Find the slant height of the pyramid.

c Use the slant height to calculate the area of one of the triangular faces of the pyramid.

d Hence find the total surface area of pyramid B.

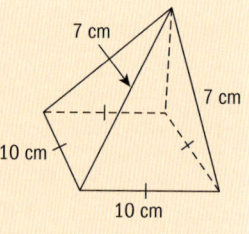

Pyramid A

The four triangles are isosceles and congruent.

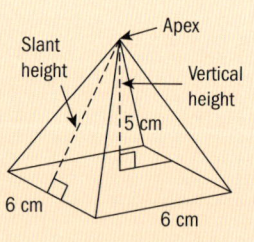

Pyramid B

Example 1

Find the surface area of this rectangular-based pyramid.

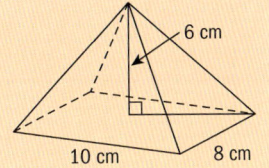

Area of base = $8 \times 10 = 80$ cm² ————————— There are three different side areas to find; the first one is the rectangular base.

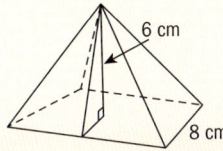 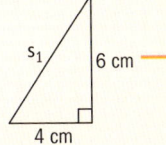

Use the Pythagorean Theorem to calculate the slant height s_1 for the front and back triangular faces.

> Use s for slant height and h for vertical height.

$$s_1^2 = 6^2 + 4^2 = 52$$
$$s_1 = 2\sqrt{13} \text{ cm}$$

Area of front triangle $= \dfrac{1}{2}b \times s_1 = \dfrac{1}{2} \times 10 \times 2\sqrt{13}$

$$= 10\sqrt{13} \text{ cm}^2$$ ————— The area of the back triangle is the same as the front triangle. Note: keep answers exact (using radicals) at each stage. Use your calculator only at the end to give your final answer correct to 3 s.f.

Similarly, calculate the slant height s_2 for the left and right triangular faces:

$$s_2 = 6^2 + 5^2 = 61$$
$$s_2 = \sqrt{61} \text{ cm}$$

Area of left triangle $= \dfrac{1}{2}b \times s_2 = \dfrac{1}{2} \times 8 \times \sqrt{61} = 4\sqrt{61} \text{ cm}^2$ ——— The area of the right side triangle is the same as the left side triangle.

Total area = area of base
+ 2 times the area of front triangle
+ 2 times the area of side triangle ————— Find the total area of all 5 faces.

$$= 80 + 2 \times 10\sqrt{13} + 2 \times 4\sqrt{61}$$

$$= 215 \text{ cm}^2 \text{ (3 s.f.)}$$

Reflect and discuss 2

- Compare and contrast the processes for finding the surface area of a square-based pyramid and a rectangular-based pyramid.

- How do you think this compares to finding the surface area of a pyramid with another regular polygon (for example, a pentagon or hexagon) as its base?

- How would you find the area of the base of a pyramid with a regular hexagon as its base? How would you find the slant height of this pyramid?

The surface area of a pyramid with an *n*-sided regular polygon base is

$S = A_{\text{base}} + nA_{\text{triangle}}$

Practice 1

In each question, copy the diagram and complete it as you solve the problem. You may need to draw more diagrams for different steps in the solution.

Find the surface area of each pyramid. If necessary, round your answer to 3 s.f.

1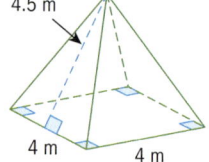
4.5 m
4 m   4 m

2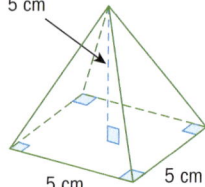
5 cm
5 cm
5 cm   5 cm

3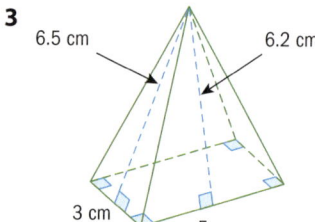
6.5 cm   6.2 cm
3 cm
5 cm

4 This square-based pyramid has four identical triangular faces. Each sloping edge measures 8 m.

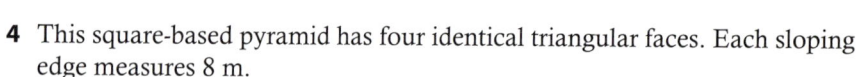
8 m   8 m
5 m   5 m
5 m

a Find the slant height.

b Hence find its surface area.

Problem solving

5 A tetrahedron is a 3D solid with all four faces equilateral triangles.
Find the surface area of a tetrahedron with side length 7 cm.

6 George bought a white plaster replica of the Great Pyramid on his trip to Egypt. Its height is 48 mm and the side length of its square base is 75 mm. George wants to paint the pyramid in stone-color to make it look more real.

a Explain which faces of the pyramid he needs to paint.

b Hence, find the area of the surface of the pyramid that he needs to paint.

7 This pyramid has a square base with side 30 cm and total surface area 2400 cm². Find its height.

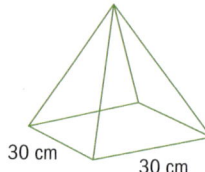
30 cm   30 cm

8 These two square-based pyramids are mathematically similar.

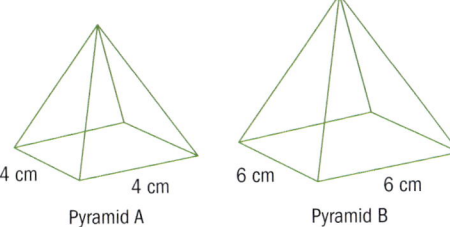

4 cm   4 cm   6 cm   6 cm

Pyramid A   Pyramid B

> When the linear scale factor is r, the area scale factor is r^2.

Pyramid A has surface area 64 cm².

Calculate the surface area of Pyramid B.

The surface area of a cone with base radius r and slant height s can be unravelled into a circle and a sector:

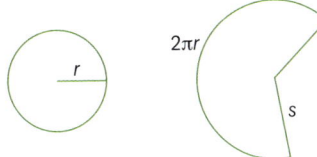

The arc length of the major sector is equal to the circumference of the circle, $2\pi r$. The radius of the sector is equal to the slant height s of the cone.

The formulae that show the relationships in a circle are:

Area of a circle $= \pi r^2$

Area of a sector $= \dfrac{\theta}{360}\pi s^2$

Arc length of a sector $= \dfrac{\theta}{360}2\pi s$

However, you know that arc length $l = 2\pi r$.

Therefore $2\pi r = \dfrac{\theta}{360}2\pi s$

$$\theta = \dfrac{360r}{s}$$

And the area of a sector $= \dfrac{\left(\dfrac{360r}{s}\right)}{360}\pi s^2$

$$= \dfrac{r}{s}\pi s^2 = \pi r s$$

Therefore the surface area of a cone $= \pi r^2 + \pi r s$.

The surface area of a cone $= \pi r^2 + \pi r s$ where r is the radius of the base and s is the slant height of the cone.

The curved surface area of the cone is $\pi r s$.

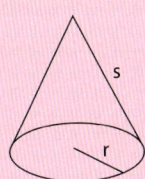

Practice 2

Find the surface area of each solid cone. If necessary, round your answer to 3 s.f.

1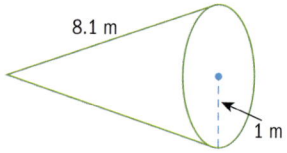
8.1 m
1 m

2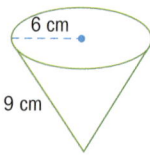
5 cm
13 cm

3 The diagram shows the dimensions of a paper cup. Calculate the area of paper used to make the cup.

6 cm
9 cm

Problem solving

4 Belgium is famous for its potato fries, which are often served in cones made from newspaper. Rene makes a paper cone from a semicircle cut from a page of his local newspaper. The page measures 410 mm by 315 mm.

a Draw a diagram to show the semicircle on the page of newspaper.

b Determine the largest possible diameter of the semicircle. Hence, find the radius.

c Find the area of the largest cone Rene can make from a page of this newspaper.

d Find the circumference of the circular base.

e Hence, find the radius of the base of the paper cone.

5 A solid cone has surface area 125.7 cm², and base radius 4 cm.

a Find the curved surface area of the cone.

b Find the slant height of the cone.

c Hence, find the vertical height of the cone.

As circles have no straight edges, you cannot use the same methods for finding the area as you would for polygons. Finding the surface area of a sphere (which has no edges at all) is not possible with methods that you know and requires more advanced mathematics.

Reflect and discuss 3

Suppose you traced around an orange several times, creating circles with the same radius as the orange. Suppose you then peeled the orange, breaking it into small pieces, and completely filled as many of the circles as possible.

- How many of the circles would you expect to fill with the orange peel pieces?

- How does this demonstrate the formula for the surface area of a sphere?

> The surface area of a sphere = $4\pi r^2$

Practice 3

Find the surface area of each sphere. If necessary, round your answer to 3 s.f.

1
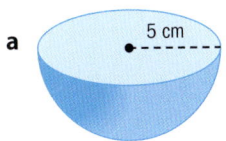
radius = 2 cm

2
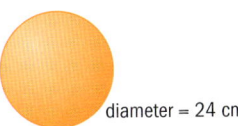
diameter = 24 cm

3 Calculate the surface area of these solids.

a
5 cm

b
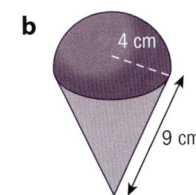
4 cm

9 cm

Problem solving

4 The surface area of a sphere is 400 cm². Calculate its radius.

5 How does the surface area of a sphere compare to the surface area of a cylinder in which it fits perfectly? (Diagram shown to the right.)

D Finding volume

- Is there a best method for finding volume?

Archimedes discovered the volume of a sphere in 225 BCE, by inscribing the sphere in a cylinder of the same radius and height as a sphere. He then sliced the sphere up, calculated the difference in volume between the cylinder and the sphere for each slice, and added up these differences to discover that the ratio between the volume of a sphere and the volume of its circumscribed cylinder is $\frac{2}{3}$.

Archimedes considered his proof for finding the volume of a sphere to be his greatest achievement.

ATL

Exploration 4

In this exploration, you will use an alternative method for finding the volume of a sphere.

You will need a golf ball (or any ball that sinks in water), a measuring cylinder and water.

Part 1 – finding the volume of a golf ball

1 Put the golf ball in the measuring cylinder. Fill the cylinder with water so that the water covers the ball.

2 Record the water level and calculate the volume of the ball and the water together.

3 Remove the golf ball. Record the new water level, and calculate the volume of the water.

4 Use your results from steps **2** and **3** to find the volume of the golf ball.

1 ml = 1 cm³

▶ Continued on next page

Part 2 – comparing spheres and cylinders

5 The diagram shows a golf ball in a cylinder.
The radius of a golf ball is approximately 4.2 cm.

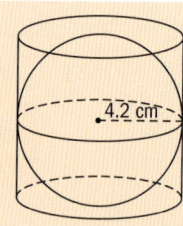

  a State the radius of the cylinder.

  b State the height of the cylinder.

6 Measure the diameter of the golf ball that you used in step **1**. Use this to find the volume of its circumscribed cylinder. Compare the volume of the golf ball with the volume of its circumscribed cylinder. Use your findings to suggest a formula for the volume of a sphere.

> When a sphere fits perfectly inside the smallest possible cylinder, the cylinder **circumscribes** the sphere.

> Archimedes of Syracuse (287 BCE – 212 BCE) was a Greek mathematician and inventor. It is said he had a sphere circumscribed by a cylinder on his tombstone, to represent his favorite mathematical proofs.

In Exploration 4, the volume of the sphere is two-thirds of the volume of its circumscribed cylinder, which has volume $2\pi r^3$. Two-thirds of this volume is $\frac{2}{3}(2\pi r^3) = \frac{4}{3}\pi r^3$.

> The volume of a sphere $= \frac{4}{3}\pi r^3$

You can use a similar method to verify the formulae for volume of a pyramid and volume of a cone.

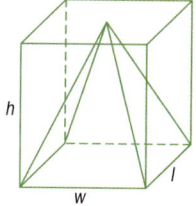

Volume of cuboid: $l \times w \times h = $ area of base $\times$ height

Volume of pyramid with same base and height: $\frac{1}{3} \times$ area of base $\times$ height

This formula can be generalized to a pyramid with any base.

Similarly, the volume of a cone is $\frac{1}{3}$ the volume of a cylinder with the same base radius and height.

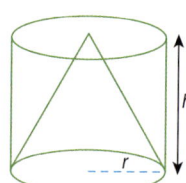

Volume of cone $= \frac{1}{3} \times$ volume of cylinder

$$V = \frac{1}{3}\pi r^2 h$$

> Volume of pyramid $= \frac{1}{3} \times$ area of base $\times$ height
>
> Volume of cone $= \frac{1}{3}\pi r^2 h$

Practice 4

Find the volume of each 3D solid.

1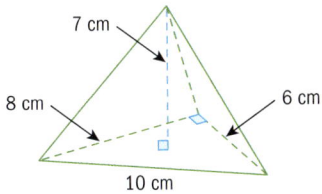
10 cm
8 cm   8 cm

2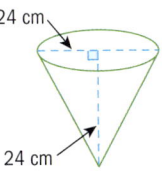
6 cm
7 cm   8 cm

3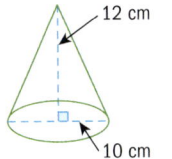
7 cm
8 cm   6 cm
10 cm

4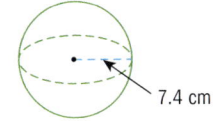
24 cm
24 cm

5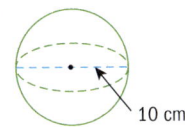
12 cm
10 cm

6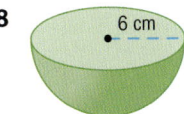
7.4 cm

7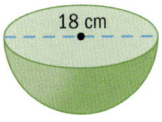
10 cm

8 6 cm

9 18 cm

10 In Practice 2 question **4**, you found the area of a newspaper cone made from a semicircle.

   a Find the volume of this newspaper cone.

   b Explain why the volume of potato in this cone of French Fries would be less than your answer to part **a**.

Problem solving

11 These two cones are mathematically similar.

   Cone A has volume 2000 cm³.

   Calculate the volume of Cone B.

10 cm   12 cm
Cone A   Cone B

> When the linear scale factor is r, the volume scale factor is r^3.

12 a Explain why any two spheres are mathematically similar.

   b The volume of a sphere of radius 4 cm is 268 cm³ (to 3 s.f.)
   Find the volume of a sphere of:
     i radius 8 cm   **ii** radius 2 cm.

13 Find the height of a cone that has volume 270π mm³ and base radius 9 mm.

14 Find the radius of a cone that has volume 8.38 cm³ and height 2 cm.

15 Find the radius of a sphere with volume 523.6 cm³.

16 Suppose you fill an empty sphere with water and then pour it into an empty cylinder that has the same height and diameter as the sphere. Find the height up the cylinder that the water would reach. Leave your answer as a fraction of the total height of the cylinder.

Summary

- A **polyhedron** is a 3D solid that has only plane (flat) faces.

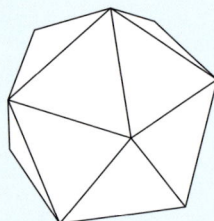

- A **pyramid** is a 3D solid with a polygon base. The other faces are triangles that meet at a point called the **apex**. A pyramid is a polyhedron.

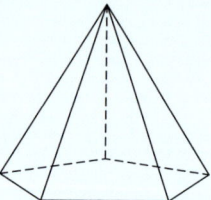

- A **cone** is a 3D solid with a circular base and an apex or vertex. A cone is not a polyhedron.

- A **sphere** is a 3D solid with one curved face. All the points on the sphere's surface are *equidistant* (the same distance) from the center. A sphere is not a polyhedron.

- The **slant height** of a pyramid is the distance from the center of one edge of the base to the apex of the pyramid.

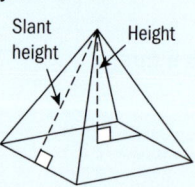

- The **surface area** is the total area of all the faces of a 3-dimensional solid.

- The **volume** of a 3-dimensional solid is the amount of space it occupies.

- The surface area of a pyramid with an n-sided regular polygon base is $S = A_{base} + nA_{triangle}$

- Volume of pyramid $= \frac{1}{3} \times$ area of base $\times$ height

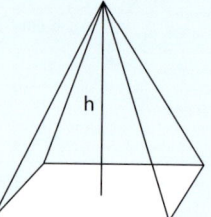

- Surface area of a cone $= \pi r^2 + \pi rs$ where r is the radius of the base and s is the slant height.

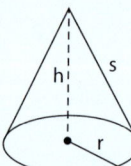

- Volume of a cone $= \frac{1}{3}\pi r^2 h$

- Surface area of a sphere $= 4\pi r^2$

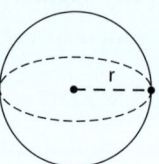

- Volume of a sphere $= \frac{4}{3}\pi r^3$

Mixed practice

1 **Find** the surface area and volume of each 3D solid.

a 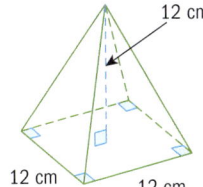 12 cm, 12 cm, 12 cm

b 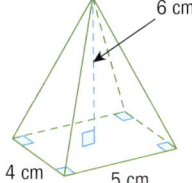 6 cm, 4 cm, 5 cm

c 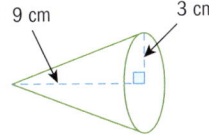 9 cm, 3 cm

d 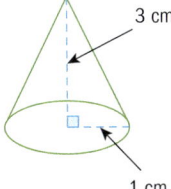 3 cm, 1 cm

e 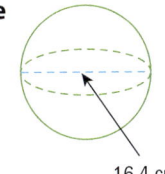 16.4 cm

f 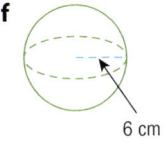 6 cm

Problem solving

2 All eight edges of a square-based pyramid are 12 cm long.

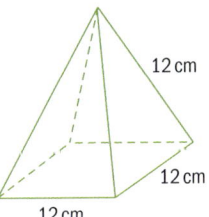 12 cm, 12 cm, 12 cm

a **Find** its surface area and its volume.

b **Find** the surface area and volume of a mathematically similar pyramid, with base a square of side 9 cm.

3 A cone has surface area 204.2 cm², and base radius 5 cm.

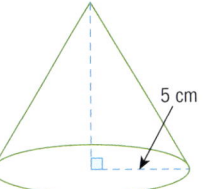 5 cm

a **Find** the slant height of the cone.

b **Find** the volume of the cone.

4 The volume of a soccer ball is 5.6 dm³.

According to the regulations, the circumference of the ball must be between 68 cm and 70 cm. **Determine** whether this soccer ball satisfies the regulations. **Justify** your answer.

5 A spherical scoop of ice cream is cut in half, and covered in chocolate (including the flat face). The total area of chocolate is 85 cm².

a **Find** the radius of the spherical scoop of ice cream.

b Hence, **find** the volume of the ice cream covered in chocolate.

6 Two paper cones are mathematically similar. The capacity of the larger cone is 8 times the capacity of the smaller cone. The surface area of the smaller cone is 50 cm².

Find the surface area of the larger cone.

Objective: **D.** Applying mathematics in real-life contexts
ii. select appropriate mathematical strategies when solving authentic real-life situations

In these real-life situations, select the strategies you have learned for finding the volume and surface area of 3D shapes to answer the questions.

Review in context

Personal and cultural expression

1 The Egyptians built square-based pyramids as part of the burial ritual for queens and pharaohs. The three largest and best preserved pyramids are located in the town of Giza, near Cairo. Many believe that the builders were influenced by the Golden Ratio (1.62).

 a Each of the sides of the base of the Great Pyramid measures 230.4 meters while the height measures 145.5 meters. How close is the ratio of side length to height to the Golden Ratio?

 b The entire pyramid was originally covered with a layer of white limestone. **Calculate** the area of limestone used.

 c **Compare** the total surface area of the sides to the area of the square base. How does this relate to the Golden Ratio?

 d **Calculate** the volume of the pyramid.

 e **Calculate** the perimeter of the base of the pyramid as well as the circumference of a circle with a radius equal to the height of the pyramid. **Describe** what you notice about these results.

2 Near Mexico City is The Temple of the Feathered Serpent, one of hundreds of pyramids in the Mesoamerican city of Teotihuacan. Archaeologists used a robot and found hundreds of spheres with circumferences ranging from about 3.5 cm to 12.5 cm. The spheres were covered in a yellow material called jarosite.

 a **Find** the amount of jarosite needed to paint:
 i the smallest ball   ii the largest ball.

 b **Find** the volume of clay needed for each size ball.

3 Potentially the earliest team sport, ballgame, was played in Mesoamerica. A very large court is still visible at the archaeological site of Chichen Itza in Mexico. Players could end the game by getting a heavy ball through a ring mounted vertically on the wall of the court (no hands allowed). If the circumference of the ring was 95 cm and the surface area of the ball was 2830 cm², **justify** why putting the ball through the hoop resulted in ending the game.

4 The Christmas tradition of decorating evergreen trees began in Germany in the 16th century. With their roughly conical shape, it was possible to decorate them and enjoy their beauty from all sides. (No decorations were put underneath the circular face.)

 a **Determine** which tree would have more area for decorations: one with a height of 215 cm and a maximum circumference of 200 cm or a tree with a height of 180 cm and a circumference of 210 cm? **Justify** your answer.

 b A tree located in Rockefeller Center in New York City is lit every year in early December. The largest tree measured 100 feet tall and had a volume equivalent to 65 500 cubic feet. **Find** the area was available for decorations.

Reflect and discuss 4

How have you explored the statement of inquiry? Give specific examples.

Statement of inquiry:

Representing transformed objects and studying their form helps us enjoy their creativity in space.

5.2 Geometric transformations

Global context: Personal and cultural expression

Related concept: Space

Objectives

- Transforming 2-D shapes on a plane by translation, rotation, reflection and enlargement
- Regular and semi-regular tessellations
- Performing combined transformations on shapes
- Replacing transformations by other transformations

Inquiry questions

- How can geometric shapes be transformed?
- How are isometric transformations defined?
- How are tessellations created?

- Can isometric transformations replace one another?
- How are geometric transformations similar to functions?

- Does the order of transformations always matter?

FORM

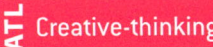
ATL Creative-thinking

Use visual diagrams to generate new ideas

Statement of inquiry:

Representing transformed objects and studying their form helps us enjoy their creativity in space.

📖 **Launch additional digital resources for this chapter.**

You should already know how to:

• enlarge a shape	**1** Copy the following diagram on a squared sheet of paper: 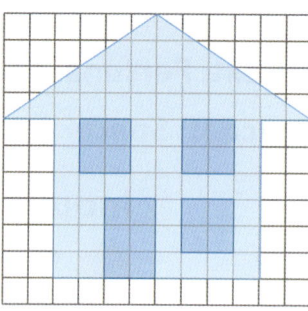 **a** Draw the same diagram, this time doubling each length. **b** Draw the same diagram, this time multiplying each length by 4.
• find the equation of a line from a graph	**2** Write down the equations of the following lines: **a** 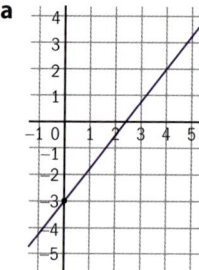 **b** 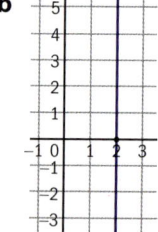 **c** 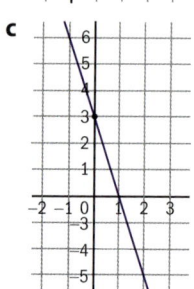

> Geometry graphing software, such as Geogebra, would be very useful throughout this question cycle.

F   Transforming shapes

- How can geometric shapes be transformed?
- How are isometric transformations defined?
- How are tessellations created?

Exploration 1

1 Take a shape (cut one out or use a tile). It can be any shape and any size.

2 Put the shape on the table, and move it to a different position on the table.

3 List the different ways in which the shape can be moved, keeping in mind that it must start off on the table and end up on the table.

Any movement or *transformation* of shapes can be described mathematically.

4 The table below lists some transformations. For each transformation listed, complete the row, determining what information is necessary to describe it. What instructions would you need to give someone else so that they would move the shape the same way you did?

Transformation	Description		Necessary information
Translation	slide	Where to?	
Rotation	turn	By how much and in which direction?	
Reflection	flip	Where is the mirror image?	

5 Using 'Yes' and 'No', complete the table below (ignoring the empty row for now) and discuss how shapes change when any of these transformations are applied.

Transformation	What changes?				
	Position	Direction	Orientation	Shape	Size
Translation					
Rotation					
Reflection					

6 Compare these transformations. How are they similar? How are they different?

7 A transformation that hasn't been discussed yet is an enlargement. Complete the empty line in the previous two tables with the fourth transformation: enlargement.

8 Discuss how an enlargement is not like the other three transformations seen so far.

> A shape on the table is either face-up or face-down. When a shape is flipped, we say that it changes *orientation*. When a shape is turned (but not flipped), we say it changes *direction*.

Geometric transformations change the position, direction and size of shapes in a plane, but they never change its shape. When a transformation does not change the size of the shape (i.e. when the original shape and its image are **congruent**), we call the transformation an **isometric transformation** (or a **congruence transformation**).

> Two objects are **congruent** when they are the same shape and size. They are **similar** when they are the same shape but have a different size.

An enlargement is not an isometric transformation. The original shape and its enlarged image are similar but not congruent.

Isometric transformations

- A **translation** displaces a shape in a plane. It changes the position of a shape, but not its shape, size, direction nor orientation. A translation is described by a displacement $\begin{pmatrix} x \\ y \end{pmatrix}$, meaning that each point in the shape is moved x units horizontally and y units vertically.

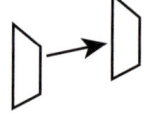

- A **rotation** turns a shape about a point, called the **center of rotation**. It changes the position and direction of a shape, but not its shape, orientation nor size. A rotation is described by the center of rotation, the angle of the turn, and the direction of the turn.

- A **reflection** changes a shape into its mirror image on the other side of a line, called the **mirror line**. The original shape and its image are symmetrical about the mirror line. A reflection flips a shape, changing its position, direction and orientation, but not its shape nor size. It is described by its mirror line.

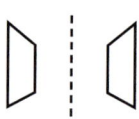

A **dilation** is a transformation of an object that produces an image of the same shape but a different size. A dilation is not an isometric transformation because it changes a shape's size, so the original shape and its image are not congruent. It is described by a **scale factor**, which is the ratio of the corresponding sides of the figure and its image. If the scale factor is larger than 1, the image is an **enlargement**; if the scale factor is smaller than 1 (but greater than 0), the image is a **reduction**.

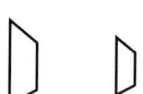

Example 1

a Triangle A maps onto triangle B. Describe the translation from A to B.

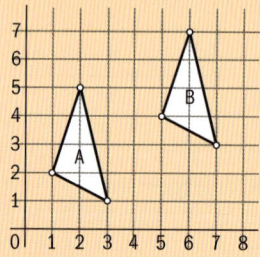

If image B is obtained by transforming image A, we say that 'A maps onto B'.

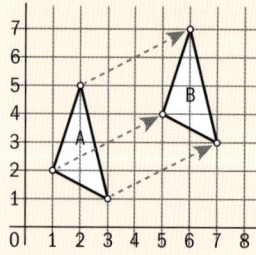

Translation by $\begin{pmatrix} 4 \\ 2 \end{pmatrix}$ —— Each vertex of the triangle is translated 4 units in the x-direction and 2 units in the y-direction.

b Draw the image of triangle A when it is rotated clockwise by 120°
around the point (5, 4).

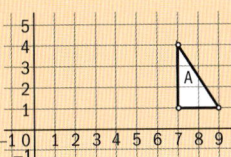

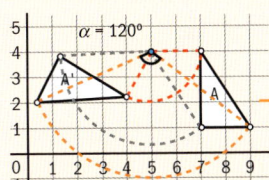

Each vertex of the triangle must be
rotated 120° clockwise from the point
(5, 4) and must remain at the same
distance from that point.

c Draw the image of the triangle A when it is reflected in the line
$y = 2x - 1$.

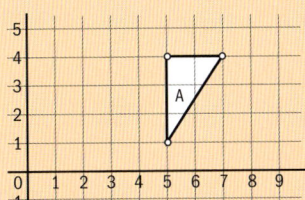

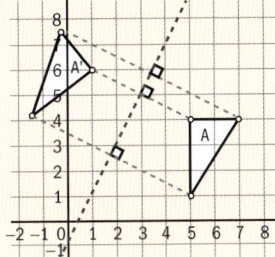

Each point of the reflected shape
must be the same perpendicular
distance from the mirror line as
its corresponding point in the
original shape.

d Draw the following shape enlarged by scale factor 3.

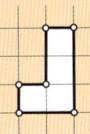

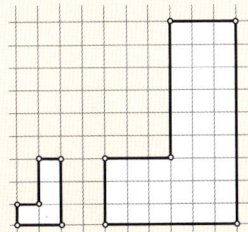

Each length in the enlarged shape is
3 times the corresponding length in
the original shape.

Practice 1

1 Describe the translations:

    a from A to B

    b from B to A

    c from A to D

    d from C to A

    e from F to E

    f from D to C.

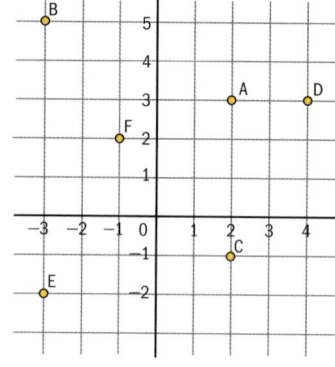

2 Reflect the following triangle in the line $x = -2$.

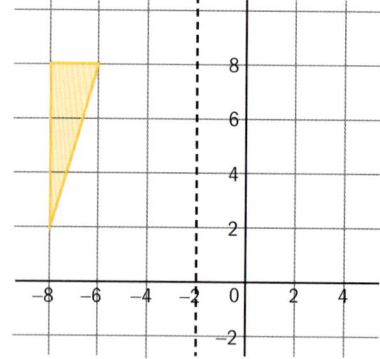

3 Rotate the following parallelogram by 90° counterclockwise around the point E(−2, 2).

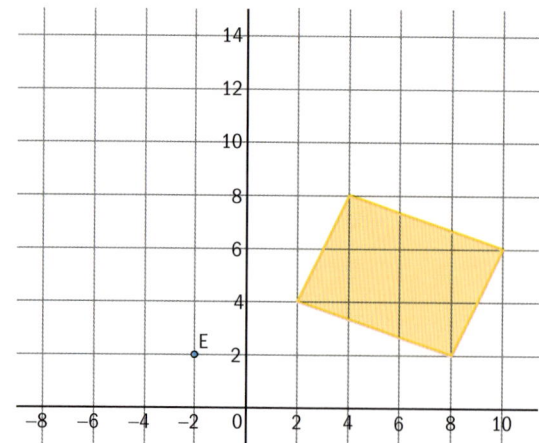

4 Transform the following shape by the translation $\begin{pmatrix} 4 \\ -2 \end{pmatrix}$.

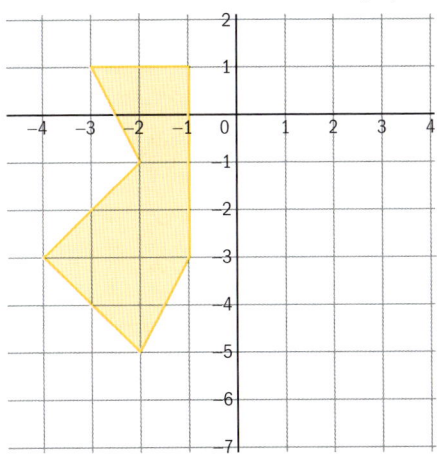

5 Reflect the triangle in the line $y = 0.5x + 2$.

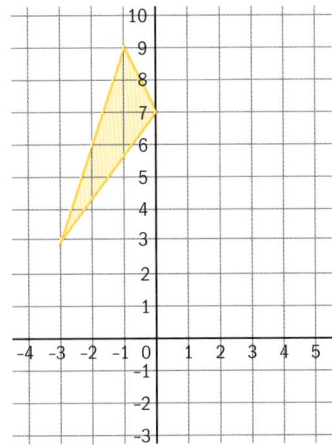

6 Using squared paper, draw the coordinate grid and label the axes from −8 to 8. Then draw the shape that has vertices (4, 0), (2, 5), (4, 6), (6, 5) on the same grid.

   a Label the shape A. Determine what type of shape it is.

Draw the following on the same graph:

   b Translate the shape −9 units in the x-direction and 2 units in the y-direction. Label the translated shape B.

   c Rotate shape A 90° clockwise around the origin. Label the rotated shape shape C.

   d Reflect shape A in the line $y = -x$. Label the reflected shape D.

7 Consider the following shape.

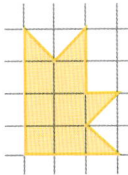

   a Draw its enlargement by factor 4.

   b Draw its enlargement by scale factor 1.5.

8 The square *ABCD* has been transformed to *A′B′C′D′*.

For each of these transformations, compare the orientations of *ABCD* and *A′B′C′D′*.

i A reflection

ii A translation

iii A rotation by 90°

iv A rotation by 180°

9 A square *ABCD* has vertices at *A*(−1, 10), *B*(3, 10), *C*(3, 6) and at *D*.

a Find the coordinates of *D*.

b Find the coordinates of *A′*, *B′*, *C′*, *D′* if *ABCD* is reflected in the line $y = 4$.

c Find the coordinates of *A″*, *B″*, *C″*, *D″* if *ABCD* is rotated by 180° around the point (1, 4).

d Find the coordinates of *A‴*, *B‴*, *C‴*, *D‴* if *ABCD* is translated −8 units in the *y*-direction.

e Compare the coordinates of the vertices of transformed square *ABCD* in the three previous questions. Discuss what you notice.

Problem solving

10 A triangle has vertices at *A*(1, 1), *B*(−4, −4), *C*(−3, 7).
After a transformation, its vertices are at *A′*(5, 1), *B′*(10, −4), *C′*(9, 7).
Describe the transformation as specifically as possible.

11 Reflect the following shape in the line $y = x$.

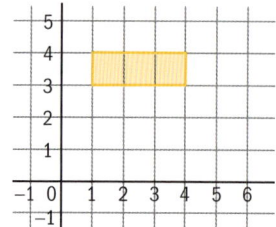

12 Describe the transformation that maps A onto A′ for the following trapezium.

a

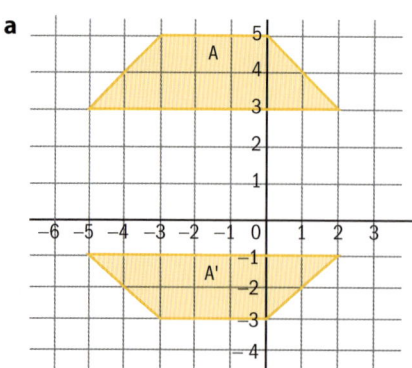

b

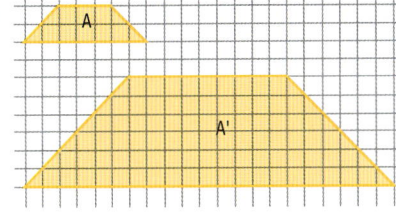

c

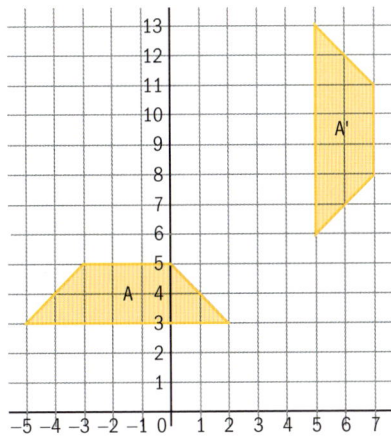

d

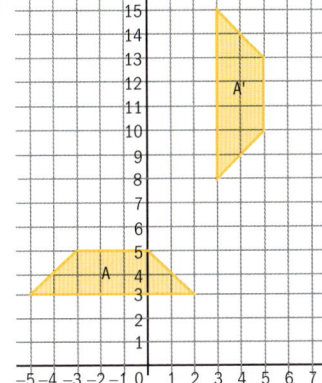

e

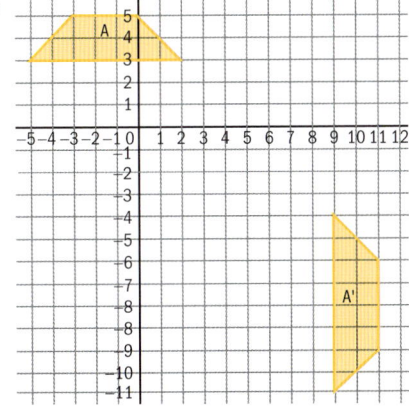

13 Digit transformations

Consider the digits 0 to 9 written as scoreboard digits.

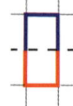

a Digit 0 can be drawn as 3 segments and their reflection along the horizontal middle segment as such:

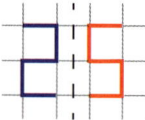

Determine how many different 2-digit numbers can be written as the segments of the top half and their reflections along the middle segment.

> Think of which digits are *symmetrical* about a horizontal line through their middle.

b The number 25 can be created using the digit 2 and its reflection along the vertical line in the middle between the 2 and the 5.

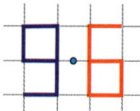

Determine how many different 2-digit numbers can be written this way.

c The number 96 can be created using the digit 9 and its rotation 180° along the point in the middle between the 9 and the 6.

Determine how many different 2-digit numbers can be written this way.

d The number 25 becomes the number 52 when it is rotated 180°.

i Determine how many different 2-digit numbers can become another 2-digit number by applying this transformation.

ii Determine how many different 2-digit numbers remain the same 2-digit number by applying this transformation.

- -

A **tessellation** is a pattern of shapes that are arranged on a plane or surface in a way that there are no gaps and no overlaps. These shapes (called **tiles**) are translated, rotated and reflected as necessary to produce a pattern.

Here are some examples of tessellations:

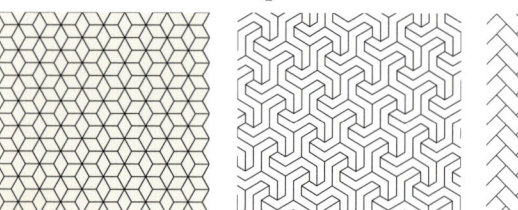

Exploration 2

Consider the following tessellations:

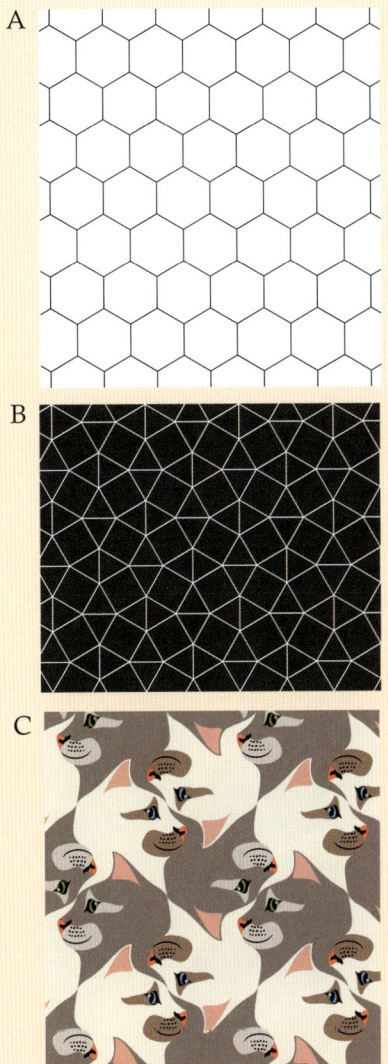

A

B

C

1 Explain how A, B, and C are all tessellations.

2 Compare A, B, and C and discuss how each one is unique.

Tessellations can be described by studying the tiles' vertices.

3 Some tessellations can be formed from regular polygons. This is the case in tessellation A.

   a Complete the following table and write down the interior angles for each regular polygon, from the equilateral triangle to the regular decagon.

The interior angle of a regular n-sided polygon is calculated using the formula $\frac{(n-2) \times 180°}{n}$.

▶ Continued on next page

Regular polygon name	Number of sides	Interior angle
Triangle	3	
Square	4	
	5	
	6	
	7	
	8	
	9	
Regular decagon	10	

b If there are no gaps and no overlaps between the tiles of a tessellation, discuss how looking at the vertices can help determine which regular polygons tessellate.

c Determine which regular polygons tessellate. Explain why the others cannot tessellate.

4 Some tessellations involve more than one regular polygon. Below are two examples of such tessellations involving only squares and equilateral triangles.

D   E

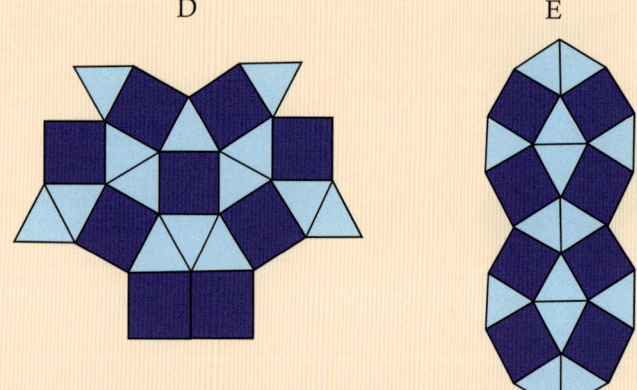

Do the following steps for each of the two tessellations D and E:

a Pick a vertex. Write down the sequence of the number of sides of each polygon that surrounds this vertex, from smallest to largest. For example, in the following tessellation the vertex is surrounded by three hexagons, which are 6-sided shapes. So this vertex is labelled '6.6.6'.

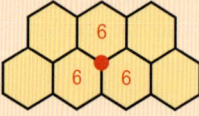

b Pick another vertex from the same tessellation (D or E), and determine whether it has the same labelling sequence as the previous vertex.

▶ Continued on next page

c Determine whether all the vertices of the tessellation have the same labelling sequence.

5 Use graphing technology to explore other tessellations of regular polygons (not just triangles and squares). How many tessellations can you create where each vertex is surrounded by the same sequence of regular polygons?

A **regular tessellation** is a tessellation where each tile is a single regular polygon. There are only three regular tessellations:

 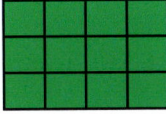 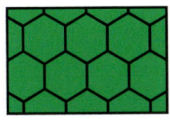

Triangles   Squares   Hexagons

Reflect and discuss 1

- Why are triangles, squares and hexagons the only regular polygons that can tessellate?

- How can looking at vertices help you justify your answer?

A **semi-regular tessellation** (or Archimedean tessellation) is a tessellation made up of more than one regular polygon, and where each vertex has the same configuration. There are only eight semi-regular tessellations:

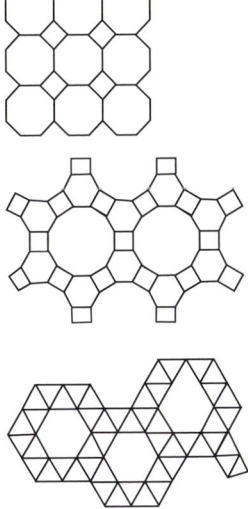 

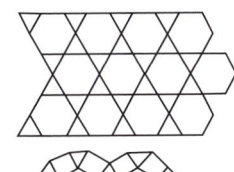

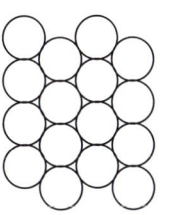 

C Understanding transformations

- Can isometric transformations replace one another?
- How are geometric transformations similar to functions?

> A **combined transformation** is the final result when one transformation is followed by one or more other transformations.

There are sometimes different ways of combining isometric transformations to obtain the same image for an original shape.

Exploration 3

Consider the following triangle.

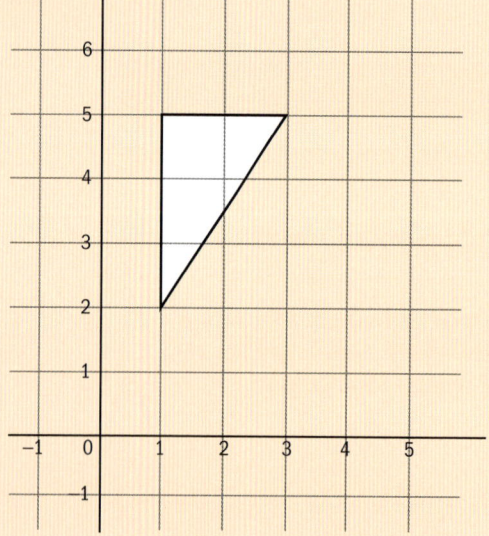

For each of the following transformations, determine whether it is possible to obtain the same indicated transformation by using one or more of the following transformations. If it is possible, justify with an example. If it isn't, explain why.

- only rotations
- only reflections
- a combination of rotations and reflections

1 Transform the triangle by the translation $\begin{pmatrix} 4 \\ 3 \end{pmatrix}$.

2 Transform the triangle by the reflection in the line $y = x$.

3 Transform the triangle by the rotation 90° clockwise around the point (1, 1).

Exploration 4

Consider the following shape.

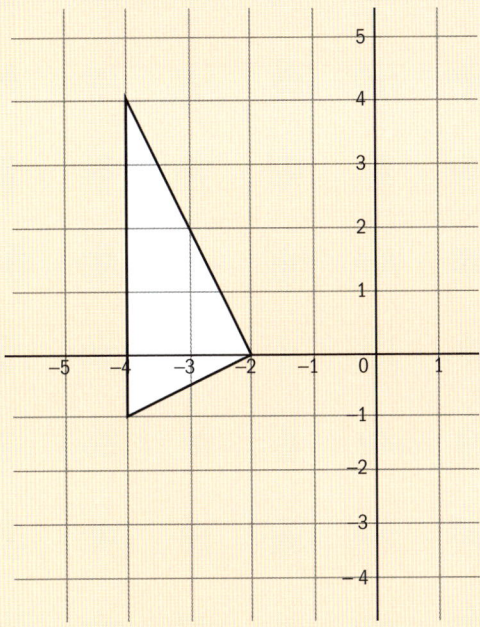

Translation

1 Draw the shape and its image when it is translated 6 units in the *x*-direction and 2 units in the *y*-direction.

2 Determine if it is possible to obtain the same image only by reflecting the original shape (possibly multiple times). If so, write down the equations of the mirror lines for each reflection.

Rotation

3 Draw the shape and its image when it is rotated 180° about the point (3, −2).

4 Determine if it is possible to obtain the same image only by reflecting the original shape (possibly multiple times). If so, write down the equations of the mirror lines for each reflection.

Glide reflection

5 Draw the shape and its image when it is reflected in the line $y = -1$ and then translated 4 units parallel to the same line.

6 Determine if it is possible to obtain the same image only by reflecting the original shape (possibly multiple times). If so, write down the equations of the mirror lines for each reflection.

7 Determine whether you think it is possible to express any isometric transformation as a succession of reflections of the original shape. If you think it is possible, determine the maximum number of reflections needed to obtain a transformation equivalent to each other type of isometric transformation.

> A **glide reflection** is a fourth isometric transformation. It is a composition of a reflection and a translation parallel to the line of reflection.

The **Fundamental Theorem of Isometries** states that any isometry of the plane is either a reflection, a translation, a rotation or a glide reflection. A consequence of this theorem is that any isometry is the composition of one, two or three reflections.

Example 2

Describe the two transformations performed sequentially on the black shape, as shown in the diagram below. Then describe the single transformation that transforms the black shape to the red shape.

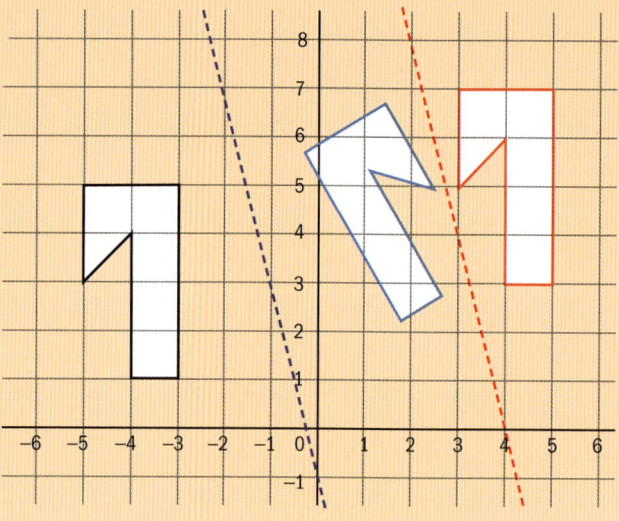

- The blue shape is the reflection of the black shape in the line $y = -4x - 1$.
- The red shape is the reflection of the blue shape in the line $y = -4x + 16$.
- The red shape is also the translation of the black shape by $\begin{pmatrix} 8 \\ 2 \end{pmatrix}$.

Example 3

Consider the following diagram:

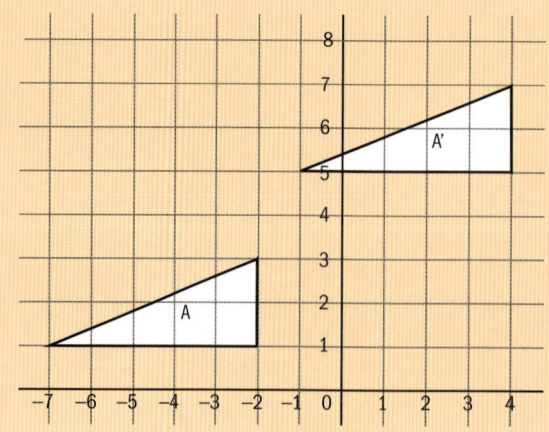

Use graphing software to play around with shapes to see how objects can move using different transformations.

▶ Continued on next page

a The transformation that maps A onto A′ is a translation by $\begin{pmatrix} 6 \\ 4 \end{pmatrix}$.

b There are multiple ways to rotate shape A to obtain shape A′.

One possible way is to rotate shape A by 180° around point (−2, 4) to obtain A″, then to rotate A″ by 180° around the point (1, 6) to obtain A′.

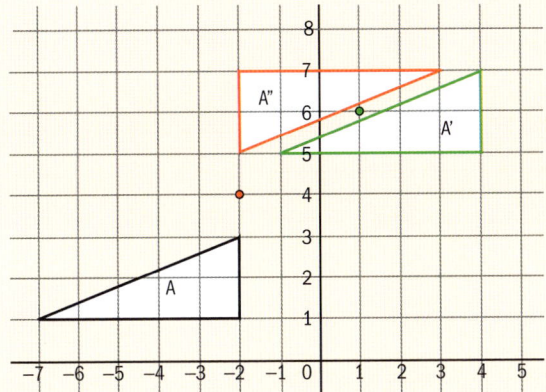

Another possible way is to rotate shape A by 180° around point (−1, 2) to obtain A″, then to rotate A″ by 180° around the point (2, 4) to obtain A′.

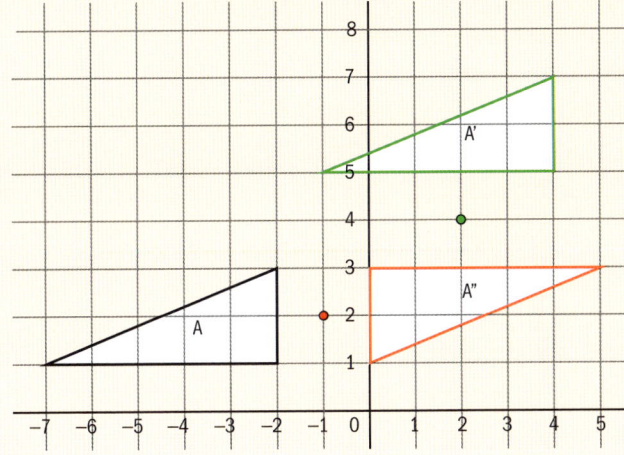

▶ Continued on next page

A third way is to rotate shape A counterclockwise by 90° around point (−1, 5) to obtain A″, then to rotate A″ clockwise by 90° around the point (4, 4) to obtain A′.

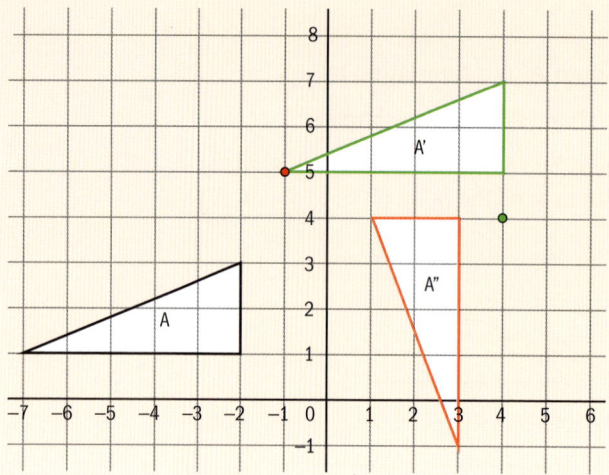

Practice 2

1 Consider the following diagrams. For each one, determine and fully describe these transformations:

i The single transformation that maps X onto X′.

ii The single transformation that maps X′ onto X″.

iii The single transformation that is equivalent to the combined transformation that maps X onto X″.

a

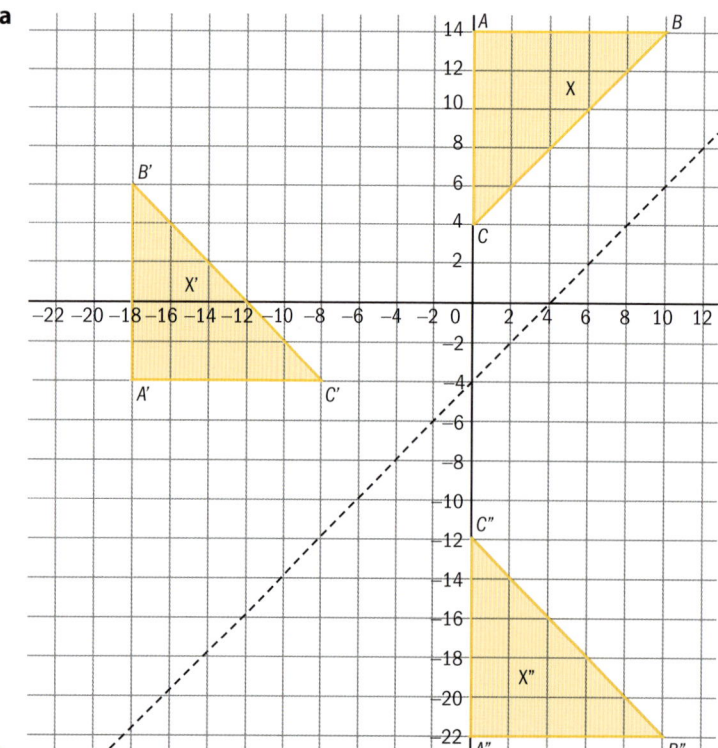

b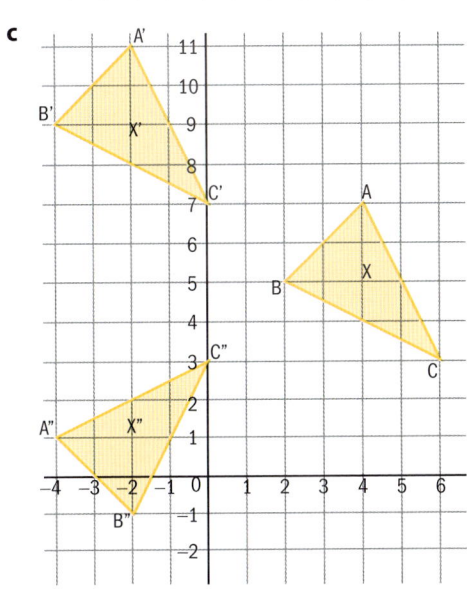

c

2 Consider the following triangle:

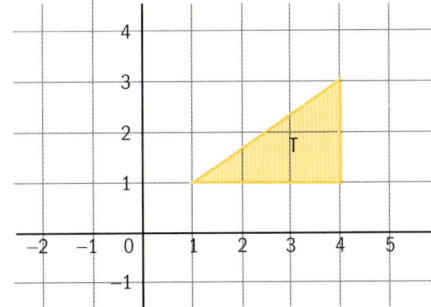

For each of the following, describe the single transformation that is equivalent to the two given transformations.

a Reflect the triangle in the line $x = 0$ and then in the line $x = 2$.

b Reflect the triangle in the line $y = -1$ and then in the line $y = -3$.

c Reflect the triangle in the line $y = 0$ and then in the line $x = -2$.

d Reflect the triangle in the line $x = -1$ and then in the line $y = 4$.

e Reflect the triangle in the line $y = 0.5x + 5$ and then in the line $y = -2x$.

3 Consider the following rectangle:

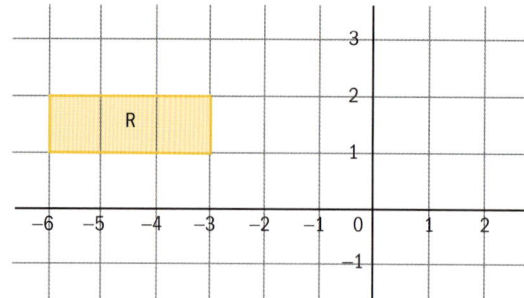

For each of the following, describe the single transformation that is equivalent to the two given rotations.

a Rotate the rectangle 90° counterclockwise around the point (0, 0). Then rotate it again in the same direction around the same point.

b Rotate the rectangle 90° counterclockwise around the point (0,0). Then rotate it 90° clockwise around the point (2, 1).

c Rotate the rectangle 90° clockwise around the point (3, 1). Then rotate it again in the same direction around the point (0, 0).

d Rotate the rectangle 90° counterclockwise around the point (2, 1). Then rotate it again in the opposite direction around the point (−2, −1).

Problem solving

4 Consider the following diagrams. For each one, describe the single transformation that maps shape A onto shape A′. Then suggest how shape A can be reflected (possibly multiple times) to obtain shape A′.

a

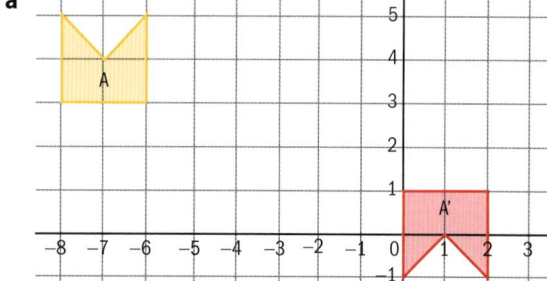

b

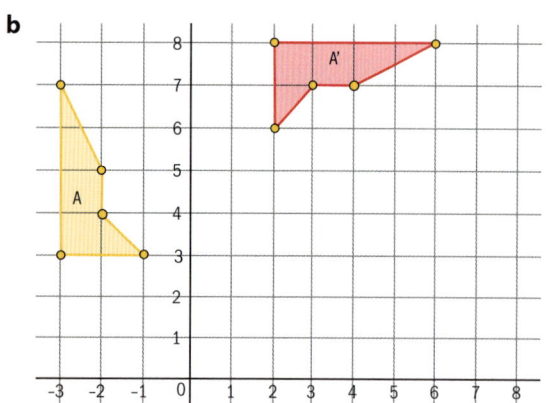

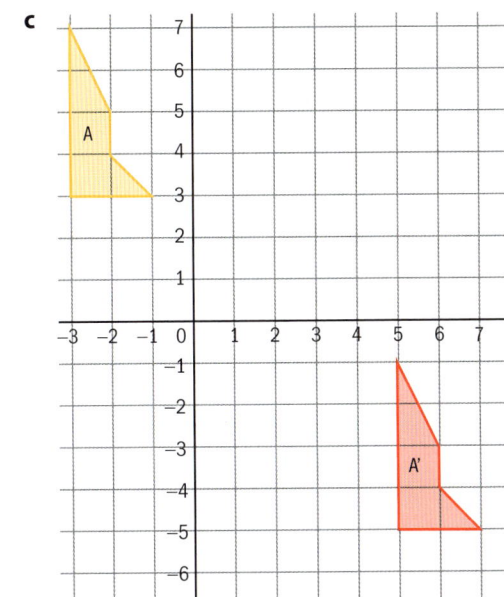

c

Exploration 5

1 Determine whether each element that composes a function (as seen in Unit 3.1) can be applied to geometric transformations:

   a There is an input (x).

   b There is an output (y).

   c There is a function (f) that maps x onto y (y is the image of x).

   d Each element in the domain matches one and only one element in the range.

2 Explain how a geometric transformation can be considered as a function of shapes.

3 Suggest possible geometric values for the transformation function $y = T(x)$:

   a What could x be?

   b What could T be?

   c What could y be?

4 Choose a geometric transformation and define its function.

   a Draw the following original shape, and its image after transforming it according to your transformation function.

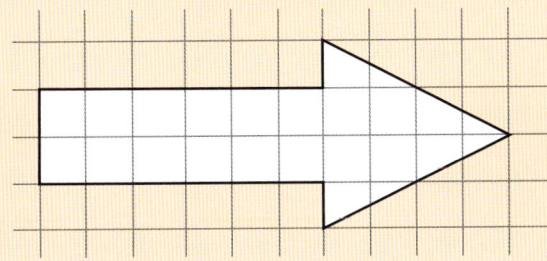

You may need to give the shape a position on a coordinate plane.

▶ Continued on next page

b Draw your own shapes, and their images in the same way. Make sure that the transformation function is specific, and that there is exactly one way to draw the image of each shape in the domain.

Exploration 6

1 Write down the properties that make a transformation an isometric transformation.

2 Consider two points x_1 and x_2 and their images $y_1 = T(x_1)$ and $y_2 = T(x_2)$, where $y = T(x)$ defines an isometric transformation. Suggest any relationships between x_1, x_2, y_1 and y_2 that are true both before and after the isometric transformation is applied.

In order for a transformation to be isometric, distance must be preserved under the transformation. This means that for the transformation T, if $y_1 = T(x_1)$ and $y_2 = T(x_2)$ the distance between x_1 and x_2 must be equal to the distance between y_1 and y_2.

D The importance of order

- Does the order of transformations always matter?

Exploration 7

1 Consider the following glide reflection:

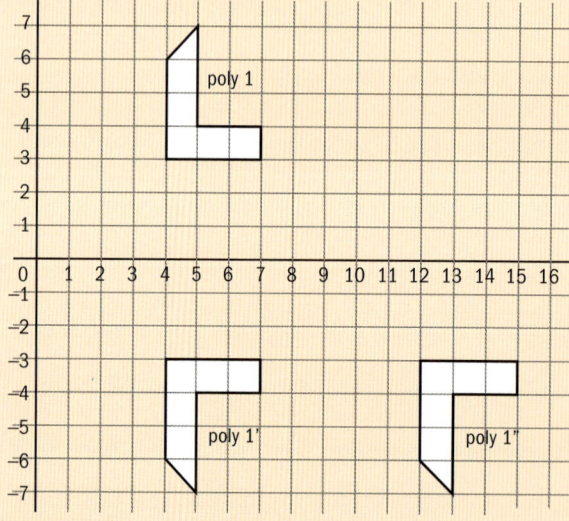

a Describe the single transformations that map poly1 onto poly1′ and poly1′ onto poly1″.

b Determine whether the same image poly1″ is obtained if the two same single transformations are performed in the opposite order.

▶ Continued on next page

2 Consider the following shape:

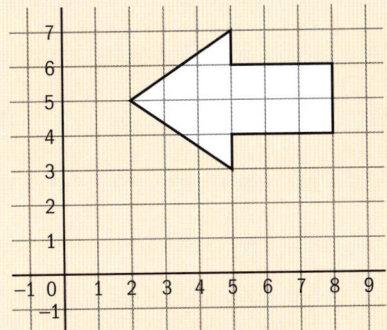

a Draw it on a squared sheet of paper, and perform the following transformations in the given order (first T1, then T2):

i T1: Rotate the shape 180° around the point (5, 0)

ii T2: Translate the shape by $\begin{pmatrix} 10 \\ 0 \end{pmatrix}$

b In a different color, perform the same transformations in the reverse order (first T2, then T1), each time using the same transformation specifications.

c Explain why the result of the two combined transformations is not the same.

d Determine whether it is possible to obtain the same image when reversing the order of the transformations (T1 then T2, and T2 then T1) by changing any or all of the following between the two combined transformations: the rotation angle, the center of rotation or the direction of the translation.

3 Discuss whether the order of transformations in a combined transformation is important or not. If combined transformations are done with the same transformations but in a different order, are the final images always/sometimes/never the same?

Summary

- Two objects are **congruent** when they are the same shape and size. They are **similar** when they are the same shape but have a different size.

- **Geometric transformations** change the position, direction and size of shapes in a plane, but they never change their shape.

- An **isometric transformation** (or a **congruence transformation**) is a transformation where the original shape and its image after transformation are congruent. Translations, rotations and reflections are isometric transformations.

- A **translation** is a displacement $\begin{pmatrix} x \\ y \end{pmatrix}$, where each point in the shape is moved x units horizontally and y units vertically .

- A **rotation** turns a shape clockwise or counterclockwise by a certain angle about a point, called the **center of rotation**.

- A **reflection** flips a shape into its mirror image on the other side of a line, called the **mirror line**.

- A **glide reflection** (also an isometric transformation) is a composition of a reflection and a translation parallel to the line of reflection.

- The **Fundamental Theorem of Isometries** states that any isometry of the plane is either a reflection, a translation, a rotation or a glide reflection. A consequence of this theorem is that any isometry is the composition of one, two or three reflections.

- A **dilation** changes the size of a shape. It is not an isometric transformation. The **scale factor** is the ratio of the corresponding sides of the shape and its image after dilation. If the scale factor is larger than 1, the image is an **enlargement**; if the scale factor is smaller than 1 (but greater than 0), the image is a **reduction**.

- A **combined transformation** is the final result when one transformation is followed by one or more other transformations. The order of transformations matters in a combined transformation.

- A **tessellation** is a pattern of shapes that are arranged on a plane or surface in a way that there are no gaps and no overlaps. These shapes (called **tiles**) are translated, rotated and reflected as necessary to produce a pattern.

  ○ A **regular tessellation** is a tessellation where each tile is a single regular polygon. There are only three regular tessellations:

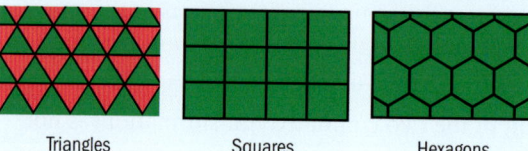

Triangles   Squares   Hexagons

  ○ A **semi-regular tessellation** (or Archimedean tessellation) is a tessellation made up of more than one regular polygon, and where each vertex has the same configuration. There are only eight semi-regular tessellations:

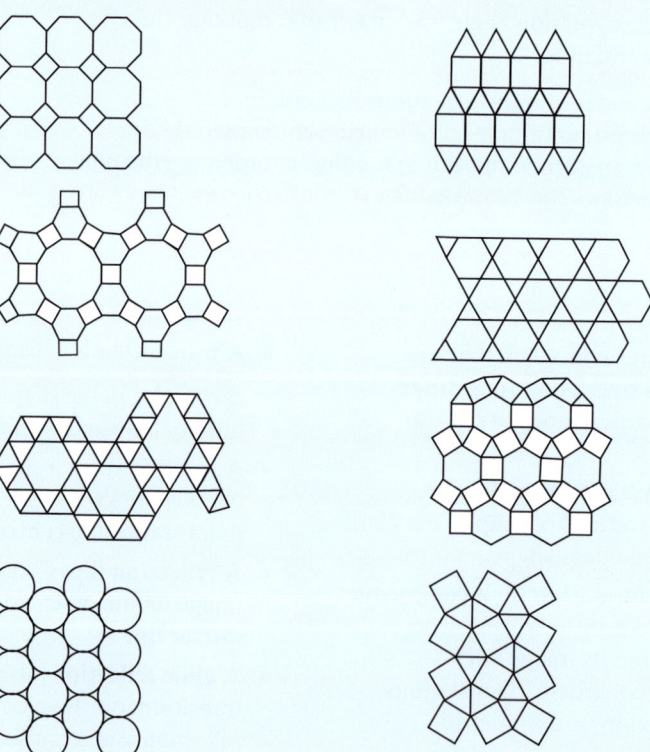

Mixed practice

1 Copy and complete the table.

Point	Translation by $\begin{pmatrix} -2 \\ 5 \end{pmatrix}$	Rotation by 180° around the origin	Reflection in the *x*-axis	Reflection in the line *y* = *x*
(0, 0)				
(5, 3)				
(3, −2)				
(−2, 5)				
(−4, −3)				

2 Draw the following shape on a Cartesian plane.

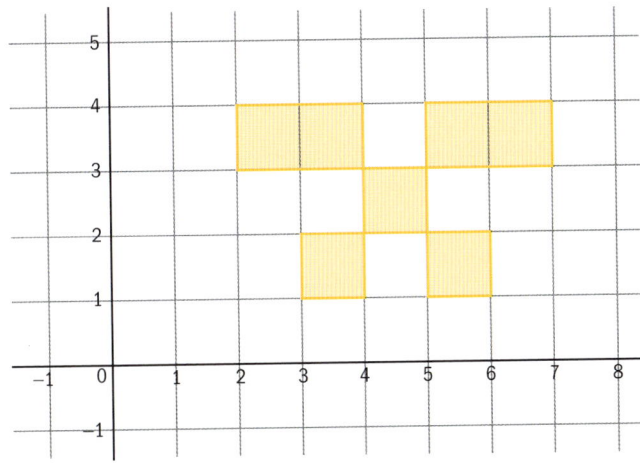

Then, in a different color each time, **draw** the image of the shape after the following transformations.

a A rotation of 90° anticlockwise around the point (1, 1).

b A rotation of 180° around the point (2, −3).

c A translation by $\begin{pmatrix} -5 \\ -2 \end{pmatrix}$

d A translation by $\begin{pmatrix} 1 \\ 3 \end{pmatrix}$

e A reflection in the *x*-axis.

f A reflection in the line *y* = −*x*.

g An enlargement by scale factor 2.

h An enlargement by scale factor 2.5.

3 Create the following shape by transforming the red shape (composed of two triangles) seven times. **Describe** each transformation. (Hint: each single transformation must always be applied to the same red triangles.)

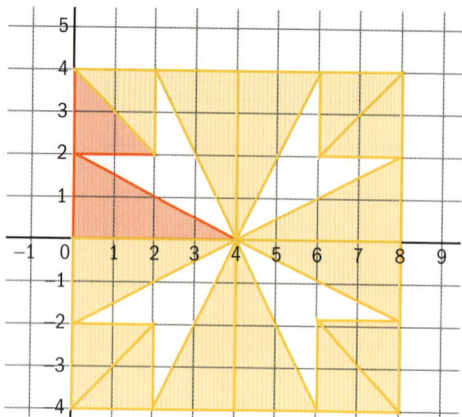

Problem solving

4 A scale drawing is a reduction of a real place or object. Conversely, a real object is an enlargement of a scale drawing. A map (considered a scale drawing) has a scale of 2:100 000.

a **Determine** the scale factor of the enlargement from the map to the real distance.

b **Find** the real-life distance that is represented by 1 cm on the map.

c The distance between Funtown and Supercity on the map is 14 cm. **Determine** the real distance between these two places.

d Strangeville is exactly halfway between Funtown and Supercity. **Determine** how far Strangeville should be from Funtown on the map.

e Ilyan drove from Funtown to Strangeville, but only recorded 6 km between the cities on his counter. **Suggest** why this might be the case.

5 **Draw** an isosceles triangle ABC where AB and AC are of equal length.

a **Draw** point D such that it is the image of point C when it is rotated 60° clockwise about point A.

b **Justify** why triangle ACD is equilateral.

6 Consider the following shape:

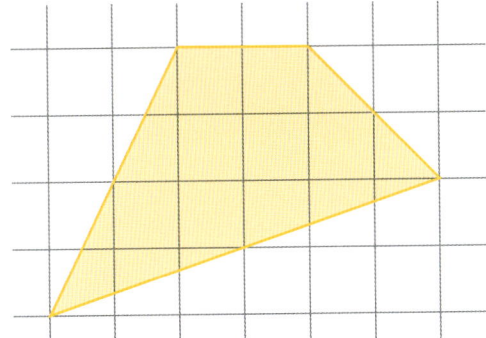

  a **Determine** whether this shape tessellates or not.

  b If it does, draw the tessellation. If it doesn't, **explain** why not.

  c If the shape tessellates, **describe** the single transformation that is repeated on a tile to obtain a new tile of the tessellation.

Reflect and discuss 2

How have you explored the statement of inquiry? Give specific examples.

Statement of inquiry:

Representing transformed objects and studying their form helps us enjoy their creativity in space.

A whole range of things

F What makes a good representation?

Representation is a visual presentation of information and can take many forms. It should be eye-catching and meaningful, relevant and purposeful. Its main aim is to present clarity and rigor to the viewer.

- What styles of representation of data can you think of?
- What do you think makes a graph useful?
- What can make a graph misleading?

C **How does understanding quantities enable you to make generalizations about trends?**

Quantity is an amount or number.

How many fish?

Suppose you want to know the quantity of fish in a lake. How would you go about this investigation? You could drain the lake and count all the dead fish; that would give you an accurate count, but it's not very practical, and not too considerate of the fish either!

One way to estimate the quantity is called the capture–recapture method:

Capture 100 fish, tag them, and then release them back into the lake. Assume that all these fish distribute themselves evenly and randomly throughout the lake.

Later, you capture 100 fish again and find that, of these, 5 are ones that you tagged previously. You know that there are 100 tagged fish in the lake. So how many batches of 100 fish would you need to capture all 100 tagged fish? If you assume you'd catch 5 tagged fish for every 100, then you would have to catch $\frac{100}{5} = 20$ batches. At 100 fish per batch that would mean there are an estimated $20 \times 100 = 2000$ fish in the lake.

- How many fish would you estimate are in the lake if you recaptured 11 tagged fish?

- What assumptions are being made in this method?

- What conclusion(s) could you draw if none of the fish you caught later on were tagged?

D **To what extent does understanding trends and relationships make decision-making more effective?**

Global context:
Globalization and sustainability

Exploration:
Exploring trends and the impact of decision-making on the environment

📖 **Launch additional digital resources for this unit.**

6.1 Univariate statistics

Global context: Globalization and sustainability

Related concept: Representation

RELATIONSHIPS

Objectives

- Categorizing data
- Constructing stem-and-leaf diagrams
- Calculating quartiles, the range and the interquartile range
- Finding a five-point summary from a set of data
- Constructing box-and-whisker plots
- Identifying outliers
- Comparing distributions

Inquiry questions

F
- What are the different types of data?
- How are the different measures of central tendency calculated?

C
- How do measures of dispersion help you describe relationships in data?
- How do different representations help you compare data sets?

D
- Should we ignore amounts or numbers that aren't typical?
- How do individuals stand out in a crowd?

ATL Communication

Organize and depict information logically

Statement of inquiry:

How quantities are represented can help to establish underlying relationships and trends in a population.

📑 Launch additional digital resources for this chapter.

You should already know how to:

• find the mode, median, mean and range of a set of data	**1** Find the mode, median, mean and range of these data sets.
	a 1, 3, 5, 3, 6, 11, 8, 3, 5, 6, 4
	b 16, 21, 19, 20, 18, 19, 21, 19, 20, 19, 19, 22, 19, 21, 17, 16, 14, 22

 Representing sets of data

- What are the different types of data?
- How are the different measures of central tendency calculated?

Statistics involves *collecting* raw data, *organizing* the data into visual representations, and *analysing* the data.

> *Data* is the plural of the Latin word *datum* meaning 'a piece of information'.

Qualitative data describes a certain characteristic (for example: color or type) using words. **Quantitative data** has a numerical value. There are two types:

- **Discrete data** can be counted (for example: number of goals scored) or can only take certain values (such as shoe size).

- **Continuous data** can be measured (for example: mass and height) and can take any numerical value.

> In order to perform statistical analysis, continuous data must be rounded to a certain degree of accuracy.

Practice 1

Categorize each set of data as qualitative or quantitative. For quantitative data, state whether it is discrete or continuous.

1 Number of red cars passing through an intersection

2 Time taken for a car to cross an intersection

3 Color of each student's eyes in your class

4 Numbers of children in each student's family in your class

5 Maximum daily temperatures in Qingdao, China

6 Heights of students in your class

7 Shoe sizes of students in your class

8 Daily intake of protein, in grams, for members of a sporting team

9 Number of milkshakes sold in a cafeteria

10 Flavors of milkshakes sold in a cafeteria

- -

A stem-and-leaf diagram is a visual representation of ordered raw data, which can then be analysed.

> Stem-and-leaf diagrams are often used in train and bus timetables.

Example 1

Here are the numbers of climate change surveys carried out by 23 students.

0, 1, 14, 11, 0, 6, 10, 1, 0, 39, 1, 13, 10, 26, 7, 4, 17, 12, 58, 22, 15, 20, 17

Construct an ordered stem-and-leaf diagram to represent this data.

0 0 0 1 1 1 4 6 7 10 10 11 12
13 14 15 17 17 20 22 26 39 58

0	0 0 0 1 1 1 4 6 7
1	0 0 1 2 3 4 5 7 7
2	0 2 6
3	9
4	
5	8

Key: 3 | 9 represents 39 surveys

Sort the data in ascending order. The data ranges from 0 to 58, so use the tens digit to form the stem.

Construct a stem-and-leaf diagram from your ordered data. Remember to include a key.

Reflect and discuss 1

- Is a stem-and-leaf diagram similar to a bar chart? Explain.
- What are the advantages of keeping raw data?

In a stem-and-leaf diagram:

- the **stem** represents the **category** figure
- the **leaves** represent the **final** digit(s) of each data point
- the **key** tells you how to read the values.

Practice 2

ATL

1 Here are the numbers of croissants a baker sold each day during a three-week period:

35, 47, 34, 46, 62, 41, 35, 47, 51, 59, 56, 73, 38, 41, 44, 51, 45, 60, 25, 35, 46

Construct an ordered stem-and-leaf diagram to represent the data.

2 The masses (in grams) of 11 Chinese striped hamsters are:

21.6, 22.4, 27.2, 30.5, 25.2, 23.1, 25.3, 21.3, 20.9, 24.5, 25.2

Construct a stem-and-leaf diagram to represent the data.

Use the whole number part as the stem and the decimal part as the leaf.

Problem solving

3 The stem-and-leaf diagram shows the distances in kilometers students, in one class, travel to school.

```
0 | 4 6 6 7
1 | 2 3 3 3 8
2 | 0 2 6 9
3 | 1 1 2 7
4 | 0
```

Key: 2 | 0 represents 20 km

a Write down the:

i least distance traveled

ii greatest distance traveled.

b Find the number of students in the class.

c Write down how many students travel 13 km.

d Students who travel more than 18 km get cheaper bus fares. Find the percentage of students who get cheaper bus fares.

4 Here are the heights of one-year-old apple trees in centimeters.

180 184 195 177 175 173 169 167 197

173 166 183 161 195 177 192 161 166

Organize and represent the data in a stem-and-leaf diagram.

Use the first two digits as the stem.

Reflect and discuss 2

- What problems might arise when using stem-and-leaf diagrams for large data sets?

- What about data sets with a small range?

For any set of data there are two categories of **summary statistics**:

- **Measures of central tendency (location)** summarize a set of data with a single value that is most typical of the data set. The mean, median and mode are all measures of central tendency.

- **Measures of dispersion (spread)** measure how spread out a set of data is. Range is a measure of dispersion.

Example 2

The stem-and-leaf diagram shows the number of emails received by Kirsty every day for 17 days. Find the mode, median and range of this data.

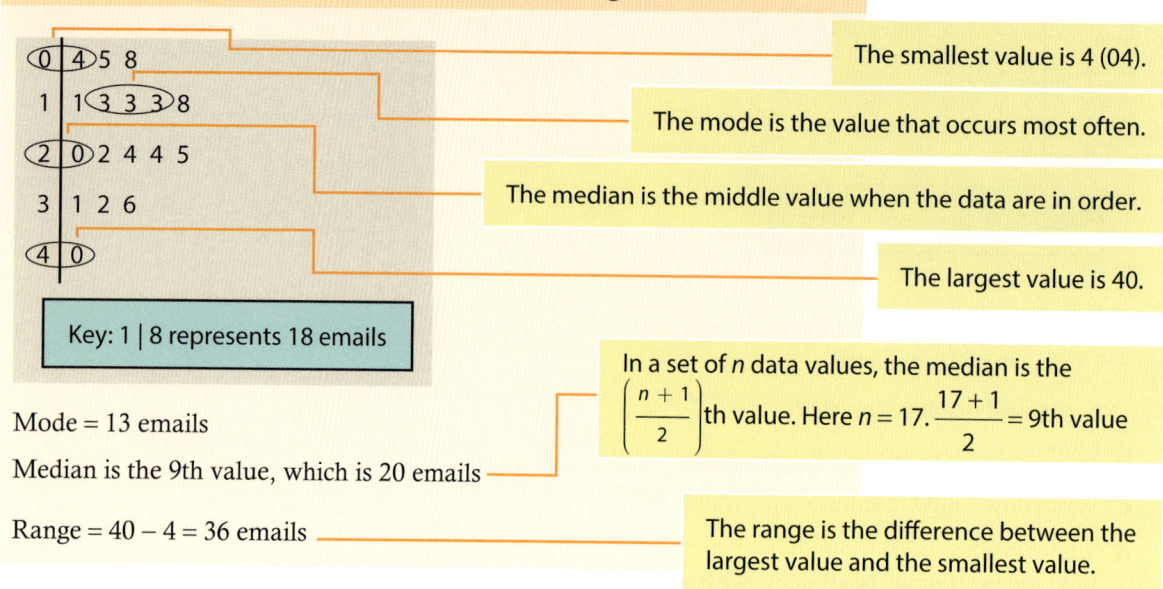

The smallest value is 4 (04).

The mode is the value that occurs most often.

The median is the middle value when the data are in order.

The largest value is 40.

Key: 1 | 8 represents 18 emails

In a set of n data values, the median is the $\left(\dfrac{n+1}{2}\right)$th value. Here $n = 17$. $\dfrac{17+1}{2} = $ 9th value

Mode = 13 emails

Median is the 9th value, which is 20 emails

Range = 40 − 4 = 36 emails

The range is the difference between the largest value and the smallest value.

Practice 3

1 The stem-and-leaf diagram shows the number of goals scored by the Welsh Wizards during a netball tournament.

Find the mode, median and range of this data.

```
2 | 7
3 | 0 3 5 7 9
4 | 1 2 2 3 3 5 7 8 9 9 9
5 | 2 5
```

Key: 4 | 1 represents 41 goals

2 The stem-and-leaf diagram shows the number of cars parked in a car park every day over a period of 20 days.

Find the mode, median and range of this data.

```
1 | 5 7 8
2 | 0 2 2 5 7 7 8
3 | 0 0 0 3 6 8
4 | 0 1 1 5
```

Key: 1 | 5 represents 15 cars

Problem solving

3 The back-to-back stem-and-leaf diagram shows the marks for a group of students following their English and Mathematics exams.

English		Mathematics
2 2	4	0 3
0	5	1 1 6 7 9
7 1	6	3 3 3
5 4 2 0	7	5
8 3	8	

Key:
2 | 4 represents 42 marks
on the English exam

4 | 0 represents 40 marks
on the Mathematics exam

a Find the number of students who took the English and Mathematics exams.

b Write down the mode of the Mathematics marks.

c Write down the mode of the English marks.

d Find the median of the English marks.

e Find the range of the English and Mathematics marks.

f Justify whether the English or Mathematics marks are the more consistent.

4 The number of minutes a sample of 13 people had to wait to see a doctor in her office are shown.

16, 28, 47, 21, 32, 19, 25, 39, 20, 12, 36, 16, 23

a Construct a stem-and-leaf diagram for this data.

b Determine how many people waited more than 30 minutes.

c Find the mode, median and range of the data.

Reflect and discuss 3

- What does the shape of a back-to-back stem-and-leaf diagram show you?

- Which statistics are easier to find from the original data and which statistics are easier to extract from the stem-and-leaf diagram?

Quartiles divide an ordered set of data values into quarters:

- The **median** is another name for the second quartile, Q_2.

- The **lower/first quartile** (Q_1) is the median of the observations to the left of the median in an arranged set of observations.

- The **upper/third quartile** (Q_3) is the median of the observations to the right of the median in an arranged set of observations.

- The **interquartile range** (IQR) is the difference between the lower quartile and the upper quartile $(Q_3 - Q_1)$.

ATL

Example 3

Find the median, lower and upper quartiles and interquartile range of this data set: 19, 5, 10, 15, 11, 2, 4, 20, 6, 13, 9, 8

2, 4, 5, 6, 8, 9, 10, 11, 13, 15, 19, 20 —— Write the data in order. There are 12 data values, so $n = 12$.

The median, $Q_2 = 9.5$

Q_2

9.5

The median is $\frac{n+1}{2} = \frac{12+1}{2} = 6.5$th value, which is the mean of 9 and 10.

2 4 5 | 6 8 9 | 10 11 13 15 19 20

The lower quartile, $Q_1 = 5.5$ —————— The lower quartile is the median of the values less than Q_2.

Q_1 Q_2

5.5   9.5

2 4 5 | 6 8 9 | 10 11 13 | 15 19 20

The upper quartile, $Q_3 = 14$ —————— The upper quartile is the median of the values greater than Q_2.

Q_1 Q_2 Q_3

5.5   9.5   14

2 4 5 | 6 8 9 | 10 11 13 | 15 19 20

Interquartile range, IQR $= Q_3 - Q_1$

$= 14 - 5.5 = 8.5$

In Example 3, the number of data values n was a multiple of 4. In this case none of the quartiles were values in the data set.

Exploration 1

1 Find Q_1, Q_2 and Q_3 for these data sets:

   a 2, 4, 5, 6, 8, 9, 10, 11, 13, 15, 19, 20, 22 $n = 13$, (multiple of 4) + 1

   b 2, 4, 5, 6, 8, 9, 10, 11, 13, 15, 19, 20, 22, 23 $n = 14$, (multiple of 4) + 2

   c 2, 4, 5, 6, 8, 9, 10, 11, 13, 15, 19, 20, 22, 23, 27 $n = 15$, (multiple of 4) + 3

> If $n + 1$ is an odd number, the median will be the mean of the two surrounding numbers.

2 Summarize your findings in a table:

n	multiple of 4	(multiple of 4) +1	(multiple of 4) +2	(multiple of 4) +3
median Q_2	not a value in original data set			
Q_1 and Q_3	not a value in original data set			

3 Determine when Q_1, Q_2 and Q_3 are values in the original data set.

- A data set has n values, where n is one less than a multiple of four. Will Q_1, Q_2 and Q_3 be values in the original data set?

- In any data set, what fraction of the data is less than or equal to:
  - ○ the median   ○ the lower quartile   ○ the upper quartile?

  Why are they are called quartiles?

- What fraction of the data lies between the lower and upper quartiles? What is this as a percentage?

- Is the IQR a measure of central tendency or a measure of dispersion? What does the IQR tell you?

Practice 4

1 Cara compared her SAT Mathematics score with ten of her friends. Their scores were:

650, 750, 700, 670, 420, 720, 750, 730, 780, 750, 780

   a Calculate the median, and the upper and lower quartiles.

   b Find the range and the interquartile range.

2 A baker records the number of doughnuts she sells each day during a three-week period:

35, 47, 34, 46, 62, 41, 35, 47, 51, 59, 56, 73, 38, 41, 44, 51, 45, 43

   a Calculate the median, and the upper and lower quartiles.

   b Find the range and the interquartile range.

3 The masses (in grams) of 11 newly hatched chicks are:

31.6, 28.4, 37.2, 31.5, 45.2, 43.1, 33.1, 35.3, 41.3, 49.9, 44.5

Find the median, range and IQR.

4 The stem-and-leaf diagram shows the time taken (in minutes) by a class of students to get to school.

Find the median, range and interquartile range of the times.

```
0 | 2 4 8 8 9
1 | 0 1 2 3 4 7
2 | 1 1 3
3 |
4 |
5 | 0
```

Key: 1 | 0 represents 10 minutes

Problem solving

5 The annual salaries of a sample of 9 senior and 9 junior employees at a law firm are shown in the back-to-back stem-and-leaf diagram.

Senior		Junior
	3	5 8
	4	0 2 8 9
9 2 0	5	0 1 3
5	6	
8 0 0	7	
2 0	8	

Key: 9 | 5 represents a salary of £59 000 for a senior employee

5 | 0 represents a salary of £50 000 for a junior employee

a Find the median salary of a senior employee.

b Find the median salary of a junior employee.

c Find the range of both the senior and junior salaries.

d Find the interquartile range of both the senior and junior salaries.

e Compare the salaries of the senior and junior employees.

Compare the medians and the measures of spreads.

6 Here are the ages of 12 people attending an evening class, in order:

22, 24, 29, 30, 30, x, 36, 45, y, 47, 53, z

The median age is 35.

The mean age is 37.5.

The upper quartile is 46.5.

Find the values of x, y and z.

7 Write two different data sets with median 5 and IQR 7.

The five-point summary of a data set is:

- the minimum value
- the lower quartile (Q_1)
- the median (Q_2)
- the upper quartile (Q_3)
- the maximum value.

Exploration 2

A box-and-whisker diagram is a visual representation of the five-point summary. Each vertical line represents one of the five-point summary values.

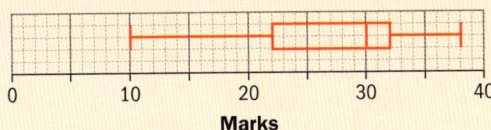

Marks

1 Write down the 5 values of the five-point summary.

2 From the information write down:

   a the median

   b the upper quartile.

3 Explain how you can calculate the range from this diagram.

4 Explain how you calculate the IQR from this diagram.

5 Determine what the box represents. What do the whiskers represent?

6 Describe a situation this diagram could represent.

American mathematician John Wilder Tukey contributed much to the field of statistics. He came up with both box-and-whisker and stem-and-leaf diagrams.

ATL Practice 5

1 The box-and-whisker diagram represents the numbers of strawberries harvested from 30 strawberry plants.

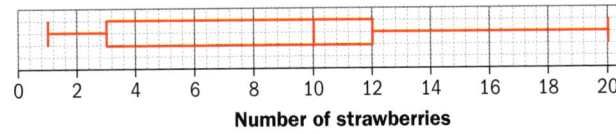

Number of strawberries

   a Find the median number of strawberries.

   b Find the maximum number of strawberries.

   c Find the IQR (interquartile range).

2 The masses of 100 male Amazon dolphins were represented in a box-and-whisker diagram.

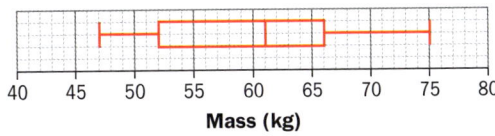

Mass (kg)

   a Write down the five-point summary of the data.

   b Calculate the range and IQR.

   c Find the number of dolphins who weigh 52 kg or less.

3 Write a five-point summary for each data set:

   a 1, 1, 2, 3, 3, 3, 4, 4, 4, 4

   b 10, 18, 15, 24, 15, 16, 21, 17, 15, 13, 12

   c 10 000, 64 000, 12 000, 11 500, 11 750, 12 250, 10 300

4 Construct a box-and-whisker diagram for this data on the number of lost property items found on a train.

Minimum	Q_1	Median	Q_3	Maximum
15	22	33	37	41

5 The number of minutes that 10 people wait to be connected to a helpline are recorded.

5, 8, 13, 19, 20, 22, 22, 27, 30, 34

a Find the median time.

b Find the lower and upper quartiles.

c Construct a box-and-whisker diagram for the data.

6 The heights, in meters, of 12 trees are:

29.2, 30.1, 36.5, 32.4, 20.0, 28.5, 32.0, 34.6, 39.1, 28.9, 34.4, 24.7

Construct a box-and-whisker diagram for the data.

7 The stem-and-leaf diagram shows the number of diners at a restaurant during a two-week period.

```
3 | 8 8 9
4 | 0 3 4 4 7 8
5 | 3 7 8 8
6 | 1
```

Key: 3 | 8 represents 38 diners

a Write down the minimum number of diners.

b Find the median number of diners.

c Find the interquartile range.

d Construct a box-and-whisker diagram for the data.

Problem solving

8 Construct a box-and-whisker diagram for a data set with:

median 32, minimum 18, Q_1 23, IQR 12, range 21, and find the values of A, B, C, D and E in the stem-and-leaf diagram here.

```
1 | A 9
2 | B 6 8
3 | C 3 4 D 8 E
```

C **Describing and comparing sets of data**

- How do measures of dispersion help you describe relationships in data?
- How do different representations help you compare data sets?

Exploration 3

A doctor is investigating how lack of sleep affects a person's ability to do simple tasks. In one task, participants were instructed to press a button as soon as they saw a red light come on. The response times were measured in seconds (to 2 d.p.). Here are two sets of data from the task:

Set 1: 0.58, 0.53, 0.58, 0.43, 0.58

Set 2: 0.66, 0.10, 0.58, 0.58, 0.78

1 Find the mean, mode, median, and interquartile range for each set.

2 The people were fully rested for one set of readings. For the other set, they had been awake for 24 hours. Decide which set is for 'fully rested' and which is for 'awake for 24 hours'. Explain the reasons for your decision.

Reflect and discuss 5

In Exploration 3:

- You could say that a typical reaction time for Set 1 was 0.58 seconds. Why would we choose this value? What does this single value tell you about the times for Set 1?

- The two data sets have the same mean. How well does the mean describe the real situation in Set 1 and in Set 2? What other measure could you use to compare the two data sets?

Distributions with one clear peak are called unimodal. Distributions with two clear peaks are called bimodal.

Example 4

The back-to-back stem-and-leaf diagram shows how much time a group of students spent studying Mathematics in one week. All times are in minutes.

a Describe the study times of the girls and boys.

b Compare the study times of the girls and boys.

Girls		Boys
	0	0 0
5 0 0	1	0 0 0
5 5 0 0	2	0 0 0 0 0 0 0 0 0 5 5
5 5 0 0 0 0 0	3	0 0 0
0 0 0 0	4	0 0 5
0 0	5	0
0 0 0	6	0
5 0	7	
	8	5

Key: 5 | 2 | 0 represents a girl studying for 25 minutes and a boy studying for 20 minutes

▶ Continued on next page

a The median is the $\frac{25+1}{2} = 13$th value. ————————— $n = 25$ for the girls and for the boys.

The median time for the girls is 35 minutes.

The median time for the boys is 20 minutes.

For the girls:

$Q_1 = 25$ minutes, $Q_3 = 50$ minutes

The interquartile range = $50 - 25 = 25$ minutes ———————

For the boys:

Use the median and interquartile range to describe the center and spread of each set of data.

$Q_1 = 20$ minutes, $Q_3 = 35$ minutes

The interquartile range = $35 - 20 = 15$ minutes

Both the distributions have only one mode (unimodal). About two-thirds of the boys spent 25 minutes or less studying Mathematics; more than two-thirds of the girls spent 30 minutes or more studying.

Use the stem-and-leaf diagram to describe the shape of each distribution.

b The median time for the girls is longer than the median time for the boys. On average, the girls spent more time studying Mathematics. The girls' IQR is ——————— greater than the boys' IQR, so the middle 50% of the girls' times has a larger spread.

Compare the measure of central tendency and the measure of dispersion for the girls and boys.

Objective: C. Communicating

iii. move between different forms of mathematical representation

In this practice you will be changing the representation of the data from tables to stem-and-leaf diagrams, and to box-and-whisker diagrams. These are examples of moving between different forms of representation.

Practice 6

1 The back-to-back stem-and-leaf diagram shows the times taken (in seconds) by some boys and girls to complete a simple jigsaw.

Girls		Boys
9 9	1	
7 5 5 4 2	2	3 5 7 7 7 9
8 8 8 5 1 0	3	1 2 3 4 4 7 8
9 6 4 3	4	5 5 6 9
7 2	5	1 2
2 1	6	9 9

Key: 3 | 4 | 5 represents a girl who took 43 seconds and a boy who took 45 seconds

a Calculate the median and interquartile range of times for the girls and boys.

b Describe the shape of the distributions.

c Compare the times taken by the girls and the boys.

Problem solving

2 The average monthly temperatures recorded over a year in the US cities of Sante Fe, New Mexico, and Saint Paul, Minnesota, are given below. All temperatures are in Fahrenheit.

On the Fahrenheit scale, zero represents the temperature produced by mixing equal masses of snow and common salt.

a Represent the data in a back-to-back stem-and-leaf diagram.

b Describe the temperatures in the two cities.

c Compare the temperatures.

	J	F	M	A	M	J	J	A	S	O	N	D
Sante Fe	44	48	56	65	74	83	86	83	78	67	53	43
Saint Paul	26	31	43	58	71	80	85	82	73	59	42	29

3 The heights (in centimeters) of one-year-old apple and pear trees are shown below.

Apple trees: 180, 184, 195, 177, 175, 173, 169, 167, 197, 173, 166, 183, 161, 195, 177, 192, 161, 166

Pear trees: 171, 160, 182, 168, 194, 177, 192, 160, 165, 178, 183, 190, 172, 174, 170, 165, 166, 193

a Represent the data in a back-to-back stem-and-leaf diagram.

b Describe the heights of the apple and pear trees.

c Compare the heights.

4 The box-and-whisker diagrams show the delayed departure of two trains, A and B.

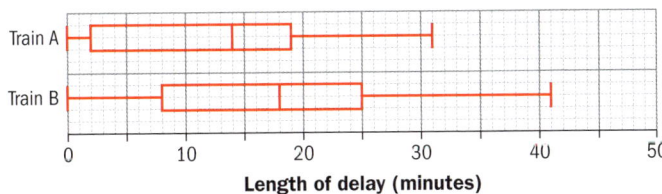

Compare the lengths of the delays.

5 The ages of a sample of subscribers to two German newspapers are shown below.

Süddeutsche Zeitung: 65, 36, 44, 25, 37, 29, 27, 19, 60, 46, 24, 35, 20, 55, 64, 30, 31, 22, 48, 53, 67

Der Tagesspiegel: 46, 18, 35, 20, 27, 25, 40, 24, 31, 29, 20, 63, 18, 30, 19, 28, 21, 34, 54, 22, 27

Use the same scale, and draw one box-and-whisker diagram above the other.

a Construct two box-and-whisker diagrams for the two data sets.

b Compare the ages.

6 Patricia and Ray work in a mobile phone store. The stem-and-leaf diagram shows Patricia's monthly sales for the previous year.

1	1 5 9
2	0 4 8 8
3	4 7
4	7
5	0 7

Key: 3 | 4 represents 34 mobile phones sold

The box-and-whisker diagram shows Ray's monthly sales for the same year.

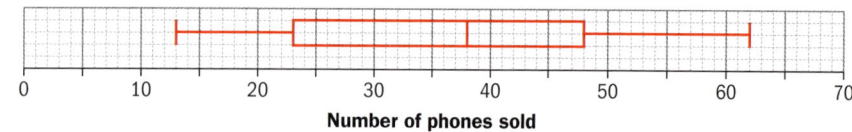

Number of phones sold

Compare Patricia's and Ray's sales.

- -

D The effect of outliers

- Should we ignore amounts or numbers that aren't typical?
- How do individuals stand out in a crowd?

An **outlier** is a member of a data set which does not fit with the general pattern of the rest of the data. A data point is an outlier if it is less than $1.5 \times IQR$ below Q_1, or greater than $1.5 \times IQR$ above Q_3.

Exploration 4

The foot lengths (measured to the nearest centimeter) of 19 students are given below.

20, 23, 22, 17, 24, 27, 27, 24, 23, 46, 18, 26, 25, 21, 24, 26, 30, 24, 20

1 a Find the lower quartile, upper quartile and interquartile range.

  b Find $1.5 \times$ interquartile range (IQR).

  c Use the definition of an outlier to determine if any of the data points can be considered outliers.

2 Find the mean, median, mode, range and interquartile range of the foot length data:

  a including any outliers

  b excluding an outlier.

Record your results in a table.

Which of the statistics are affected by the outlier? Justify this result.

Reflect and discuss 6

In Exploration 4:

- What might account for any outliers?

- When the outlier is included, which measure of central tendency and which measure of dispersion would you use to describe the distribution?

- What are some potential results of ignoring outliers?

When a set of data has outliers, you need to decide whether or not to use them when calculating the measures of central tendency and spread. If you think a result occurred by human error (typing error, misreading a measuring device, broken measuring device) then you can ignore the outlier. If it is a genuine data point, then decide whether or not to keep it.

Generally speaking, the range is a good indication of the dispersion of a set of data, but it can be greatly affected by just one extreme value. You may need to exclude any outliers before calculating the range.

> To describe a distribution:
>
> **1** identify any outliers
>
> **2** use a measure of central tendency (center) and a measure of dispersion (spread) and
>
> **3** describe the shape.
>
> The median and interquartile range are not affected by outliers.

Practice 7

1 A group of 17 young children were tested to see how long it took each of them to assemble a set of interconnecting bricks. Their times (in seconds) are shown here.

8, 12, 16, 23, 24, 25, 25, 27, 28, 30, 31, 31, 32, 32, 40, 48, 51

a Find the mean, median and mode of the times.

b Determine whether it is better to use the mean, median or mode for this data set. Give reasons for your answer.

2 The number of text messages sent by 17 adults in one week are shown below.

36, 40, 22, 8, 16, 19, 48, 62, 27, 22, 34, 31, 36, 28, 30, 12, 20

a Find the mean and median number of texts sent.

b Find the interquartile range.

c Determine if any of the data values can be considered outliers.

d Find the range. Give a reason why any outliers have been included or excluded in your calculation.

e Which measure of central tendency is more appropriate in this case? Explain.

3 Look back at the data on Mathematics study times in Example 4.

   a Determine if any of the data values can be considered outliers.

   b Find the range of study times for the girls and boys. Give a reason why any outliers have been included or excluded in your calculations.

Problem solving

4 The back-to-back stem-and-leaf diagram shows the masses (to the nearest kg) of 30 male and 30 female northern hairy-nosed wombats.

Male wombat		Female wombat
	0	8
9 8 5 2 0	1	0 5 7 8 9
8 8 7 7 1 0 0 0	2	0 0 0 0 5 7 8 8
8 8 7 5 2 2 2 1 1 0	3	0 0 1 1 1 2 5 5 6 8 8
4 3 2 2 0	4	2 2 3 4
0	5	0
	6	
	7	
	8	
	9	
0	10	

Key: 0 | 4 | 2 represents a male wombat with mass 40 kg and a female wombat with mass 42 kg

   a Decide whether there are any outliers.

   b Describe the masses of the male and female wombats.

   c Compare the masses of the male and female wombats.

5 The table shows the percentage of households that speak English in the 26 cantons of Switzerland.

   a Construct a stem-and-leaf diagram and determine whether there are any outliers.

   b Suggest how any outliers could have occurred.

   c Describe the distribution.

Switzerland has four official languages. From 2010 the Swiss Federal Statistical Office has allowed citizens to indicate more than one language as their main language so the total for all languages exceeds 100%.

ZH	BE	LU	UR	SZ	OW	NW	GL	ZG
6.4	3.0	2.9	1.6	3.8	2.8	2.6	1.2	8.4
SO	BS	BL	SH	AR	AI	SG	GR	AG
2.5	8.6	4.2	3.6	2.1	2.4	2.5	2.5	3.5
TI	VD	VS	NE	GE	JU	FR	TG	
3.1	7.4	2.6	3.3	10.7	1.5	2.5	2.4	

Summary

- In a stem-and-leaf diagram:
  - the **stem** represents the **category** figure
  - the **leaves** represent the **final** digit(s) of each data point
  - the **key** tells you how to read the values.

stem	leaf
0	0 0 0 1 1 1 4 6 7
1	0 0 1 2 3 4 5 7 7
2	0 2 6
3	9

Key: 1|0 represents 10

- For any set of data there are two categories of **summary statistics**:
  - **Measures of central tendency (location)** describe where most data lies. They answer the question 'What is an average data value?'
  - **Measures of dispersion (spread)** describe how spread out the data is. They answer the question 'How much variation is there between the values?'

- The **lower/first quartile (Q_1)** is the median of the observations to the left of the median in an arranged set of observations.

- The **upper/third quartile (Q_3)** is the median of the observations to the right of the median in an arranged set of observations.

- The **interquartile range (IQR)** is the difference between the lower quartile and the upper quartile ($Q_3 - Q_1$).

- The median is another name for the second quartile, Q_2.

- A five-point summary of a data set is:
  - the minimum data point (min)
  - the lower quartile (Q_1)
  - the median (Q_2)
  - the upper quartile (Q_3)
  - the maximum data point (max).

- A box-and-whisker diagram represents the five-point summary:

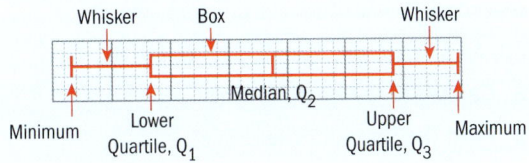

- **Qualitative data** – describes a certain characteristic using words (color, animal).

- **Quantitative data** – has a numerical value.

Quantitative data has a numerical value. There are two types:

- **Discrete data** – can be counted (number of goals scored) or can only take certain values (shoe size)

- **Continuous data** – can be measured (mass, height) and can take any value.

- The **distribution** of a data set describes the behavior of all the data points in the set.

- An **outlier** is a member of the data set which does not fit with the general pattern of the rest of the data. It could be an anomaly in the data or an inaccurate reading.

- A data point is an outlier if it is less than $1.5 \times IQR$ below Q_1, or greater than $1.5 \times IQR$ above Q_3.

Mixed practice

1 **Write down** whether these are qualitative or quantitative data.

  a The color of flowers

  b The prices of graphic calculators

  c The areas of public parks

  d The numbers of people at a store

2 **Write down** whether these are discrete or continuous data.

  a The time taken to run a marathon

  b The number of carriages on a train

  c The heights of Humboldt penguins

  d The temperature at midday in Iceland

3 The masses (in kilograms) of a group of people are given below.

46, 52, 64, 60, 82, 48, 72, 61, 70, 75, 59

a **Construct** a stem-and-leaf diagram to represent the data.

b **Write down** the number of people who weigh less than 60 kg.

c **Find** the median mass.

d **Find** the range.

4 During a one-hour study break, the amount of time students spent on social media sites was recorded. Their times, in minutes, were:

20, 45, 37, 29, 48, 52, 41, 32, 26, 50, 32, 44

a **Calculate** the median time.

b **Find** the interquartile range.

c **Find** the range.

Problem solving

5 Sebastian collected data on the number of pairs of shoes owned by every student in his class. The values are in order.

5, 6, 7, 7, 9, 9, r, 10, s, 13, 13, t

He calculated that the median of the data set was 9.5 and the upper quartile Q_3 was 13.

a **Write down** the value of r and s.

b The mean of the data set is 10.

Find the value of t.

6 All the dogs attending a veterinary surgery were weighed. Their masses, in kilograms, were:

26, 18, 54, 32, 30, 25, 6, 32, 43, 90, 16, 5, 27, 18, 3, 23, 27

a **Find** a five-point summary for the data.

b **Construct** a box-and-whisker diagram for the data.

7 This box-and-whisker diagram represents the results from a survey that asked: 'How old were you when you got your first smartphone?'

The interquartile range is 20 and the range is 40.

a **Write down** the median value.

b **Find** the values of a and b.

c 160 people were surveyed. **Find** the number of people who were 30 or older.

Problem solving

8 The box-and-whisker diagrams show the ages of people watching two different films at a cinema.

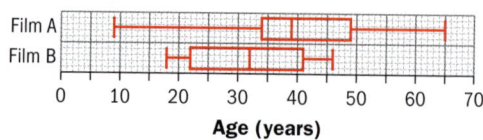

a **Compare** the ages.

b **Deduce** which film is categorized as a family film. Give reasons for your answer.

9 The profits made by a small business during the last 11 years are as follows:

$45 000, $560 000, $1000, $85 000, $160 000, $170 000, $62 000, $250 000, $3100, $120 000, $38 000

a **Find** the interquartile range.

b **Determine** if any of the data values can be considered outliers.

c **Find** the range. Give a reason why any outliers have been included or excluded in your calculation.

d **Find** the measure of central tendency which is most appropriate in this case. **Justify** your choice.

Problem solving

10 The table shows the masses (in kilograms) of Blackface sheep on two farms.

Farm A	63	48	60	55	45	49	19	55
Farm B	54	71	68	57	62	70	54	49
Farm A	65	49	57	56	64	43	64	48
Farm B	66	68	72	50	56	49	70	64

a **Construct** a back-to-back stem-and-leaf diagram to represent the data.

b **Compare** the masses of the Blackface sheep on the two farms.

c The table shows the average adult bodyweight of Blackface sheep for different grazing conditions.

Poor hill	45–50 kg
Average/good hill	50–65 kg
Upland	70 kg

Deduce the grazing conditions available to the sheep on the two farms. Give reasons for your answer.

ATL

ATL

ATL

Review in context

Globalization and sustainability

1 The table shows the percentage of land covered by forest in 19 European Union states in 2010.

Austria	46.7%
Belgium	22.0%
Czech Republic	34.3%
Denmark	11.8%
Estonia	53.9%
Finland	73.9%
France	28.3%
Germany	31.7%
Greece	29.1%
Hungary	21.5%
Ireland	9.7%
Italy	33.9%
Lithuania	33.5%
Netherlands	10.8%
Poland	30.0%
Portugal	41.3%
Slovakia	40.1%
Sweden	66.9%
United Kingdom	11.8%

a **Construct** a box-and-whisker diagram to represent the data.

b **Determine** if there are any outliers in this data.

2 The box-and-whisker diagram shows the forest coverage for the same EU states in 2012.

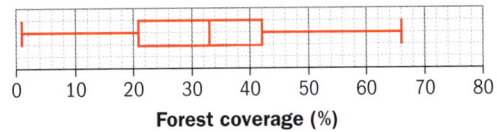

Forest coverage (%)

Compare the data for 2010 and 2012 and **identify** any changes between the two years.

3 **Use** the UNECE (United Nations Economic Commission for Europe) website to find more forestry data. **Use** an appropriate form of representation and prepare a short report to present to your classmates, and show how you can move between different forms of representation. **Explain** the conclusions you can draw from your diagram.

Reflect and discuss 7

How have you explored the statement of inquiry? Give specific examples.

Statement of inquiry:

How quantities are represented can help to establish underlying relationships and trends in a population.

Global context: Globalization and sustainability

Related concept: Quantity

Objectives

- Finding the mean, median, mode and range from a grouped frequency table
- Representing grouped data in a cumulative frequency curve
- Finding the five-point summary from a cumulative frequency curve
- Constructing a box-and-whisker diagram from a cumulative frequency curve
- Finding percentiles on a cumulative frequency curve

Inquiry questions

F
- How can you quantify the measures of central tendency from a grouped frequency table?
- How can you represent grouped data in a cumulative frequency curve?

C
- How does the type of data affect the way it can be represented and quantified?

D
- How can real data ever be misleading?
- How do individuals stand out in a crowd?

ATL Communication

Organize and depict information logically

Statement of inquiry:

How quantities are represented can help to establish underlying relationships and trends in a population.

📖 **Launch additional digital resources for this chapter.**

You should already know how to:

• understand inequality notation	**1** Which of these values satisfy the inequality $3 < x \le 6$? **a** 4.2　**b** 3.0　**c** 6.4　**d** 6.0
• recognize discrete and continuous data	**2** Is each data set discrete or continuous? 　**a** Numbers of eggs laid by 6 hens 　**b** Heights of sunflower plants 　**c** Shoe sizes 　**d** Lap times in a Formula 1 car race
• calculate the mean from a frequency table	**3** The frequency table shows the ages of children in a playgroup. Calculate the mean age. | Age	1	2	3	4	5
---	---	---	---	---	---
Frequency	0	2	6	4	3	
• write a five-point summary and construct a box-and-whisker diagram	**4 a** Construct a box-and-whisker diagram for this data on the ages of a Scout group. 11, 12, 13, 13, 13, 14, 15, 15, 17, 18, 18, 20, 21 **b** Find the interquartile range.
• identify how quartiles divide a data set	**5** In any data set, what fraction of the data is less than or equal to: **a** the lower quartile **b** the median **c** the upper quartile? Write each fraction as a percentage.

 ## Working with grouped data

- How can you find the measures of central tendency from a grouped frequency table?
- How can you represent grouped data in a cumulative frequency curve?

When you have a large set of data it is often convenient to organize the data into groups before doing any statistical analysis.

Example 1

The lengths of 50 Eelgrass leaves were measured. The results are given below, to the nearest tenth of a centimeter.

46.3	35.6	75.2	43.7	49.0	42.6	47.1	50.3	50.7	55.6
56.0	52.7	57.3	57.3	34.2	58.0	37.0	59.3	68.1	59.9
53.6	34.0	74.4	70.9	44.2	41.3	64.9	39.3	44.2	68.3
54.2	40.7	76.8	38.2	70.3	33.5	64.3	64.6	68.7	69.9
48.9	51.6	51.7	46.0	52.0	45.6	64.1	63.4	45.1	62.0

> Measuring a leaf gives continuous data; this has to be rounded to a certain degree of accuracy to be used in statistical analysis.

a Construct a grouped frequency table to represent the data.

b Find the class interval that contains the median.

c Write down the modal class.

a The minimum value is = 33.5 cm. The maximum value is = 76.8 cm

range = 76.8 – 33.5 = 43.3 cm

$\frac{43.3}{10} = 4.33$ so use a class width of 5 cm

> Choose a class width to give between 5 and 15 equal width classes. (In this case, 10.)

> Write the class intervals using inequality notation.

Length, x (cm)	Frequency	Cumulative frequency
$30 < x \le 35$	3	3
$35 < x \le 40$	4	7
$40 < x \le 45$	6	13
$45 < x \le 50$	7	20
$50 < x \le 55$	8	28
$55 < x \le 60$	7	35
$60 < x \le 65$	6	41
$65 < x \le 70$	4	45
$70 < x \le 75$	3	48
$75 < x \le 80$	2	50

> Add a Cumulative frequency column to help find the class interval that contains the median.

> The cumulative frequency is the sum of the frequencies for every class, up to and including the current one. Here, the cumulative frequency is $3 + 4 + 6 = 13$.

> The 25th and 26th values are in this class.

b $n = 50$, so the median is the $\frac{n+1}{2} = \frac{50+1}{2} = 25.5$th data value.

The class interval that contains the median is $50 < x \le 55$.

c The modal class is $50 < x \le 55$.

> The modal class is the class interval with the highest frequency.

Reflect and discuss 1

- What does cumulative frequency represent?
- Why can't you find the exact value of the median from a grouped frequency table?
- How would you estimate the range from a grouped frequency table? Estimate the range of lengths of Eelgrass leaves.

The **class width** is the difference between the maximum and the minimum possible values in a class interval.

The class $18 < x \leq 20$ has class width 2, because $20 - 18 = 2$.

An estimate for the range from a grouped frequency table is (upper bound of highest class interval) − (lower bound of lowest class interval).

When the class widths are equal, the **modal class** is the class containing the most data. It has the highest frequency.

For grouped data, you can find the class interval that contains the median.

Add a cumulative frequency column to the frequency table to find which class interval contains the $\left(\frac{n+1}{2}\right)$th value.

Grouped data has a modal class instead of one mode value.

Practice 1

1 The table shows the heights of a group of students on their 14th birthdays.

Height, x (cm)	Frequency
$1.20 < x \leq 1.30$	4
$1.30 < x \leq 1.40$	6
$1.40 < x \leq 1.50$	8
$1.50 < x \leq 1.60$	6
$1.60 < x \leq 1.70$	6

   a Write down the modal class.

   b Find the class interval that contains the median.

2 Here are the times taken for some students to complete a 1500 m race (measured to the nearest whole second).

325	580	534	500	532	328	600	625	450	435
450	340	357	370	401	456	388	626	532	399

   a Construct a grouped frequency table for this data. Use class widths of equal size and first class interval $300 < x \leq 350$.

   b Find the modal class.

   c Determine which class interval contains the median value.

3 The heights of one-year-old apple trees are shown below, measured to the nearest cm.

| 180 | 184 | 195 | 177 | 175 | 173 | 169 | 167 | 197 |
| 173 | 166 | 183 | 161 | 195 | 177 | 192 | 161 | 166 |

a Construct a grouped frequency table for this data.

b Write down the modal class.

c Determine which class interval contains the median value.

Problem solving

4 The table shows the masses of apples picked from one tree.

Mass, w (g)	Frequency	Cumulative frequency
$30 < w \leq 40$	a	5
$40 < w \leq 50$	7	12
$50 < w \leq 60$	5	b
$60 < w \leq 70$	c	19
$70 < w \leq 80$	8	d
$80 < w \leq 90$	3	30

a Calculate the values of a, b, c and d.

b Verify that the median lies in the class $50 < w \leq 60$.

Exploration 1

1 Look back at the grouped frequency table for Eelgrass leaves in Example 1. Imagine you had not received the raw data.

a Assume that all the data in each class interval has the value of the upper class boundary. For example, in the class $30 < x \leq 35$ assume all the values are 35. Using this assumption, calculate an estimate for the mean length of the leaves.

b Now assume that all the data in each class interval has the value of the lower class boundary. For example, in the class $30 < x \leq 35$ assume all the values are 30. Using this assumption, calculate an estimate for the mean length of the leaves.

> The lower boundary of the interval is 30 (not 31 or 30.1, etc.).

c Compare your two estimates. How would choosing a different value of the class interval affect the estimate of the mean?

d What value would be better than the upper or lower class boundaries to represent all the data in a class interval?

To calculate an estimate of the mean from a grouped frequency table:

- Find the midpoint or mid-interval value of each class interval by adding the upper and lower class boundaries and dividing by 2.
- Use the midpoint of each class interval to calculate the mean.

▶ Continued on next page

2 To calculate an estimate of the mean for the Eelgrass leaves, add a column for mid-interval value and a column for mid-interval value × frequency.

Length, x (cm)	Frequency	Mid-interval value	Mid-interval value × frequency
$30 < x \leq 35$	3	32.5	$32.5 \times 3 = 97.5$
$35 < x \leq 40$	4	37.5	$37.5 \times 4 = 150$
$40 < x \leq 45$	6	42.5	
$45 < x \leq 50$	7	47.5	
$50 < x \leq 55$	8	52.5	
$55 < x \leq 60$	7	57.5	
$60 < x \leq 65$	6	62.5	
$65 < x \leq 70$	4	67.5	
$70 < x \leq 75$	3	72.5	
$75 < x \leq 80$	2	77.5	
Total frequency (number of observations)		Sum of mid-interval value × frequency	

For grouped data the mean is defined as:

$$\bar{x} = \frac{\text{sum of (mid-interval value} \times \text{frequency)}}{\text{number of observations}}$$

For individual points in a set of data the mean is defined as:

$$\bar{x} = \frac{\text{sum of observations}}{\text{number of observations}}$$

Copy and complete the table, and calculate an estimate for the mean.

 You can also calculate an estimate of the mean using a GDC.

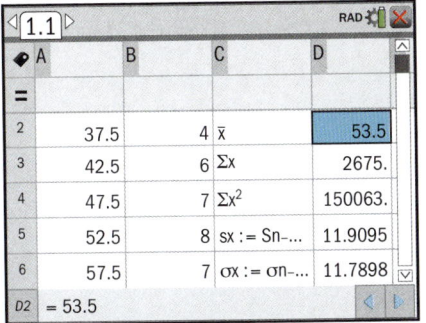

Enter the mid-interval values and frequencies into your GDC.

$\bar{x}$ is the mean.

Reflect and discuss 2

- In Exploration 1, what does the mid-interval value represent for the Eelgrass leaves? What does the mid-interval × frequency value represent?

- Why can you calculate only an *estimate* for the mean from a grouped frequency table? Is the estimate for the mean likely to be one of the original data values?

- Use the raw data in Example 1 to calculate the mean length of the Eelgrass leaves. Compare the calculated mean with your estimate for the mean from Exploration 1.

Practice 2

1 The table shows the number of hours a group of 50 students spent watching online videos in one week.

Time, t (hours)	Frequency	Mid-interval value	Mid-interval value × frequency
$0 < t \leq 10$	8	5	40
$10 < t \leq 20$	12		
$20 < t \leq 30$	16		
$30 < t \leq 40$	11		
$40 < t \leq 50$	3		
Total			

To find the mid-interval value, add the upper and lower class boundaries and divide by 2.

a Copy and complete the table.

b Calculate an estimate for the mean time each student spent watching online videos.

2 The masses of the Irish Wolfhounds at a dog show are shown in the table.

Mass, w (kg)	Frequency
$45 < w \leq 48$	2
$48 < w \leq 51$	5
$51 < w \leq 54$	12
$54 < w \leq 57$	13
$57 < w \leq 60$	8

a Calculate an estimate for the mean mass of the dogs.

b Write down the modal class.

c Find the number of dogs who weighed 54 kg or less.

d Determine the class interval that contains the median.

Problem solving

3 The table below shows the masses (w) of fish caught one morning.

Mass, w (kg)	Frequency (f)
$0.6 < w \leq 0.8$	16
$0.8 < w \leq 1.0$	35
$1.0 < w \leq 1.2$	44
$1.2 < w \leq 1.4$	23
$1.4 < w \leq 1.6$	10

a Estimate, correct to the nearest 0.1 kg, the mean mass of the fish.

b Find the modal class.

c Any fish caught that weighs no more than 1.0 kg must be returned to the sea. Find the number of fish returned.

d Find the class interval that contains the median.

e Estimate the range of the masses.

f A fish weighing 1.2 kg was incorrectly recorded in the class $1.2 \leq w < 1.4$. Without doing any calculations, explain whether or not the mean and median will stay the same.

Many types of scale can be used to weigh fish but only some are recognized by the International Game Fish Association for potential records. If the scale reading is between two marks the angler must round down to the heaviest known mass.

- -

Cumulative frequency curves

A cumulative frequency curve is a graph with the upper class boundaries plotted on the x-axis, and the cumulative frequencies on the y-axis.

You can find the five-point summary from a cumulative frequency curve.

For a set of n data values on a cumulative frequency curve, to find the estimate for:

- the lower quartile Q_1, find the value on the x-axis which corresponds to 25% of n

- the median Q_2, find the value on the x-axis which corresponds to 50% of n

- the upper quartile Q_3, find the value on the x-axis which corresponds to 75% of n.

The cumulative frequency curve here represents the grouped frequency table of the Eelgrass data in Example 1.

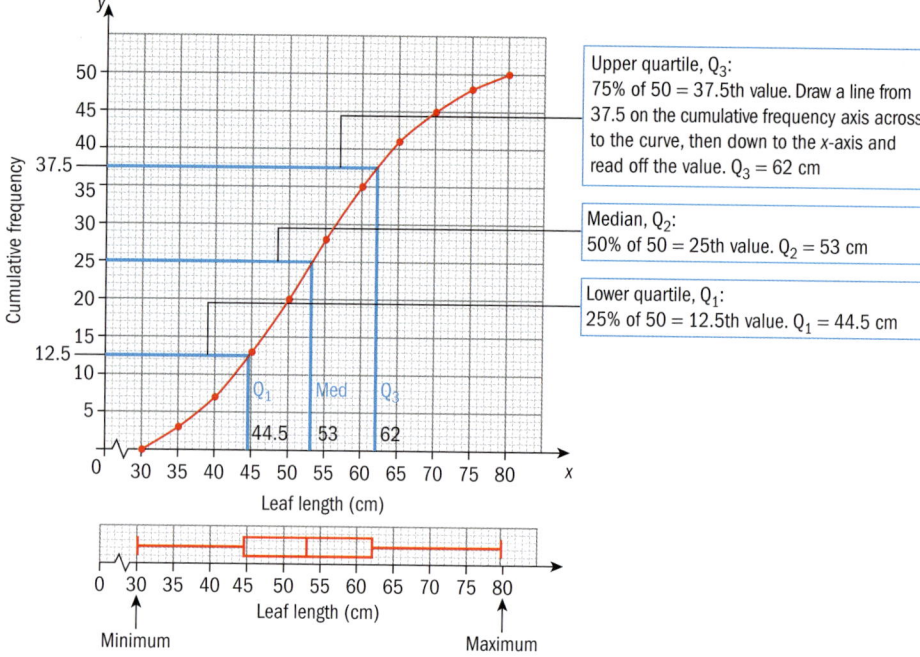

Upper quartile, Q_3:
75% of 50 = 37.5th value. Draw a line from 37.5 on the cumulative frequency axis across to the curve, then down to the x-axis and read off the value. $Q_3 = 62$ cm

Median, Q_2:
50% of 50 = 25th value. $Q_2 = 53$ cm

Lower quartile, Q_1:
25% of 50 = 12.5th value. $Q_1 = 44.5$ cm

You can take the five-point summary from the cumulative frequency curve and use it to draw the box-and-whisker diagram at the same scale.

Reflect and discuss 3

- Why are the percentiles 25%, 50% and 75% used to find estimates for Q_1, Q_2 and Q_3 respectively?

- Find the five-point summary from the raw Eelgrass data in Example 1.

- Do the values from the cumulative frequency curve agree with the values from the raw data in Example 1? Which values are the most accurate?

- How could you use the cumulative frequency curve to estimate the number of leaves with lengths less than or equal to 62 cm? Or greater than 62 cm? Or between 53 and 62 cm?

Percentiles

You have seen that the quartiles refer to the data set having been split into four equal parts. An extension of this is splitting the data set into 100 equal parts and finding percentiles,

- For a set of n data values on a cumulative frequency curve, to find an estimate for the 14th percentile, find the value on the x-axis which corresponds to 14% of n.

Example 2

The heights of 40 players in a basketball club are given in the following table.

Height in meters (x)	Frequency	Cumulative frequency
$1.75 \leq x < 1.80$	1	1
$1.80 \leq x < 1.85$	1	2
$1.85 \leq x < 1.90$	4	
$1.90 \leq x < 1.95$	13	
$1.95 \leq x < 2.00$	14	
$2.00 \leq x < 2.05$	3	
$2.05 \leq x < 2.10$	3	
$2.10 \leq x < 2.15$	1	40

a Complete the cumulative frequency column.

b Construct a cumulative frequency curve.

c Calculate the following:

   i the lower quartile Q_1

   ii the median Q_2

   iii the upper quartile Q_3

d Calculate:

   i the 16th percentile

   ii the 84th percentile.

a The completed cumulative frequency table is given below.

Height in meters (x)	Frequency	Cumulative frequency
$1.75 \leq x < 1.80$	1	1
$1.80 \leq x < 1.85$	1	2
$1.85 \leq x < 1.90$	4	6
$1.90 \leq x < 1.95$	13	19
$1.95 \leq x < 2.00$	14	33
$2.00 \leq x < 2.05$	3	36
$2.05 \leq x < 2.10$	3	39
$2.10 \leq x < 2.15$	1	40

b

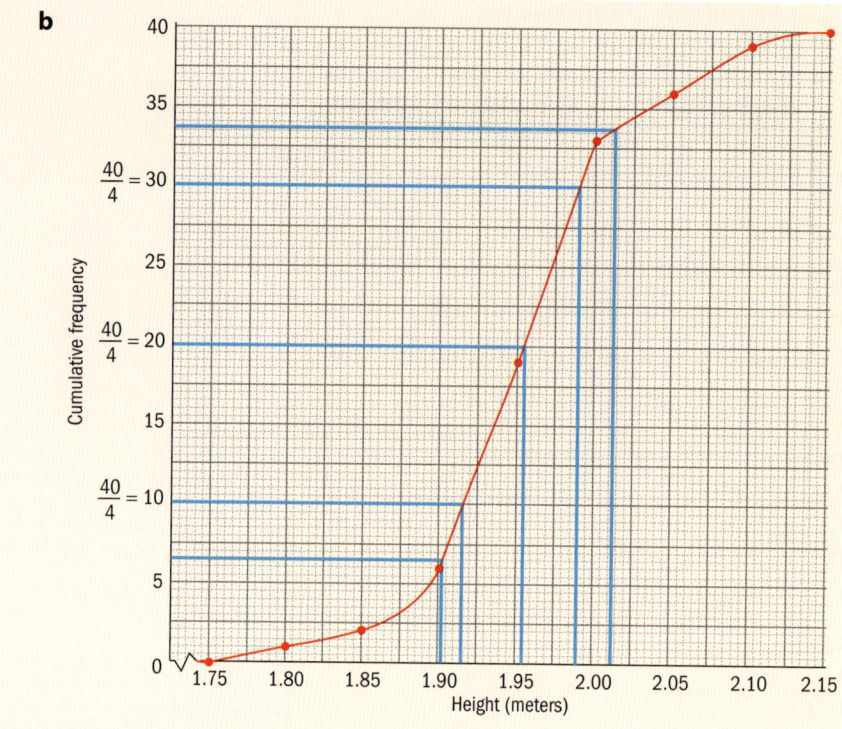

c i 1.915

ii 1.955

iii 1.99

d i The 16th percentile refers to the shortest 16% of players
16th percentile $\equiv \dfrac{16}{100} \times 40 = 6.4$th item giving 1.90 m.

ii The 84th percentile refers to the tallest 16% of players
84th percentile $\equiv \dfrac{84}{100} \times 40 = 33.6$th item giving 2.01 m.

Practice 3

1 The cumulative frequency curve
shows the heights of the basketball
players in a university league.

a Find an estimate for the median
height of the players.

b Find an estimate for the upper
and lower quartiles.

c Find an estimate for the
interquartile range.

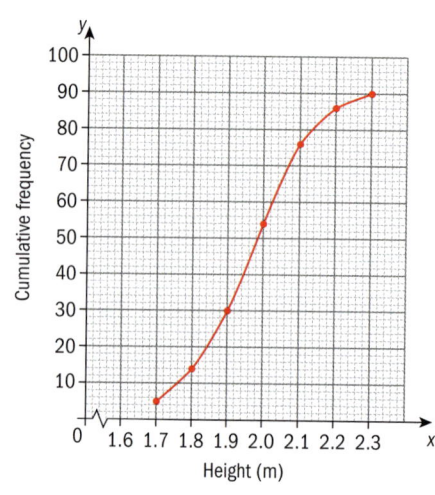

The shortest
player in National
Basketball
Association history
measured 1.6 meters,
while the tallest was
2.31 meters.

2 The table shows the distances walked (in kilometers) by members of a walking group in one week.

Distance, d (km)	Frequency	Cumulative frequency
$0 < d \leq 3$	4	4
$3 < d \leq 6$	14	18
$6 < d \leq 9$	6	
$9 < d \leq 12$	8	
$12 < d \leq 15$	4	

a Copy and complete the table.

b Construct a cumulative frequency curve to represent this data.

c Find estimates for the median and quartiles.

d Find estimates for the range and interquartile range.

> Plot the points (3, 4), (6, 18) and so on, then join with a smooth curve.

3 The table shows the masses of the Great Danes at a rehoming shelter.

Mass, m (kg)	$65 < m \leq 70$	$70 < m \leq 75$	$75 < m \leq 80$	$80 < m \leq 85$	$85 < m \leq 90$
Frequency	7	13	9	12	9

a Construct a cumulative frequency curve to represent this data.

b Write a five-point summary for the data.

c Construct a box-and-whisker diagram.

Problem solving

4 For the fish data in Practice 2, question **3**:

a Construct a cumulative frequency curve.

b Construct a box-and-whisker diagram.

c Use your cumulative frequency curve to decide whether these statements are true or false.

   i 90 fish weigh 1.1 kg or less.

   ii 60 fish weigh between 1.1 kg and 1.5 kg.

d 25% of the fish are classed as too heavy. By using the calculated upper quartile, find the minimum mass at which a fish is classed as too heavy.

5 The table shows the masses (in grams) of apples in a box.

Mass, m (kg)	$30 < m \leq 40$	$40 < m \leq 50$	$50 < m \leq 60$	$60 < m \leq 70$	$70 < m \leq 80$	$80 < m \leq 90$
Frequency	5	7	5	2	8	3

a Construct a cumulative frequency curve for this data.

b Apples weighing less than 45 g cannot be sold.

Find an estimate for the number of apples that cannot be sold.

c 10% of the apples weigh more than x grams. Find x. Which percentile is this?

6 This box-and-whisker diagram shows the times taken by 100 people to complete a simple word puzzle. Construct a cumulative frequency curve for the data.

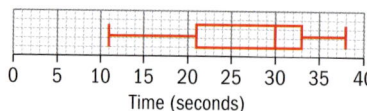

Time (seconds)

Problem solving

7 The cumulative frequency curve here shows the speeds (in kilometers per hour) of some cars on motorway A.

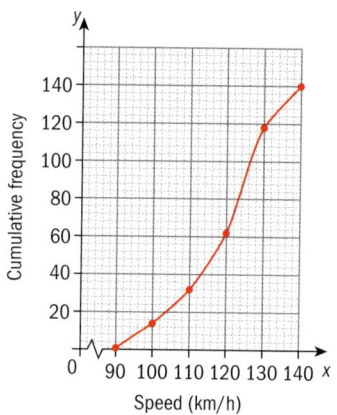

Speed (km/h)

> Only three countries on the world give the motorway speed limit in miles per hour rather than kilometers per hour: the Great Britain, the United States and Burma.

a Find an estimate for the median speed.

b Find the 15th and 85th percentiles.

c The speed limit on the motorway is 130 km/h.

Find an estimate for the percentage of cars exceeding the speed limit.

d Construct a box-and-whisker diagram for the speed data for motorway A.

The box-and-whisker diagram below shows the speeds of some cars on motorway B.

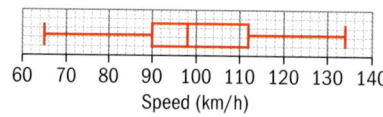

Speed (km/h)

e Compare the speeds of the cars on motorway A and motorway B.

- -

C Grouping discrete data

- How does the type of data affect the way it can be represented and analysed?

When you represent data in a frequency table, you first need to decide if the data is discrete or continuous, as this affects how you write the class intervals.

	Continuous data has overlapping boundary values and is written with continuous intervals, with one < sign and one ≤, for example:	Discrete data has no overlapping boundary values and there are gaps between the class intervals. Both inequalities are ≤, for example:
	$35 < x \leq 40$	$35 \leq x \leq 40$
	$40 < x \leq 45$	$41 \leq x \leq 45$

When you have decided on the class intervals, you can calculate an estimate of the mean in the same way as for grouped continuous data.

For continuous data, for example $35 < x \leq 40$, $40 < x \leq 45$, plot the cumulative frequencies against the upper class boundaries 40 and 45.

For discrete data, for example $35 \leq x \leq 40$, $41 \leq x \leq 45$, plot the cumulative frequencies against the point halfway between the upper bound of one interval (40) and next lower bound (41), at 40.5.

All values < 40.5 round down to 40, and all values ≥ 40.5 round up to 41.

ATL

Example 3

Dieter recorded the number of trucks driving past his house in 5-minute intervals over a period of 3 hours. His results are shown below.

3	14	6	16	21	6	20	14	4	11
12	19	1	12	19	14	11	16	24	20
6	18	8	27	7	23	2	7	11	12
11	7	27	24	12	22	15	29	9	25
14	10	10	16	15	19	1	17	8	12

Construct a cumulative frequency curve for this data.

Number of trucks	Frequency	New upper boundary	Cumulative frequency
$1 \leq x \leq 5$	5	$\frac{5+6}{2} = 5.5$	5
$6 \leq x \leq 10$	11	$\frac{10+11}{2} = 10.5$	16
$11 \leq x \leq 15$	15	$\frac{15+16}{2} = 15.5$	31
$16 \leq x \leq 20$	10	$\frac{20+21}{2} = 20.5$	41
$21 \leq x \leq 25$	6	$\frac{25+26}{2} = 25.5$	47
$26 \leq x \leq 30$	3	$\frac{30+31}{2} = 30.5$	50

Find the new upper boundary for each class interval – the value halfway between the upper class boundary of one interval and the lower class boundary of the next.

Add a Cumulative frequency column to the table.

▶ Continued on next page

339

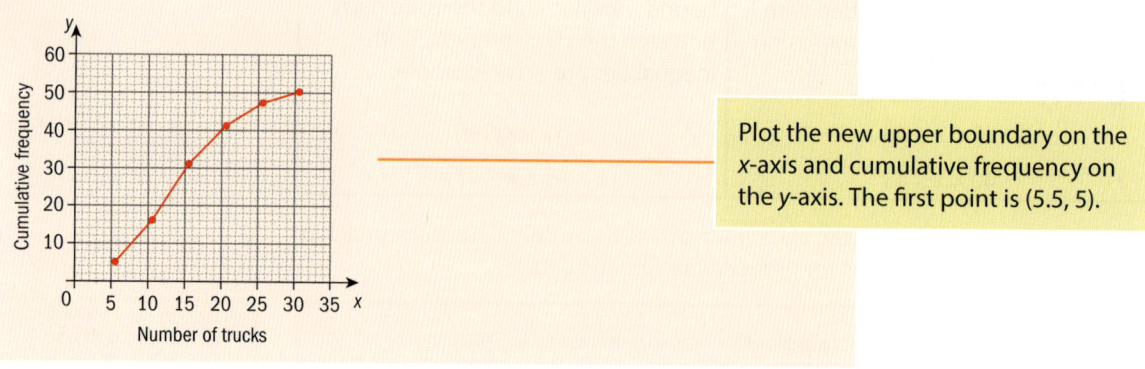

Plot the new upper boundary on the *x*-axis and cumulative frequency on the *y*-axis. The first point is (5.5, 5).

You can obtain a five-point summary and draw a box-and-whisker diagram for discrete data in exactly the same way as for continuous data.

Practice 4

1 a State whether these class intervals represent continuous or discrete data, and give reasons for your answers.

b Write down the class width of each interval.

i $10 < x \leq 20$	**ii** $14 \leq x \leq 18$	**iii** $6 < x \leq 9$	**iv** $20 - 39$
$20 < x \leq 30$	$19 \leq x \leq 23$	$9 < x \leq 12$	$40 - 64$

2 The table here shows the number of words in each of 100 sentences in a book.

Number of words	Frequency
$0 \leq x \leq 4$	17
$5 \leq x \leq 9$	25
$10 \leq x \leq 14$	30
$15 \leq x \leq 19$	12
$20 \leq x \leq 24$	10
$25 \leq x \leq 29$	3
$30 \leq x \leq 34$	2
$35 \leq x \leq 39$	0
$40 \leq x \leq 44$	1

a Calculate an estimate for the mean number of words in each sentence.

Does your answer make sense in the context of this question?

b Find the class interval that contains the median.

c Write down the modal class.

3 Beatrice records the number of goals scored by her unihockey team for each of the 25 matches in the season.

Number of goals scored	$0 \leq x \leq 3$	$4 \leq x \leq 7$	$8 \leq x \leq 11$	$12 \leq x \leq 15$	$16 \leq x \leq 19$
Frequency	3	5	6	6	5

a Calculate an estimate for the mean number of goals scored per match.

b Explain why this data is bimodal.

c Find the class interval that contains the median.

d Estimate the range.

4 The table shows the Extended Essay scores of 50 DP students.

Score	Frequency
$1 \leq x \leq 5$	1
$6 \leq x \leq 10$	9
$11 \leq x \leq 15$	15
$16 \leq x \leq 20$	15
$21 \leq x \leq 25$	5
$26 \leq x \leq 30$	5

a By drawing a new table with the correct upper boundary for discrete data and the cumulative frequency, construct a cumulative frequency curve.

b Using your cumulative frequency curve, write down the median score.

c Find an estimate for the upper and lower quartiles.

d Draw a box-and-whisker diagram to represent the information.

Problem solving

5 Brooke recorded the number of text messages she sent every day for a month in this table:

Number of messages sent	$0 \leq x \leq 4$	$5 \leq x \leq 9$	$10 \leq x \leq 14$	$15 \leq x \leq 19$	$20 \leq x \leq 24$	$25 \leq x \leq 29$	$30 \leq x \leq 34$
Frequency	10	7	3	4	3	2	1

a Calculate the values of a and b in this cumulative frequency table for the text message data.

Upper boundary	Cumulative frequency
≤ 4.5	10
≤ 9.5	17
≤ 14.5	a
≤ 19.5	24
≤ 24.5	27
≤ 29.5	b
≤ 34.5	30

> ≤ 9.5 means 'all the values up to and including 9.5'.

b Draw a cumulative frequency curve for this data.

c Use your curve to calculate each value in the five-point summary. Hence represent the data in a box-and-whisker plot.

6 The ages (in years) of the first 30 people visiting the Tuileries Gardens in Paris on a certain day are shown.

25	65	34	48	4	55
32	45	23	43	23	37
45	36	26	39	43	45
29	15	15	20	64	37
61	25	17	23	45	36

a Construct a grouped frequency table for this data.

b Construct a cumulative frequency curve.

c Use your cumulative frequency curve to estimate the percentage of visitors who are 25 or under.

d Estimate the percentage of visitors who are older than 40.

7 The cumulative frequency curves give information about the ages of pedestrians and pedal cyclists killed in Great Britain in 2014.

a Draw a box-and-whisker diagram for the pedestrians.

b Draw a box-and-whisker diagram for the pedal cyclists.

c Compare the ages of the pedestrians and pedal cyclists.

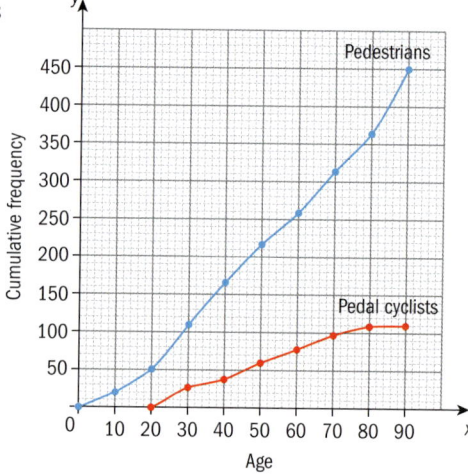

Use the same scale and draw one box-and-whisker diagram above the other.

Exploration 2

1 In your class, record 500 random numbers between 1 and 30 generated in the following way:

Use technology to produce random 3-digit numbers and record the last two digits of each, ignoring any over 30.

For example:

Random number	Action
307	record 7
951	51 > 30 so ignore
823	record 23
430	record 30

Construct a grouped frequency table with carefully chosen intervals. As a class, try different sized class intervals. Use technology to calculate the measures of central tendency.

2 Compare your results with other students who chose different class intervals. What are the differences?

Use the random number button on your calculator, a spreadsheet formula, or random number tables. You could find 15 random numbers each and combine them into one class set.

▶ Continued on next page

3 Discuss how choosing different class intervals affects the mean, median class and modal class.

4 Why would it not be sensible to represent this data in a stem-and-leaf diagram?

5 Represent the data in a cumulative frequency curve and box-and-whisker diagram.

6 Compare your results with others.

Reflect and discuss 4

If a set of data is grouped in equal class width intervals:

- Does the choice of class interval affect the estimate of the mean? What about the median class and modal class? Explain.

- Does the choice of class interval affect the cumulative frequency curve and box-and-whisker diagram? Explain.

- Discuss the advantages and disadvantages of having too few classes. Do likewise for too many classes.

D Misleading statistics

- How can real data ever be misleading?
- How do individuals stand out in a crowd?

Exploration 3

The table gives the ages of fathers at the birth of their first child, in Switzerland in 2013.

Age	Freq	Age	Freq	Age	Freq	Age	Freq	Age	Freq
≤12	0	22	388	32	5522	42	2203	52	189
13	0	23	598	33	5766	43	1773	53	146
14	0	24	958	34	5612	44	1487	54	128
15	0	25	1414	35	5516	45	1187	55	95
16	2	26	1815	36	5225	46	856	56	86
17	13	27	2365	37	4703	47	717	57	61
18	26	28	3073	38	4126	48	579	58	45
19	69	29	3792	39	3705	49	442	59	40
20	132	30	4382	40	3210	50	365	≥60	174
21	251	31	5108	41	2703	51	290		

1 Draw a grouped frequency table to represent this data. Use equal class width intervals $1 \le x \le 10$, $11 \le x \le 20$, and so on. Assume that all the fathers were under 70. What will the highest class interval be?

2 Calculate an estimate for the mean and the five-point summary of the age of fathers from your table.

▶ Continued on next page

3 Peter uses the class intervals below so that the frequencies in all the classes are roughly equal.

$0 \le x \le 25$, $26 \le x \le 29$, $30 \le x \le 34$, $35 \le x \le 38$, $39 \le x \le 43$, $44 \le x \le 50$, $51 \le x \le 100$

Construct a grouped frequency table using his class intervals. Calculate an estimate for the mean and the five-point summary from this new table.

Reflect and discuss 5

- In Exploration 3, which grouping of the data gives a five-point summary that best represents the data?

- How should you group data so that it accurately represents a data set? Consider:

  - the number of classes

  - class width

  - the upper and lower boundaries of the class intervals.

- Do you need to consider the size of the data set?

Summary

The **class width** is the difference between the maximum and the minimum possible values in a class interval.

When the class widths are equal, the **modal class** is the class interval containing the most data. It has the highest frequency.

For grouped data, you can find the class value that contains the median. Add a cumulative frequency column to the frequency table to find which class interval contains the $\left(\frac{n+1}{2}\right)$th value.

To calculate an estimate of the mean from a grouped frequency table:

- Find the midpoint or mid-interval value of each class interval by adding the upper and lower class boundaries and dividing by 2.

- Use the midpoint of each class interval to calculate the mean.

For grouped data the mean is defined as:

$$\bar{x} = \frac{\text{sum of (mid-interval value} \times \text{frequency)}}{\text{number of observations}}$$

An estimate for the range from a grouped frequency table is (upper bound of highest class interval) – (lower bound of lowest calls interval).

A cumulative frequency curve is a graph with the upper class boundaries plotted on the horizontal axis, and the cumulative frequencies on the vertical axis.

- For continuous data, for example:
  $35 < x \le 40$, $40 < x \le 45$, plot the cumulative frequencies against the upper class boundaries 40 and 45.

- For discrete data, for example:
  $35 \le x \le 40$, $41 \le x \le 45$, plot the cumulative frequencies against the point halfway between the upper bound of one interval (40) and next lower bound (41), at 40.5.

Objective: C. Communicating
v. organize information using a logical structure.

In the mixed practice you will be specifically looking at organizing information using a logical structure to represent the data given.

Mixed practice

1 The masses of 35 desert hedgehogs are listed here. All masses are to the nearest gram.

290	455	342	465	480	400	500
325	460	328	284	436	280	370
450	368	295	310	390	435	450
315	505	510	495	310	400	375
347	450	474	298	380	463	360

a **Construct** a grouped frequency table to represent the data.

b **State** the modal class.

c **Determine** the class interval that contains the median.

d **Calculate** an estimate for the mean mass.

2 The table shows learner drivers' marks in a hazard perception test.

Mark, m	Frequency
$16 \leq m \leq 27$	9
$28 \leq m \leq 39$	21
$40 \leq m \leq 51$	18
$52 \leq m \leq 63$	23
$64 \leq m \leq 75$	19

a **Estimate** the range of the marks.

b **Construct** a cumulative frequency table.

c **Construct** a cumulative frequency curve.

3 The tails of a random sample of 200 adult foxes were measured in cm. The results are represented in the cumulative frequency curve.

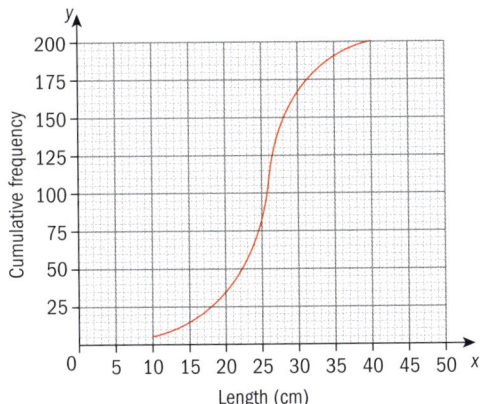

a **Estimate** the median length of fox tail in the sample.

b **Estimate** the interquartile range for the length of fox tails in the sample.

c Given that the shortest length was 11 cm and the longest 37 cm, **draw** and label a box-and-whisker plot for the data.

4 The box-and-whisker diagram shows the masses of 80 frogs at a zoo. **Construct** a cumulative frequency curve for the data.

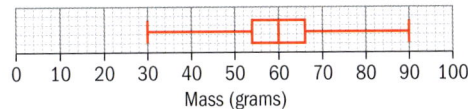

Mass (grams)

Problem solving

5 The speeds of cars passing a speed camera on a highway are recorded in this table.

Speed, v (km/h)	Number of cars
$v \leq 60$	0
$60 < v \leq 70$	10
$70 < v \leq 80$	22
$80 < v \leq 90$	61
$90 < v \leq 100$	74
$100 < v \leq 110$	71
$110 < v \leq 120$	39
$120 < v \leq 130$	17
$130 < v \leq 140$	6

a **Calculate** an estimate for the mean speed of the cars.

b Here is a cumulative frequency table for the same data.

Speed, v (km/h)	Number of cars	Cumulative frequency
$v \leq 60$	0	0
$v \leq 70$	10	10
$v \leq 80$	22	32
$v \leq 90$	61	93
$v \leq 100$	74	a
$v \leq 110$	71	238
$v \leq 120$	39	b
$v \leq 130$	17	294
$v \leq 140$	6	300

Write down the values of a and b.

c On graph paper, **construct** a cumulative frequency curve to represent this information.

d 25% of cars exceed the speed limit. By calculating the upper quartile, **estimate** the speed limit on this stretch of highway.

6 The cumulative frequency curve shows the masses, in grams, of a selection of oranges.

  a Use the graph to **estimate**:

   i the median

   ii the upper quartile.

   Give your answers to the nearest gram.

  b 10% of the oranges weigh more than x grams. **Find** x.

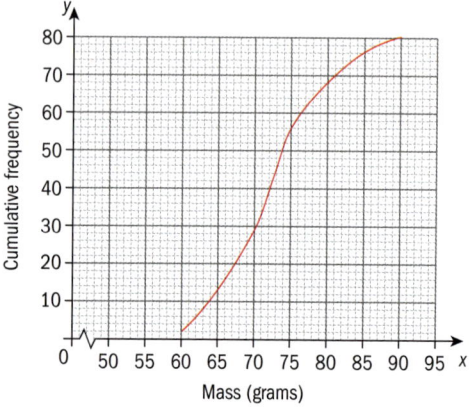
Mass (grams)

7 A fisherman catches 200 halibut. The table shows the lengths of these halibut to the nearest cm.

Length, x (cm)	Frequency
$10 < x \le 15$	24
$15 < x \le 20$	38
$20 < x \le 25$	53
$25 < x \le 30$	39
$30 < x \le 35$	29
$35 < x \le 40$	10
$40 < x \le 45$	7

  a **Calculate** an estimate for the mean length of the halibut.

b The cumulative frequency diagram shows the lengths of the halibut.

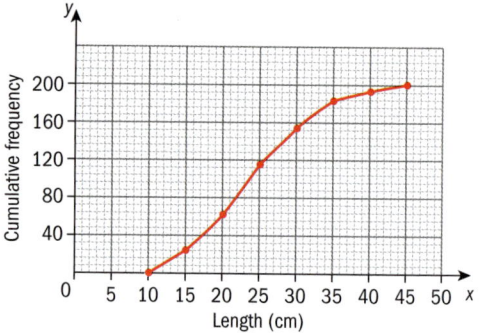
Length (cm)

Estimate the interquartile range.

c The fisherman returns any fish smaller than 20 cm to the river. **Calculate** an estimate for the number of fish he returns.

d Fish greater than or equal to 20 cm but less than 28 cm are classified as small fish. Fish that are 28 cm or longer are classified as large fish.

   Estimate the number of fish in each category.

e The fisherman sells small fish for $6 and large fish for $10. **Estimate** how much money he will earn if he sells all the fish.

8 The cumulative frequency curves show the ages of foreign male and foreign female residents in Switzerland in 2013.

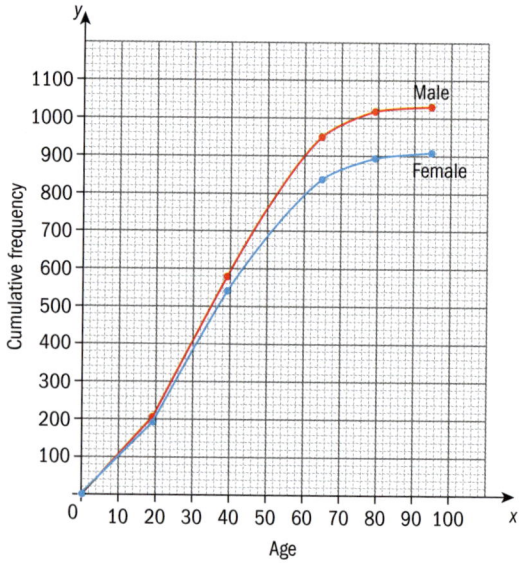
Age

By constructing a double box-and-whisker plot, **compare** the ages of the foreign male and foreign female residents.

Review in context

Globalization and sustainability

1 A marine biologist is studying rainbow trout in a local river. To the nearest centimeter, she records the lengths of a sample of 100 rainbow trout from the river.

Rainbow trout	
Length, *x* (cm)	Frequency
$25 < x \leq 27$	1
$27 < x \leq 29$	5
$29 < x \leq 31$	9
$31 < x \leq 33$	21
$33 < x \leq 35$	29
$35 < x \leq 37$	19
$37 < x \leq 39$	16

a Construct a cumulative frequency table for this data.

b Draw a cumulative frequency curve.

c Use the cumulative frequency curve to write a five-point summary for the data.

d Copy and complete this statement:

75% of the rainbow trout are over _____ cm in length.

e The rainbow trout feed on smaller fish of other species, so the biologist records the lengths of 100 female fish and 100 male fish of other species, from the same river.

These are shown in the box-and-whisker diagrams.

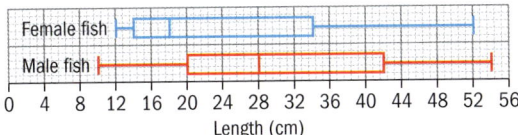

i Estimate the number of female fish that are smaller than 75% of the rainbow trout in the river.

ii Estimate the number of male fish that are smaller than 75% of the rainbow trout.

iii Hence **estimate** the percentage of the fish of other species in the river that 75% of the rainbow trout can feed on.

Reflect and discuss 6

How have you explored the statement of inquiry? Give specific examples.

Statement of inquiry:

How quantities are represented can help to establish underlying relationships and trends in a population.

6.3 Histograms

Global context: Globalization and sustainability

Related concept: Generalization

RELATIONSHIPS

Objectives

- Constructing bar charts and histograms
- Interpreting frequency and relative frequency histograms
- Visualizing characteristics of a data set

Inquiry questions

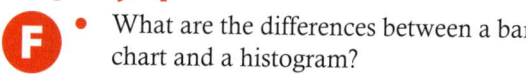

F
- What are the differences between a bar chart and a histogram?

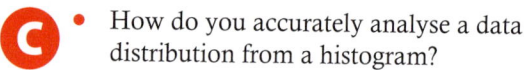

C
- How do you accurately analyse a data distribution from a histogram?

D
- How can generalizations made from real data ever be misleading?

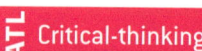

ATL Critical-thinking

Revise understanding based on new evidence and information

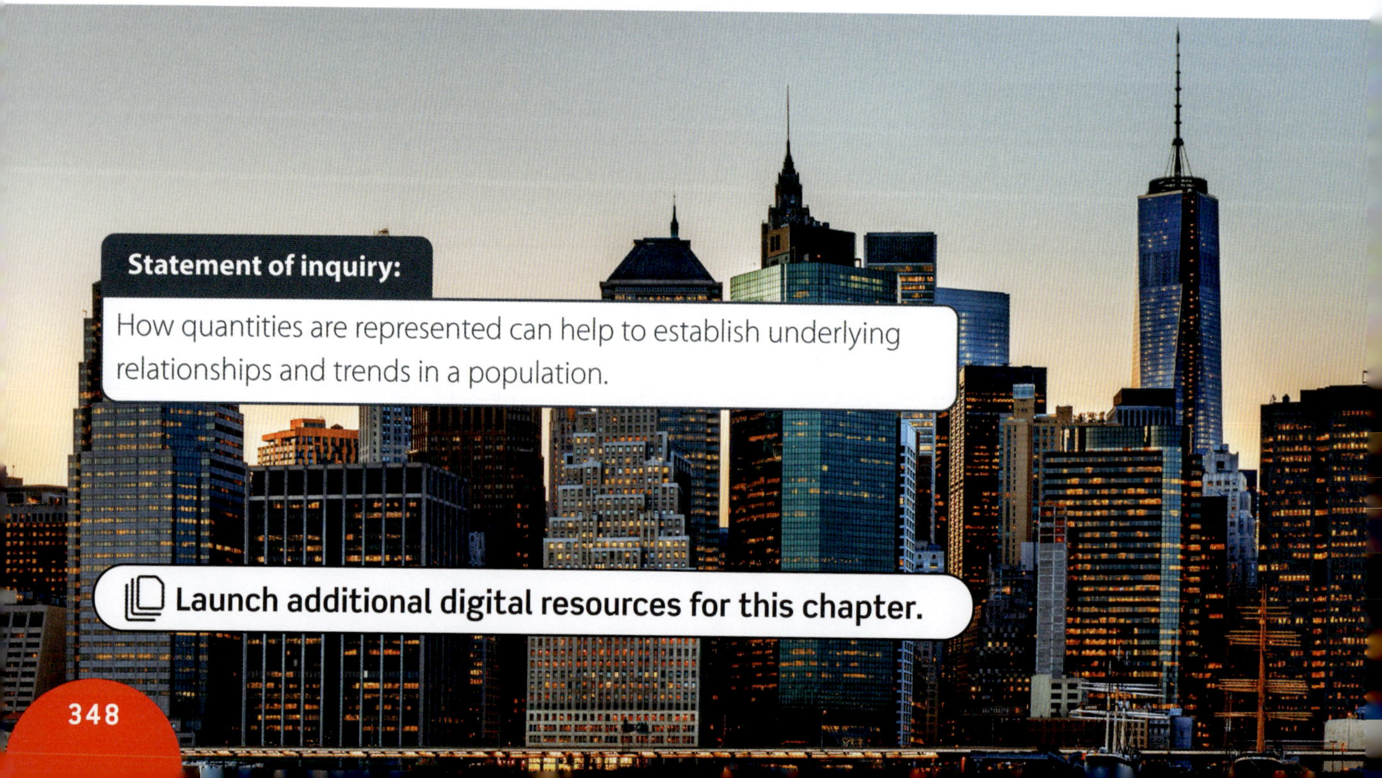

Statement of inquiry:

How quantities are represented can help to establish underlying relationships and trends in a population.

Launch additional digital resources for this chapter.

You should already know how to:

• represent continuous and discrete data in a grouped frequency table	**1** The heights in cm of 24 seedlings (rounded to 1 d.p.) are: 2.4, 3.1, 5.2, 2.6, 5.8, 2.2, 4.9, 3.0, 4.7, 5.3, 2.6, 4.5, 3.7, 2.3, 5.4, 5.7, 3.5, 2.1, 4.0, 4.2, 3.6, 2.5, 2.8, 4.1 Construct a grouped frequency table with equal class widths for this data.
• find measures of central tendency and dispersion from a grouped frequency table	**2** From your grouped frequency table, find the modal class and the class that contains the median. Calculate estimates for the mean and the range.
• recognize qualitative and quantitative data	**3** Classify as qualitative or quantitative data: **a** shoe size **b** shoe color **c** shoe price.

F Bar charts and frequency histograms

- What are the differences between a bar chart and a histogram?

Before now, you may have drawn bar charts for both qualitative and quantitative discrete data. However, strictly speaking, a chart with bars representing quantitative data is a histogram.

A **bar chart** represents qualitative data.

- All the bars have equal width.
- There are spaces between the bars.
- The *height* of the bar represents the frequency.
- Frequency is on the vertical axis.

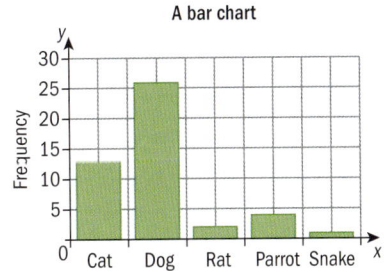

A bar chart

A **histogram** represents quantitative discrete data and all continuous data.

- The bars may or may not be of equal width.
- There are no spaces between the bars.
- The *area* of the bar represents the frequency.
- Frequency, relative frequency or frequency density are on the vertical axis.

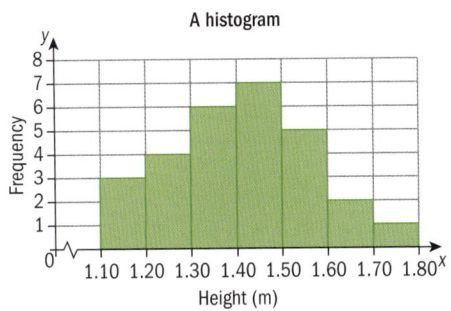

A histogram

Reflect and discuss 1

ATL

Decide which of these graphs are bar charts, which are histograms and which are neither. Justify your answers.

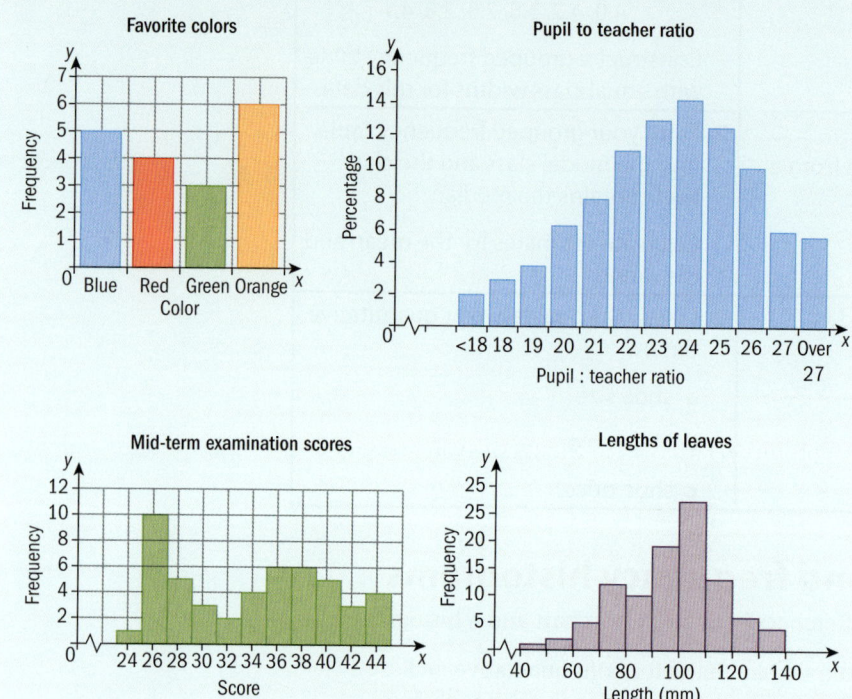

The word *histogram* originates from Greek words: *histos* meaning 'stands upright' and *gram* meaning 'a drawing'.

As the scores do not start at zero, the zigzag symbol indicates that some values are not included on the scores axis.

Frequency histograms for continuous data

Example 1

The table shows the masses in grams of 50 baby chicks hatched at a farm in one week. Draw a histogram to represent the data.

Mass, x (grams)	Frequency	Mass, x (grams)	Frequency
$19.5 < x \le 20.0$	3	$22.5 < x \le 23.0$	4
$20.0 < x \le 20.5$	5	$23.0 < x \le 23.5$	6
$20.5 < x \le 21.0$	1	$23.5 < x \le 24.0$	5
$21.0 < x \le 21.5$	6	$24.0 < x \le 24.5$	5
$21.5 < x \le 22.0$	2	$24.5 < x \le 25.0$	6
$22.0 < x \le 22.5$	6	$25.0 < x \le 25.5$	1

▶ Continued on next page

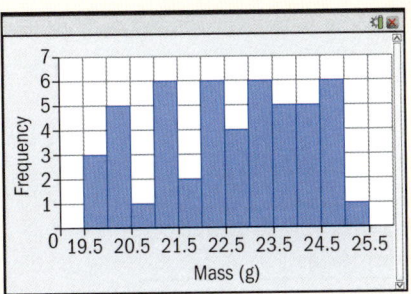

Use your frequency table to draw the histogram on graph paper.

Plot the class boundaries on the x-axis and the frequency on the y-axis. Draw the bars with no gaps between them.

Use a GDC to check your histogram.

In Example 1, the masses are continuous data, even though they are rounded to one decimal place, so a histogram is the correct representation.

The class intervals are sometimes called *bins*.

ATL

Reflect and discuss 2

Ages are rounded differently to most data. If a fir tree is 10 meters tall to the nearest meter, its height h satisfies $9.5 \leq h < 10.5$.

If a woman is 40 years old, her age a satisfies $40 \leq a < 41$, where a is a continuous quantity.

The table gives the ages of musicians in an orchestra.

Age	18–25	26–33	34–41	42–50
Frequency	5	8	10	7

- How would you draw bars on a histogram to show these ages?
- What are the class boundaries for each class?
- How would you write the class interval, using $\leq$ and $<$, for the class 18–25?

Practice 1

1 The heights of the chicks from Example 1, measured to the nearest centimeter, are recorded in this grouped frequency table:

Height (cm)	Frequency
$1.5 \leq x < 2.5$	1
$2.5 \leq x < 3.5$	3
$3.5 \leq x < 4.5$	7
$4.5 \leq x < 5.5$	14
$5.5 \leq x < 6.5$	18
$6.5 \leq x < 7.5$	5
$7.5 \leq x < 8.5$	2

Draw a frequency histogram to represent the data.

2 The ages of 100 shoppers randomly chosen for a survey are given in the table.

Age (years)	$14 \le x < 24$	$24 \le x < 34$	$34 \le x < 44$	$44 \le x < 54$	$54 \le x < 64$
Number of users	41	30	15	8	6

Draw a frequency histogram to represent the data.

Problem solving

3 The incomplete table and frequency histogram give some information about the masses (to the nearest kilogram) of some female polar bears.

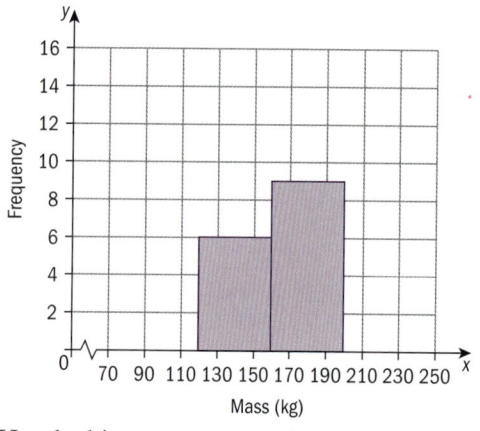

Class interval	Class boundaries	Frequency
80–119	79.5–119.5	15
120–159		
160–199		
200–239		8

a Use the histogram to complete the table.

b Complete the histogram.

Frequency histograms for discrete data

You can represent ungrouped discrete data with a vertical line graph.

This type of graph is not suitable for grouped discrete data. A single vertical line to represent the category 1–3 eggs could be misleading, but separate lines at 0, 1, 2 and 3 could be confusing.

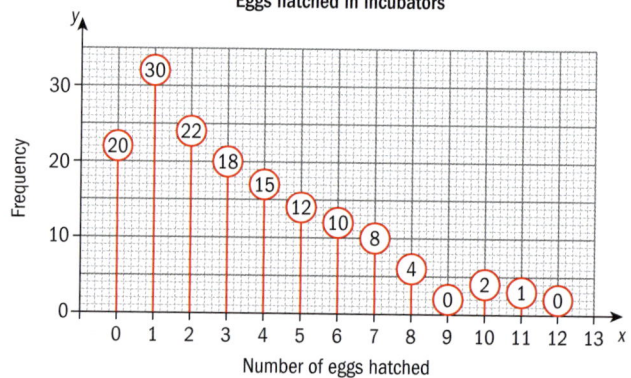

A histogram for grouped discrete data uses bars to represent each group.

For discrete data, 1–3, 4–6, 7–9, and so on, plot the bars from the point halfway between the upper boundary of one class interval and the lower boundary of the next.

For 4–6, plot the bar between 3.5 and 6.5. Start the first bar at 0.5, to make all the bars the same width.

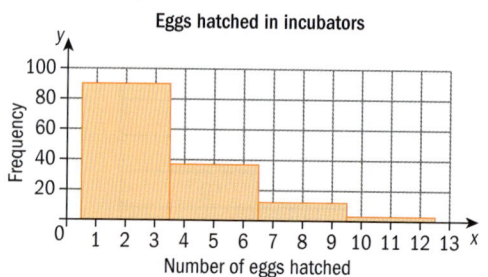

A histogram for ungrouped discrete data
1, 2, 3, 4 … uses bars from
0.5 to 1.5, 1.5 to 2.5, and so on.

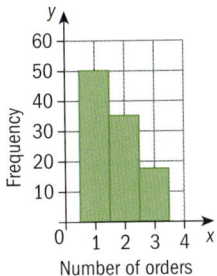

Number of orders

You plot the class intervals of cumulative frequency curves in a similar way.

Practice 2

1 The table shows the numbers of people traveling in 33 cars.

Number of people	1	2	3	4	5	6
Frequency	8	11	6	4	2	2

  a Classify the data as discrete or continuous, grouped or ungrouped.

  b Represent the data in a frequency histogram.

2 There were 25 trays of eggs in an incubator. Each tray started with 24 unhatched eggs. The numbers of eggs that hatched from each tray were:

12 18 17 13 9

21 2 5 12 1

5 14 11 13 15

18 21 14 15 9

12 14 15 16 24

  a Construct a grouped frequency table for the data.

  b Construct a frequency histogram for this data.

3 The lengths of 30 Swiss cheese plant leaves were measured to the nearest cm. The table shows the results.

Length of leaf (to the nearest cm)	$10 \le x < 15$	$15 \le x < 20$	$20 \le x < 25$	$25 \le x < 30$
Frequency	3	8	12	7

  a Determine whether this is discrete or continuous data.

  b Draw a frequency histogram to represent the data.

4 A taxi driver records the distances of his journeys, to the nearest km, over the course of a long weekend shift.

Distance (km)	1–5	6–10	11–15	16–20	21–25
Frequency	10	6	8	5	2

  a Write down the modal class.

  b Determine the class boundaries for each class.

  c Draw a frequency histogram for this data.

For grouped continuous data, 9–12, 13–16 and so on, are the class intervals. The class boundaries are 8.5–12.5 or $8.5 < x \le 12.5$, and so on.

Problem solving

5 This histogram has no title or axes labels.

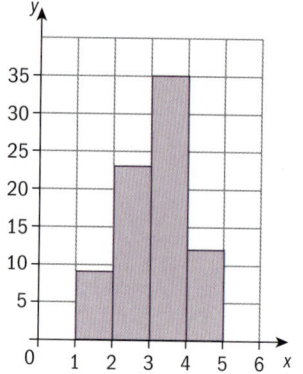

  a Determine whether it represents discrete or continuous data.

  b Suggest what the data could be.

  c Do you think that the data represented here contains any outliers? If not, why not?

6 The histogram shows the number of hours that Macey spent doing homework each day in June.

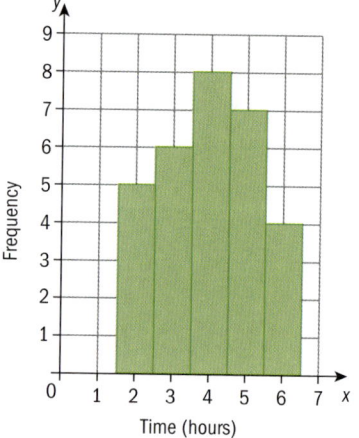

  a Use the information in the frequency histogram to construct a grouped frequency table.

  b Use your frequency table to calculate an estimate for the mean time that Macey spent doing homework.

C Distributions in histograms

- How do you accurately analyse a data distribution from a histogram?

Examining a histogram can help you visualize certain characteristics of the data set it represents.

To comment on the distribution of data, describe:

Center   measure of central tendency

Spread   measure of dispersion

Outliers   extreme data values that don't fit the pattern

Shape   unimodal, bimodal or multimodal

Example 2

This frequency histogram shows the lengths in centimeters of 57 fish caught in the Kispiox River, British Colombia, Canada.

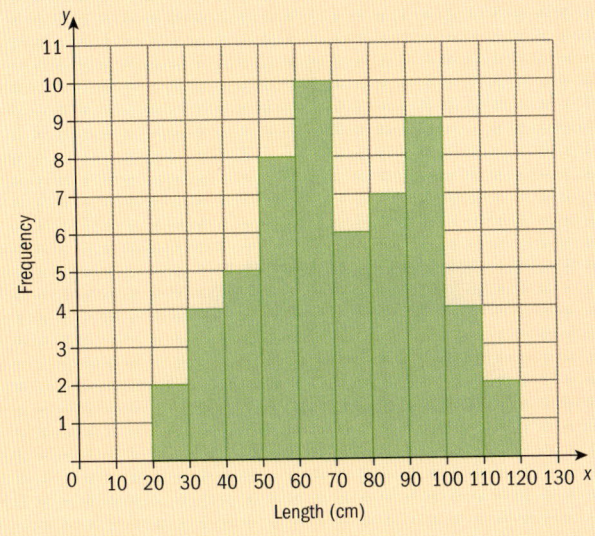

a Find:

   i the modal class

   ii the class interval that contains the median

   iii an estimate for the range.

b Describe the distribution.

a **i** The modal class is $60 \leq x < 70$.

   ii 57 data items

     The median $= \frac{57+1}{2} = $ 29th item of data. ⎯⎯⎯⎯⎯⎯⎯⎯
> Count the number of data items in each bar, until you reach the 29th.

     The class $60 \leq x < 70$ contains the median.

   iii Estimate for the range $= 120 - 20 = 100$ cm

b The median lies in the class $60 \leq x < 70$ and this is also the modal class. The lengths of the fish caught are widely spread from 20 cm to 120 cm. There are no outliers. The distribution is bimodal. Most fish caught have length $60 \leq x < 70$ cm or $90 \leq x < 100$ cm.

> To describe a distribution, use a measure of central tendency (center) and a measure of dispersion (spread). State if there is an outlier, and describe the shape.

These three histograms all show the masses, to the nearest gram, of the same 50 eggs measured one week before hatching. The first histogram, for ungrouped data, appears to be a multimodal distribution.

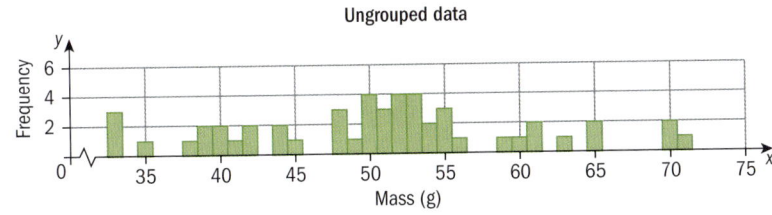

This appears to be a unimodal distribution (at $43 \leq w < 53$) that is not symmetrical.

10 class intervals

This appears to be a bimodal distribution that is fairly symmetrical.

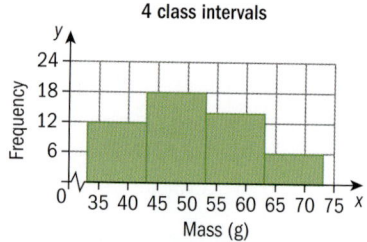

4 class intervals

Reflect and discuss 3

- How can changing the class intervals change the shape of a distribution?
- What are the effects of having too few classes? What about too many classes?
- How many class intervals should you use? Do you need to consider the size of the data set when deciding on the number of classes?

Practice 3

1 Determine whether each histogram:

i is symmetrical   **ii** is unimodal, bimodal or multimodal   **iii** contains outliers.

a

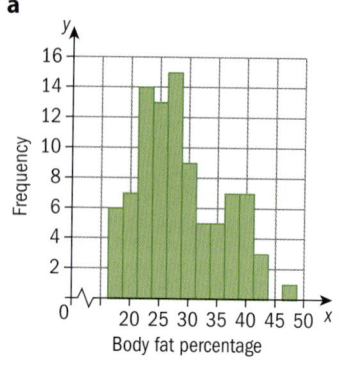

Body fat percentage

b

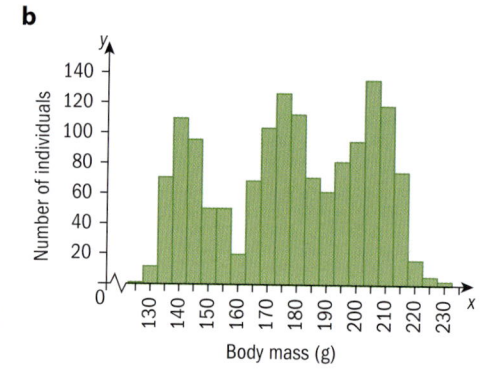

Body mass (g)

c

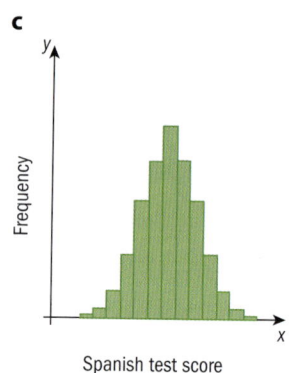

Spanish test score

2 The histogram shows the lengths of 26 black rats.

a Write down the modal class.

b Find the class interval that contains the median.

c Calculate an estimate for the range.

d By first constructing a grouped frequency table, calculate an estimate for the mean length.

e Describe the distribution.

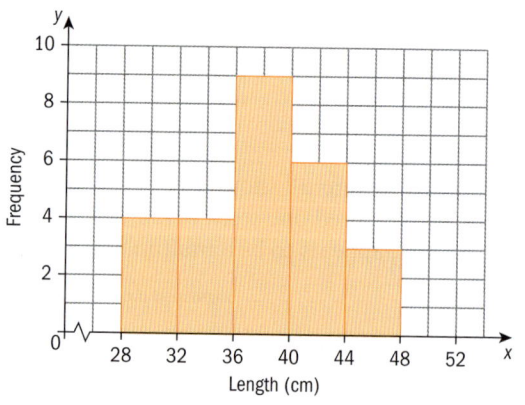

Problem solving

3 The histogram shows the amounts of money, to the nearest $10, some families spend on food each week.

a Write down the total number of families.

b Calculate an estimate for the mean amount spent on food.

c Comment on the distribution of the data.

4 Imogen asked everyone in her class to tell her their birthday month.

a Explain why she should use a bar chart to show the results.

b Sketch a bar chart to predict what the distribution would look like.

5 Here are the masses (to the nearest whole kg) of 50 emus in an Australian nature reserve in the Snowy Mountains.

```
33   19   24   35   36   24   29   29   29   34
38   35   35   35   36   60   35   50   34   48
41   41   51   42   35   36   32   61   30   40
41   19   33   34   17   35   35   38   35   42
20   29   50   33   37   28   49   58   45   40
```

a Construct a frequency histogram for this data.

b Describe the distribution.

D Can real data ever be misleading?

● How can generalizations made from real data ever be misleading?
● How do individuals stand out in a crowd?

Relative frequency histograms

In order to make fair comparisons between data sets with different numbers of data points, you can use a *relative frequency histogram*. Relative frequency shows the proportion of the total frequency in each class interval. It is plotted on the vertical axis.

Exploration 1

The frequency tables show the lengths of fish caught in the Au Sable and Kalamazoo rivers.

Au Sable River			
Length, x (cm)	Frequency	Length, x (cm)	Frequency
$10 < x \leq 20$	2	$80 < x \leq 90$	30
$20 < x \leq 30$	52	$90 < x \leq 100$	40
$30 < x \leq 40$	93	$100 < x \leq 110$	25
$40 < x \leq 50$	30	$110 < x \leq 120$	30
$50 < x \leq 60$	25	$120 < x \leq 130$	5
$60 < x \leq 70$	33	$130 < x \leq 140$	7
$70 < x \leq 80$	30	Total frequency	

Kalamazoo River			
Length, x (cm)	Frequency	Length, x (cm)	Frequency
$10 < x \le 20$	0	$80 < x \le 90$	7
$20 < x \le 30$	8	$90 < x \le 100$	7
$30 < x \le 40$	15	$100 < x \le 110$	8
$40 < x \le 50$	30	$110 < x \le 120$	1
$50 < x \le 60$	10	$120 < x \le 130$	2
$60 < x \le 70$	11	$130 < x \le 140$	4
$70 < x \le 80$	10	Total frequency	

1 Draw a frequency histogram for each data set. Use the same scale for both, with the y-axis from 0 to 100.

2 a Copy each table, adding a third column for 'Relative frequency'.

b Find the total frequency of each data set.

c For each class interval, calculate the relative frequency: $\left(\dfrac{\text{frequency}}{\text{total frequency}}\right)$

Round the values to 2 decimal places and add to your tables.

d Draw a relative frequency histogram for each data set. Plot the class boundaries on the x-axis and relative frequency on the y-axis.

3 Look at your histograms.

a Which pair of histograms should you use to compare the distribution of fish lengths in the two rivers? Explain fully.

b Which pair of histograms should you use to find the measures of central tendency? What about the measures of dispersion?

Objective:
D. Applying mathematics in real-life contexts
v. justify whether a solution makes sense in the context of the authentic real-life situation

This exploration encourages students to see mathematics as a tool for solving problems in an authentic real-life context. The students should be able to justify whether or not the comparison of data makes sense in this specific case.

Relative frequency is the proportion (or percentage) of the data set belonging in the class interval.

For a data set with n members, a class interval with frequency f has relative frequency $\dfrac{f}{n}$.

Practice 4

ATL

1 The tables show the length of time some men and women spent on their mobile phones one day.

Time spent in minutes (men)	Frequency
$0 \le x < 15$	5
$15 \le x < 30$	8
$30 \le x < 45$	10
$45 \le x < 60$	5
$60 \le x < 75$	2

Time spent in minutes (women)	Frequency
$0 \le x < 15$	4
$15 \le x < 30$	5
$30 \le x < 45$	7
$45 \le x < 60$	14
$60 \le x < 75$	20

When comparing two distributions, use descriptive words such as: wider, narrower, more varied, less varied.

a Explain why you need to use a relative frequency histogram to compare these data distributions.

b Calculate the relative frequencies for each class interval.

c Draw relative frequency histograms for the two sets of data.

d Describe each distribution.

e Compare the length of time spent on the phone by the men and women.

2 The tables show the masses of some male and female Siberian huskies.

Male Siberian husky	
Mass, m (kg)	Frequency
$17 \leq m < 19$	3
$19 \leq m < 21$	6
$21 \leq m < 23$	6
$23 \leq m < 25$	11
$25 \leq m < 27$	9

Female Siberian husky	
Mass, m (kg)	Frequency
$17 \leq m < 19$	5
$19 \leq m < 21$	8
$21 \leq m < 23$	4
$23 \leq m < 25$	2
$25 \leq m < 27$	0

a Calculate the relative frequency of each class interval as a percentage.

b Draw relative frequency histograms for each data set.

c Comment on the distribution of the masses of the male and female Siberian huskies.

Problem solving

3 The histogram shows the relative frequency of items sold at different prices at a community fundraising event. There were 32 items in total.

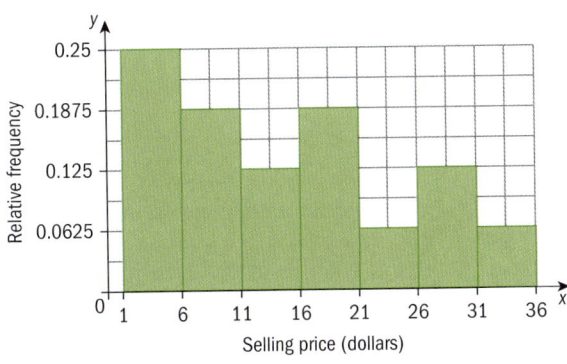

Calculate how many items sold for less than 16 dollars.

Summary

A **bar chart** represents qualitative data.

- All the bars have equal width.

- There are spaces between the bars.

- The **height** of the bar represents the frequency.

- Frequency is on the vertical axis.

A **histogram** represents quantitative discrete data and all continuous data.

- The bars may or may not be of equal width.

- There are no spaces between the bars.

- The **area** of the bar represents the frequency.

- Frequency, relative frequency or frequency density are on the vertical axis.

To comment on the distribution of data, describe:

Center   measure of central tendency

Spread   measure of dispersion

Outliers   extreme data values that don't fit the pattern

Shape   unimodal, bimodal or multimodal.

Relative frequency is the proportion (or percentage) of the data set belonging in the class interval.

Mixed practice

1 The table shows the heights of 24 students.

Height, x (cm)	Frequency
$140 \leq x < 150$	6
$150 \leq x < 160$	7
$160 \leq x < 170$	6
$170 \leq x < 180$	4
$180 \leq x < 190$	1

  a Explain why a frequency histogram can be used to represent this set of data.

  b Construct the frequency histogram.

2 A restaurant records the number of pizzas served from 8pm to 9pm on consecutive nights during one week. The table shows the results.

Number of pizzas served	5	6	8	9	10
Frequency	3	8	12	4	5

  Draw a frequency histogram for this data.

3 The masses of 50 hoglets are recorded to the nearest gram.

```
93   88  105  90   92   89   90   88  108  86
103  96   94  100  104  98  100  120 115  94
84  130  110  125  115 112  105  129 118 105
95  124  112  96   114 128  132  95  129 122
120  85   93  108  105  88   95  105 123  97
```

  a Construct a grouped frequency table for this data.

  b Construct a histogram to represent this data.

4 Fifty students recorded how much they spent on eating out in one month (to the nearest dollar). The results are shown in the partially complete frequency table:

Amount spent ($)	Class boundaries	Frequency
1–10	0.50–10.50	14
11–20	10.50–20.50	13
21–30		15
31–40		0
41–50		4
51–60		3
61–70		1

  a Draw and clearly **label** a frequency histogram to represent this information.

  b State the modal class.

  c State the class that contains the median.

  d Describe the distribution.

5 The table shows the age distribution of teachers in a school.

Age, x (years)	Number of teachers
$20 < x \leq 30$	6
$30 < x \leq 40$	4
$40 < x \leq 50$	3
$50 < x \leq 60$	2
$60 < x \leq 70$	2

  a Calculate an estimate for the mean age.

  b Construct a histogram to represent this data.

  c Describe the distribution.

6 The heights of 14-year-old students from Sri Lanka and Peru are given in the frequency tables below.

Heights of students in Sri Lanka (measured to the nearest cm)	Frequency
120–129	3
130–139	11
140–149	14
150–159	8
160–169	6

Heights of students in Peru (measured to the nearest cm)	Frequency
120–129	22
130–139	41
140–149	32
150–159	6
160–169	6

  a Explain why it is necessary to construct a relative frequency histogram to compare these data sets.

  b Comment on the distributions of the heights of 14-year-old students in Sri Lanka and Peru.

Problem solving

7 The histogram shows the lengths of a sample of European otters.

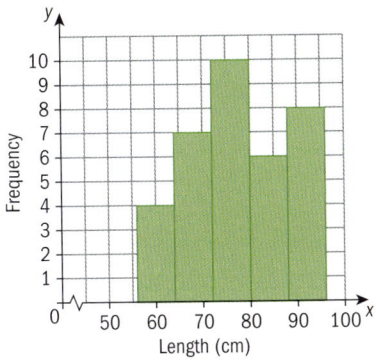

Length (cm)

a Find the class interval that contains the median.

b Calculate an estimate for the mean length.

Review in context

Globalization and sustainability

1 Twenty-five women from Mexico were asked how many children they had. The results are shown in the frequency histogram.

Number of children per woman

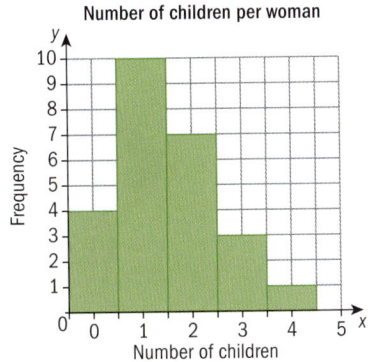

Number of children

Number of children	0	1	2	3	4	5
Frequency	4	8	5	4	5	2

Use the results from parts **a** and **b** to **describe** and **compare** the distribution of the numbers of children per woman in Australia and Mexico.

2 The amount of land covered by rainforest in the Amazon has been rapidly declining over the past decades. This frequency table show the percentage of deforestation for 20 South American regions.

0.4%	0.3%	1.6%	2.1%	0.3%
2.7%	2.2%	3.5%	2.0%	9.2%
3.2%	0%	3.0%	3.3%	4.0%
0.6%	0.5%	4.0%	1.7%	2.6%

a Sketch a frequency histogram for this data.

b Comment on the distribution.

c Determine any data that could be outliers.

a Show that the mean number of children per woman is 1.48.

b A group of 25 women from Australia were asked the same question. The results are given in the table.

Reflect and discuss 4

How have you explored the statement of inquiry? Give specific examples.

Statement of inquiry:

How quantities are represented can help to establish underlying relationships and trends in a population.

7 How do they measure up?

Statement of inquiry:

Systems use logic to validate generalizations and increase our appreciation of the aesthetic.

Key concept:

Logic is used as a process in making decisions about numbers, shapes and variables.

F **When is a measurement an approximation?**

An approximation is a quantity or a representation that is nearly, but not exactly, correct.

How big is it?

Although we have sophisticated measuring tools and standard units, most people are not very good at visualizing or interpreting measurements.

- Would a sofa measuring 160 cm × 80 cm × 70 cm fit in a family car?

C How can understanding logic help us to make generalizations?

A generalization is a general statement made on the basis of specific examples.

Horse sense

Your friend says she passes a field every day on the way to school and each day, without exception, she sees a farmer wearing a straw hat feeding a carrot to a brown horse.

Look at the following general statements and rank them in order from most likely to be true to least likely to be true. Can you think of any other general statements that could be made based on your friend's specific observations?

- The horse never eats anything but carrots.
- The farmer feeds the horse only on school days.
- The farmer is the only person who feeds the horse.
- Your friend never walks to school.
- The farmer always wears a hat.
- The horse is not a racing horse.
- Your friend travels to school at the same time every day.

D To what extent does understanding systems help you make more aesthetic solutions?

Systems are groups of interrelated elements.

Gödel's incompleteness theorems

Mathematician Kurt Gödel (1906–1978) proved that no matter what axioms you choose to start with, any axiomatic system will eventually run into statements that cannot be proven true or false – they just 'are'.

Gödel's revolutionary theorems turned mathematical and philosophical thinking on its head, and paved the way for new ideas in the field of logic and the foundation of mathematics.

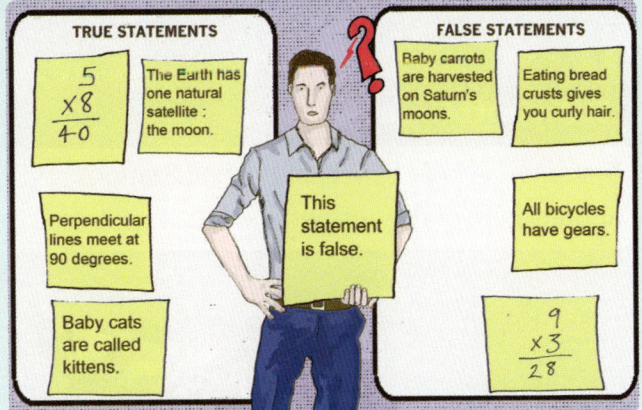

Global context: Personal and cultural expression

Exploration: Explore your appreciation of the aesthetic

 Launch additional digital resources for this unit.

LOGIC

Global context: Personal and cultural expression

Related concept: Approximation

Objectives

- Solving problems in right-angled triangles using trigonometric ratios
- Knowing the properties of trigonometric ratios
- Solving problems that include angles of elevation and angles of depression
- Solving problems using bearings

Inquiry questions

- How do you find measurements of immeasurable objects?
- What are the relationships in the special triangles?

- How do relationships between sides and angles in right-angled triangles help you find real-life measurements?

- How does understanding the trigonometric ratios help you create and understand mathematical models?

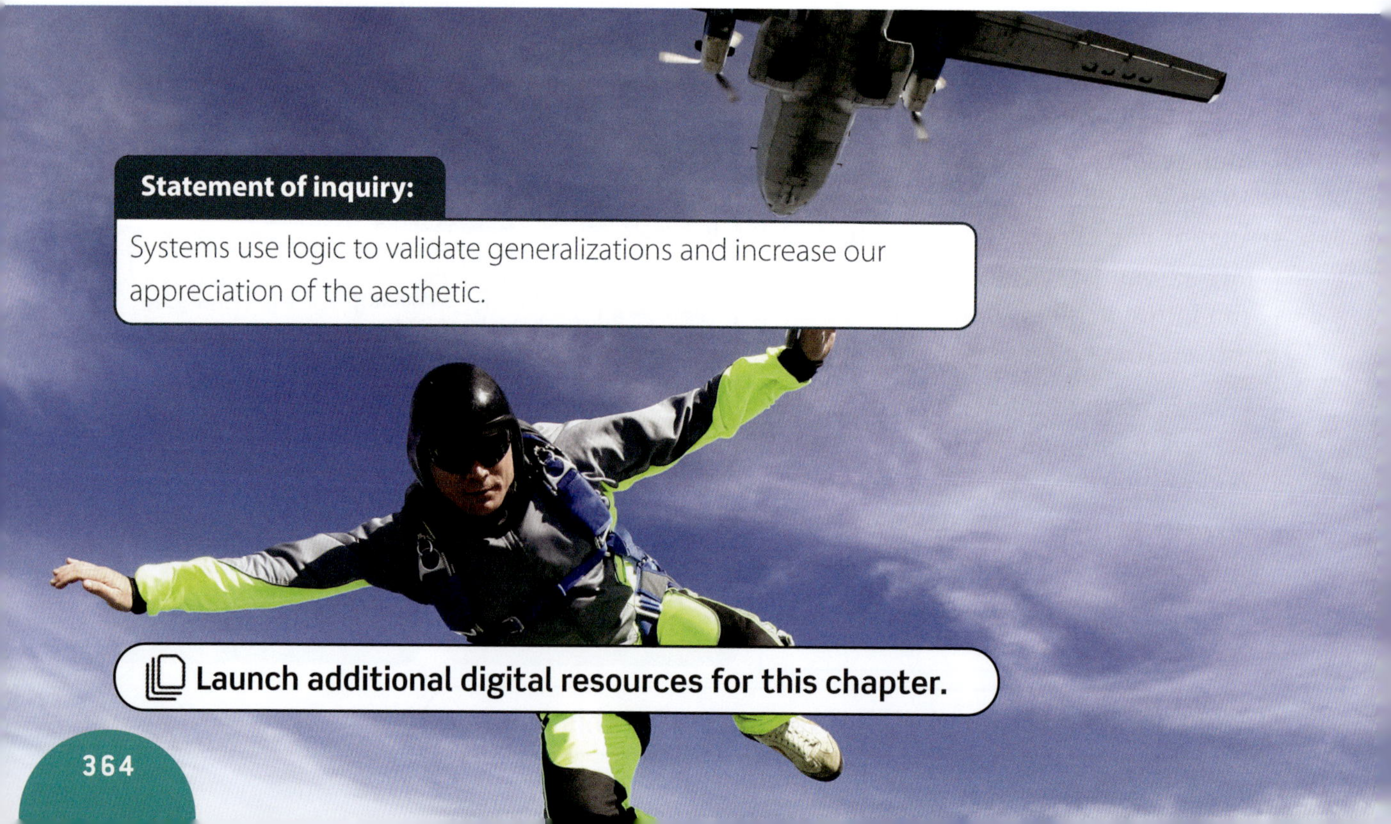

Statement of inquiry:

Systems use logic to validate generalizations and increase our appreciation of the aesthetic.

 Launch additional digital resources for this chapter.

You should already know how to:

• use the Pythagorean Theorem to find the missing side in a right-angled triangle	**1** Find the missing side in each triangle, accurate to 3 s.f. All measurements are in cm. 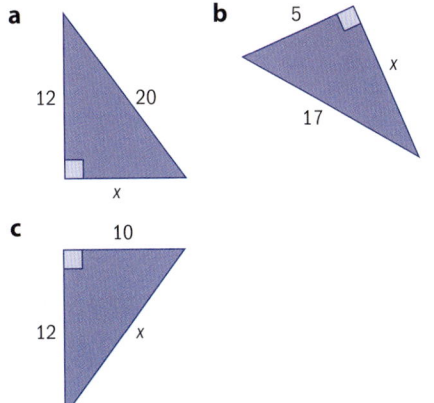
• relate angles and sides of a right-angled triangle using the trigonometric ratios (sine, cosine and tangent)	**2** Find sin A, cos B, tan A and tan B in terms of a, b and c. 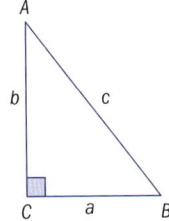
• solve simple problems using the trigonometric ratios	**3** Find the value of x in each triangle, accurate to 3 s.f. 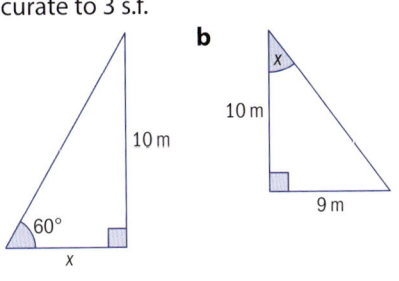

F ## Right-angled triangles and trigonometric ratios

- How do you find measurements of immeasurable objects?
- What are the relationships in the special triangles?

The right angle is the most common angle in our world – after all, we stand at right angles to our earth, and the homes we live in are built at right angles to their foundations. This fundamental angle is at the heart of the study of geometry and trigonometry.

ATL

Activity

1 Make a list of different methods you could use to find the height of a very tall building. For each method, state where you are standing in relation to the building.

2 Write down the advantages and disadvantages of using each method.

3 Discuss these methods with others and rank them starting with the best method first. Explain your ranking order.

4 If you were standing on the ground in front of a building, what measurements would you need to take in order to calculate its height? Draw a diagram and write an equation relating these measurements.

Land surveyors determine property boundaries and prepare maps and survey plots accordingly. In their job they are always calculating immeasurable distances and angles.

5 Research what kind(s) of tools land surveyors use to measure far distances and angles between the line of vision and an object.

6 How would land surveyors use their instruments, together with the trigonometric ratios of sine, cosine, and tangent, to determine immeasurable heights and angles?

You have already learned about the trigonometric ratios in a right-angled triangle, but did you know that they can help you determine immeasurable distances? In order to do so, you will need to review how to find the trigonometric ratios with a calculator.

Practice 1

1 Use your calculator to evaluate these, either exact or to three significant figures.

a $\sin 47°$	**b** $\cos 32°$	**c** $\tan 17°$	**d** $\sin 2°$
e $\tan 89°$	**f** $\cos 60°$	**g** $\tan 45.8°$	**h** $\sin 0.789°$
i $\cos 0°$	**j** $\tan 30°$		

2 Find the angle in each expression, either exact or to one decimal place.

a $\sin A = 0.467$	**b** $\cos B = \dfrac{\sqrt{2}}{2}$	**c** $\tan C = 1$
d $\cos \alpha = 0.898$	**e** $\sin \beta = 0.5$	**f** $\tan \theta = \sqrt{3}$
g $\cos \varphi = 0.123$	**h** $\tan A = 27.3$	

> Make sure that your calculator is in degree mode (not in radian mode) when you are using degrees to measure angles.

Reflect and discuss 1

Take a closer look at the values of the trigonometric ratios in the questions of Practice 1.

- What do you notice about the range of values for each?

- Can you explain the reason for your observation?

Some people use the memory aid **SOH-CAH-TOA** for remembering the trigonometric ratios in a right-angled triangle. Given a right-angled triangle with acute angle α:

SOH — $\text{Sin}\,\alpha = \dfrac{\text{side } \mathbf{O}\text{pposite to }\alpha}{\mathbf{H}\text{ypotenuse}}$

CAH — $\text{Cos}\,\alpha = \dfrac{\text{side } \mathbf{A}\text{djacent to }\alpha}{\mathbf{H}\text{ypotentuse}}$

TOA — $\text{Tan}\,\alpha = \dfrac{\text{side } \mathbf{O}\text{pposite to }\alpha}{\text{side } \mathbf{A}\text{djacent to }\alpha}$

Practice 2

1 Use your knowledge of the trigonometric ratios to find the side marked x in each triangle. Round your answers to the nearest hundredth where necessary.

a
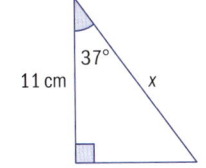

b
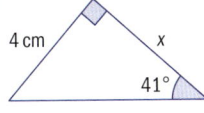

c
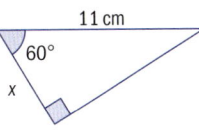

d
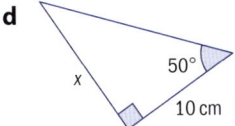

e
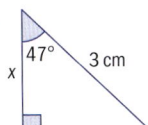

f
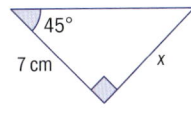

2 Find the angle θ in each triangle. Round your answers to the nearest tenth where necessary. All lengths are in meters.

a
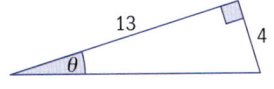

b
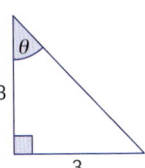

c
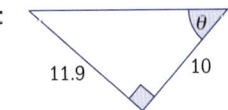

d
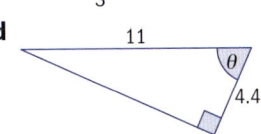

3 Find all missing sides and angles in these right-angled triangles. Round your answers to 1 d.p. where necessary.

a
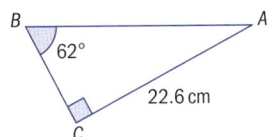

b
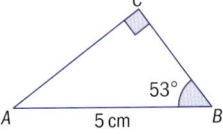

c
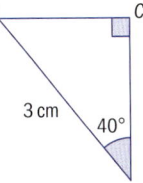

d
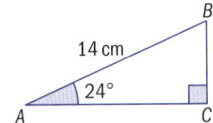

e
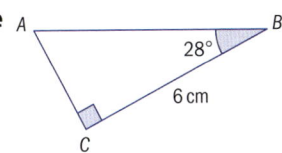

Objective: C. Communicating

i. use appropriate mathematical language (notation, symbols and terminology) in both oral and written explanations

In this exploration, you will need to use appropriate and accurate notation in your sketches to be able to convince others that your answers are justified.

Exploration 1

One method you may have discussed in the Activity is to use the shadow of a building to measure its height. You are now going to explore two methods to find out how tall your school is without actually measuring its height.

Method 1: Shadow

1 Sketch the building and its shadow in your notebook, and draw the right-angled triangle that is represented by this situation. Label the sides of the triangle.

2 Determine what measurements you would need to make in order to use trigonometric ratios to calculate the height of the building. If you can, make these measurements.

3 Use your sketch to determine which trigonometric ratio will help you find the height of the building. Write down the trigonometric equation that represents the situation. (Solve it if you have actual measurements.)

Method 2: Mirror

1 Put a small mirror on the ground and stand far enough away that you can see the top of the building in the middle of the mirror.

2 Measure your distance to the mirror, your height and the distance of the building to the mirror.

3 Sketch the situation and indicate the measurements in your diagram.

4 Justify how the two triangles in your diagram are related.

5 Explain how you could calculate the height of the building **a** using trigonometric ratios and **b** without using trigonometric ratios.

Reflect and discuss 2

- Which method do you think is more accurate, the shadow or the mirror method? Justify your answer.

Exploration 2

1 **a** Using the Pythagorean Theorem, find the length of the hypotenuse of this triangle. Leave your answer as a radical.

   b Identify what type of triangle this is, and thus find the missing angles.

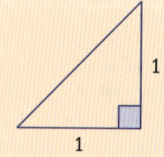

▶ Continued on next page

c Hence, use your knowledge of trigonometric ratios in a right-angled triangle to find the following values (leaving your answers as radicals):

- ○ sin 45°   ○ cos 45°   ○ tan 45°

Now consider the equilateral triangle shown here:

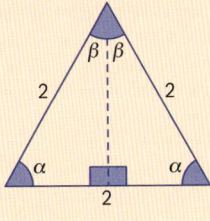

2 a Using your knowledge of equilateral triangles, find angle α.

b Assume that the dotted line is the perpendicular bisector of the base. Using your knowledge of the angle sum in a triangle, find angle β.

c Using the Pythagorean Theorem, find the length of the dotted line.

d Hence, use your knowledge of trigonometric ratios in a right-angled triangle to find the following values (leave your answers in surd form):

- ○ sin 30°   ○ cos 30°   ○ tan 30°
- ○ sin 60°   ○ cos 60°   ○ tan 60°

3 Check your results in steps **1 c** and **2 d** by comparing the surd form with the values from your calculator

4 In step **2**, which was the longest side of the right-angled triangle and which was the greatest angle? Where were these in relation to each other? What about the shortest side and the smallest angle?

> The results of this exploration are very useful to memorize, as are the methods used to find these angles.

These triangles are known as 'special triangles'. Recognizing these ratios can help you solve problems.

Practice 3

By using the special triangles, find the unknown measurements.
Leave your answers in radical form where appropriate.

1

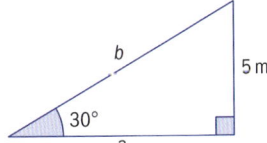

2

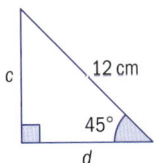

3

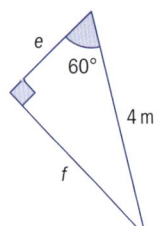

> You can check your answers using the Pythagorean Theorem.

4

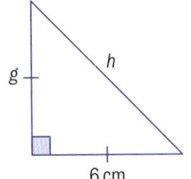

5

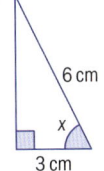

C Real-life applications

- How do relationships between sides and angles in right-angled triangles help you find real-life measurements?

Example 1

You are standing 9 m away from a building, and your eyes are 160 cm from the ground. Using a surveyor, you read the angle of elevation of the top of the building is 50°. Find the height of the building to the nearest meter.

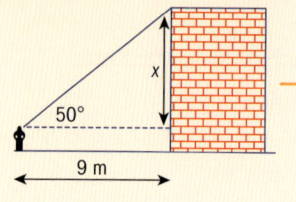

Draw a sketch and label the given information.

$\tan 50° = \frac{x}{9} \Rightarrow x = 9 \times \tan 50° = 10.726$

In relation to the angle, you are given the side adjacent and you are looking for the opposite side, hence use tangent.

$1.6 + 10.726 = 12.326$

The building is about 12 m tall.

Add your height to the answer and round to the nearest meter.

An **angle of depression** is the angle between the horizon and an object below the horizon.

An **angle of elevation** is the angle between the horizon and an object above the horizon.

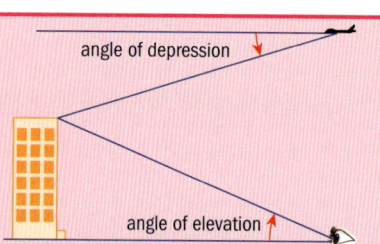

angle of depression

angle of elevation

Reflect and discuss 3

- Why do we refer to sine, cosine and tangent as trigonometric *ratios*?
- The angles and sides of right-angled triangles are measured in specific units. What are the units of the trigonometric ratios? Justify your answer.
- Why are the angles of elevation and depression equal?

angle of depression

angle of elevation

Practice 4

Problem solving

1 The famous Leaning Tower of Pisa 'leans' at an angle of 4°, and its top is 55.86 m above the ground. Determine the height to the nearest meter of its top above the ground when it was originally built (standing at right angles to the ground).

2 To a person standing 130 m away from the base of a building, determine the angle of elevation of the top of a building that is 58 m high. Explain the limitations on the accuracy of your answer.

3 Gina is flying a kite that makes a 50° angle with the ground. Determine how high the kite is above the ground when she has let out 150 m of string.

4 A vertical stick 1m long casts a shadow which is 1.3 m long. Determine the altitude of the sun (its angle of elevation).

5 A ladder that is 6 m long is leaning against the side of a building making an angle of 60° with the ground. Determine how far the ladder's base is from the building, and how far up it is on the building.

6 A ship is on the surface of the water, and its radar detects a submarine at a distance of 238 m away underwater, at an angle of depression of 23°. Find the depth of the submarine.

Reflect and discuss 4

- For Practice 3, question **2**, what happens to the angle of elevation as you get closer to the building, and as you get farther from the building?

- For Practice 3, question **4**, describe what happens to the length of the shadow of the stick as the sun's altitude changes.

> It is important to understand, at this point, that a trigonometric ratio is a relationship between specific sides of a right-angled triangle. That ratio is normally represented as either a fraction or decimal.

Example 2

Find the length of the side labelled x to 3 s.f.

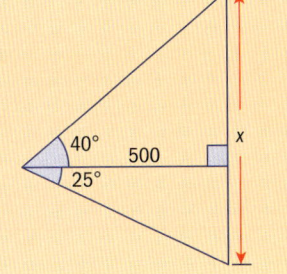

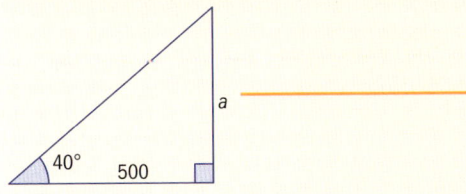

> Separate the triangle into two right-angled triangles. Label the unknown side in the upper triangle and use the trigonometric ratios to find it. Since the final answer is required to 3 s.f., all calculations before the final answer must be carried out to at least one more s.f.

$$\tan 40° = \frac{a}{500} \Rightarrow a = 500 \times \tan 40° = 419.5$$

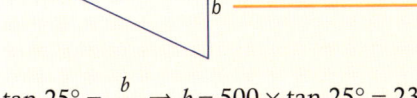

> Label the unknown side in the lower triangle and use trigonometric ratios to find it.

$$\tan 25° = \frac{b}{500} \Rightarrow b = 500 \times \tan 25° = 233.2$$

$x = a + b$

$\quad = 419.5 + 233.2 = 652.7 = 653$ (3 s.f.)

> Add the two lengths that make up the unknown side, and round to the required degree of accuracy.

Example 3

In the diagram, $AC = 52$ m. The angle of depression from C to B is $28°$, and the angle of depression from C to D is $42°$. Find the distance between B and D.

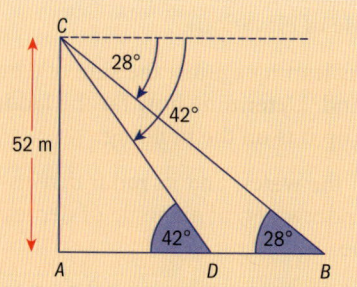

In $\triangle ABC$, $\tan 28 = \dfrac{52}{AB} \Rightarrow AB = \dfrac{52}{\tan 28} = 97.80$ m

Use the trig ratios to find the required sides.

In $\triangle ADC$, $\tan 42 = \dfrac{52}{AD} \Rightarrow AD = \dfrac{52}{\tan 42} = 57.75$ m

$\Rightarrow BD = 97.80 - 57.75 = 40.1$ m (3 s.f.)

Bearings are used to describe the direction of one point from another on the surface of the Earth. The bearing of point B from point A is always given in degrees and measured clockwise from north. Bearings are usually given as three figures (using leading zeroes if necessary) and correct to the nearest degree.

In order to help you find a bearing, you may find it useful to imagine that you are standing at A and facing due north. The bearing is how far you must turn to your right until you are facing B.

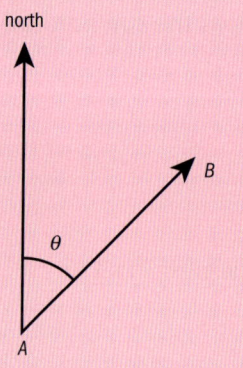

Example 4

An air ambulance helicopter needs to attend an emergency. The location of the emergency is 6 km north and 3 km west of the helicopter's start point.

a Find the bearing along which the helicopter should travel.

b Find the distance to the location of the emergency and the time it would take to fly there at 150 km/h.

a

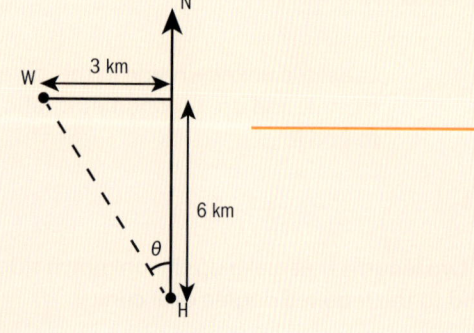

First draw a diagram showing the given distances.

▶ Continued on next page

$\tan \theta = \dfrac{3}{6}$ so $\theta = \arctan\left(\dfrac{1}{2}\right) = 27°$ (to the nearest degree) — This angle is measured counterclockwise from north, so it is not the bearing.

The bearing is $360 - 27 = 333°$ — The bearing must be measured clockwise from north.

b $d = \sqrt{6^2 + 3^2} \approx 6.71$ km (3 s.f.) — Use the Pythagorean Theorem to find the length of the diagonal.

$\text{time} = \dfrac{\text{distance}}{\text{speed}}$ so $t = \dfrac{6.71}{150} \approx 0.0447$ hours

$0.0447 \times 60 = 2.68$ minutes or 2 minutes 41 seconds — Give your answer in sensible units.

Practice 5

1 Find the missing length x in each diagram.

a
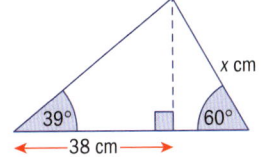

b
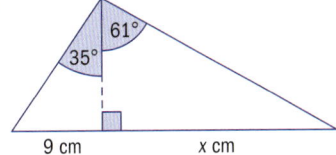

2 Find the side length x in each triangle.

a
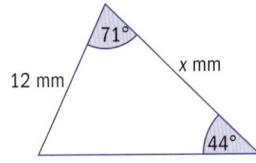

b
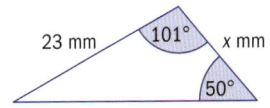

> In question **2**, you will need to decide where to draw a dotted line in order to solve the problem.

3 Find the angle θ.

4 Find the distance m in the diagram.

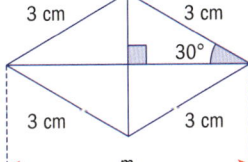

5 Find the heights from the ground of A, B and C.

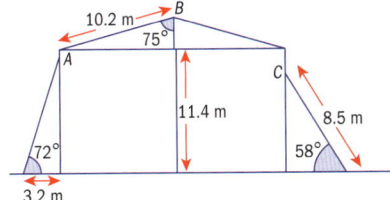

6 Find the side length x in this diagram.

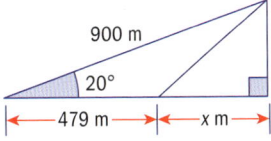

Problem solving

7 A single engine private plane flies due north for an hour and 18 minutes at an average speed of 110 km/h. It then turns and flies at the same average speed for an hour and a half on a bearing of 130°. At the end of this time, determine:

   a how far the plane has traveled

   b its bearing from its initial position.

8 Two ships leave port at 10:00 and each one travels on a straight line course. The first one travels on a bearing of 60° at 23 km/h and the second one travels on a bearing of 115° at 28 km/h. Determine how far the two ships are from one another at 12:00 noon.

9 A lookout post is on top of a hill that is 100 m above sea level. From the base of the lookout post, the angle of depression of a boat out at sea is 30°, and from the top of the lookout post, the angle of depression of the boat is 60°. Find the height of the lookout post.

- -

Reflect and discuss 5

- How does trigonometry help determine immeasurable distances?

- How do you think we solve problems when the triangle isn't a right-angled triangle?

- Why is it important to follow a convention when using bearings?

D More on the trigonometric ratios

- How does understanding the trigonometric ratios help you create and understand mathematical models?

Exploration 3

1 Using your calculator, find the sines, cosines and tangents of several angles between 0° and 90°.

2 What is the range of values of each of the three ratios?

3 Summarize your findings in a table.

Reflect and discuss 6

- Considering right-angled triangles, give reasons why the sines and cosines of angles cannot be greater than 1.

- What was the greatest value you found for a tangent ratio? By choosing a bigger angle, could you have found an even greater value?

- What does your calculator say when you enter tan 90°? Why is this? Why is there no maximum value for the tangent ratio?

So far, you should have been able to make the following generalizations related to right-angled triangles:

- The lengths of the sides of a right-angled triangle are proportional to the measures of their opposite angles. The longest side will therefore be opposite the largest angle, and the shortest side will be opposite the smallest angle. Since the largest angle in a right-angled triangle is $90°$, the longest side of the triangle has to be the hypotenuse.

- The sine and cosine ratios are the length of one of the legs divided by the length of the hypotenuse. Since the hypotenuse is always the longest side, the denominator of the fraction is always larger than the numerator; hence the ratio is always less than 1.

- The tangent of an angle is the ratio of the leg opposite the angle to the leg adjacent to the angle. The legs that make up the right angle are either equal, or one is larger than the other. The tangent can therefore be less than 1 (but greater than zero), greater than 1, or equal to 1.

Exploration 4

1 Draw a right-angled triangle where one of the legs is very short (very close to length 0) and the hypotenuse is 5 cm. Label it like this:

2 Measure lengths a and b.

3 Using the definition of sine and cosine, find $\sin A$, $\cos A$, $\sin B$ and $\cos B$.

4 Explain what happens to $\sin A$ as side a gets smaller.
Generalize the effect on $\sin A$ and $\cos A$ as angle A gets closer to zero.
Generalize the effect on $\sin B$ and $\cos B$ as angle B gets closer to $90°$.

> You might want to look at the effects on $\tan A$ and $\tan B$ as angle A gets closer to zero.

In Exploration 5 you will see how the tangent ratio is related to another mathematical concept you have studied.

Exploration 5

1 Plot the points $(5, 0)$ and $(10, 4)$ on graph paper. Calculate the gradient of the line segment joining these two points.

2 Measure the angle between the line and the x-axis and use your calculator to find the tangent of the angle.

3 Write down the relationship you notice between the gradient of the line and the tangent of the angle.

4 Plot the points $(0, -2)$ and $(3, 4)$ and find the gradient of the line segment joining them. Find the tangent of the angle between the line segment and the x-axis. Then, find the tangent of the angle between the line segment and the line $y = -2$. Write down what you notice between the two tangent values, and the relationship between the gradient of the line and the tangent of the angle formed by the line segment and a line parallel to the x-axis.

5 Justify the relationships you noticed in steps **3** and **4**.

> The gradient of a straight line between (x_1, y_1) and (x_2, y_2) is $m = \frac{y_2 - y_1}{x_2 - x_1}$.

▶ Continued on next page

6 Consider again the line segment in step **1**. Write down what happens to the gradient of the line segment as you move the point (10, 4) closer to the y-axis. Reflect on the change of the tangent of the angle formed by the line and the x-axis as you move the point closer to the y-axis. Determine the gradient of the line segment when you move this point on to the y-axis. What is the tangent of the angle when the point is on the y-axis?

7 Plot the points (5, 0) and (0, 4) and find the gradient of the line segment between the two points. Find the tangent of the angle formed between the line segment and the x-axis. Explain why the tangent of the angle should be a negative value.

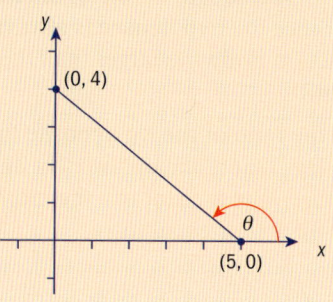

Note that you find the angle between the line and the *positive x*-axis. So θ is obtuse (>90°).

The use of trigonometric ratios for angles that cannot be represented in a right-angled triangle will be explored further in the MYP 4 & 5 Extended book.

Summary

- The trigonometric ratios in a right-angled triangle help you to make measurements that you couldn't easily make otherwise.

- The largest angle in a right-angled triangle is the right angle. The two other angles are always acute angles.

- The longest side in a right-angled triangle is the hypotenuse (opposite the right angle) and the other sides, called legs, are shorter.

- In a right-angled triangle, the values of sin and cos are always between 0 and 1. However, the value of tan can be any value greater than 0.

- The following results hold true for sin, cos and tan:

sin 0° = 0	cos 0° = 0	tan 0° = 0
sin 90° = 1	cos 90° = 0	tan 90° = *undefined*

- Some results worth knowing:

$\sin 45° = \dfrac{\sqrt{2}}{2}$	$\sin 30° = \dfrac{1}{2}$	$\sin 60° = \dfrac{\sqrt{3}}{2}$
$\cos 45° = \dfrac{\sqrt{2}}{2}$	$\cos 30° = \dfrac{\sqrt{3}}{2}$	$\cos 60° = \dfrac{1}{2}$
$\tan 45° = 1$	$\tan 30° = \dfrac{\sqrt{3}}{2}$	$\tan 60° = \dfrac{\sqrt{3}}{1}$

- The gradient of a line is equal to the tangent of the angle that the line makes with the positive x-axis.

- Angles of depression and elevation:

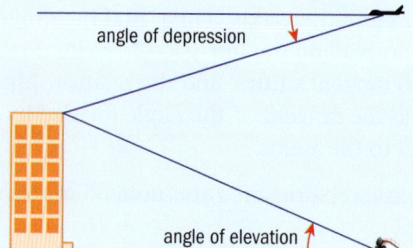

Mixed practice

1 Eric travels for 4 km on a bearing of 048° and then travels for a further 5 km on a bearing of 129°. **Determine** whether his final position is north or south of his original position, and by how much.

2 An historic building is being moved because a new road is being constructed. The building is to be moved 5 km west and 7 km south.
Find the bearing of its new position from its old position.

3 Reading lies 11.1 km from Wokingham on a bearing of 296°. Write down the bearing from Reading to Wokingham.
For the journey from Reading to Wokingham, **determine** how far must be traveled east and south.

4 A kite string is 48 m long. As the wind blew, the angle between the kite and the ground went from 27 degrees to 54 degrees. **Determine** the increase in the vertical height of the kite above the ground.

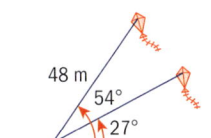

5 **Find** length x in each diagram.

a

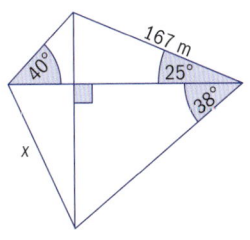

b

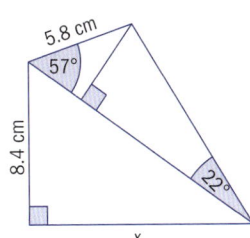

6 $ABCD$ is a square, where $AP = 5$ cm, $QC = 7$ cm and $PB = 12$ cm.

Calculate:

a the size of the angle marked x

b the length of AB

c the length of DQ

d the length of PD

e the size of $\angle BQD$.

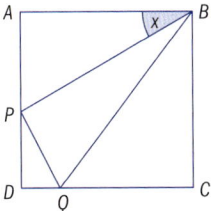

7 In a house that is being renovated, two corridors meet at right angles, as shown in the diagram. Workmen attempting to take a ladder around the corner get the ladder stuck when it is at an angle of 45° to each wall.

a **Determine** the length of the ladder.

b **Determine** the length of a second ladder that got stuck when it was at an angle of 60° with the wall of the 1 m corridor.

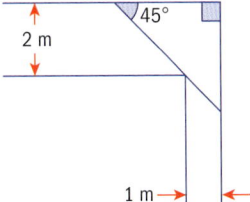

Problem solving

8 A 5 m ladder is resting against a vertical wall. The base of the ladder is 2 m from the wall. Keeping its base fixed, the ladder is rotated so that it now rests against the opposite wall which is 1 m away. **Determine** the angle through which the ladder has been rotated.

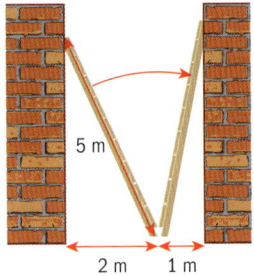

9 A coast guard attendant atop a cliff 120 m high observes two boats in line with him at angles of depression of 45 degrees and 69 degrees.

Determine how far apart the boats are.

Review in context

1 In 1852, an Indian mathematician, Radhanath Sikdar, used measurements and trigonometry to calculate the height of Peak XV in the Himalayas (later to be named Mount Everest). This required the use of a device that measured angles from the ground to the top of an object. By measuring the angle to the top of Peak XV from two different spots, and knowing the distance between these spots, Sikdar may have come up with a drawing like the following:

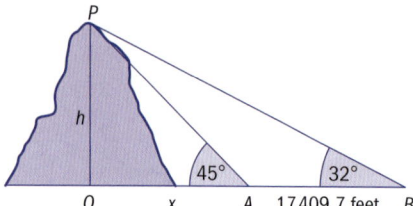

The angle of elevation to the top of the peak (from point *B*) was measured to be 32°. From a point 17 409.7 feet closer (point *A*), the angle of elevation was 45°.

Find the height Sikdar calculated for Peak XV.

2 You are the pilot of a light aircraft, returning to the airfield after a parachuting trip. Your altitude is 3050 m and you are heading towards the landing strip which is currently 14 km away. **Find** the angle of depression you should use so that you touch down on the landing strip at the closest point.

> Legend has it that the value Sikdar calculated was so perfect that he thought nobody would believe him. Supposedly, he added 2 feet to make it more believable! History books record his calculated height to be 29 002 feet.

Reflect and discuss 7

How have you explored the statement of inquiry? Give specific examples.

Statement of inquiry:

Systems use logic to validate generalizations and increase our appreciation of the aesthetic.

7.2 Properties of circles

Global context: Personal and cultural expression

Related concept: Generalization

Objectives

- Knowing the terms chord, arc, segment and sector
- Finding the length of an arc of a circle
- Finding the angle in a sector of a circle
- Finding the perimeter and area of a sector of a circle
- Finding the length of a chord

Inquiry questions

F • How can you find the measurements for the different parts of a circle?

C • How are the parts of a circle related?

D • Is it advantageous to make your own generalizations?

LOGIC

ATL Communication

Use and interpret a range of discipline-specific terms and symbols

Statement of inquiry:

Systems use logic to validate generalizations and increase our appreciation of the aesthetic.

📖 **Launch additional digital resources for this chapter.**

You should already know how to:

• find the circumference of a circle using $C = 2\pi r$ or πd	**1** Find the circumference of a circle: **a** of radius 2.4 cm **b** of diameter 5.75 m. Give your answers to 1 d.p.
• find the area of a circle using $A = \pi r^2$	**2** Find the area of the two circles above. Give your answers to 1 d.p.
• find missing lengths in a right-angled triangle using trigonometric ratios	**3** Find the missing length x in this triangle. 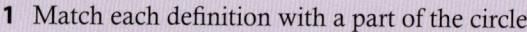5 cm x 30°

F Parts of a circle

- How can you find the measurements for the different parts of a circle?

ATL

Activity

1 Match each definition with a part of the circle.

- A **diameter** is a chord that passes through the center of a circle.

- A **chord** is a line segment with its endpoints on a circle.

- A **secant** is a line that intersects a circle at two points.

- A **tangent** is a line that touches a circle at only one point.

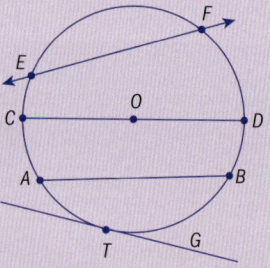

2 Match the following definitions with the parts of the circle in the diagram.

The **major segment** is the larger segment.

The **minor segment** is the smaller segment. ('Segment' usually refers to the minor segment.)

The larger arc is the **major arc**.

The smaller arc is the **minor arc**.

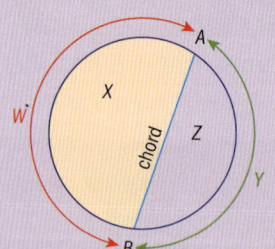

A **sector** is a 'slice' of a circle between two radii. The center of a circle is usually labelled O, so the sector here is BOC. 'Sector' usually means the minor sector.

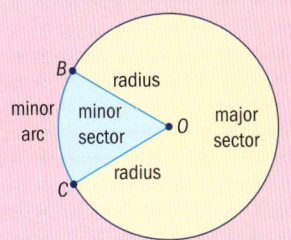

ATL

Reflect and discuss 1

How are secants and chords similar? How are they different?

Exploration 1

1 Use a set of compasses to draw a circle. Clearly mark its center. Draw a chord that is **not** the diameter of the circle.

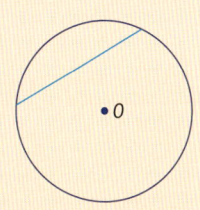

2 Draw radii from the center of the circle to each endpoint of the chord. Determine which type of triangle you have drawn.

3 Use a protractor to measure the angle of the sector you have drawn.

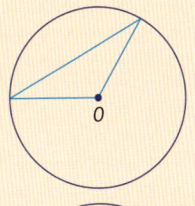

4 Draw a line segment from the center of the circle, O, to the midpoint of the chord, M.

a Explain why this line segment:

- divides the triangle in half

- divides the angle of the sector in half (measure to check that it does).

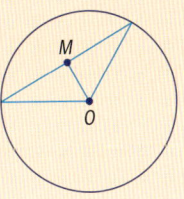

b Calculate the angle that the new line segment makes with the chord. Measure to check.

Use symmetry.

In a circle, two radii and a chord form an isosceles triangle. A line from the center of the circle to the midpoint of the chord forms two right-angled triangles.

When you know the angle at the center, you can use trigonometry in one of the right-angled triangles to find the length of the chord.

Example 1

Find the length of chord *XY*.

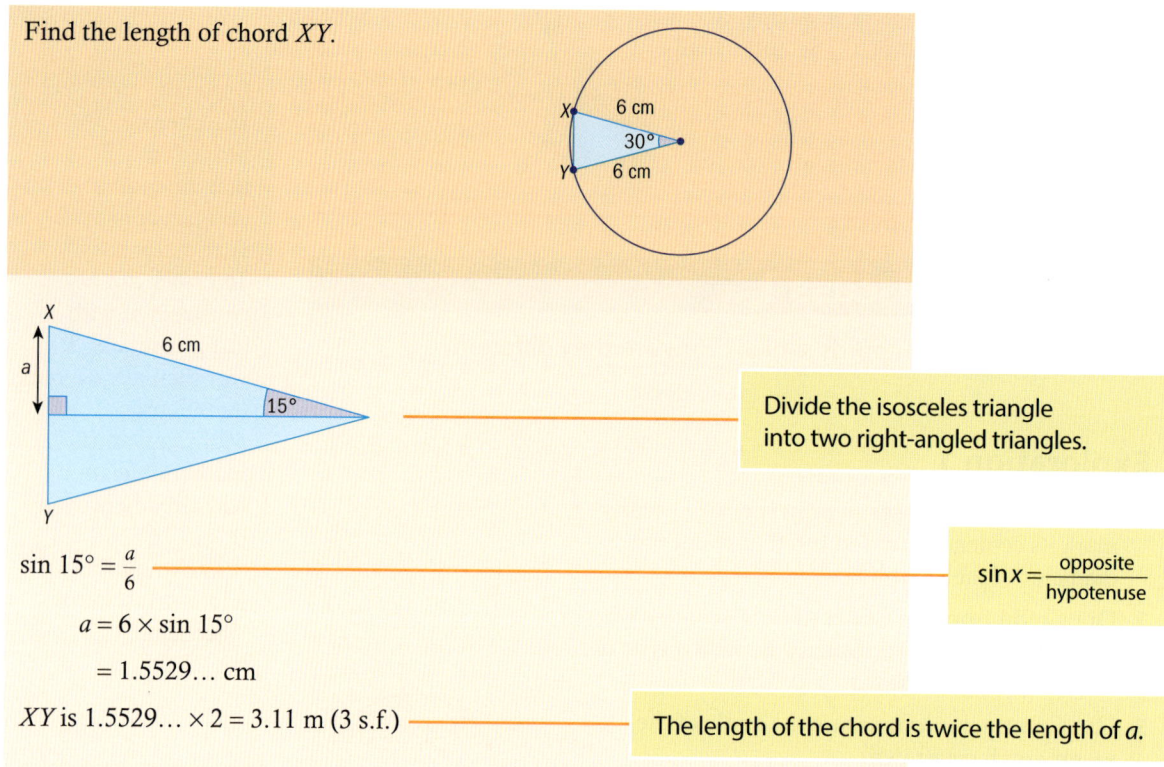

sin 15° = $\frac{a}{6}$

$a = 6 \times \sin 15°$

$= 1.5529...$ cm

XY is $1.5529... \times 2 = 3.11$ m (3 s.f.)

> Divide the isosceles triangle into two right-angled triangles.

> $\sin x = \frac{\text{opposite}}{\text{hypotenuse}}$

> The length of the chord is twice the length of *a*.

Practice 1

Give your answers to 1 decimal place.

1 Find the length of chord *JK*.

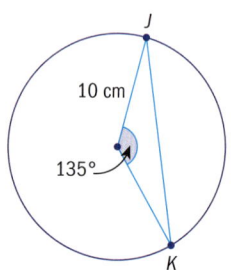

2 Find the length of chord *LM*.

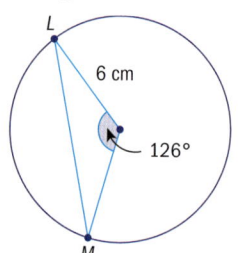

Problem solving

3 The sector *AOB* is one third of the circle.
Find the length of chord *AB*.

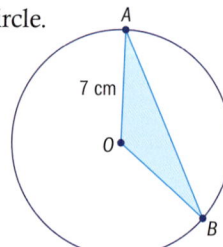

> First find the angle of the sector.

4 *POQ* is a sector of a circle.
The angle of the sector is 75°.
Chord *PQ* has length 8 cm.
Find the radius of the circle.

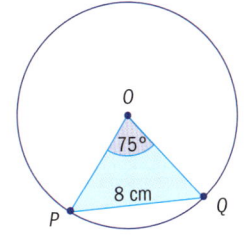

5 *ROS* is a sector of a circle of radius 5 cm.
Chord *RS* is 8 cm.
Find the angle of sector *ORS*.

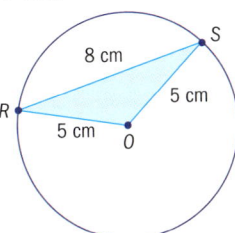

The Mesopotamians used a sexagesimal system, that is, base 60. We use this today when measuring time (60 seconds in a minute, 60 minutes in an hour) and also for angles ($360° = 60° \times 6$).

C Relationships between measurements in a circle

- How are the parts of a circle related?

Exploration 2

1 Draw a circle with a set of compasses and then draw a chord that is not the diameter of the circle. Label the chord *c*.

2 Draw radii from the center of the circle to each endpoint of the chord. Indicate the angle, θ, in the center of the sector.

3 By drawing a line segment from the center of the circle to the midpoint of the chord *c*, use trigonometry to show that the relationship between θ, *r* and *c* can be expressed as $\theta = 2\arcsin\left(\frac{c}{2r}\right)$.

Verify that your formula works for questions **1**, **2** and **3** in Practice 1.

Explain what changes you would have to make to your formula for questions **4** and **5** in Practice 1.

When sharing a pizza, the more equal slices you cut, the smaller each slice will be. To describe the size of a pizza slice you could measure:

1 the fraction of the pizza

2 the **central angle** θ (angle at the center of the sector), sometimes called the **measure of the sector**

3 the length of the crust, or **arc length**, *l*

4 the perimeter of the sector, *P*

5 the area of the sector, *A*.

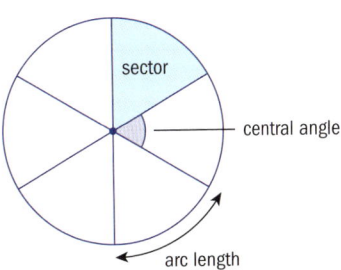

'You better cut the pizza in four pieces because I'm not hungry enough to eat six.'

Lawrence Peter 'Yogi' Berra

Objective: **B.** Investigating patterns
ii. describe patterns as general rules consistent with findings

In this exploration you will search for patterns and generalize the relationships between the different measurements in a circle.

ATL

Exploration 3

In this exploration you will generalize the relationship between the measurements.

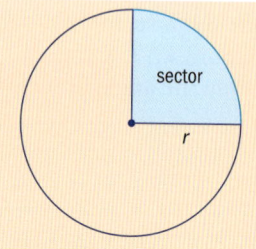

For a pizza of radius r cut into four equal slices or sectors.

1 State the fraction of the pizza in each sector.

2 State the central angle for each sector.

3 What fraction of the circumference is the arc length of each sector? Write down an expression for the arc length of each sector.

4 Describe how you can use the arc length of a sector to find the perimeter of a sector. Write down an expression for the perimeter of each sector.

5 What fraction of the area of the circle is the area of each sector? Write an expression for the area of each sector.

> When answering questions about the length of arcs and sectors, your final answer should always include the appropriate units.

6 Copy and complete the table.

Number of equal sectors	Fraction	Central angle	Arc length	Sector perimeter	Sector area
1 (the whole circle)	$\frac{1}{1}=1$	360°			
2	$\frac{1}{2}$	$\frac{360°}{2}=180°$	$\frac{2\pi r}{2}$	$\pi r + 2r$	$\frac{\pi r^2}{2}$
3	$\frac{1}{3}$	$\frac{360°}{3}=120°$	$\frac{2\pi r}{3}$		$\frac{\pi r^2}{3}$
4					
	$\frac{1}{5}$				
		60°			
			$\frac{2\pi r}{8}$		
					$\frac{\pi r^2}{9}$
			$\frac{2\pi r}{10}$		
		12°			
		10°			
		9°			
n					
$\frac{360}{\theta}$					

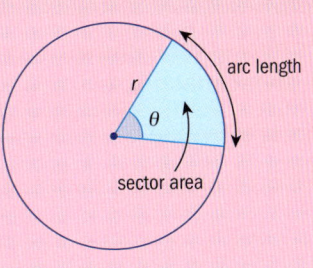
Example 2

Find the area and circumference of
this circle in terms of π.

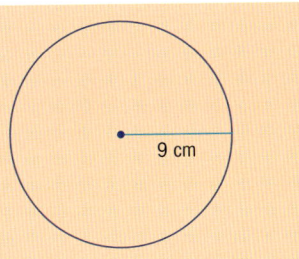

9 cm

'In terms of π'
means leave π in
your answer.

$\text{Area} = \pi r^2 = \pi \times 9^2 = 81\pi \ \text{cm}^2$

$\text{Circumference} = 2\pi r = 2 \times \pi \times 9 = 18\pi \ \text{cm}$

Remember to include the correct units.

Example 3

Find the length of arc XY in terms of π,
and as a number to 2 decimal places.

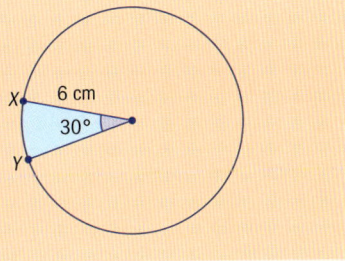

X — 6 cm — 30°
Y

$\theta = 30°$

$r = 6 \ \text{cm}$

Arc length $XY = \dfrac{\theta}{360°} \times 2\pi r$

$= \dfrac{30}{360} \times 2 \times \pi \times 6$

$= \pi \ \text{cm}$

$\approx 3.14 \ \text{cm}$

Use the arc length formula.

Reflect and discuss 2

Circle and sector problems may ask for lengths and areas in terms of π, or to a given number of decimal places.

- Which gives the most accurate value?
- What degree of accuracy do you think is necessary?

Example 4

Find the area of sector PQ.
Give your answer to 3 s.f.

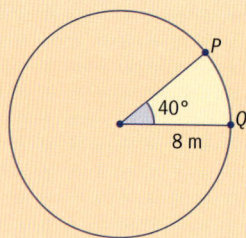

$\theta = 40°$

$r = 8$ m

Area of sector $PQ = \dfrac{\theta}{360°} \times \pi r^2$ ——————— Use the formula for the area of a sector.

$ = \dfrac{40}{360} \times \pi \times 8^2$

$ = \dfrac{1}{9} \times \pi \times 64$

$ = 22.3402...$

Area of sector $PQ = 22.3$ m² (3 s.f.) ——————— Remember to include the units.

Practice 2

1 Find the area and circumference of each circle.
Give your answers in terms of π.

a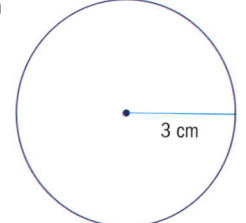
3 cm

b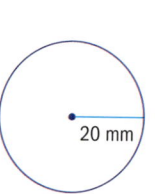
20 mm

c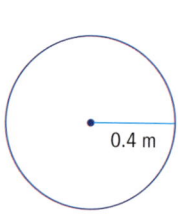
0.4 m

2 Find the area and perimeter of the half circle and quarter circle.
Give your answers to 2 d.p.

a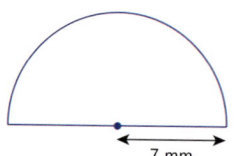
7 mm

b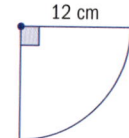
12 cm

3 The radius of this circle is 8 cm.

  a Find the arc length *HI*.

  b Hence find the perimeter of sector *HI*.

  c Find the perimeter of sector *KJ*.

  d Find the area of sector *HK*.

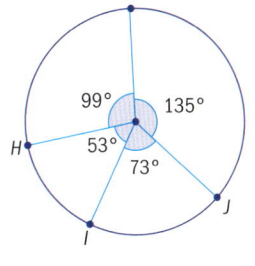

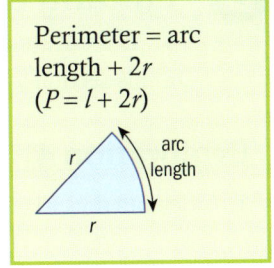

Perimeter = arc length + 2*r*
(*P = l + 2r*)

arc length

4 In this question, give all your answers in terms of π.

  a Find the length of arc *AB*.

  b Find the perimeter of the shaded sector.

  c Find the area of the shaded sector.

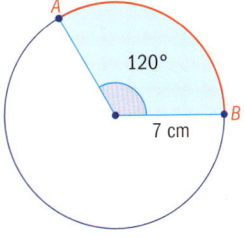

5 This is a sector of a circle.

  a Find the perimeter of the sector.

  b Find the area of the sector.

  Give your answers to 2 d.p.

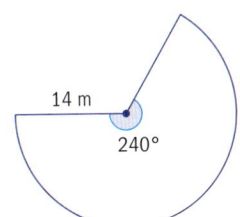

6 a Find the length of the major arc.

  b Find the perimeter of the major sector.

  c Find the area of the major sector.

  Give your answers to 2 d.p.

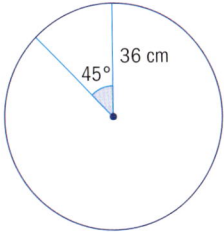

Problem solving

7 *VX* and *UW* are both diameters of the circle; *VX = UW* = 12 cm. Find the perimeter of sector *XOW* to 2 d.p.

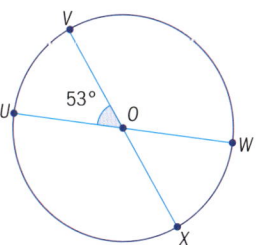

8 A frame for a mirror is in the shape of a rectangle with a curved top as shown in the diagram. The vertical sides of the frame are 50 cm long, and the top is an arc with central angle 97° and radius 20 cm. Calculate the perimeter of this frame to 2 d.p.

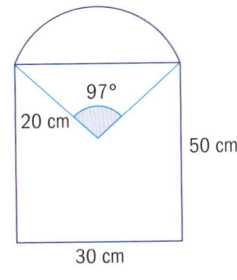

9 Calculate the volume of this prism to 2 d.p. The end face is a sector of a circle, radius 4 cm.

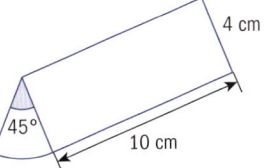

10 A light hardwood dowel has a semi-circular cross-section of radius 3 cm, and is 2 m in length. Calculate the volume of wood in the dowel to 2 d.p.

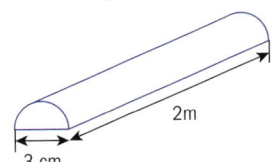

D Finding unknown values in circles

● Is it advantageous to make your own generalizations?

In this section you will generate more of your own formulae.

ATL

Exploration 4

1 Calculate the circumference of each whole circle in terms of π.

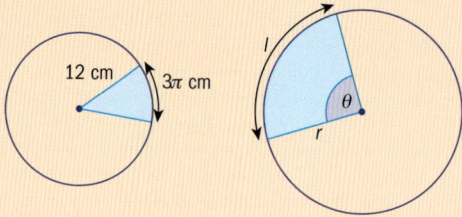

Use the arc length to work out the fraction of each circle that is shaded. Write down a general formula for finding the angle of sector θ given the arc length l and the radius r.

2 Calculate the area of each whole circle in terms of π.

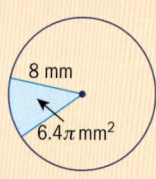 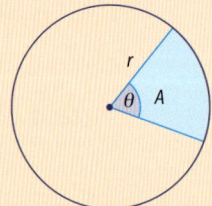

Use the sector area to work out the fraction of the circle that is shaded. Write down a general formula for finding the angle of the sector θ given the area A and the radius r.

3 Rearrange the formula you found in step **1** to make arc length l the subject.

4 Make r the subject of the formula.

5 Rearrange the formula you found in step **2** to make area A the subject.

6 Solve the formula for r.

> π has fascinated people for centuries. The Great Pyramid at Giza has dimensions that relate very closely to it. The base is a square, the perimeter of which is equal to the circumference of a circle with a radius equal to the pyramid's height.

Example 5

Find the measure of arc θ, to the nearest degree.

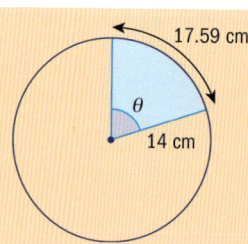

arc length $= 17.59 = \dfrac{\theta}{360°} \times 2\pi r$ —— Use the arc length formula.

$17.59 = \dfrac{\theta}{360°} \times 2 \times \pi \times 14$ ——

$\dfrac{17.59 \times 360}{28\pi} = \theta$ —— Rearrange and solve to find θ.

$\theta = 71.988\ldots$

The measure of θ to the nearest degree is 72°.

Example 6

Find the radius of the circle to 3 s.f.

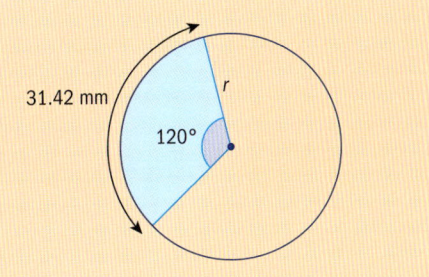

arc length = 31.42 mm

$$= \frac{\theta}{360°} \times 2\pi r$$

————————————————— Use the formula for the arc length.

$$31.42 = \frac{120}{360} \times 2\pi r$$

$$= \frac{1}{3} \times 2\pi r$$

$$r = \frac{31.42 \times 3}{2\pi}$$

————————————————— Rearrange and solve for r.

$$= 15.0019...$$

The radius of the circle is 15.0 mm (3 s.f.)

Practice 3

1 Find the measure of the central angle of the sector in each circle. Give your answers to the nearest degree.

a

9.599 mm

5 mm

b
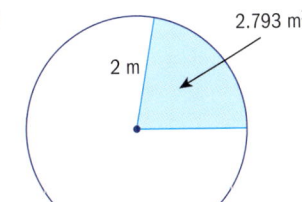
2.793 m²

2 m

2 a Find the angle in the sector.

b Find the length of the arc AB.

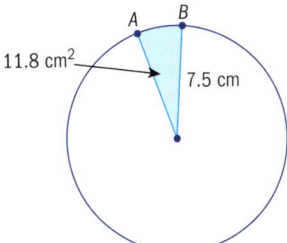
11.8 cm²   7.5 cm

3 a Find the measure of the central angle of the major sector.

b Find the length of the major arc.

c Find the perimeter of the major sector.

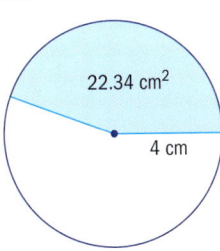
22.34 cm²   4 cm

4 Find the radius of each circle. Give your answers to 3 s.f.

a

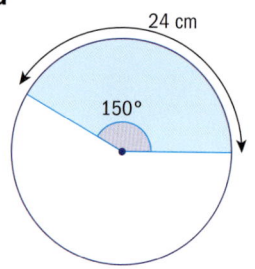

24 cm

150°

b

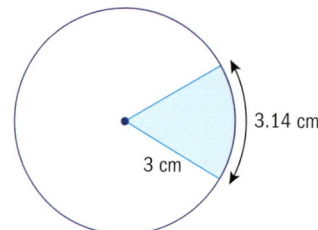

84 m²

200°

5 Find the perimeter of the major sector to 2 d.p.

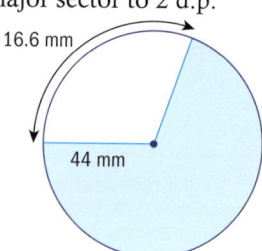

16.6 mm

44 mm

6 Find the area of the minor sector.

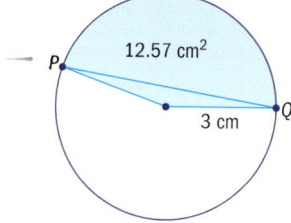

3.14 cm

3 cm

> In question **6**, first find the angle of the sector.

Problem solving

7 Ellie plans to make a paper cone from a sector of a circle with angle 220°. What size circle does she need to start with to make a cone with curved surface area 120 cm²? Give your answer in terms of the circle's radius, accurate to 1 d.p.

8 Find the length of chord *KM*.

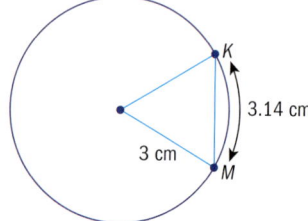

K

3.14 cm

3 cm

M

9 Find the length of chord *PQ*.

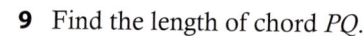

P

12.57 cm²

3 cm

Q

10 The landing zone for a javelin competition is a sector of a circle with radius 120 m. The central angle of the sector is 40°.

a Draw a diagram to represent this landing zone.

b Find the perimeter of the landing zone.

c Find the area of the landing zone.

d Find the shortest distance between the two outer corners of the landing zone. Give your answers to 2 d.p.

Summary

- A **chord** is a line segment with its endpoints on a circle.
- A **diameter** is a chord that passes through the center of a circle.
- A **secant** is a line that intersects a circle at two points.
- A **tangent** is a line that touches a circle at only one point.

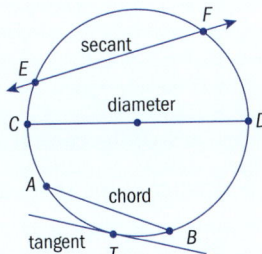

- A chord divides a circle into two **segments**.
- The larger segment is the **major segment**. The smaller segment is the **minor segment**. 'Segment' usually means the minor segment.
- An **arc** is a part of the circumference of a circle.
- The larger arc is the **major arc**. The smaller arc is the **minor arc**.

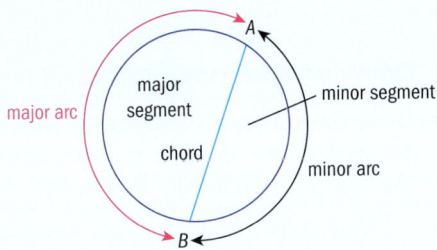

- A **sector** is a 'slice' of a circle between two radii. The center of a circle is usually labelled O, so the sector is sector BOC. 'Sector' usually means the minor sector.

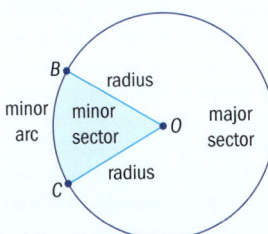

- Two radii and a chord form an isosceles triangle. A line from the center of the circle to the midpoint of the chord forms two right-angled triangles.

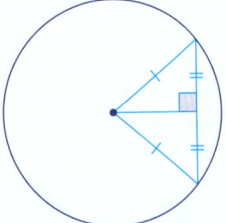

- The formula for the length of a chord, c, in a sector radius r with angle θ is $c = 2r \sin \frac{\theta}{2}$ or $\theta = 2 \arcsin\left(\frac{c}{2r}\right)$.

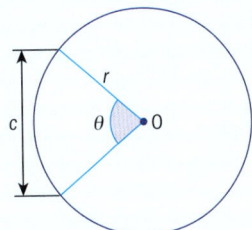

- Arc length $= \dfrac{\theta}{360°} \times 2\pi r$

- Sector area $= \dfrac{\theta}{360°} \times \pi r^2$

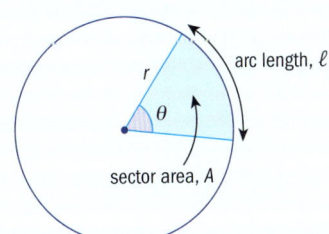

$$\theta = \frac{180\ell}{\pi r} \qquad \theta = \frac{360A}{\pi r^2}$$

$$r = \frac{180\ell}{\theta r} \qquad r = \sqrt{\frac{360A}{\theta \pi}}$$

$$\ell = 2\pi r \frac{\theta}{360} \qquad A = \pi r^2 \frac{\theta}{360}$$

Mixed practice

1 a Find the arc length of sector *DC*.

  b Find the perimeter of sector *BD*.

  c Find the area of sector *EB*.

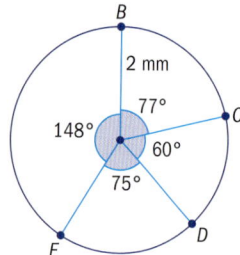

2 a Find the length of the major arc *QR*.

  b Find the area of the major sector.

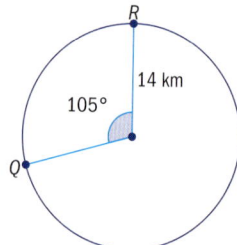

3 Find the perimeter and area of:

  a the minor sector

  b the major sector.

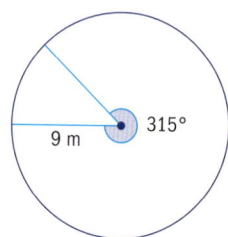

4 a Find the length of the minor arc.

  b Find the perimeter of the minor sector.

  c Find the area of the major sector.

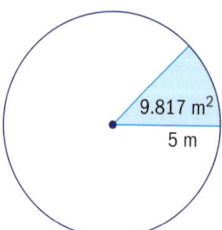

5 a Find the measure of the central angle.

  b Find the length of the minor arc.

  c Find the perimeter of the shaded sector.

  d Find the length of the chord *MN*.

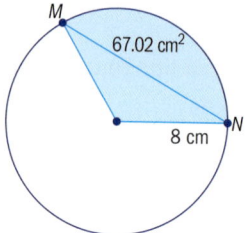

6 a Find the measure of the central angle.

  b Find the perimeter of the shaded sector.

  c Find the length of the chord *UV*.

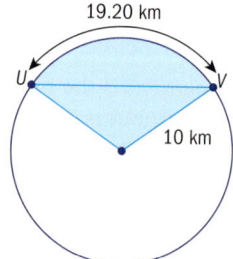

7 Toni has a rectangular lawn 8 m by 10 m. Her lawn sprinkler sprays water up to 5 m.

  a Draw and label a scale diagram of the lawn.

  b By using compasses to draw the region watered by the sprinkler to scale, **determine** the best position for the sprinkler so that it waters as much of the lawn as possible.

  c Divide the circle that lies inside the garden boundary into two sectors and two isosceles triangles. **Hence, calculate** the area of the lawn watered by the sprinkler.

  d Calculate the percentage of the lawn that is not watered by the sprinkler.

Problem solving

8 A regular hexagon is constructed in a circle of radius 5 cm. **Calculate** the perimeter of the hexagon. Give your answer to a suitable degree of accuracy.

Review in context

Personal and cultural expression

1 'Pendulum dowsing' as a means of finding water, gold or even answers to questions has been used throughout history and has been recorded as far back as the time of the pharaohs in Egypt. In one version, a pendulum is held above a cloth with 'yes' or 'no' written on it and the degree to which the pendulum sways to one side or the other is an indication of how likely or unlikely the event in question is going to happen.

   a If the pendulum has a total length of 30 cm, **calculate** the distance traveled if it moved a total of 45 degrees.

   b If the pendulum starts facing straight down and it travels an arc of 10 cm, **calculate** the turned angle.

2 The diagram shows the landing area for the shot put. The throwing circle has a diameter of 2.135 m, and the landing area is a sector with angle 34.92° and sector lines 25 m long, starting from the center of the circle. The distance thrown is measured from the circumference of the throwing circle to the imprint made in the soil by the shot in the landing area.

   a **Find** the area enclosed by the entire sector.

   b **Find** the area enclosed by the sector inside the throwing circle.

   c Hence, **find** the area of the landing area. Give your answers to 4 s.f.

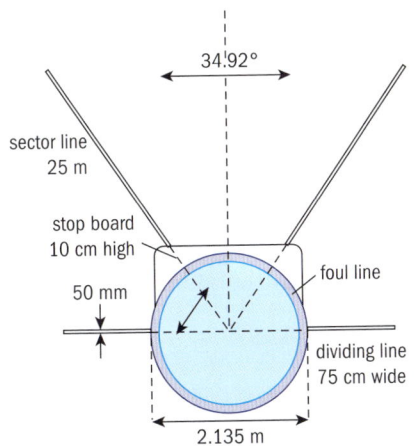

3 'Medicine wheels' were used by native Americans for a variety of rituals. The Big Horn Medicine Wheel is a circle of stones with a diameter of about 24 meters. It is divided into 28 approximately equal sections, likely to represent the 28 days of the lunar calendar.

   a **Calculate** the approximate central angle of each sector.

   b **Calculate** the area of each sector.

   c Different spots along the circle have been found to correspond to specific astronomical events (winter solstice, rising of stars). Two spots related to the rising of the star Sirius are 20 meters apart. **Calculate** their approximate distance apart along the circle.

   d The rising of the star Aldebaran happens between two points whose central angle measures 80 degrees. **Calculate** the shortest distance between them. Give your answers to 4 s.f.

Reflect and discuss 3

How have you explored the statement of inquiry? Give specific examples.

Statement of inquiry:

Systems use logic to validate generalizations and increase our appreciation of the aesthetic.

7.3 Circle theorems 1

Global context: Personal and cultural expression

Related Concept: Systems

LOGIC

Objectives

- Finding angles and lengths using circle theorems
- Proving results using circle theorems
- Examining 'If ... then ...' statements and testing the truth of their converses

Inquiry questions

F
- What are the circle theorems?

C
- How do we validate mathematical systems?

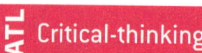

D
- Is the opposite of a true statement always false?
- Can aesthetics be calculated?

ATL Critical-thinking

Draw reasonable conclusions and generalizations

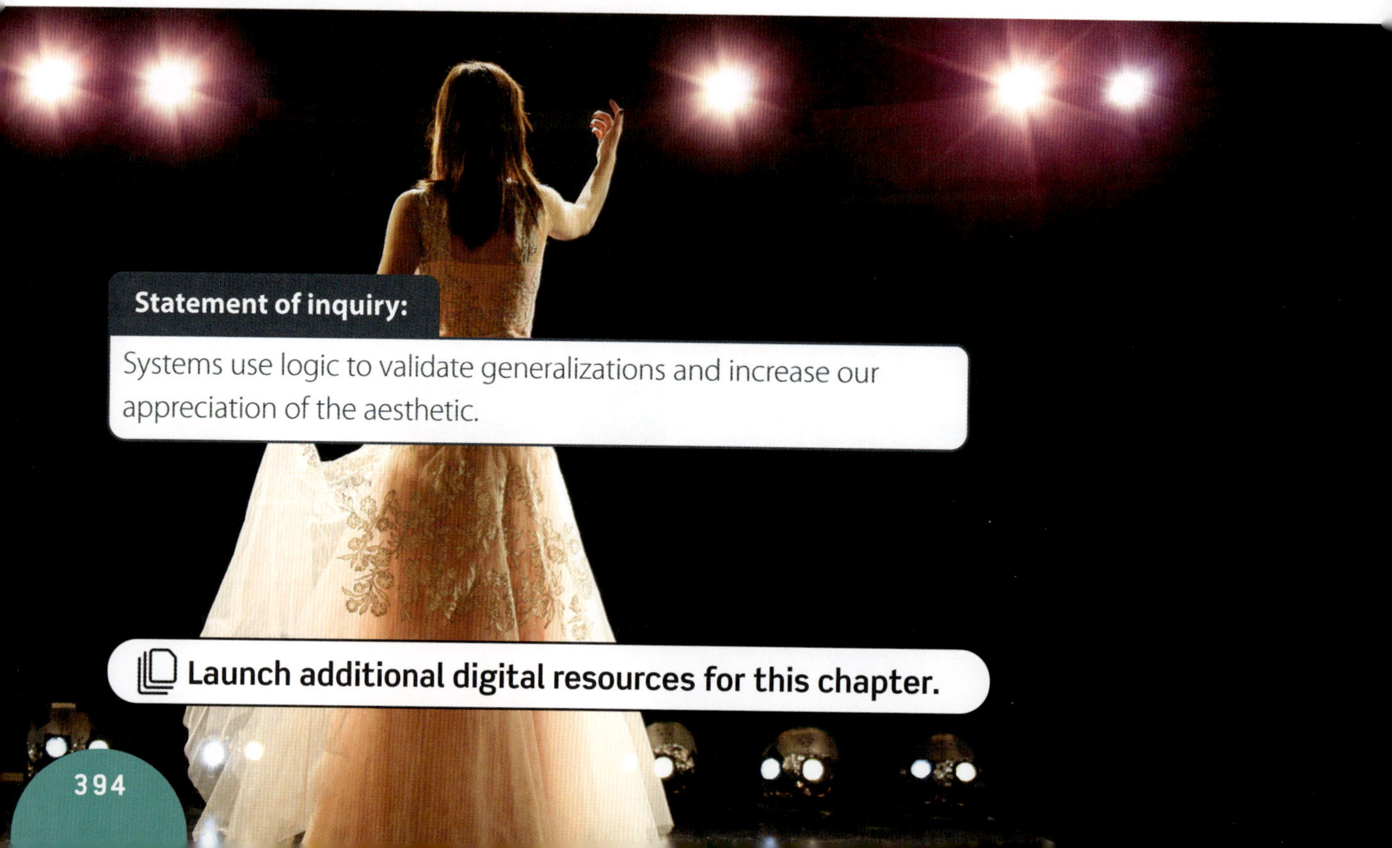

Statement of inquiry:

Systems use logic to validate generalizations and increase our appreciation of the aesthetic.

Launch additional digital resources for this chapter.

You should already know how to:

• name the parts of a circle	**1** Draw a circle, then draw and label:
	     a a radius
	     b a diameter
	     c a chord
	     d a segment
	     e an arc
	     f the center
	     g the circumference.

(F) Discovering the basic circle theorems

• What are the circle theorems?

These diagrams all illustrate tangent lines.

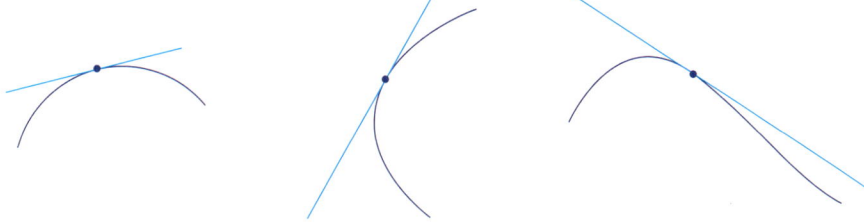

In each case, the tangent line touches the curve at the point of contact and does not pass through the curve.

A tangent line has the same gradient (slope) as the curve at the point where the tangent touches the curve.

> Line L is the **tangent** to a circle at point P if L intersects the circle at only one point, P.

ATL

Exploration 1

1   Using a GDC or dynamic geometry software, construct a circle with center O which passes through a second point, P. Add a third point Q, not on the circle. Draw a line segment joining O to P, and add the line PQ.

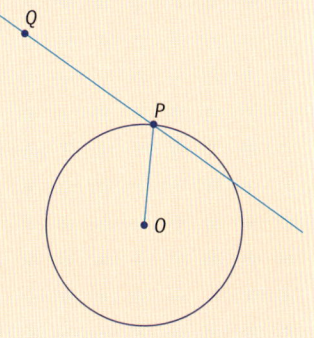

> A line **segment** connects two points, but a line extends in both directions.

▶   Continued on next page

2 Move the point Q freely until the line PQ is a tangent to the circle at P. Repeat a few times by repositioning P (and hence changing the circle) and finding a new position for Q so that PQ is a tangent to the circle.

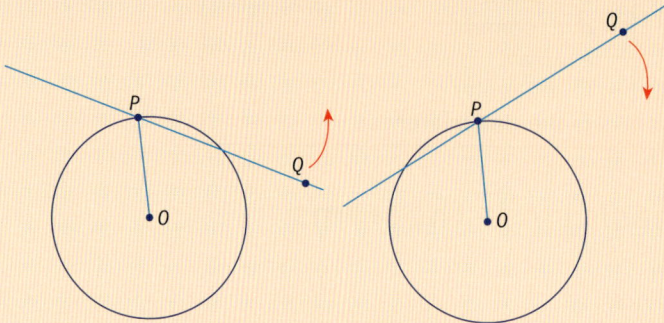

3 Now use your GDC or dynamic geometry software to measure $\angle OPQ$. Describe anything you notice about angle OPQ when PQ is a tangent to the circle. Compare your findings with others. Form a conjecture about the relationship between a tangent and the radius at a point P on the circumference of a circle.

If P is a point on the circumference of a circle, the tangent to the circle at P is perpendicular to the radius OP.

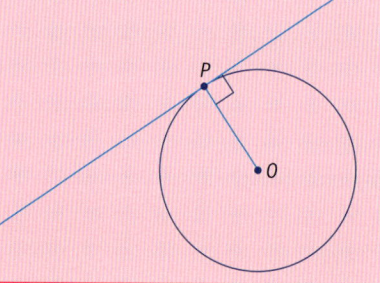

Exploration 2

1 Using a GDC or dynamic geometry software, draw a circle with center O and diameter AB. Draw another point, P, on the circumference of the circle. Draw the line segments AP and BP.

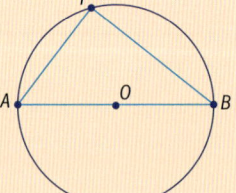

2 Use the software to measure $\angle APB$.

3 Move point P around the circumference of the circle. Describe anything you notice about $\angle APB$.

4 Repeat with circles of different diameters.

5 Compare your findings with others. Form a conjecture based on your findings.

Exploration 3

1 Using a GDC or dynamic geometry software, draw a circle with center O and chord AB. Draw another point, P, on the circumference of the circle. Draw the line segments AP and BP.

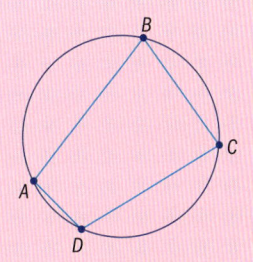

2 Use the software to measure $\angle APB$.

3 Without moving A or B, move point P around the circumference of the circle. Describe anything you notice about $\angle APB$.

4 Now reposition A or B (or both). Describe the effect of this on $\angle APB$.

5 Move point P around the circumference of the circle, without moving A and B. Describe anything you notice about $\angle APB$.

6 Compare your findings with others. Form a conjecture based on your findings.

A **cyclic quadrilateral** is a quadrilateral whose vertices all lie on the circumference of a circle.

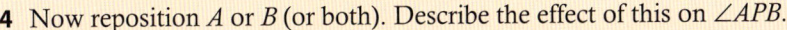

Exploration 4

1 Using a GDC or dynamic geometry software, draw a circle and mark four points P, Q, R and S on the circumference. Join the four points with straight line segments so that $PQRS$ is a cyclic quadrilateral.

2 Use the software to measure $\angle PQR$ and $\angle RSP$.

3 Now reposition any or all of the points. Describe anything you notice about the relationship between $\angle PQR$ and $\angle RSP$ as the cyclic quadrilateral changes.

4 Compare your findings with others. Form a conjecture based on your findings.

> Make sure the points P, Q, R and S are in order, so your quadrilateral does not cross itself.

The **major arc** is the long way around and the **minor arc** is the short way around a circle. To show the direction you can include a third point on the circumference of the circle, for example, ADB.

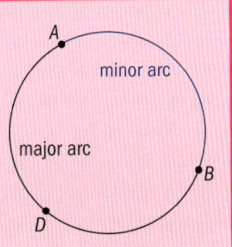

Exploration 5

1 Using a GDC or dynamic geometry software, draw a circle with center *O*. Mark two points *A* and *B* on the circumference. Draw another point, *P*, on the major arc *AB*. Draw the line segments *AP*, *BP*, *AO* and *BO*.

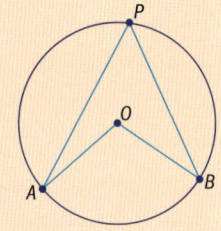

2 Measure $\angle AOB$ and $\angle APB$.

3 Move points *A*, *B* and *P*, keeping *P* in the major arc. Describe anything you notice about the relationship between $\angle AOB$ and $\angle APB$ as you vary the positions of *A*, *B* and *P*.

4 Repeat the exploration with a circle of a different diameter.

5 Compare your findings with others. Form a conjecture based on your findings.

Exploration 6

1 Using a GDC or dynamic geometry software, draw a circle with center *O* and points *A*, *B* and *C* on its circumference. Draw the line segments *AB*, *BC* and *CA*. Also draw the tangent to the circle at *A*.

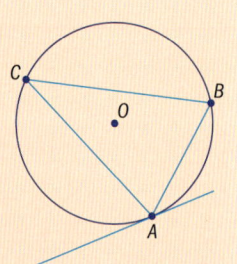

2 Measure $\angle ABC$ and $\angle ACB$. Measure the acute angles between *AB* and the tangent, and *AC* and the tangent.

3 Move points *A*, *B* and *C*. Describe anything you notice.

4 Repeat the exploration with a circle of a different diameter.

5 Compare your findings with others. Form a conjecture based on your findings.

> Your software should be able to construct a tangent to a circle automatically.

Activity

Did you find it difficult to explain the rules you discovered in Explorations 2 to 6? Below are five ways of writing these rules and five diagrams to illustrate them. Read the five rules, look at the diagrams, and then answer the questions below the diagrams.

Five rules:

i *Thales' Theorem*: An angle inscribed in a semicircle is a right angle.

ii Opposite angles in a cyclic quadrilateral are supplementary.

iii Angles in the same segment subtended by equal chords are equal in size.

iv *Alternate segment theorem*: the angle between a chord and tangent at a point is equal to the angle subtended by the chord in the alternate segment.

▶ Continued on next page

v The angle subtended by a chord at the center (central angle) is twice the angle at the circumference (inscribed angle) in the same segment subtended by the same chord.

Five diagrams:

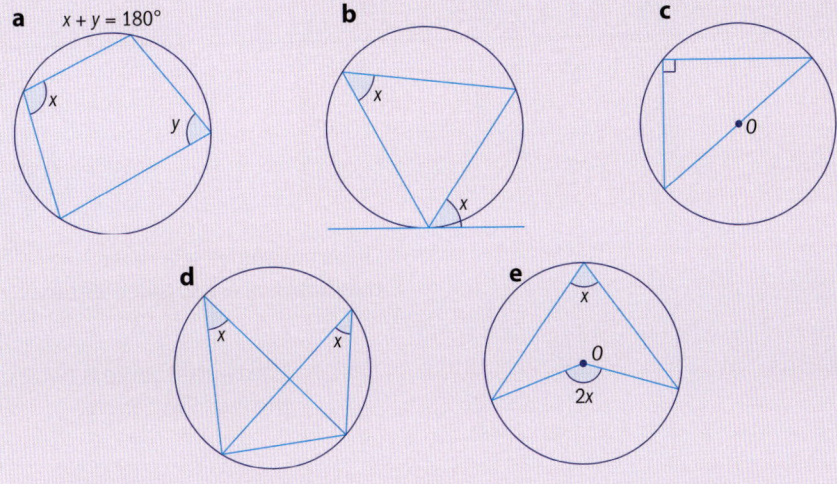

a $x + y = 180°$

b

c

d

e

- What do these terms mean? *subtended, supplementary, opposite angle, inscribed, same segment, alternate segment.* Look them up if you need to.

- Match each rule to its diagram.

- Match each rule to one of the Explorations 2 to 6.

> Make sure you understand all these terms, so that you can understand the information given in a question.

You can use these five results to find angles in geometric problems.

Example 1

Find the value of angle *t*, and justify your reasoning.

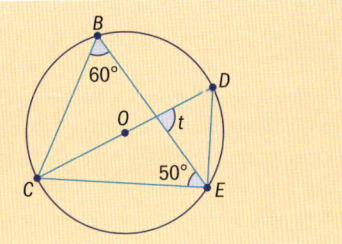

$\angle CDE = 60°$ because $\angle CDE$ and $\angle CBE$ are angles in the same segment.

'Justify' means 'give clear reasons for your answers'.

$\angle CED = 90°$ because the angle inscribed in a semicircle is a right angle.

CD passes through O, so it is a diameter.

$\angle BED = 90 - 50$
$\qquad = 40°$ because $\angle CED = 90°$

$t = 180 - 60 - 40$
$\quad = 80°$ because the interior angles in a triangle sum to $180°$.

Example 2

Calculate $\angle BOD$.

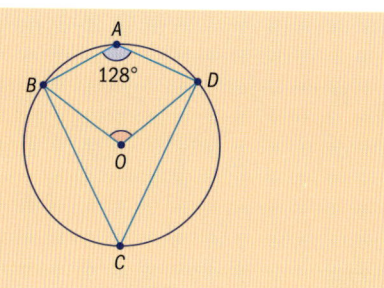

$\angle BCD = 180 - 128$ ————————————————— **Opposite angles in a cyclic quadrilateral are supplementary.**

$\quad = 52°$

$\angle BOD = 2 \times 52$ ————————————————— **The central angle is twice the inscribed angle.**

$\quad = 104°$

Example 3

Prove that $\angle BOD = 64°$.

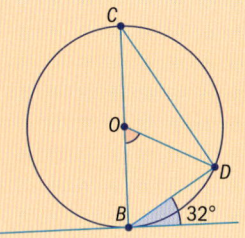

$\angle BCD = 32°$ by the alternate segment theorem.

$\angle BOD = 64°$ because the central angle is twice the inscribed angle.

Practice 1

1 Calculate the size of the marked angles in each diagram.

> **Calculate** and **find** both mean that you should show relevant stages in your working, but you do not need to justify all your reasoning.

a

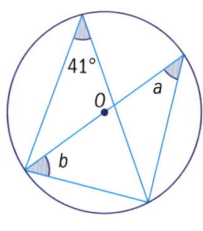

b

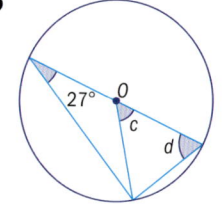

c

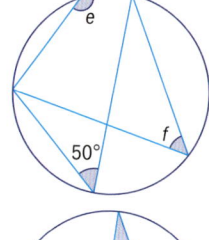

d

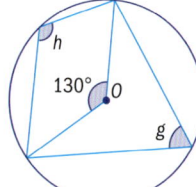

e

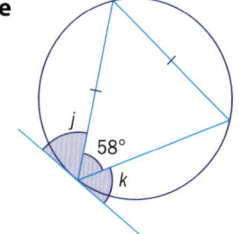

f

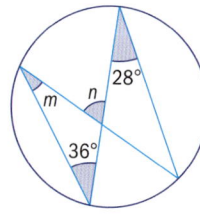

Problem solving

2 Find the size of the marked angle in each diagram.
In each case, justify your answer.

a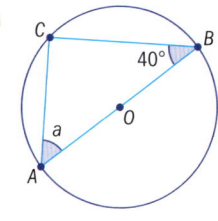

b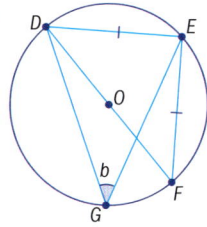

c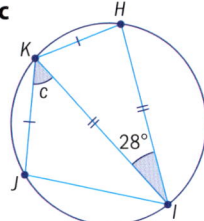

d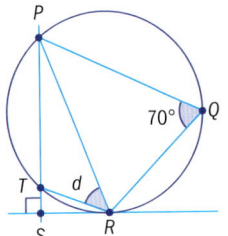

e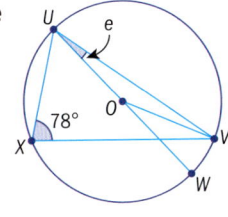

f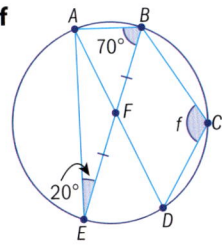

- -

C Justifying the circle theorems

● How do we validate mathematical systems?

In this section you will use direct (deductive) proof to justify the circle theorems.

Objective: C. Communicating
iv. communicate complete, coherent and concise mathematical lines of reasoning

The following two proofs complete the proof of the cyclic quadrilateral theorem.
Make sure your proofs are concise and that they make sense.

Exploration 7

1 Copy and complete this skeleton proof.

Theorem
Opposite angles in a cyclic quadrilateral are supplementary.

Proof
Consider a cyclic quadrilateral *ABCD* inscribed in a circle with center *O*.

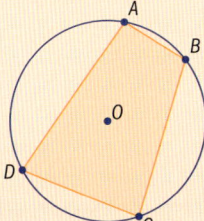

A diagram makes it easier for readers to understand your proof.

▶ Continued on next page

$OA = OB = OC = OD$ because _____

Therefore $\triangle OAB$, _____, _____,
and _____ are all _____ triangles. ———————— What type of triangle is $\triangle OAB$?

Therefore $\angle OAB = \angle OBA$, _____ = _____,
_____ = _____, and _____ = _____ ———— Use the 'triangle fact' from the line above.
because _____

$\angle OAB + \angle OBA +$ ____ + ____ + ____ + ____ + ____ + ____ $= 360°$

$\Rightarrow 2(\angle OAB + \angle OAD +$ _____ + _____ $) = 360°$ ———————— $\Rightarrow$ means 'implies'

$\Rightarrow \qquad 2(\angle DAB +$ _____ $) = 360°$ ———— Notice how $\angle OAB + \angle OAD = \angle DAB$.

$\Rightarrow \qquad\qquad$ _____ + _____ $= 180°$

Therefore the angles at A and C are supplementary, and the angles at
B and D are supplementary.

2 The proof is incomplete as you need to consider two other cases.
By drawing suitable diagrams and modifying the proof, prove
that the opposite angles are supplementary in cyclic quadrilaterals
where:

  a one edge of the quadrilateral passes through the center of the circle
  b the center of the circle is not inside the quadrilateral.

Exploration 8

Copy and complete this skeleton proof of Thales' Theorem.

Theorem

Any angle inscribed in a semicircle is a right angle.

Proof

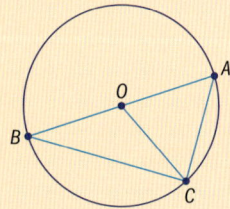

Consider a circle with center O where AB is a diameter. Let C be any
point on the circumference of the circle.

$\triangle OAC$ and $\triangle OCB$ are _____ triangles.

Hence $\angle OCA =$ _____ and $\angle OCB =$ _____

$\angle ACB = \angle OCA + \angle OCB$

$\angle AOC =$ _____ + _____ and $\angle BOC =$ _____ + _____ ———————— Exterior angle = sum of
interior opposite angles.

▶   Continued on next page

$\Rightarrow \angle AOC = 2\angle OCB$ and $\angle BOC = 2\angle OCA$

$\Rightarrow \angle AOC + \angle BOC = 2(\underline{\hspace{1cm}} + \underline{\hspace{1cm}})$

$\Rightarrow \angle AOC + \angle BOC = 2\underline{\hspace{1cm}}$

$\Rightarrow 2\underline{\hspace{1cm}} = 180°$ ———————————————— $\angle OCA + \angle OCB = \angle ACB$

$\Rightarrow \underline{\hspace{1cm}} = 90°$

Exploration 9

Copy and complete this skeleton proof.

Theorem

Angles in the same segment are equal.

Proof

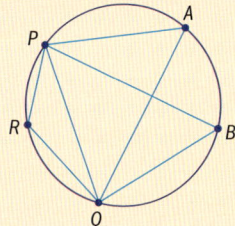

Consider points A and B that lie in the same segment of a circle divided by the chord through P and Q. Point R lies in the opposite segment.

$\angle PAQ + \angle PRQ = \underline{\hspace{1cm}}$

$\angle PBQ + \angle PRQ = \underline{\hspace{1cm}}$

because \underline{\hspace{5cm}}

Hence $\angle PAQ = \underline{\hspace{1cm}}$

Example 4

A circle, center O, has points S and T on its circumference. RST is a straight line segment. Prove that $\angle SOT = 2 \times \angle RSO - 180°$.

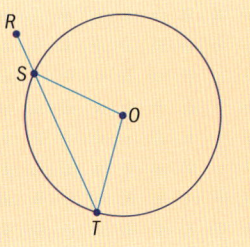

$\angle OST = 180° - \angle RSO$ (angles on a straight line)

$\angle OST = \angle OTS$ (base angles in an isosceles triangle)

$\angle SOT = 180° - \angle OTS - \angle OST$ (angles in a triangle sum to $180°$)

$\Rightarrow \angle SOT = 180° - 2\angle OST$

$\Rightarrow \angle SOT = 180° - 2(180° - \angle RSO)$

$\Rightarrow \angle SOT = 2 \times \angle RSO - 180°$

Practice 2

Problem solving

1 Points A, B and C lie on a circle with center O such that A, B and C all fall within the same semicircle. Prove that $\angle ABC = 180° - \frac{1}{2}\angle AOC$.

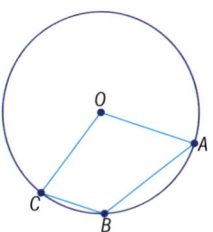

2 Points P, X and Y lie on the circumference of a circle. The tangents to the circle at X and Y meet at Q. Let O be the center of the circle. Prove that

$\angle XPY = \frac{1}{2}(180° - \angle XQY)$.

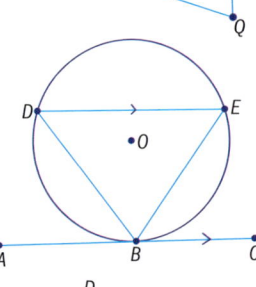

3 Points B, D and E lie on a circle. ABC is a tangent to the circle at B. DE is parallel to ABC. Prove that $\triangle BDE$ is isosceles.

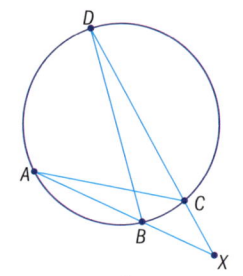

4 A, B, C and D lie on the circumference of a circle, and when the line segments AB and DC are extended they meet at X, outside the circle.

Prove that $\triangle ACX$ is similar to $\triangle DBX$.

> Remember that two triangles are similar if their angles are the same.

5 A, B, C, D, E and F lie on the circumference of a circle, with $AB = BC$ and DF perpendicular to BE. AE, BE and CE meet DF at X, Y and Z respectively.

Prove that $\angle EXY = \angle EZY$.

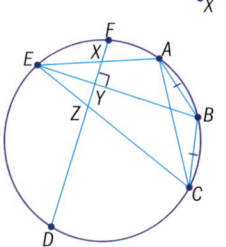

> 'Bisect' means to cut in half exactly.

- -

D **The converse of the circle theorems**

- Is the opposite of a true statement always false?
- Can aesthetics be calculated?

The theorems you have proved are all of the form 'If p, then q', where p and q are statements. For example, 'If points A, B and C lie on the circumference of a circle and AC is a diameter, then $\angle ABC$ is a right angle'. You can see that the statement can be split into two parts, the premise (the 'if' part) and the conclusion (the 'then' part).

- If ABC is a triangle, then $\angle ABC + \angle BCA + \angle CAB = 180°$.
- If x is a whole number which ends in a zero, then x is not prime.
- If $x^2 = 4$, then $x = 2$.
- If $x + 3 = 7$, then $x = 4$.

You can also write the statement 'If p then q' as $p \Rightarrow q$. This is read as 'p implies q'.

Reflect and discuss 1

Which of the 'If … then …' statements above are true?

The converse of a statement takes its two constituent parts and places them in the opposite order. So the converse of 'If p then q' is 'If q then p'.

These statements are the converses of the four previous statements.

- If $\angle ABC + \angle BCA + \angle CAB = 180°$, then ABC is a triangle.
- If x is not prime, then x is a whole number which ends in a zero.
- If $x = 2$, then $x^2 = 4$.
- If $x = 4$, then $x + 3 = 7$.

Reflect and discuss 2

- Which of the preceding list of 'If … then …' statements are true?
- If the original statement is true, then is the converse also true?
- If the original statement is false, then is the converse also false?

You should have seen that statements and their converses can be true or false independently of one another. This means that you have to be careful when working with proof and justification; proving an 'If … then …' statement does not necessarily mean that its converse is true.

Consider Thales' Theorem once more: 'If points A, B and C lie on the circumference of a circle and AC is a diameter, then $\angle ABC$ is a right angle'. The converse of the theorem would be: 'If $\angle ABC$ is a right angle then points A, B and C lie on the circumference of a circle, and AC is a diameter'. It's a little harder to see exactly what the converse means – and certainly it is not obvious whether or not it is true.

Exploration 10

1 Use a GDC or dynamic geometry software to draw two points A and C.
2 Draw a third point D, and the line segment AD.
3 Draw a line perpendicular to AD through C. Let point B be the intersection of AD and the perpendicular through C.
   You have created a set of three points, A, B and C that satisfy the 'if' part of the converse of Thales' Theorem: three points such that $\angle ABC$ is a right angle. By moving point D, you should see that as B moves $\angle ABC$ stays the same size.
4 Use the Trace facility of your GDC or software to track the position of point B. Vary the position of B by moving D.
5 Explain if your diagram supports the converse of Thales' Theorem.

Your software should be able to construct a perpendicular to a line through a point.

Reflect and discuss 3

Is Exploration 10 a proof of the converse of Thales' Theorem? If not, is it sufficiently convincing that you believe the converse to be true anyway?

Exploration 11

Use a GDC or dynamic geometry software to verify that the converses of the other four circle theorems also hold. Some are significantly easier than others, provided you know how to use the software to produce an angle that is the same size as another. Exploring the converse of the theorem that the opposite angles in a cyclic quadrilateral are supplementary is quite tricky – so tackle this one last!

Summary

- Line L is the **tangent** to a circle at point P if L intersects the circle at only one point, P.

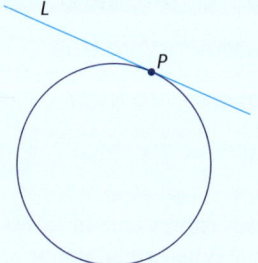

- A **cyclic quadrilateral** is a quadrilateral whose vertices all lie on the circumference of a circle.

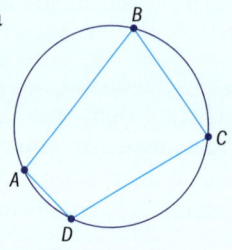

- The **major arc** is the long way around the circle; the **minor arc** is the short way around. To indicate a major arc you can include a third point on the circumference of the circle, for example, ADB.

- A tangent to a circle at a point P on its circumference is perpendicular to its radius OP.

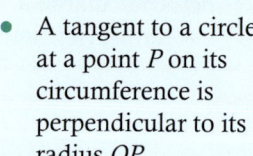

- **Thales' Theorem:** An angle inscribed in a semicircle is a right angle.

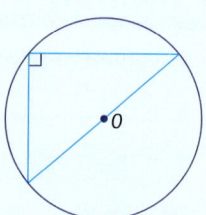

- Opposite angles in a cyclic quadrilateral are supplementary.

$$x + y = 180°$$

- Angles in the same segment subtended by equal chords are equal in size.

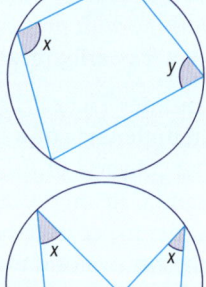

- **Alternate segment theorem:** The angle between a chord and tangent at a point is equal to the angle subtended by the chord in the alternate segment.

- The angle subtended by a chord at the center is twice the angle at the circumference in the same segment subtended by the same chord.

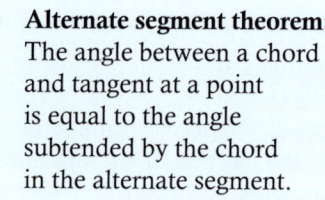

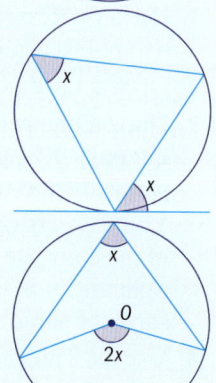

Mixed practice

1 Find the size of the marked angles.

a

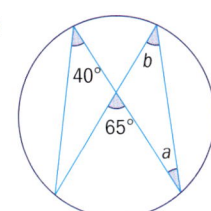

b

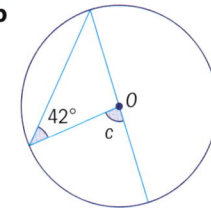

2 Find the size of the marked angle.

a

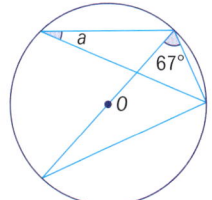

b

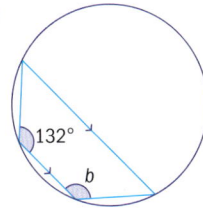

3 For each statement, **write down** the converse. Determine which statements, and which of their converses, are true. **Justify** your answers.

a If $a = 7$ then $3a - 2 = 19$.

b If $b = a$ then $a - b = 0$.

c If it is a bird then it has wings.

d If a polygon has four sides, then it is a square.

e If $c = 9$ then $c^2 = 81$.

f If a right-angled triangle is drawn with its vertices on the circumference of a circle then its hypotenuse is a diameter of the circle.

4 In the cyclic quadrilateral $ABCD$, $\angle DAB \cong \angle ABC$.

Prove that $AD = BC$.

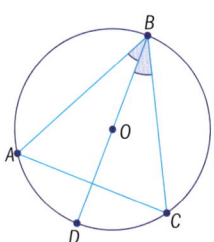

5 A, B, C and D lie on a circle center O, and DOB bisects $\angle ABC$.

Prove that $\triangle ABC$ is isosceles.

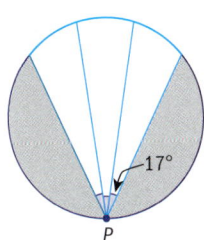

Review in context

Personal and cultural expression

1 A circular auditorium has a stage across the end of it. When a patron sits at O, the center of the auditorium, the stage occupies 88° of the patron's field of vision.

Find the amount of the field of vision that the stage would occupy when viewed from P, at the very edge of the auditorium.

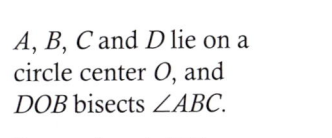

2 Three projectors, used to display images on the wall of a circular performance space, are mounted on the opposite wall. The projectors each have a beam width of 17°, and are placed one above another at a single point P.

The circle has diameter 6 m.

Find the total length of the wall projected on when the projectors are positioned so their beams overlap by 20 cm.

Reflect and discuss 4

How have you explored the statement of inquiry? Give specific examples.

Statement of inquiry:

Systems use logic to validate generalizations and increase our appreciation of the aesthetic.

7.4 Circle theorems 2

Global context: Personal and cultural expression

Related concept: Systems

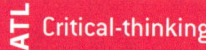

Objectives

- Using circle theorems to find lengths of chords
- Finding lengths using the intersecting chord theorem

Inquiry questions

F
- What is the intersecting chords theorem?
- How can you apply the theorem?

C
- How can theorems within systems have different cases?

D
- Can aesthetics be calculated?

ATL Critical-thinking

Test generalizations and conclusions

Statement of inquiry:

Systems use logic to validate generalizations and increase our appreciation of the aesthetic.

📚 **Launch additional digital resources for this chapter.**

You should already know how to:

• solve quadratic equations	**1** Solve the equation $2x^2 - x - 3 = 0$ for x by factorizing.
• apply the circle theorems	**2** A circle of radius 5 cm has a tangent at a point on the circumference. If a point on the tangent is 13 cm from the center of the circle, how far is this point from the point where the tangent touches the circle?

F Intersecting chords

- What is the intersecting chords theorem?
- How can you apply the theorem?

Exploration 1

1 Draw a circle of radius 5 using a GDC or dynamic geometry software.
Draw four points A, B, C and D on the circumference of the circle.
Draw line segments AB and CD. You should have a diagram similar to this one.

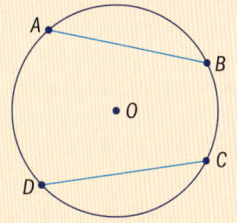

2 Note that chords AB and CD do not meet in this diagram. By varying the position of the points, modify your diagram so that chords AB and CD intersect.
State a suitable condition on the points A, B, C and D such that chords AB and CD will intersect. Label the point of intersection of AB and CD as X.

3 Use the software to measure the lengths AX, BX, CX and DX.

4 Find the values of $AX \times BX$ and $CX \times DX$.
Vary the position of the points. Describe anything you notice, and suggest a suitable general rule.
The rule you have discovered is known as the **intersecting chords theorem**. It has a number of cases, of which this is the first.

5 Verify that the theorem holds true as you continue to vary the positions of points A, B, C and D. Determine whether it continues to hold when you change the radius of the circle. Describe any limitations to the rule you have observed.

Reflect and discuss 1

The result that you have just found is proved in the Extended chapter on circle theorems. In Exploration 1 you justified the intersecting chords theorem by demonstrating that it works in all the situations you have seen. A mathematical proof must show the result to be true beyond any doubt. Do you think that the dynamic geometry approach does this?

Theorem: If A, B, C and D are points on the circumference of a circle such that AB meets the chord CD at a point X interior to the circle then $AX \times BX = CX \times DX$.

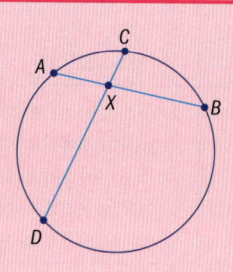

Example 1

In the circle shown here, chords AB and CD meet at P. Find the value of x.

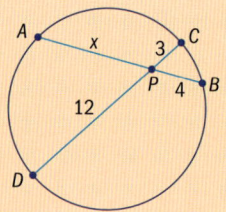

$AP \times BP = CP \times DP$ ——————————— Make sure that you correctly identify the sides involved.

$x \times 4 = 3 \times 12$

$x = \dfrac{36}{4} = 9$

Example 2

In this circle, chords PR and QS meet at T. Find the value of x and hence find the possible values of the lengths of PT, RT and QT.

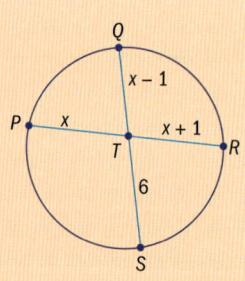

$PT \times RT = QT \times ST$

$x \times (x+1) = (x-1) \times 6$ ——————————— Substitute in the known values.

$x^2 + x = 6x - 6$

$x^2 - 5x + 6 = 0$

$(x-2)(x-3) = 0$ ——————————— Factorize.

So $x = 2$ or $x = 3$. ——————————— There are two possible values of x.

$PT = 2$ or 3, $RT = 3$ or 4 and $QT = 1$ or 2.

Practice 1

1 Find the value of x in each diagram. Hence find the missing lengths.

a
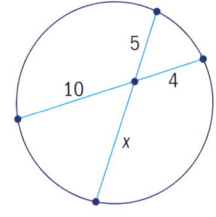

b
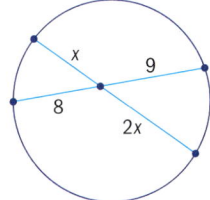

c
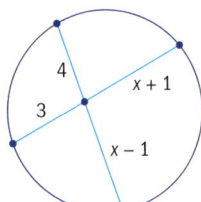

d
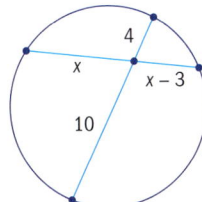

e
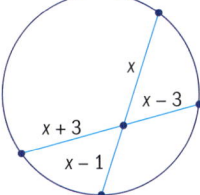

f
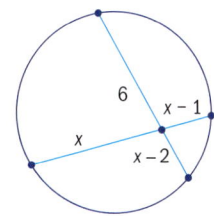

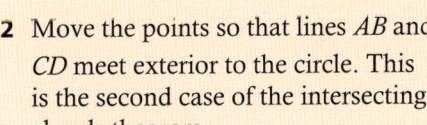

C Chords that intersect outside the circle

- How can theorems within systems have different cases?

Exploration 2

1 Draw a circle using a GDC or dynamic geometry software.

Draw four points A, B, C and D on the circumference of the circle.

Draw lines AB and CD.

Draw point X, where AB and CD and intersect.

You should have a diagram similar to this.

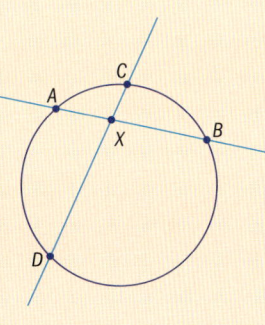

2 Move the points so that lines AB and CD meet exterior to the circle. This is the second case of the intersecting chords theorem.

Using the software, measure the lengths AX, BX, CX and DX. Verify that the relationship $AX \times BX = CX \times DX$ still holds when the lines AB and CD intersect exterior to the circle. Can you describe any conditions under which it would not be possible to say that $AX \times BX = CX \times DX$?

> Note that a **line** continues in both directions, unlike a **line segment** which stops at its endpoints.

The intersecting chords theorem referred to chords that intersect at an interior point. You have now seen that the theorem is identical if point P is exterior to the circle.

Example 3

Points J, K, L and M lie on the circumference of a circle. The lines that pass through JK and LM intersect at P. Find the value of x.

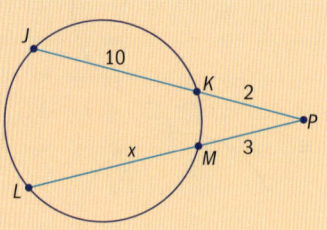

$JP \times KP = LP \times MP$

$12 \times 2 = (x+3) \times 3$ ———————————— Substitute in the known values.

$24 = 3(x+3)$

$8 = x+3$

$x = 5$

Practice 2

1 Use the intersecting chords theorem to find the value of x in each diagram. Hence find the missing lengths in the diagrams.

a

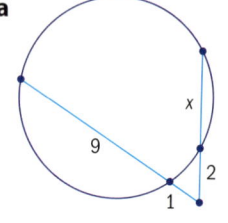

b

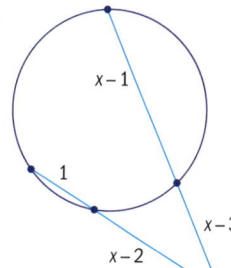

c

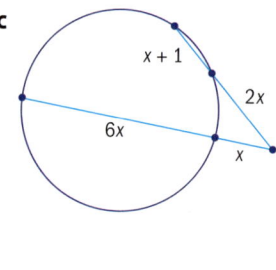

- -

D ## When a chord becomes a tangent

- Can aesthetics be calculated?

Exploration 3

1 Recall the diagram from Exploration 2 step **2** where the lines AB and CD meet externally at X.

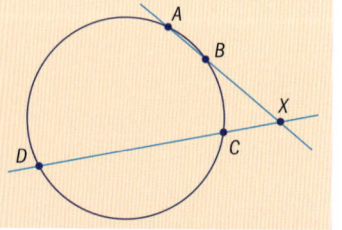

You may need to move A to make sure that X remains on the page.

▶ Continued on next page

2 Use the software to measure the lengths of AX, BX, CX, and DX and confirm that $AX \times BX = CX \times DX$.

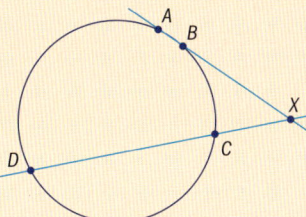

3 Move the point B so that it gets closer to A. You should make sure that the other three points remain stationary. Re-measure the four lengths and check that the intersecting chords theorem still applies.

4 What do you notice about the two lengths AX and BX as B approaches A?

5 Repeat steps **3** and **4** a few more times, allowing B and A to get as close as possible.

6 From your observations, make a conjecture about the limiting case as B approaches A. Test your conjecture.

Reflect and discuss 2

- In Exploration 3, what happened to the line AX as the point B approached the point A? What other line does this resemble?

- Make a conjecture for a *tangent-secant theorem* that is the limiting case of the intersecting chord theorem.

- Use the software to construct a tangent to a circle and confirm that your conjecture is true.

The tangent-secant theorem:

If TX is a tangent to a circle at T and PQX meets the circle at P and Q, then $PX \times QX = TX^2$.

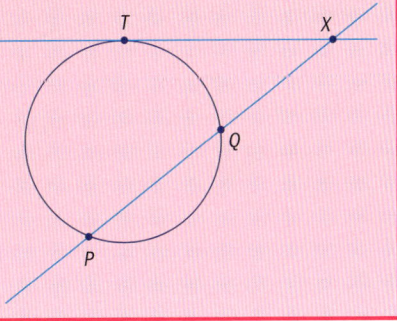

Just as in Explorations 1 and 2, you have used software to form and test a conjecture. To fully justify the conjectures that you have made, a proof is needed.

If you have already written proofs using similar triangles, you might be able to prove the theorems in this section for yourself. To get started, see if you can explain why triangles PTX and TQX are similar.

A soccer player running down the sideline wants to take a shot with the best chance of scoring a goal. It turns out that the best chance for a successful shot happens when the player is at the point of tangency of the circle that passes through the goal posts and is tangent to the sideline.

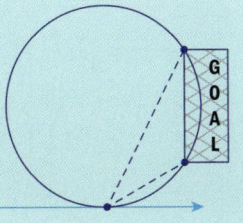

Summary

- The intersecting chords theorem:
  If A, B, C and D are points on the circumference of a circle such that AB meets the chord CD at a point X interior to the circle then $AX \times BX = CX \times DX$.

- The tangent-secant theorem:
  If TX lies tangent to a circle at T and PQX meets the circle at P and Q, then $PX \times QX = TX^2$.

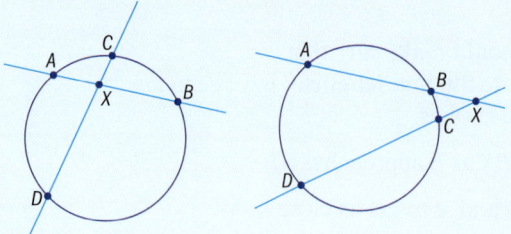

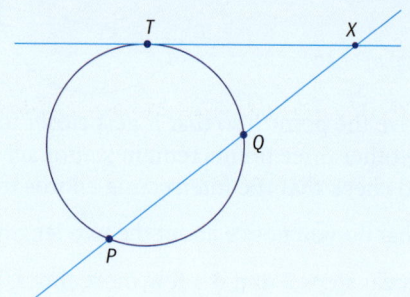

Mixed practice

1 A circle has points A, B, C and D on its circumference. Chords AB and CD have length 11 and 7 respectively, and meet interior to the circle at point X.

  a **Sketch** the circle and indicate points A, B, C, D and X on the sketch.

  b Given that AX, BX, CX and DX are integers, **find** the possible values that they can take.

2 **Find** the value of the unknown(s) in each diagram.

a

b

c

d

e

f

3 **Find** the values of x, y and z.

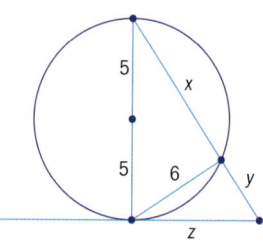

4 In the diagram, BC is a chord and meets a diameter AB at B. $AO = BO = 3$ and $BC = 8$. **Find** x and y.

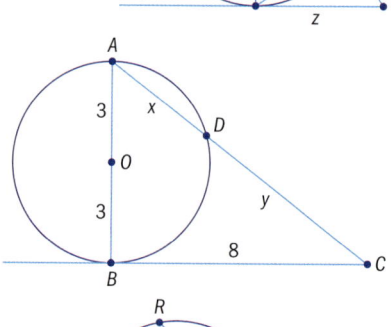

5 **Find** the values of x and y.

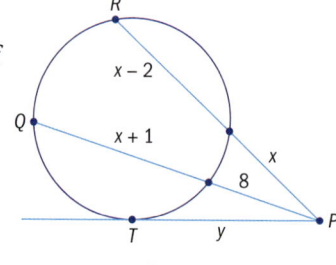

6 In this diagram:

  a **show** that $3x = 4y$

  b hence **find** the values of x and y.

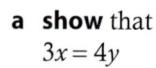

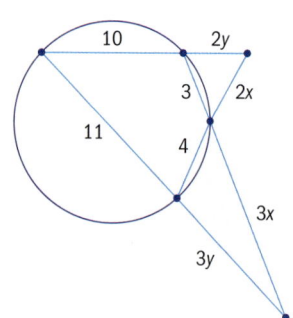

For each of the questions below, consider the geometry of the real-life situation and determine which version of the intersecting chords theorem you need to use.

Review in context

Personal and cultural expression

1 A fragment of a bowl, bearing an ancient inscription, dates from the 7th century BCE. Archaeologists believe the original bowl was circular.

Points A and B are chosen on the edge of the bowl and AB is measured to be 5 cm. M is the midpoint of AB, and MC is perpendicular to AB where C lies on the circumference of the bowl. MC is measured to be 0.25 cm.

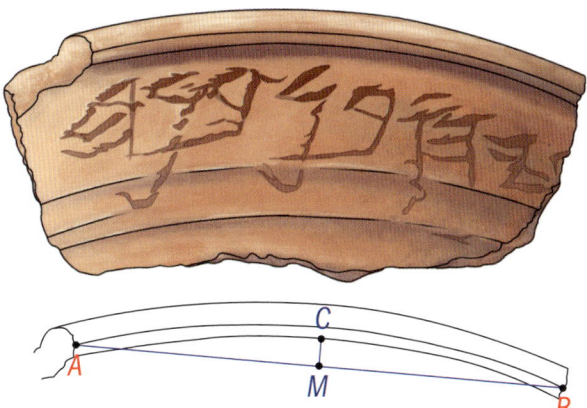

a **Sketch** the complete bowl, including the line segments AB and MC.

b **Show** that the line segment MC passes through the center of the bowl when extended.

c **Use** the intersecting chords theorem to **find** the diameter of the bowl.

2 Huge stone circles have been discovered in Jordan in the Middle East. Archaeologists have been attempting to find out more about these circles. Measuring hundreds of meters across, one of the challenges has been to measure them accurately, especially as some of them are incomplete.

Two points, A and B are marked on the circle and the distance between them is measured. The mid-point of AB is found and the distance from this point to the nearest point on the circle is measured.

Surveyors found that AB was 114 m and the distance from the midpoint was 9 m.

a **Use** this information to **calculate** the diameter of the circle.

A second group of archaeologists use a different technique. From a point outside the circle they make a straight line which is a tangent to the circle and measure the distance to the point of contact. Then they measure the shortest distance from the original point to the circle.

The distances are 150 m and 52 m respectively.

b **Calculate** the diameter from these measurements and then **compare** the two results.

Reflect and discuss 3

How have you explored the statement of inquiry? Give specific examples.

Statement of inquiry:

Systems use logic to validate generalizations and increase our appreciation of the aesthetic.

8 What comes next?

Statement of inquiry:

Representing patterns and change in a variety of forms has helped humans apply their understanding of scientific principles.

Key concept:

Form is the shape and underlying structure of an entity or piece of work.

F Which patterns exist in real-life situations?

Patterns are sets of numbers or objects that follow a specific order or rule.

Patterns in music

Steve Reich is an American composer who experiments with pattern and structure in his music. One of his famous works is titled 'Clapping Music for two people', and consists of a single rhythm repeated over 150 times, but with variation created by one musician starting half a beat later every 8 bars.

Search online for 'Steve Reich clapping music' to listen to a live performance and see if you can follow any patterns.

C How can changing the form help to visualize a pattern?

Hilbert's Hotel Infinity

Are there different *forms* of infinity denoting different *sizes* of infinity? David Hilbert's thought experiment imagined a hotel with an infinite number of rooms – with the motto 'always room for one more!'

- What if a guest arrives, but all the infinite number of rooms in the hotel are already occupied? No problem – the guest in room 1 moves to room 2, the guest in room 2 moves to room 3, and so on. Room 1 is now free, and everyone is happy.

- And what if an *infinite* number of guests arrive at the same time but all rooms are occupied? Still no problem – the guest in room 1 moves to room 2, the guest in room 2 moves to room 4, and so on, so that the one in room n moves to room $2n$. All the even-numbered rooms are now occupied, but all the odd numbered rooms are free.

D To what extent does changing the form help you understand the scientific principles in real-life situations?

The symbol for infinity is called a lemniscate. The word lemniscate is of Latin origin, and means 'pendant ribbon'.

- Why do you think this form was chosen to symbolize infinity?

- Can you design an alternative symbol that would effectively signify infinity?

This curve is known as the Lemniscate of Bernoulli; on the Cartesian plane its equation is:

$$(x^2 + y^2)^2 = 2a^2(x^2 - y^2)$$

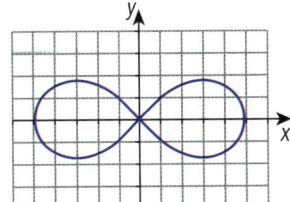

- Use a GDC to graph this equation and create a slider for the variable a from -5 to 5. What effect does the variable a have on the graph?

Global context: Scientific and technical innovation

Exploration: Exploring how humans apply their understanding of scientific principles to real-life situations

📖 Launch additional digital resources for this unit.

8.1 Sequences

Global context: Scientific and technical innovation

Related concept: Patterns

FORM

Objectives

- Understanding and using recursive and explicit formulae for sequences
- Recognizing linear sequences
- Recognizing patterns in real-life contexts
- Solving problems involving sequences in real-life contexts

Inquiry questions

- What is a sequence?
- How can you describe the terms of a sequence?

- What is a general formula for a sequence?

- How does the pattern of a sequence help you identify its form?

- How does the pattern of a sequence help you find its general formula?

- What are the similarities/differences in the forms of linear sequences and linear functions?

ATL Critical-thinking

Identify trends and forecast possibilities

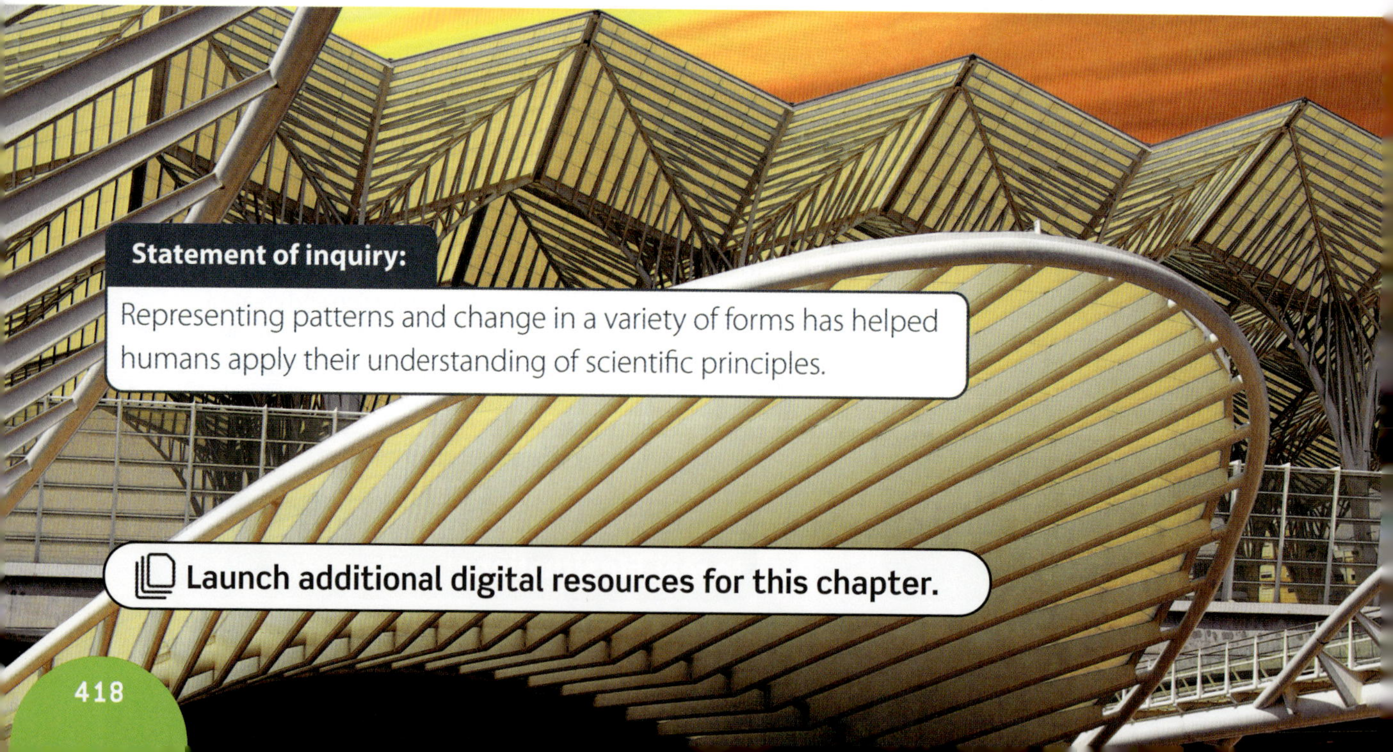

Statement of inquiry:

Representing patterns and change in a variety of forms has helped humans apply their understanding of scientific principles.

📖 **Launch additional digital resources for this chapter.**

You should already know how to:

• identify the next term in a sequence	**1** Write down the next two terms in each sequence. **a** 2, 4, 6, 8, … **b** 4, 9, 14, 19, …
• substitute into formulae	**2** Find the value of: **a** $6n + 3$, when $n = 4$ **b** $-2n + 7$, when $n = 10$
• solve simple linear and quadratic equations	**3** Solve for n. **a** $3n + 7 = 19$ **b** $5n - 2 = 14$
• write a general formula for simple number patterns	**4** Find a formula for the nth term of each sequence. **a** 4, 8, 12, 16, 20, … **b** 12, 24, 36, 48, … **c** −3, −6, −9, −12, −15, …

F Introduction to sequences

- What is a sequence?
- How can you describe the terms of a sequence?
- What is a general formula for a sequence?

ATL

Exploration 1

1 Describe each list of numbers. Compare your descriptions with others.

   a 1, 3, 5, 7, 9   **b** 1, 4, 9, 16, 25   **c** 7, 10, 13, 16, 19

   d 1, 2, 1, 2, 1   **e** 6, 12, 24, 48, 96   **f** 0, 1, 8, 6, 5

Predict the next three numbers in each list. Compare your results with others.

2 Here are two different ways of continuing the list 3, 1, 4, 1, 5, …

3, 1, 4, 1, 5, 1, 6, 1, 7, 1, 8

3, 1, 4, 1, 5, 9, 2, 6, 5, 3, 5

Explain the pattern in each one.

> Search online for
> '3 1 4 1 5 9 2 6 5 3 5'
> if you need help
> identifying the
> pattern.

Reflect and discuss 1

Here is a way of continuing the list from step **1f** in Exploration 1:

0, 1, 8, 6, 5, 5, 5, 6, 7, 6, 7

Is there a pattern?

Try searching online for the numbers grouped like this: 01865 556 767.

- Does this list of numbers count as a pattern?
- Could you have identified the sequence without an internet search?
- If one digit was missing, would you be able to find out what it was?

A **sequence** is an ordered list of numbers. Each number in the list is called a **term**.

In some sequences the terms follow a pattern, specific rule or order.

Describing terms in a sequence

You can use u_1 to represent the first term of the sequence, u_2 to represent the second term, and so on. The subscripts 1, 2, 3, match the term number. For the sequence 1, 3, 5, 7, 9, …

1st term	2nd term	3rd term	4th term	5th term
$u_1 = 1$	$u_2 = 3$	$u_3 = 5$	$u_4 = 7$	$u_5 = 9$

Reflect and discuss 2

- Why is the notation $u_1, u_2, u_3, u_4, u_5, …$ more useful than labelling the terms $a, b, c, d, e, …$?
- What does u_n mean?

Describing a sequence using an explicit formula (position-to-term rule)

An **explicit formula** uses the term's position number, n, to calculate its value.

The formula

$$u_n = 2n - 1 \text{ for } n \geq 1$$

tells us that the value of the nth term (u_n) is given by $2n - 1$ for any value of n greater than or equal to 1. When you are working with sequences, n is always an integer.

The subscript is sometimes called the **index** of the term. As the word 'index' is also used to mean 'exponent', you need to work out its meaning from the context.

Be careful when you talk about 'the first term' – do you mean u_0 or u_1?

You could also use u_0 for the first term, so that:

1st term $u_0 = 1$
2nd term $u_1 = 3$
3rd term $u_2 = 5$
4th term $u_3 = 7$
5th term $u_4 = 9$

Sequences starting from u_0 are often used in computer programs. When u_0 starts the sequence, the subscripts do not match the term number.

Example 1

A sequence is given by the explicit formula $u_n = 3n^2 - 2$ for $n \geq 1$.

a Find:

   i the first, second and tenth terms of the sequence

   ii the term of the sequence with value 673.

b Determine whether or not 524 is a term of the sequence.

a **i** Since $n \geq 1$, the terms required are u_1, u_2 and u_{10}.

$$u_1 = 3 \times 1^2 - 2 = 1$$ Substitute $n = 1$ for the 1st term.

$$u_2 = 3 \times 2^2 - 2 = 10$$ Substitute $n = 2$ for the 2nd term.

$$u_{10} = 3 \times 10^2 - 2 = 298$$ Substitute $n = 10$ for the 10th term.

  ii $3n^2 - 2 = 673$ Solve the explicit formula for the specific value of 673.

$$3n^2 = 675$$

$$n^2 = 225$$

$$n = \pm 15$$

As $n \geq 1$, $n \neq -15$, so $n = 15$.

When $n = 15$, $u_n = 3 \times 15^2 - 2 = 3 \times 225 - 2 = 673$ ✓   Check your solution.

b If 524 is a term in the sequence, then

$$3n^2 - 2 = 524$$

$$3n^2 = 526$$

$$n^2 = 175.333\ldots$$

n is not an integer, so 524 is not a term in the sequence.

Practice 1

1 Find the first five terms of each sequence.

  a $u_n = 4n - 1$ for $n \geq 1$ **b** $u_n = 6n^2 + 2$ for $n \geq 1$

  c $u_n = 10 - \dfrac{1}{4}n^2$ for $n \geq 1$ **d** $u_n = 2^n - 2$ for $n \geq 1$

2 Find the tenth term of the sequence given by $u_n = 5n - 3$ for $n \geq 1$.

3 Determine if 54 is a term in the sequence $u_n = 4n - 1$ for $n \geq 1$.

4 Determine which term of the sequence $u_n = 3n - 5$ has value 61.

5 Find the fifteenth term of the sequence given by $u_n = 10 - \dfrac{10}{n}$ for $n \geq 1$.

6 Find the value of the fourth term of the sequence given by $u_n = 2n + 12$ for $n \geq 0$.

Problem solving

7 Identify which explicit formula, **a** to **f**, corresponds to each sequence, **i** to **vi**.

The command term **identify** requires you to state briefly how you have made your decisions.

a $u_n = 4n + 1$ for $n \geq 0$

b $u_n = 2n + 3$ for $n \geq 1$

c $u_n = 5n - 4$ for $n \geq 1$

d $u_n = 3n$ for $n \geq 1$

e $u_n = 3n - 2$ for $n \geq 0$

f $u_n = 2n + 1$ for $n \geq 0$

i 3, 6, 9, 12, 15, …

ii 1, 3, 5, 7, 9, …

iii −2, 1, 4, 7, 10, …

iv 1, 5, 9, 13, 17, …

v 5, 7, 9, 11, 13, …

vi 1, 6, 11, 16, 21, …

Describing a sequence using a formula (term-to-term rule)

> A **recursive formula** gives the relationship between consecutive terms. When you know one term, you can work out the next.

With this recursive formula you are given the value of u_1:

$$u_{n+1} = u_n + 2, \ u_1 = 1 \text{ for } n \geq 1$$

$$u_1 = 1$$

Substituting $n = 1$ gives the 2nd term:

$$u_{1+1} = u_1 + 2$$

$$u_2 = 1 + 2 = 3$$

Substituting $n = 2$ gives the 3rd term:

$$u_{2+1} = u_2 + 2$$

$$u_3 = 3 + 2 = 5$$

and so on.

u_n is the nth term of a sequence, so u_{n+1} is the next term or $(n + 1)$th term. u_{n-1} is the term before the nth term.

Example 2

A sequence has term-to-term rule $u_{n+1} = \frac{1}{2}u_n + 8$ for $n \geq 1$, and $u_1 = 12$.

Find the 2nd and 3rd terms of the sequence.

$u_2 = \frac{1}{2}u_1 + 8$ ——— The 2nd term is found when $n = 1$.

$\quad = \frac{1}{2} \times 12 + 8$

$\quad = 14$

$u_3 = \frac{1}{2}u_2 + 8$ ——— Use the value you just got for u_2 to find the 3rd term.

$\quad = \frac{1}{2} \times 14 + 8$

$\quad = 15$

Practice 2

1 Find the first five terms of each sequence.

   a $u_{n+1} = 4u_n - 1$, $u_1 = 1$ for $n \geq 1$

   b $u_{n+1} = 2u_n + 1$, $u_1 = 2$ for $n \geq 1$

   c $u_{n+1} = u_n + 7$, $u_1 = -4$ for $n \geq 1$

   d $u_{n+1} = \frac{1}{2}u_n + 1$, $u_1 = 3$ for $n \geq 1$

2 A sequence is given by $u_{n+1} = 3 - u_n$ and $u_1 = -3$.
Find the first four terms of the sequence.

3 A sequence is given by $u_{n+1} = \frac{u_n - 1}{u_n}$, $u_1 = 2$ for $n \geq 1$.

   a Find the first six terms of the sequence.

   b Describe any patterns you notice.

   c Predict the next few terms of the sequence.

> It can be useful to list a few terms to explore an unfamiliar sequence.

Problem solving

4 A sequence is given by $u_{n+1} = 2u_n - 1$, $u_1 = 2$ for $n \geq 1$.

   Find the term of the sequence that has value 257.

5 A sequence is given by $u_{n+1} = 3u_n - 2$, $u_1 = 2$ for $n \geq 1$.

   Find the value of the largest term in the sequence that is less than 10 000.

C   The structure of linear sequences

- How does the pattern of a sequence help you identify its form?
- How does the pattern of a sequence help you find its general formula?

ATL

Exploration 2

1 For each sequence, write down the first five terms.

   $a_n = 3n + 7$ $c_n = 5n - 2$

   $b_n = 3 - 2n$ $d_n = 4n + 5$

2 **a** Copy and complete the diagram for the sequence given by $a_n = 3n + 7$, filling in missing terms in the sequence and the first difference row.

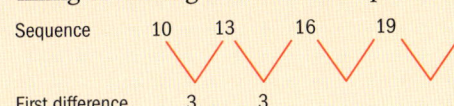

Sequence   10   13   16   19

First difference   3   3

> The first difference is the difference between consecutive terms.

   b Make a similar diagram for the other sequences in step **1**.

3 Look at your diagrams.

   a Describe anything you notice.

▶ Continued on next page

b Compare the first difference for each sequence with its explicit formula. Describe anything you notice. Suggest a relationship between the explicit formula and the value of the first difference.

c What do the explicit formulae of these sequences have in common?

Sequences like the ones in Exploration 2, where the terms increase or decrease by a constant number, are called linear sequences.

For a **linear sequence**, the difference between consecutive terms is constant and the explicit formula is of the form $u_n = a + bn$.

Reflect and discuss 3

- If you plotted the terms of a sequence from Exploration 2, what type of graph would you get?

- Plot the graph of $a_n = 3n + 7$ to check your answer. Plot coordinate pairs as (n, a_n).

A **general formula** for a sequence is a rule that can be used to generate each term. Usually the general formula is an explicit formula.

Example 3

Find a general formula for u_n, the nth term of the sequence 11, 17, 23, 29, …

Sequence   11   17   23   29

First difference   6   6   6

Find the first differences.

The first difference is 6, so compare to the sequence $u_n = 6n$.

The first difference is constant so this is a linear sequence.

n	1	2	3	4
u_n	11	17	23	29
$6n$	6	12	18	24

$+5$

Look for a pattern connecting u_n and $6n$. Adding 5 to $6n$ gives u_n.

The general formula is $u_n = 6n + 5$.

Note that the general formula you find describes the terms you were given. It doesn't necessarily mean that the pattern will continue. To know that, you need more information about the sequence, for example, if it is linear.

Practice 3

1 Find a general formula to describe the terms in each sequence.

> You can check your general formula is correct by working out the first few terms.

a $a_1 = 8, a_2 = 16, a_3 = 24, a_4 = 32$

b $b_1 = 14, b_2 = 17, b_3 = 20, b_4 = 23$

c $c_1 = -14, c_2 = -28, c_3 = -42, c_4 = -56$

d $d_1 = 49, d_2 = 38, d_3 = 27, d_4 = 16$

e $e_1 = 11, e_2 = 29, e_3 = 47, e_4 = 65$

f $f_1 = 17, f_2 = 17.5, f_3 = 18, f_4 = 18.5$

g $g_1 = 8\frac{1}{3}, g_2 = 7\frac{2}{3}, g_3 = 7, g_4 = 6\frac{1}{3}$

h $h_1 = -1.4, h_2 = 3.2, h_3 = 7.8, h_4 = 12.4$

i $i_1 = 15, i_2 = -3, i_3 = -21, i_4 = -39$

2 Each set of terms below is part of a linear sequence.

Find a general formula describing the terms of each sequence.

a $a_5 = 9, a_6 = 11, a_7 = 13, a_8 = 15$

b $b_{11} = 17, b_{12} = 14, b_{13} = 11, b_{14} = 8$

c $c_9 = 13.5, c_{10} = 14, c_{11} = 14.5, c_{12} = 15$

d $d_5 = 7, d_7 = 15, d_9 = 23, d_{11} = 31$

Problem solving

3 A string of decorative lights are wired as shown.

a Explain why it takes 500 cm of cable to connect the first bulb, and then another 20 cm to connect the next bulb.

b Let d_n be the total length of cable needed to connect the nth bulb. Find a general formula for d_n.

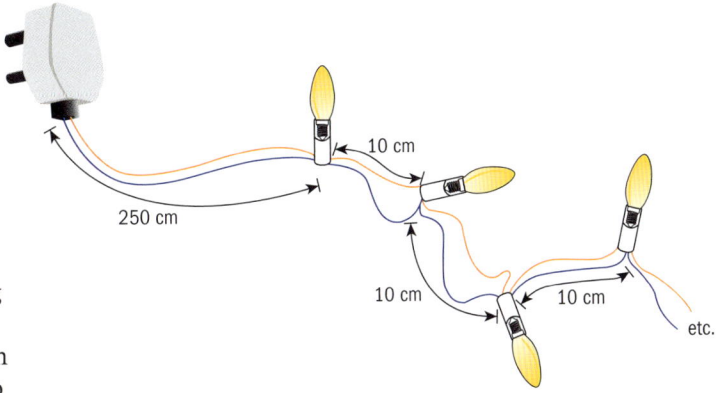

4 A railway train is stored overnight in a depot which is 6 km from its starting station. It then spends all day moving from its starting station, back and forth along a section of track 14 km long, so in each complete journey it travels 28 km.

a Explain why after its first complete journey of the day it has traveled 34 km.

b Find a general formula for the distance it has traveled after n journeys up and down the track.

c The train can travel 400 km before refuelling. Find the number of complete journeys it can make before refuelling.

5 The first five terms of a linear sequence are −3, 4, 11, 18, 25.

   a Find the 100th term of the sequence.

   b Show that 102 is a member of the sequence and find its term number.

6 A sequence has formula $u_{n+1} = u_n + 5$ and $u_1 = -1$.

   Find a formula for the nth term of the sequence.

Problem solving

7 A linear sequence has terms $u_{10} = 25$ and $u_{15} = 70$.

   a Find the difference between consecutive terms.

   b Write down the value of **i** u_9 and **ii** u_1.

8 A linear sequence begins 191, 173, 155, …

   Find the first term that is less than 65.

9 A linear sequence has first term 108 and second term 103.

   Find its first negative term.

D Is there a connection between linear sequences and linear functions?

- What are the similarities and differences in the forms of linear sequences and linear functions?

Exploration 3

A sign in a marina advertises boat hire:

BOAT HIRE!

$40 hire fee then
$20 per hour or part thereof

The phrase '$20 per hour or part thereof' means that customers get charged for a full hour, even if they have only used the boat for a minute.

1 Let x_n denote the cost of hiring the boat for n hours.
Explain why x_n forms a linear sequence and find a formula for x_n in terms of n.

▶ Continued on next page

2 These graphs represent different attempts to graph the cost of hiring a boat for up to four hours. Describe the differences between the graphs and evaluate their suitability to describe this situation.

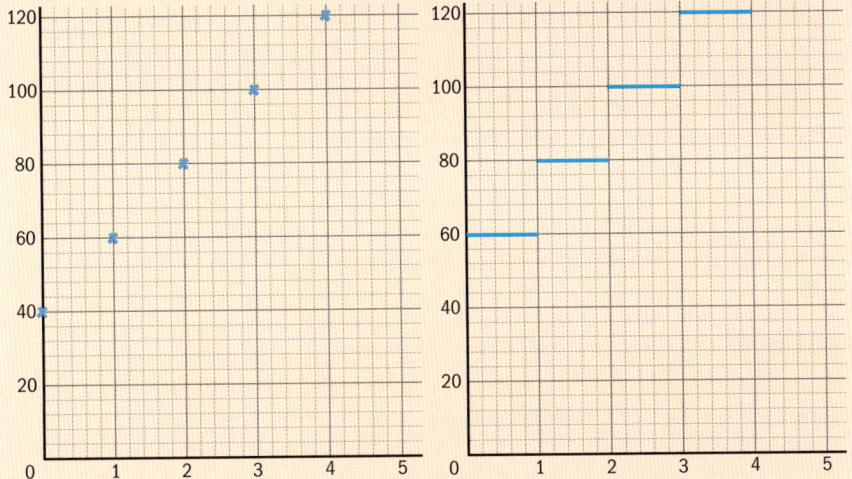

3 The hire company modifies its pricing structure. It is still going to charge a flat fee of $40 and then $20 per hour, but the total will now be calculated for each completed 15-minute period (so up to an hour and a quarter would be $45, up to an hour and a half would cost $50 and so on). Sketch some graphs like those in question **2** to represent this pricing structure.

4 Describe how the graphs would change if the company started charging by 10-minute interval, or by 5-minute interval.

Reflect and discuss 4

What would happen to the graphs if the company started charging by the minute? Or by the second?

In many real-life applications, quantities do not increase in steps like sequences do – especially when considering problems where a quantity is increasing over time. However, you might have noticed that the equation of the linear sequence in Exploration 3:

$$x_n = 20n + 40$$

is very similar to the equation of the line which was obtained when the charging interval became very small. Letting C be the cost and t be the time taken, the equation would be:

$$C = 20t + 40$$

This is a straight line with gradient 20 and an intercept on the C-axis (the vertical axis) of 40. The gradient is 20 because there is a charge of $20 per hour, and the intercept is $40 because this amount is charged even if the time is 0 hours.

Any situation which features a quantity growing at a constant rate can be modelled using a linear function.

If a linear function is used to model a scenario which involves a quantity q growing at a regular rate r per unit time, starting from a fixed amount f, then $q = rt + f$

The rate, r, will be the gradient of the straight-line graph, which will meet the vertical axis at f.

Example 4

A plumber charges an $80 fee to cover travel expenses, and then $30 per hour for labor while working.

a Form an equation for the plumber's charge $\$C$ in terms of the time taken, t hours.

b Use your equation to determine the cost of a four-hour visit.

c Use your equation to determine the cost of a visit lasting $2\frac{1}{4}$ hours.

d Use your equation to determine the length of a visit costing $150.

a The amount charged per hour is $30.
So t hours will cost $\$30t$.
In addition, there is a fixed charge of $80.
So $C = 30t + 80$

b When $t = 4$, —————————————— Substitute in the value of t.
Don't forget to include units.

$C = 30 \times 4 + 80 = 120 + 80 = \$200$

c When $t = 2\frac{1}{4}$, ——————————— The value of t could be a decimal or a fraction, but it must be measured in hours.

$C = 30 \times 2\frac{1}{4} + 80 = 67.5 + 80 = \$147.50$.

d When $C = 150$, ——————————— Substitute your value of C into the equation.

$150 = 30t + 80$

$70 = 30t$

$t = 2\frac{1}{3}$ hours ——————————————— This answer is the right value, but an unusual way to present a time.

So t is 2 hours and 20 minutes ————— Convert the answer into hours and minutes.

Practice 4

1 An electrician charges for home visits. The cost, $\$C$, of a visit lasting t hours is given as $C = 35t + 60$.

a Find the cost of a visit lasting 3 hours.

b Find the cost of a visit lasting 1 hour and 15 minutes.

c Find the duration of a visit costing $191.25.

d Write down the electrician's hourly rate.

2 A monthly mobile phone bill costs €10 plus an additional €1.20 for each gigabyte of mobile data used.

Let €y be the value of the bill in a given month and x be the amount of data used in gigabytes.

  a Write an equation for the cost y in terms of x.

  b Hence find the cost if 2.4 gigabytes of mobile data are used in a month.

  c Find the amount of data used if a month's bill totals €18.04.

3 Two picture framers each charge a fixed fee to cover the cost of glazing and mounting, and then a cost per centimeter for the material for the edge of the frame:

Company	Fixed fee	Charge per cm
EZ-Framers	16	0.14
Perfect Pictures	10	0.18

  a Write an equation for the cost, €y, in terms of x, the length of the edge of the frame, for each of the two companies.

  b Use your equations to find the cost of a frame with edge length 60 cm from each framer. Determine which framer would charge more for this frame.

  c Determine the frame size for which the two framers would charge the same amount.

4 A tree is already 3 m tall when planted in a garden. It then grows at a rate of 50 cm per year.

  a Find an equation linking the height of the tree h m to the amount of time passed since it was planted t years.

  b Find the height of the tree after 6 years.

  c Use this model to find the height of the tree after 7 years and 6 months.

  d Comment on the limitations of this model.

Summary

- A **sequence** is an ordered list of numbers. Each number in the list is called a **term**.

- An **explicit formula** uses the term's position number, n, to calculate its value.

- A **recursive formula** gives the relationship between consecutive terms. When you know one term, you can work out the next.

- A **general formula** for a sequence is a rule that can be used to generate each term. Usually the general formula is an explicit formula.

- Sequences where the terms increase or decrease by a constant number, are called **linear sequences**.

- For a **linear sequence**, the difference between consecutive terms is constant and the explicit formula is of the form $u_n = a + bn$.

- If a linear function is used to model a scenario which involves a quantity q growing at a regular rate r per unit time, starting from a fixed amount f, then $q = rt + f$.

- The rate, r, will be the gradient of the straight-line graph, which will meet the vertical axis at f.

Mixed practice

1 **Find** a formula for the nth term of each sequence.

   a 6, 10, 14, 18, 22, 26, …

   b 42, 35, 28, 21, …

   c 2, 5, 10, 17, 26, 37, …

   d 3, 8, 15, 24, 35, …

   e 2.5, 7, 11.5, 16, 20.5, …

   f −0.5, 4, 13.5, 28, 47.5, …

   g 9, 13, 13, 9, 1, …

   h 6, 7, 7, 6, 4, …

2 A linear sequence begins 14, 17, 20, …

   Find its hundredth term.

3 A sequence has formula $u_n = u_{n-1} - 5$ and $u_1 = 12$.

   a **Write down** the first five terms.

   b **Find** a formula for the nth term of the sequence.

Problem solving

4 A sequence has formula $u_{n+1} = u_n + 7$ and $u_0 = 15$.

   a **Write down** the first five terms of the sequence.

   b **Show** that 85 is a member of the sequence.

5 A linear sequence begins 18, 33, 48, ...

   Find the first term greater than 1000.

6 A linear sequence has terms $u_3 = 6$ and $u_6 = 27$.

   a **Find** the difference between successive terms.

   b **Write down** the value of u_7.

7 A 12-storey tall building has an elevator that stops at every floor.

The elevator takes 8 seconds to travel one floor, 14 seconds to travel two floors, 20 seconds to travel three floors and 26 seconds to travel four floors.

Let T_n be the time taken to travel n floors.

   a **Show that** T_n forms a linear sequence.

   b **Find** a formula for T_n.

   c **Find** the greatest number of floors that the elevator could travel in under a minute.

8 A mobile phone company offers three possible tariffs. Each has a fixed monthly charge and then charges an additional amount based on the amount of mobile data used. The tariffs are as follows:

	Fixed cost	Data charge per gigabyte
Red	£10.00	£1.20
Green	£16.00	£0.80
Blue	£6.00	£2.00

   a **Find** equations for the cost in pounds of the a month's bill in terms of x, the amount of data used, according to each of the three plans.

   b If 5 gigabytes of data are used, two of the plans would cost the same amount. **Determine** which plans.

   c **Determine** the conditions under which the green plan would be the cheapest.

Review in context

Scientific and technical innovation

1 Engineers are laying signalling cable alongside a railway track. They place fixed lengths of cable separated by junction boxes.

The total length of cable for 1, 2, 3 or 4 junction boxes is 12 m, 18 m, 24 m or 30 m.

Let u_n be the cable length for n junction boxes.

a **Find** a formula for u_n.

b **Use** your formula to **predict** the length of cable needed for 30 junction boxes.

2 The number of passengers, P_n, who will comfortably fit into an n-carriage train is given by the following table for small values of n:

n	1	2	3	4
P_n	40	110	180	250

a **Show** that P_n forms a linear sequence.

b **Find** a formula for P_n.

c **Predict** the number of passengers that an eight-carriage train could comfortably hold.

d **Suggest** a reason why a two-carriage train might hold more than twice the number of passengers of a one-carriage train.

Reflect and discuss 5

How have you explored the statement of inquiry? Give specific examples.

Statement of inquiry:

Representing patterns and change in a variety of forms has helped humans apply their understanding of scientific principles.

8.2 Rearranging formulae and proportion

Global context: Scientific and technical innovation

Related concept: Change

FORM

Objectives

- Changing the subject of a formula
- Finding a constant of proportionality
- Setting up direct and indirect proportion equations to model a situation
- Graphing direct and indirect relationships
- Recognizing direct and inverse proportion from graphs
- Identifying direct and inverse proportion from tables of values

Inquiry questions

 F
- What is the subject of a formula?
- How can you change the subject of a formula?
- How do you find a constant of proportionality?
- What does a proportional relationship look like?

 C
- What does it mean to be proportional?
- How does changing one variable in a proportional relationship affect the other?

 D
- Can situations seem proportional when they are not?
- Is simpler always better?

 **ATL** | Transfer

Combine knowledge, understanding and skills to produce products and solutions

Statement of inquiry:

Representing patterns and change in a variety of forms has helped humans apply their understanding of scientific principles.

📖 **Launch additional digital resources for this chapter.**

You should already know how to:

• simplify fractions	**1** Simplify: **a** $\dfrac{4}{16}$ **b** $\dfrac{14}{35}$ **c** $\dfrac{x^2}{x^3}$ **d** $\dfrac{20x^2}{(20x)^2}$
• solve a linear equation algebraically	**2** Solve: **a** $2x - 1 = 5$ **b** $5x - 7 = 8$ **c** $8x + 1 = 4x + 17$
• express a ratio as a fraction	**3** Express each ratio as a fraction in its simplest form. **a** $5:3$ **b** $2:4$ **c** $4.5:13.3$ **d** $0.2:1.2$
• write linear functions to model real-life situations	**4 a** John earns £10 per hour. Write a function for the amount he earns in h hours. **b** A taxi ride costs \$2 plus \$4.50 per mile. Write a function for the cost of any journey.
• draw graphs of linear functions	**5** Draw graphs of the two functions above.
• draw graphs of quadratic functions	**6** Draw the graph of $y = x^2$ for integer values of x from -3 to $+3$.

Rearranging formulae

- What is the subject of a formula?
- How can you change the subject of a formula?
- How do you find a constant of proportionality?
- What does a proportional relationship look like?

You already know how to solve linear equations like $5x - 7 = 8$, which has solution $x = 3$. This is sometimes called 'isolating the x' or 'rearranging the equation to solve for x'. You also know how to use substitution to solve equations that show relationships between variables, for example, solving $c^2 = a^2 + b^2$ when $a = 3$ and $b = 4$.

$5x - 7 = 8$ and $c^2 = a^2 + b^2$ are both equations, but $c^2 = a^2 + b^2$ is also a formula.

> A **formula** is an equation that describes an algebraic relationship between two or more sets of values. Each variable in a formula can take different values, depending on the values of the other variables.

$c^2 = a^2 + b^2$ is valid for $a = 3$, $b = 4$, $c = 5$. It is also valid for $a = 5$, $b = 12$, $c = 13$ and an infinite number of other combinations of values a, b, and c.

By substituting values for a and b you can find a corresponding value for c. Similarly, by substituting values for b and c you can find a corresponding value for a. In other words, you can solve for any of the variables, given the values of the other two.

Exploration 1

The relationship between degrees Celsius and degrees Fahrenheit is given by the formula: $F = \dfrac{9}{5}C + 32$.

1 Find the temperature in °F when it is 35°C.

2 Find the temperature in Celsius when it is 77°F. To find a temperature in °C, you need to solve an equation. Carefully write down the steps you have used to solve the equation.

3 Using the same steps as you used in step **2**, begin with the formula for finding F and finish with a formula for C. C is now the 'subject' of the formula.

4 Use your new formula from step **3** to find the temperature in Celsius when it is 77°F. Compare your answer to that in step **2**.

5 Write down what you think it means to 'change the subject of the formula', and the necessary steps to do this.

> The Fahrenheit scale was based on a mixture of salt and water freezing at 0°F. In this scale, water freezes at 32°F and boils at 212°F. The Celsius scale is based on water freezing at 0°C and boiling at 100°C.

Changing the subject of the formula is a way of rearranging algebraic relationships. When you change the subject of a formula, you solve a different variable in the formula.

Reflect and discuss 1

- In Exploration 1, does changing the subject of the formula change the relationship between F and C?

- What are similarities and differences between changing the subject of a formula and solving an equation?

- When could it be useful to change the subject of a formula?

Example 1

The Pythagorean Theorem states that in a right-angled triangle, the relationship between the side lengths is $c^2 = a^2 + b^2$, where c is the hypotenuse and a and b are the other two sides.

Rearrange $c^2 = a^2 + b^2$ to make a the subject of the formula.

$$c^2 = a^2 + b^2$$

$$c^2 - b^2 = a^2 + b^2 - b^2 \qquad \text{Subtract } b^2 \text{ from both sides.}$$

$$c^2 - b^2 = a^2$$

▶ Continued on next page

$$a^2 = c^2 - b^2$$ ————— Rearrange the terms so that the variable a is on the left-hand side.

$$\sqrt{a^2} = \sqrt{c - b^2}$$ ————— Take the square root of both sides. a is a length, so you can ignore the negative square root.

$$a = \sqrt{c^2 - b^2}$$ ————— Now a is the subject of the formula.

When the variable you are trying to isolate appears more than once in the formula, factorize so that the variable appears only once.

Example 2

Rearrange $F = \frac{mv - mu}{t}$ to make m the subject.

$$F = \frac{mv - mu}{t}$$

$$Ft = mv - mu$$ ————— Multiply both sides by the denominator of the right-hand side.

$$Ft = m(v - u)$$ ————— Factor out m to isolate it.

$$\frac{Ft}{v - u} = m$$ ————— Divide both sides by $v - u$.

Practice 1

1 Rearrange each formula to make the variable in brackets the subject.

a $y = 5x - 4$ $[x]$ b $y = \frac{1}{3}x^2 + 3$ $[x]$

c $p = \sqrt{m + 2}$ $[m]$ d $V = (2w - 5)^2$ $[w]$

e $V_f^2 = V_i^2 + 2ad$ $[V_i]$ f $V_f = V_i + at$ $[a]$

> You may have seen some of these in science.

g $I = \frac{V}{R + r}$ $[R]$ h $F = \frac{mV^2}{r}$ $[r]$

i $F = \frac{mV^2}{r}$ $[V]$ j $F = \frac{1}{2}mV^2 + mgh$ $[m]$

k $\mu = \sqrt{\frac{3RT}{M}}$ $[M]$ l $c = (3a + 2b)^2 - 1$ $[a]$

2 Write down the formula for the area A of a circle with radius r. Make r the subject of the formula.

3 The formula for the volume V of a cone with height h and base of radius r is $V = \frac{1}{3}\pi r^2 h$. Make r the subject of the formula.

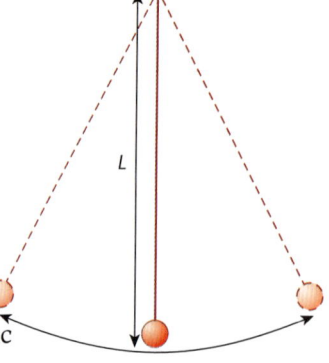

4 When driving a car, if you accelerate from rest at a constant rate a for an amount of time t, the distance d traveled is given by the formula $d = \frac{1}{2}at^2$. Rearrange the formula to make t the subject.

5 The time taken (T) for a pendulum to swing once each way and back to its starting position is given by the formula $T = 2\pi\sqrt{\frac{L}{g}}$, where L is the length of the pendulum.
Rearrange the formula to make L the subject.

Problem solving

6 Between any two charged particles with charge q_1 and q_2, there is an electric force. You can calculate this force using the formula $F = \dfrac{kq_1q_2}{r^2}$, where r is the distance between the particles. Rearrange the formula to make r the subject.

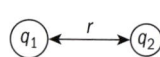

Sometimes when working with related quantities, you might not be told all the details of the relationship. Instead you may be told how changes to one quantity affect the other. For example, if you sell identical items, say mouse mats, the money you make varies with the number of mouse mats you sell. If you sell twice as many mouse mats, you will make twice as much money. If you sell half as many, you make half as much money. We say the two quantities are directly proportional.

> Two variables are said to be in **direct proportion** if, and only if, their ratio is a constant for all values of each variable.
>
> $y \propto x$ means 'y varies directly as x' or 'y is directly proportional to x'.

ATL

Exploration 2

A store sells regular light bulbs for 2 Euros per bulb.

1 Write down a function to represent the store's income from selling regular bulbs. Identify your variables and justify your choice of letters to represent each variable.

2 Determine which variable is dependent, and which one is independent.

3 Draw a graph representing the amount of money made from selling up to 10 light bulbs.

4 From your graph, determine what happens to the income when you multiply the number of light bulbs sold:

    a by 2   **b** by 4   **c** by 5   **d** by 12   **e** by 14.

To meet the growing demand for more efficient bulbs, the station also sells LED bulbs for 7 Euros per bulb.

▶   Continued on next page

5 Using the same variables as in step **1**, write down a new function to represent the amount of income from selling LED bulbs. Draw a line on your graph to represent this relationship.

6 Determine whether the amount of money made is in direct proportion to the number of light bulbs sold. Justify your answer.

Reflect and discuss 2

- Justify why the graphs you drew in Exploration 2 go through the origin.

- Describe a situation where, if one quantity increases, the other increases, but not in direct proportion.

$y \propto x$ means that $y = kx$ for a constant k, where $k \neq 0$.

k is called the **proportionality constant**, or **constant of variation**.

The function $y = kx$ is called a **linear variation function**.

In other words, if y is proportional to x, then the relationship between x and y is a function of the form $y = kx$.

Reflect and discuss 3

- In Exploration 2, identify the proportionality constant for the function for:

  o regular light bulbs

  o LED light bulbs.

- For linear relationships of the form $y = kx$, the proportionality constant k is also called the constant ratio of x and y. Explain why you think this is.

Example 3

A shop charges €1.50 for a liter of mineral water.

a Write down a function to represent the relationship between the number of liters of mineral water and the total price of mineral water purchased.

b Hence, determine the proportionality constant.

c Show that number of liters and price are in direct proportion by drawing a graph.

▶ Continued on next page

a P = price ——————————————— Define the variables.

l = number of liters

$P(l) = 1.50l$

b $k = 1.50$ ——————————— For every extra liter the price increases by €1.50.

c The graph is a straight line that passes through the origin, so P and l are in direct proportion.

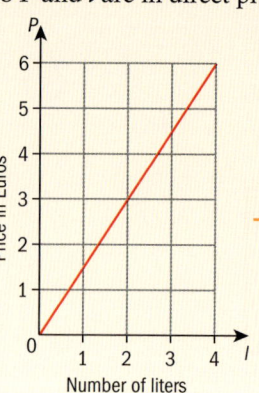

The total price depends on the number of liters, so P is the dependent variable and N is the independent variable.

If the graph is a straight line passing through the origin then the equation of the graph can be written as $y = kx$, and x is directly proportional to y.

Reflect and discuss 4

- How is the proportionality constant represented on the graph of a direct linear proportion?

- Explain why a linear graph that does not go through the origin does not represent a proportional relationship.

Example 4

The variable y varies as x. When $x = 4$, $y = 10$.

Find the value of y when $x = 7$.

'y varies as x' means 'y is directly proportional to x'.

$y \propto x$ means that $y = kx$

$10 = k \times 4$

$k = \dfrac{10}{4} = 2.5$

When $x = 7$, $y = 2.5 \times 7 = 17.5$ ——————— Use the proportionality constant to find y when $x = 7$.

Practice 2

1 The variable c is directly proportional to the variable b. Write an equation to represent this relationship. State what happens to:

a c if b is doubled   **b** b if c is tripled

c c if b is multiplied by $\frac{2}{3}$ **d** c if 4 is added to b.

2 The variable v is directly proportional to the variable t. When $t = 5$, $v = 40$.

a Write the function that represents the relationship of proportionality.

b Find the value of the constant of proportionality.

c Find v when $t = 25$.

3 P is directly proportional to V. When $V = 3.2$, $P = 8.64$.

Find V when $P = 5.4$.

4 Two variables x and Q are in direct proportion.

Find the missing values from this table:

x	0	4.7	6.1	
Q		6.58		13.72

Problem solving

5 In order to reduce trash in landfills, many people are beginning to compost food waste. Composting produces rich soil that can then be used in gardens or farms. In a science experiment, Kent records the number of containers of food waste dumped in a composter at one time and the mass of soil produced.

Number of containers	2	3	7	9
Mass of soil (kg)	1.6	2.4	5.6	7.2

a Verify that the number of containers and mass of soil are in direct proportion.

b Find the constant of proportionality.

c Calculate the amount of soil produced from 5 containers of food waste.

6 Determine which of these functions represent direct proportion, and find the constant of proportionality for those that do.

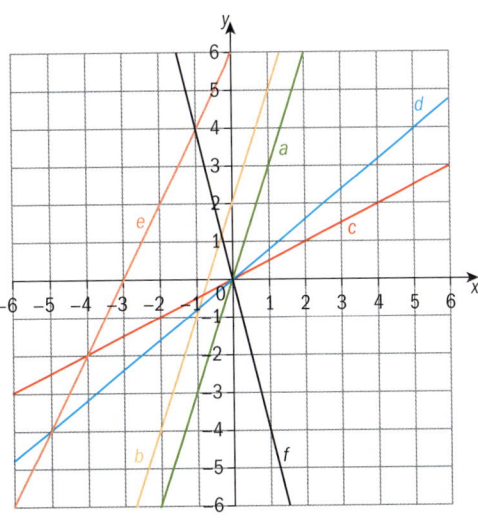

Objective: B. Investigating patterns
ii. describe patterns as general rules consistent with findings

In this exploration, you will find a general rule in terms of a specific function that models the relationship between the time needed to plant trees and hourly income.

ATL

Exploration 3

In an effort to replace trees that have been harvested for consumer products, students can take a summer job that pays 8 cents per tree that they plant. One student can plant 300 trees in one hour.

Find the total income from planting 2400 trees.

1 Determine how long it would take one student to plant 2400 trees. Hence, find this student's income per hour.

2 Copy and complete the table to show the time taken and income per hour for the different groups of students.

	1 student	2 students	4 students	8 students
Time (t) needed to plant 2400 trees (h)	8	4		
Income (I) per hour ($/h)	24			

3 Predict the time needed and income per hour for 16 students. Do some calculations to check your predictions. Add the values for 16 students to your table.

4 Identify a pattern from this table. Generalize this pattern, and write down a function to represent the relationship between the number of students planting trees and the income per hour.

5 Describe the relationship between the number of students and the time needed to plant 2400 trees.

In Exploration 3, one relationship is directly proportional: doubling the number of students doubles the income per hour. But doubling the number of students halves the time taken to plant 2400 trees. The time taken to plant the trees is *inversely proportional* to the number of students doing the planting.

Two variables x and y are **inversely proportional** if multiplying one of them by a non-zero number results in the other variable being divided by the same non-zero number.

If x and y are in an inverse linear proportion, you can say 'y varies inversely as x' or 'y is inversely proportional to x', and you can write $y \propto \dfrac{1}{x}$ and $y = \dfrac{k}{x}$.

Reflect and discuss 5

- Write the relationship between the number of students (s) and time taken to plant 2400 trees (t) from Exploration 3 as a function.

- Does the function have a constant of proportionality? Explain.

> If y is inversely proportional to x, then y is directly proportional to $\frac{1}{x}$.
> An equation $y = k \times \frac{1}{x}$ or $y = \frac{k}{x}$ represents a relationship of inverse proportion or an **inverse relationship**.

> Graphs of $y = \frac{k}{x}$ are called reciprocal graphs.

Example 5

It takes one person 2 days to prepare one hectare of field for planting and there are 16 hectares to be prepared.

a Find the time for one person to prepare the 16 hectares for planting.

b Determine if this relationship represents direct or inverse proportion.

c Write down a function to represent the relationship between the time to prepare the field and the number of workers.

d Draw the graph of this function.

a $2 \times 16 = 32$ days ——— One person, two days' prep time per person, total time = 32 days.

b

w: number of workers	1	2	4	8
t: time to prepare 16 hectares	32	16	8	4

The prep time halves as the number of workers doubles.

This describes an inverse proportion.

c $t \propto \dfrac{1}{w} \Rightarrow t(w) = \dfrac{k}{w}$ ——— Substitute values for t and w, and solve for k.

$$32 = \frac{k}{1}$$

$$k = 32$$

$$t = \frac{32}{w}$$

d

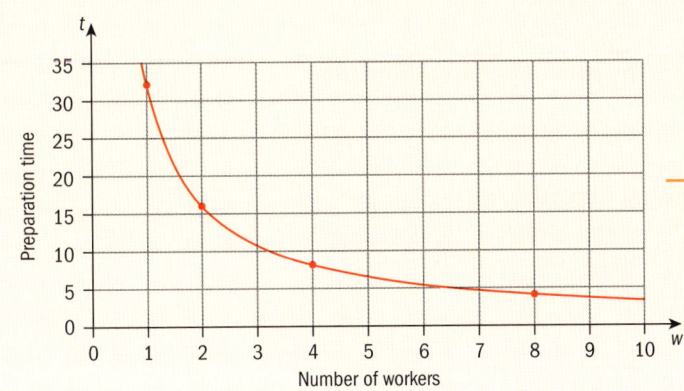

Number of workers

Plot the points from the table of values. Even though the function is in its own right a smooth curve, only the points with integer values on the n axis are meaningful since there can't be a non-integer number of workers.

Practice 3

1 For each part **a** to **e**:

  i Determine whether there is a relationship of direct proportion, inverse proportion or neither. Justify your answer.

  ii If there is a proportional relationship, find k.

  a The perimeter p of an equilateral triangle with side length l.

  b The number of liters n of paint needed to paint an area A, given that 3 liters will paint a 15 m² area.

  c $y = 4x$ **d** $y = \dfrac{3}{x}$ **e** $y = \dfrac{x}{5}$

2 The variable f is inversely proportional to the variable v. When $v = 6, f = 4$.

  a Write the function that represents the relationship of proportion.

  b Find the value of the constant of proportionality.

  c Find f when $v = 2$.

3 y is in inverse proportion to x. When $x = 5.2, y = 2$.

  Find y when $x = 1.6$.

4 T is inversely proportional to m. When $m = 1.8$, $T = 4$.

  Find T when $m = 3.1$.

5 Two variables s and t are in inverse proportion.
  Find the missing values in this table:

s	4		4.8
t	0.8	2	

Problem solving

6 To balance a seesaw, Archimedes' Law of the Lever says that the distance d of each person from the pivot must be inversely proportional to their mass w.

  a Write down a function to represent the Law of the Lever.

  b Mark weighs 20 kg and is 1.5 m from the pivot. The seesaw is balanced when Emilie sits 1.25 m from the pivot. Use this information to find k.

  c Hence, find Emilie's mass.

7 Milijenko has decided to encourage her class to participate in 'Adopt a Sumatran Tiger' which funds research and conservation of these critically endangered animals. The cost of adoption per person depends on the number of people participating as shown in the table below:

Number of people	1	4	8	10	20
Cost per person	$300	$75	$37.50	$30	$15

  a Verify that the number of people and the cost per person are inversely proportional.

  b Find the constant of proportionality.

  c Calculate the cost per person when 25 people participate.

8 Conservation efforts, like the adoption program, are trying to double the number of tigers in the wild. The amount spent on conservation is related to the increase in the number of wild tigers as shown in the table below:

Amount spent on conservation (millions of US $)	1.5	2.4	4.9	8.3
Increase in tiger population	390	624	1274	2158

  a Determine whether or not this relation is in a proportion, and if so, state the type of proportion. Justify your answer.

  b Write down an equation relating the two variables.

  c Determine how much will need to be spent on conservation for the goal of adding 3 200 tigers to the wild to be met. (This will double their population.)

9 During a storm, a bolt of lightning strikes a distance d m away from an observer and causes a loud thunderclap. Because of distance, the observer will not see the lightning strike or hear the thunder immediately. Light travels at 3×10^8 ms^{-1}. Sound travels at 340 ms^{-1}

  a Determine whether the following relationships are proportional relationships. Justify your answer.

    i The relationship between the distance and the time to see the lightning

    ii The relationship between the distance and the time to hear the thunder

    iii The relationship between the time to see the lightning and the time to hear the thunder

  b Lightning strikes 5 km away.

    i Find how long it takes to see the lightning.

    ii Find how long it takes to hear the thunder.

 Different types of variation

- What does it mean to be proportional?
- How does changing one variable in a proportional relationship affect the other?

You have seen examples of these proportional relationships:

- $y = kx$ is a relationship of direct proportion between x and y
- $y = \dfrac{k}{x}$ is a relationship of inverse proportion between x and y

In the next Exploration, you will see that y can vary, directly or inversely, with higher powers of x as well.

Exploration 4

This circle has radius r.

1 Write down the formula for the area A of the circle, in terms of r.

2 **a** Find the new area if you double the radius.

   b Find the new area if you triple the radius.

   c Find the new area if you halve the radius.

   d Multiply the radius by a few more factors, and find the new area each time.

   e Suggest a general rule for what happens to the area when the radius of the circle is multiplied by a constant c, where $c \neq 0$.

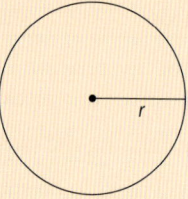

3 Justify whether or not the formula represents a proportional relationship between the area and the radius of the circle.

4 Write a statement of proportionality linking area A and radius r. Find the constant of proportionality.

5 This cube has side length x.

Write down the formula for the volume V of the cube. Find what happens to the volume if you double, halve or triple the side length. Suggest a general rule for what happens to the volume when the side length is multiplied by a constant c, where $c \neq 0$.

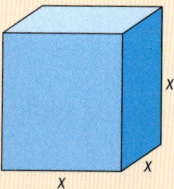

6 Justify whether or not the formula represents a proportional relationship between the volume and the side length of the cube.

7 Write a statement of proportionality linking volume V and side length x. Find the constant of proportionality.

Two variables x and y are in **direct non-linear proportion** if y is proportional to a power of x, or $y \propto x^n$, $n > 0$.

The variation function is $y = kx^n$, $k \neq 0$ and $n > 0$.

y varies directly as x^n or y is in direct proportion to x^n.

Exploration 5

Diego plans to tile a wall with square tiles of side length l.

1 Write down the formula for the area A_t of a square tile.

2 Let A_w represent the area of the wall.

Let the number of tiles $= n$.

   a Write down an expression for n in terms of A_w and A_t.

   b Write down an expression for n in terms of A_w and l.

▶ Continued on next page

3 Determine whether the number of tiles is directly or inversely proportional to the area of the tile.

4 State the proportional relationship between the number of tiles and the side length of each tile. Find the constant of proportionality.

Diego changes his mind, and tiles the wall with square tiles of side length $\frac{2}{3}l$.

5 Write down the formula for the area A_s of this smaller tile.

6 Find the number m of new tiles he needs to cover A_w. Write down an expression for m:

    a in terms of A_w and A_s

    b in terms of A_w and l.

7 Compare m and n. How does changing to tiles with $\frac{2}{3}$ the side length affect:

    a the number of tiles needed

    b the proportionality constant?

Reflect and discuss 6

- Do you think that there has to be a whole number of tiles along the length and height of the wall?

- Does this affect the number of tiles you need to cover the wall entirely?

Two variables x and y are in an **inverse non-linear proportion** if y is proportional to a power of $\frac{1}{x}$, or $y \propto \frac{1}{x^n}$, $n > 0$. You can also write this as $y \propto x^{-n}$, $n > 0$.

The variation function is $y = \frac{k}{x^n}$, $k \neq 0$ and $n > 0$.

y varies inversely as x^n or y is inversely proportional to x^n

---

In Exploration 5 you should have found that:

- the smaller the tile, the more tiles you need for the given area

- the number of tiles is inversely proportional to the side length of each tile

- the proportionality constant k changes only when the initial conditions of the problem change.

Exploration 6

1 Explain what happens to y when x is multiplied by a constant c in these variation functions:

    $y = kx$ $y = kx^2$ $y = kx^3$

    $y = \frac{k}{x}$ $y = \frac{k}{x^2}$

2 Generalize your results first for $y = kx^n$, $n > 0$, and then for $y = \frac{k}{x^n}$, $n > 0$.

$y = kx^n$ is a relationship of direct variation. When x is multiplied by a constant c, then y is multiplied by c^n.

$y = \dfrac{k}{x^n}$ is a relationship of inverse variation. When x is multiplied by a constant c, then y is divided by c^n.

Example 6

The light intensity on a movie screen varies inversely with the square of the distance between the screen and the projector.

a When the screen is 3 m from the projector, the light intensity is 24 units.

Find the light intensity when the screen is 6 m away.

b Describe what happens to the light intensity when the distance between the projector and the screen is halved.

c The distance between the projector and the screen is increased by 25%. Find the effect on the light intensity on the screen.

d Draw a graph to represent the variation function.

a $I(d) = \dfrac{k}{d^2}$ ———————— Choose sensible variable names and write the variation function.

$24 = \dfrac{k}{3^2}$ ———————— Substitute the known values and solve for k.

$k = 24 \times 9 = 216$

$\Rightarrow I(6) = \dfrac{216}{6^2} = 6$ ———————— Find I when $d = 6$.

The light intensity at 6 m is 6 units of illumination.

b $I(d) = \dfrac{k}{d^2}$

$I_{new}(d) = \dfrac{k}{\left(\frac{1}{2}d\right)^2} = \dfrac{k}{\frac{1}{4}d^2} = 4\dfrac{k}{d^2}$ ———————— Replace d with $\frac{1}{2}d$ and substitute this into the variation function.

$= 4 I_{original}(d)$

When the distance is halved, the light intensity is 4 times as great.

c $d_n = 1.25d = \dfrac{5}{4}d_o$ ———————— Increasing d by 25% gives 1.25d or $\frac{5}{4}d$.

$I_n = \dfrac{k}{\left(\frac{5}{4}d_o\right)^2} = \dfrac{k}{\frac{25}{16}d_o^2} = \dfrac{16k}{25d_o^2} = \dfrac{64k}{100d_o^2}$ ———————— $k \div \dfrac{25}{16} = \dfrac{16}{25}k$

$= 0.64$

When the distance is increased by 25% the light intensity is reduced to 64% of the original.

▶ Continued on next page

d $I = \frac{216}{d^2}$

d is the independent variable, as the illumination *I* depends on the distance.

Distance (m)

All points on the curve have meaning, as you can have any distance *d* on the horizontal axis.

Example 7

The table shows the resistances of four 1 m cables of the same material, but each a different radius.

Radius of cable (mm)	1	2	5	10
Resistance of 1 m of cable (ohms)	1.5	0.375	0.06	0.015

a Determine if this relationship between the radius and the resistance of the cable is one of direct variation, inverse variation or neither. Justify your answer.

b Hence, if the relationship is a variation function, write down the equation of the function.

a Let r = radius (mm)

R = resistance (ohms)

Define the variables.

As r increases, R decreases. There is either inverse variation, or no variation.

Compare the changes in the variables.

If $R = \frac{k}{r}$, then $k = r \times R$

For $R = \frac{k}{r}$, k must be constant.

1st pair of values gives $k = 1 \times 1.5 = 1.5$

2nd pair of values gives $k = 2 \times 0.375 = 0.75$

Test with pairs of values from the table.

k is not constant, so $R \neq \frac{k}{r}$

If $R = \frac{k}{r^2}$ then $k = r^2 \times R$

Try $R = \frac{k}{r^2}$

1st pair of values gives $k = 1^2 \times 1.5 = 1.5$

2nd pair of values gives $k = 2^2 \times 0.375 = 1.5$

Test with pairs of values from the table.

3rd pair of values gives $k = 5^2 \times 0.06 = 1.5$

4th pair of values gives $k = 10^2 \times 0.015 = 1.5$

Therefore, k is constant.

$R = \frac{k}{r^2}$, which is an inverse variation relationship, because k is constant.

b $R = \frac{1.5}{r^2}$

Use the value of k from part **a**.

Reflect and discuss 7

- What conditions must always be met for direct or inverse variation?

- What do you think it means to be 'proportional'?

Practice 4

1 i For each table of values, determine whether the functions are a direct variation function, an inverse variation function or neither. Justify your answer.

ii If it is a variation function, write down the equation of the function.

a

x	1	2	3	4
y	1	8	27	64

b

x	1	2	3	4
y	24	12	8	6

c

x	−2	0	3	4
y	20	0	45	80

d

x	2	4	6	12
y	30	15	10	5

e

x	−2	0	2	5
y	−0.5	undefined	0.5	0.032

f

x	1	2	4	9
y	40	22	13	8

2 When $x = 2$, $y = 12$. Find the value of y when $x = 4$ if:

a y varies directly as x^2 **b** y varies directly as x^3

c y varies inversely as x **d** y varies inversely as x^2.

3 $y = 24$ when $x = 5$. Find the value of x when $y = 2$ if:

a y varies directly as x **b** y varies directly as x^3

c y varies inversely as x^2 **d** y varies inversely as x^3.

4 The surface area of a sphere varies directly as the square of its radius. The surface area of a sphere with radius 5 cm is 100π cm^2.

a Find the surface area of a sphere with radius 2 cm.

b From the information above, or otherwise, write down the formula for the surface area of a sphere.

c State what happens to the surface area of a sphere when the radius is enlarged by a factor of 5.

d Determine the effect on the radius of halving the surface area of a sphere.

Problem solving

5 The weight of an object in Newtons (N) varies inversely with the square of its distance in km from the center of the Earth. The radius of the Earth is approximately 3670 km. A certain astronaut weighs 850 N at the surface of the Earth. Find the weight of the same astronaut when she's on the International Space Station, which orbits at an average of 400 km from the surface of the Earth.

6 The rings of Saturn have been found to be made up of particles of a variety of sizes. Amazingly, the abundance is inversely proportional to the cube of the size of the particle. If a 2-meter size particle has an abundance of 10%, determine the abundance of a 3-meter size particle, to the nearest tenth of a percent.

7 Under the right conditions, pyrite (often called fool's gold) will form in the shape of a perfect cube. The cost of an ounce of this pyrite varies directly with its volume. If a cube with side length of 5 cm costs $24 per ounce, determine the length of the side of a piece of pyrite that costs $40 per ounce.

8 The use of low-flow shower heads has become an easy way to reduce our water consumption. Regular shower heads use 30 liters of water per minute while low-flow shower heads may use only 8 liters per minute. This volume of water is directly proportional to the square of the radius of the pipe in the shower head. If a regular shower head has a pipe with a radius of 5 cm what should be the radius of a pipe in a low-flow shower head?

Exploration 7

If your calculator/software has a slider bar or similar function you can change the parameters of the variation function and see how the shape of the graph changes.

Direct variation functions

Graph the direct variation function $y = kx^n$. Insert a slider so that you can change the value of k between -10 and 10, and the value of n between 1 and 3. If your calculator has a split-screen, you will be able to see the graph and table of values simultaneously.

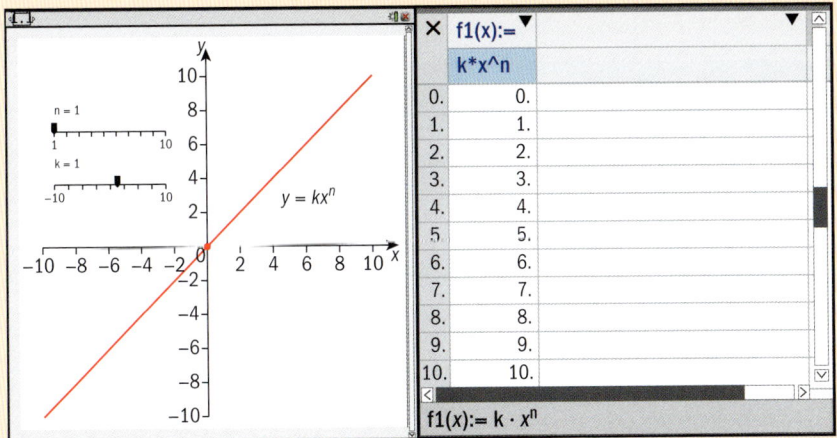

1 Start with the values $k = 1$ and $n = 1$. Change the value of k using the slider, and describe how the graph changes. State what does *not* change in the graph as you change the value of k.

2 State what k represents on the graph.

3 Repeat steps **1** and **2** for $n = 2$ and $n = 3$.

▶ Continued on next page

Inverse variation functions

Graph the inverse variation function $y = \dfrac{k}{x^n}$.

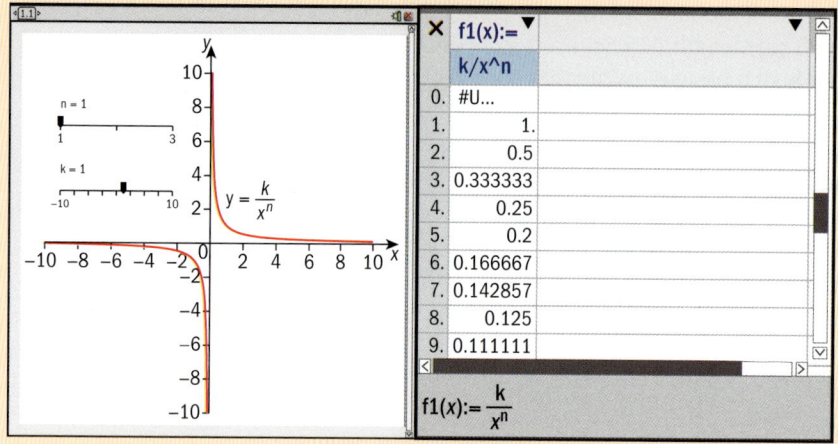

This reciprocal graph includes negative values of x.

4 Start with the values $k = 1$ and $n = 1$. Change the value of k using the slider, and describe how the graph changes.

5 State what happens as x gets closer to $+10$ and -10.

State what happens as x gets closer to 0 (from the positive side and from the negative side).

6 Explain how the proportionality constant affects the graph.

7 Repeat steps **4** to **6** for $n = 2$ and $n = 3$.

Reflect and discuss 8

- Consider the direct variation function $y = kx^n$.
  - Describe how n affects the shape of the graph.
  - Describe how k affects the shape of the graph.
  - Justify what happens when $x = 0$.
  - Justify what happens as x becomes extremely large in both the positive and the negative directions.

- Repeat these four steps for the inverse variation function $y = \dfrac{k}{x^n}$.

- Describe how you can recognize a direct variation function from a graph.

- Describe how you can recognize an inverse variation function from a graph.

Practice 5

1 Write down the variation function and sketch its graph.

    a y varies directly as x, and when $y = 30$, $x = 5$.

    b y varies inversely as x, and when $y = 2$, $x = 6$.

    c y varies directly as the square of x, and when $x = 4$, $y = 120$.

    d y varies inversely as the square of x, and when $x = 4$, $y = 5$.

    e y varies directly as the cube of x, and when $x = 2$, $y = 62.5$.

    f y varies inversely as the cube of x, and when $x = \frac{1}{2}$, $y = 4$.

Problem solving

2 Determine whether the following graphs show a direct variation function, an inverse variation function, or neither. Justify your answer.

a

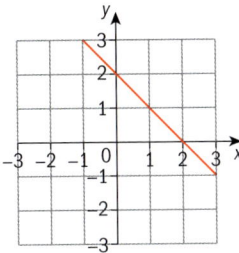

b

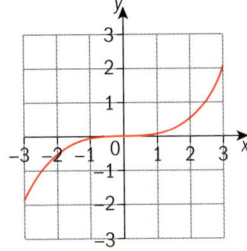

c

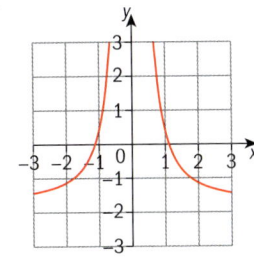

d

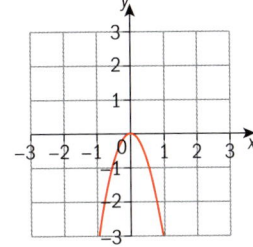

e

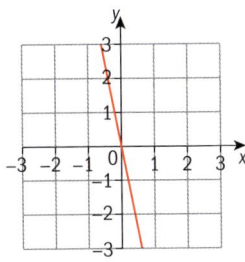

f

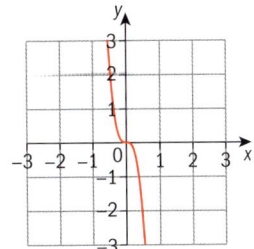

3 Sketch the graph of the variation function $y = \dfrac{2}{x^2}$.

    a Determine whether or not y can have a negative value. Justify your answer.

    b Explain what happens to y as x gets extremely large.

    c Explain what happens to y as x gets closer and closer to 0.

    d Hence, explain why this is an inverse variation function.

D Modelling proportional relationships

- Can situations seem proportional when they are not?
- Is simpler always better?

Until now you have been dealing with variation functions that are either direct variation or inverse variation. Are there situations in which, even though a change in one variable causes a similar change in another, there is no direct or inverse variation?

Exploration 8

When you go to the coffee shop, you can either pay €4.50 for your favorite drink, or you can buy a cup for €5 and refill it every time, though each refill will cost you €3.50.

1 Write down an equation for each option and sketch a graph that represents the total cost as it relates to the number of drinks bought.

2 Determine which option represents a direct variation, and which one is not a direct variation. Justify your answers.

3 Suggest a rule for determining whether or not a function is a variation function:

  a from its equation

  b from its graph.

4 Describe a situation where one quantity increases as the other decreases, but that is not an inverse variation function. Explain how you know it is not a variation function.

In most of the examples and practice problems you have seen so far, the proportionality constant k has been positive. However, according to the definitions of direct and inverse proportion, k can be any number except 0, so technically, it could be negative.

Exploration 9

1 Sketch the graphs of these functions:

  a $y = 3x$ **b** $y = -3x$ **c** $y = \dfrac{3}{x}$ **d** $y = -\dfrac{3}{x}$

2 Explain why they are all variation functions.

3 For each variation function, determine whether the following statements are true or false:

  a As x increases, y increases

  b As x decreases, y decreases

  c As x increases, y decreases

  d As x decreases, y increases

4 Explain what happens as x gets closer and closer to 0.

5 Explain what happens as x gets farther and farther away from 0, in the positive and negative directions.

Reflect and discuss 9

- Summarize your findings. What is the difference between negative proportionality and inverse proportionality?

- Describe a real-life situation in which there is a negative variation between two variables.

Summary

A **formula** is an equation that describes an algebraic relationship between two or more sets of values. Each variable in a formula can take different values, depending on the values of the other variables.

Proportional relationships	General shape of the graph
<ul><li>Two variables are said to be in **direct proportion** if, and only if, their ratio is a constant for all values of each variable.</li><li>$y \propto x$ means 'y varies directly as x' or 'y is directly proportional to x'.</li><li>$y \propto x$ means that $y = kx$ for a constant k, where $k \neq 0$. k is called the **proportionality constant**, or **constant of variation**.</li><li>The function $y = kx$ is called a **linear variation function**.</li></ul>	$k > 0$ $k < 0$ $y = \dfrac{k}{x}$ direct linear proportion
<ul><li>Two variables x and y are **inversely proportional** if multiplying one of them by a non-zero number results in the other variable being divided by the same non-zero number.</li><li>If x and y are in an inverse linear proportion, you can say 'y varies inversely as x' or 'y is inversely proportional to x', and you can write $y \propto \dfrac{1}{x}$ and $y = \dfrac{k}{x}$.</li><li>If y is inversely proportional to x, then y is directly proportional to $\dfrac{1}{x}$.</li><li>An equation $y = k \times \dfrac{1}{x}$ or $y = \dfrac{k}{x}$ represents a relationship of inverse proportion or a **reciprocal relationship**.</li></ul>	$k > 0$ $k < 0$ $y = \dfrac{k}{x}$ inverse linear proportion
<ul><li>Two variables x and y are in **direct non-linear proportion** if y is proportional to a power of x, or $y \propto x^n$, $n > 0$.</li><li>The variation function is $y = kx^n$, $k \neq 0$ and $n > 0$.</li><li>y varies directly as x^n or y is in direct proportion to x^n.</li><li>$y = kx^n$ is a relationship of direct variation. When x is multiplied by a constant c, then y is multiplied by c^n.</li></ul>	$k > 0$ $k < 0$ $y = kx^n$ direct non-linear proportion, when n is even $k > 0$ $k < 0$ $y = kx^n$ direct non-linear proportion, when n is odd

- Two variables x and y are in an **inverse non-linear proportion** if y is proportional to a power of $\frac{1}{x}$, or $y \propto \frac{1}{x^n}, n > 0$. You can also write this as $y \propto x^{-n}, n > 0$.

- The variation function is $y = \frac{k}{x^n}, k \neq 0$ and $n > 0$.

  y varies inversely as x^n or y is inversely proportional to x^n

- $y = \frac{k}{x^n}$ is a relationship of inverse variation. When x is multiplied by a constant c, then y is divided by c^n.

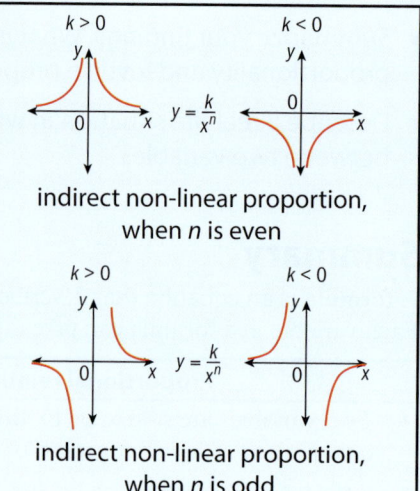

indirect non-linear proportion, when n is even

indirect non-linear proportion, when n is odd

Mixed practice

Rearrange the formulae to make the variable in brackets the subject.

1 $V = \frac{4}{3}\pi r^3$ $\quad[r]$

2 $P = \frac{500T}{v}$ $\quad[T]$

3 $F = G\frac{m_1 m_2}{r^2}$ $\quad[r]$

4 $W = \frac{1}{2}CU^2$ $\quad[C]$

5 $E = mc^2$ $\quad[c]$

6 $v = v_0\sqrt{\frac{c-v}{c+v}}$ $\quad[c]$

7 **Sketch** the graph of each variation function and **determine** whether it is a direct or inverse relationship.

a $y = 5x$

b $y = \frac{x}{3}$

c $y = 1.4x^2$

d $y = \frac{2}{x^2}$

e $y = \frac{7}{x}$

f $y = \frac{1}{3x}$

g $y = \frac{3x^2}{5}$

h $y = \frac{3}{5x^2}$

8 The variable x is directly proportional to the variable t. When $t = 4.6$, $x = 3.45$

a **Find** the value of the constant of proportionality.

b **Write down** the function relating t and x.

c **Find** x when $t = 8.2$

9 P is inversely proportional to y. When $P = 15$, $y = 0.2$. **Find** P when $y = 1.5$

10 M varies directly as the square of c. When $M = 12.6$, $c = 3$. **Find** c when $M = 17.15$

11 p is inversely proportional to the square of q. **Find** the missing values in this table:

p	100		1
q		0.4	2

12 **Write down** the function connecting x and y for each table of values:

a

x	−1	3	5	8
y	0.25	2.25	6.25	16

b

x	−2	−1	0.5	4
y	2.5	5	−10	−1.25

13 A supermarket sells 300 ml bottles of ketchup for £1.30 a bottle.

a **Explain** why total cost of ketchup is in direct proportion to the number of bottles of ketchup bought.

b In a special offer, if you buy two bottles you get one free.

Is the total cost still in direct proportion to the number of bottles bought? **Justify** your answer.

Problem solving

14 The force needed to break a board varies inversely with the length of the board. It takes a force of 120 Newtons to break a board 60 cm long. **Find** the force needed to break a board 20 cm long.

15 The number of tennis balls you can pack in a box varies inversely with the volume of the balls. **Write down** the variation function that expresses the relationship between the number of balls that can fit in a box and the radius of the balls.

16 A giraffe's mass varies directly with the cube of the animal's height. An adult giraffe is 5 m tall and weighs 1.1 metric tonnes. **Find** the mass of a 2 m tall baby giraffe.

17 During freefall, the distance an object falls is directly proportional to the square of the time spent falling. An object falls 40.8 m in 20 s. **Find** how far it falls in 1 minute.

18 The shutter speed of a camera varies inversely with the square of the aperture setting. When the aperture setting is 8, the shutter speed is 125. **Find** the shutter speed when the aperture setting is 4.

19 The volume of a cylinder is given by the formula $V = \pi r^2 h$, where r is the radius of the base and h is the height of the cylinder.

a If the cylinder has a fixed height, **write down** the variation function between V and r. Hence, **write down** the proportionality constant in this case.

b If the cylinder has a fixed radius, **write down** the variation function between V and h. Hence, **write down** the proportionality constant in this case.

Review in context
Scientific and technical innovation

Problem solving

1 An important relationship in the study of motion is $V = \dfrac{d}{t}$, where V is the velocity of an object, d is distance and t is the time taken. An Airbus A333 has a cruising speed of 870 km/h. In this exercise, consider this speed to be the average speed for the entire flight.

a On a flight from Brussels to Montreal, it is flying with a headwind of 40 km/h. **Find** the actual speed of the A333.

b On the return flight, it is flying with a tailwind of 30 km/h. **Find** the actual speed of the A333.

c **Write down** an expression for the actual speed of the A333 with a tailwind of x km/h.

d **Write down** an expression for the actual speed of the A333 with a headwind of y km/h.

The distance between Brussels and Montreal is 5560 km.

e Make t the subject of the formula.

f **Find** the time it takes to travel without any wind.

g **Find** the time it took on the flight described in part **a**.

h **Find** the time it took on the return flight described in part **b**.

i **Find** the wind speed and direction (headwind or tailwind) if the flight took 6 hours and 57 minutes.

j **Find** the wind speed and direction (headwind or tailwind) if the flight took 6 hours 2 minutes and 30 seconds.

2 In order to reduce overcrowding in their cities, Boomcity and Alphatown have begun pricing office real estate in a way that they hope will encourage developers to construct buildings outside the city center.

In Boomcity, the price of a building plot varies inversely with the distance of the plot from the city's center.

In Alphatown, the price of a plot varies inversely with the square of the distance from the center.

In both Alphatown and Boomcity, a plot 5 km from the center costs $250 000.

Find the cost of a plot 10 km from the center of each city.

3 The amount of water that flows through a water pipe is directly proportional to the square of the diameter of the pipe. A pipe of diameter 10 cm can serve 50 houses.

 a Make a table of the number of houses served by water pipes of diameter 10 cm, 20 cm, 30 cm, 40 cm and 50 cm.

 b **Use** your table to **estimate** the number of houses that can be served by a water pipe with diameter 25 cm.

 c **Draw** a graph of the variation function that represents the relationship between the diameter of the water pipe and the number of houses served.

 d Now **use** your graph to **estimate** the number of houses that can be served by a water pipe with diameter 25 cm.

 e **Use** the equation of the variation function to **find** the actual number of houses that can be served by a water pipe with diameter 25 cm.

 f **Discuss** how far off your estimations were from the actual number of houses.

 g Water conservation is a priority in many parts of the world, yet humans want and need water for so many of our activities. **Discuss** what the trade-offs might be between using larger diameter of pipes and our need to conserve water.

The average water consumption per head varies widely between the northern and southern hemispheres. But there is also great variation between European countries. Luxembourg's average of 80 cubic meters per person per year is 5 times less than Germany's average of 400 cubic meters per person.

Problem solving

4 Generating electricity, whether through hydroelectricity, fossil fuels, wind or nuclear energy, can have serious negative effects on the environment. We should all do our part to decrease the amount of energy we consume; something that will also save money.

In the construction of an office building, a heating engineer tries to place a heater in the spot where it will be most efficient. The heat received at X is inversely proportional to the square of the distance from the heat source. The engineer plans to put the heater at position A, however, the company's manager prefers position B.

Determine how much moving the heater to B will reduce the heat received at X. Give your answer as a percentage.

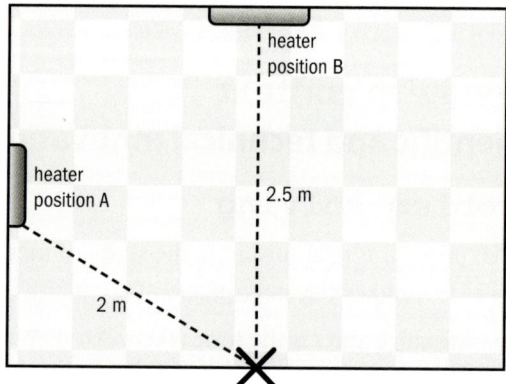

5 The 'urban heat island effect' occurs when buildings and parking lots are constructed, covering grass and dirt with concrete. Temperatures in these areas tend to be higher than normal, leading to health issues. To combat this, some cities now have ordinances that require the planting of trees to provide shade and decrease these temperature changes. Suppose the temperature change varies directly with the cube of the diameter of the trees planted. Trees with a diameter of 1.5 meters produce an average temperature change of −0.3°C.

 a **Find** the temperature change that would be expected for a tree with a diameter of 2 meters.

 b If a temperature change of −1°C was desired, **determine** what size trees should be used.

6 Companies use a variety of ways to try to entice consumers to buy their products. One of those is by setting a price that will encourage people to purchase their goods. A clothing company makes jeans in a variety of price ranges. The Bootcut jeans sell for $25 while the Classic jeans sell for $160. The demand for this company's jeans is inversely proportional to the square of the price.

a If 50 000 pairs of the Bootcut jeans were bought, **find** how many of the Classic jeans were bought.

b If the company wanted to double the number of pairs of Classic jeans bought, **determine** at what price they should be sold. Your answer should be to the nearest dollar.

7 Since the volume of a sphere is given by $V = \dfrac{4}{3}\pi r^3$, you would think that the price of ice cream should vary directly with the cube of the radius of the scoop. However, at Dave's Ice Cream Shop the price of one small scoop of ice cream (radius = 3 cm) is $2.50 and the price of a large scoop of ice cream (radius = 5 cm) is $5.00.

a **Show that** this does not represent a direct cube variation.

b If this were a direct cube variation, **determine** the price of one large scoop.

c **Suggest** reasons why the price does not seem to vary based on the volume of the ice cream.

Reflect and discuss 10

How have you explored the statement of inquiry? Give specific examples.

Statement of inquiry:

Representing patterns and change in a variety of forms has helped humans apply their understanding of scientific principles.

9 So, what do you think?

Statement of inquiry:

Generalizing and representing relationships can help to clarify trends amongst individuals.

Key concept:

Relationships are the connections and associations between properties, objects, people and ideas.

F Can relationships always be generalized?

A generalization is a general statement made on the basis of specific examples.

In mathematics we talk about two different types of generalization. The first involves looking at specific information and trying to find out about something less specific that might underlie it. The other is to tackle specific problems by looking at more general ones.

'All generalizations are dangerous, even this one.'

Alexandre Dumas

C How can relationships be best represented?

Representation is the manner in which something is presented.

Biological relationships

To reproduce and survive, living organisms must coexist and interact with each other. Ecological relationships between living organisms are either oppositional or symbiotic.

In oppositional relationships, one organism eats others (predation) or organisms compete for the same resources (competition).

In symbiotic relationships, one organism lives in or on another. Sometimes this relationship is beneficial to both (mutualism), such as the clownfish and anemone (top pair of photographs on opposite page). The anemone protects the clownfish (which is immune to its toxin) and the clownfish's waste provides food for the anemone.

▶

The suckerfish (bottom left) attaches itself to a host like this turtle and eats its parasites.

A symbiotic relationship may benefit one organism but have no effect on the other (commensalism). Corals and anemones provide camouflage for commensal shrimps and pygmy seahorses but do not benefit from them (bottom right).

D **To what extent do generalized representations provide a true picture of trends within individuals?**

Global context: Identities and relationships

Exploration: Exploring trends and characteristics amongst individuals

📖 **Launch additional digital resources for this unit.**

9.1 Sampling techniques

Global context: Identities and relationships

Related concept: Generalization

Objectives

- Selecting samples and making inferences about populations
- Understanding the purpose of taking a sample
- Using different sampling techniques
- Understanding when it is appropriate to generalize from a sample to a population
- Understanding the effect of sample size on the reliability of your generalizations
- Calculating response rates

Inquiry questions

F
- What are the different sampling methods?

C
- How are generalizations made from experimental data?
- How do you determine the validity of the generalizations?

D
- How do we know when to say 'when'?

ATL Critical-thinking

Recognize unstated assumptions and bias

Statement of inquiry:

Generalizing and representing relationships can help to clarify trends among individuals.

📑 **Launch additional digital resources for this chapter.**

You should already know how to:

• represent data using both stem-and-leaf diagrams and box-and-whisker diagrams	**1** Below are the number of customers per day at a noodle bar over the course of 20 days. Present this data in a stem-and-leaf diagram. 65 54 77 71 73 89 55 19 17 53 70 75 88 29 34 33 67 71 55 50 Represent the same data on a box-and-whisker diagram.
• represent data using cumulative frequency graphs	**2** 35 people made note of how many radio adverts they had heard on their commute to work, shown here. Create a cumulative frequency graph from this data. <table><tr><th>Adverts</th><th>Frequency</th></tr><tr><td>$0 < t \le 4$</td><td>7</td></tr><tr><td>$5 < t \le 9$</td><td>14</td></tr><tr><td>$10 < t \le 14$</td><td>10</td></tr><tr><td>$15 < t \le 19$</td><td>3</td></tr><tr><td>$20 < t \le 24$</td><td>1</td></tr></table>
• calculate the mean and the median for a set of data	**3** The heights of students (in meters) in a school football team were measured as follows: 1.55, 1.64, 1.49, 1.72, 1.81, 1.58, 1.73, 1.68, 1.75, 1.70, 1.69 Calculate the mean and median heights. Calculate the range.
• calculate the range and interquartile range for a set of data	Calculate the lower and upper quartiles and hence the interquartile range.

The need for sampling

- What are the different sampling methods?

Some things we learn from first-hand experience, while others are based on deductions we draw from the evidence we have. Using observation and background knowledge to draw a conclusion is known as *inference*. For example, if you walk into your classroom and your teacher has laid out a sheet of paper on each desk, you might infer that you were having an assessment.

> To *infer* means to draw conclusions based on evidence or reasoning.

Inference in statistics

The mathematics eAssessment results for two schools where the same teacher taught in consecutive years are shown in the stem-and-leaf diagram here.

Crescent Moon High School		Oyster Bay Academy
4	4	
7 5 4 3	5	
9 8 6 4 3 1	6	
8 7 5 3 3 2 0 0	7	2 7
8 4 2 1	8	0 3 5 5 8 9
5 3	9	1 2 4 4 5 8
8 1	10	4 4 6 7
1	11	3

Key: 1|8|5 means 81 for Crescent Moon and 85 for Oyster Bay

Reflect and discuss 1

Look at the stem-and-leaf diagram and compare the performance of the two schools.

- What generalizations can you draw based on this data?

- How do your generalizations differ from those of others?

- Did you come up with any answers that they did not?

- Did you come up with any conflicting generalizations?

Inference is the process of drawing conclusions about general characteristics from specific pieces of information. In the eAssessment scenario, it's difficult to make inferences from the data because you are given so little information about it. Various factors, such as time spent on revision, personal circumstances, and even class size might explain the difference in performance between one school and the other.

If you don't know anything about the quality or the nature of the data, it's difficult to make generalizations about any underlying trends. In this case, you may have reached conclusions about the school, or the students, which were unfair or unrepresentative.

Reflect and discuss 2

Calculate the median score for the classes from the two schools. Which of the following statements do you think are valid?

- The students at Oyster Bay Academy are more intelligent than the students at Crescent Moon High.

- The teacher did a better job of teaching the class at Oyster Bay than at Crescent Moon.

- The class at Crescent Moon scored lower on average than the Oyster Bay class.

Again, it's difficult to compare the schools, or to compare the teacher's performance, because we don't know enough about the factors surrounding the data. The only statement that we can be really confident of is saying that on average, the Crescent Moon class scored lower than the Oyster Bay class, but even this is problematic, since they sat the eAssessment in different years and you don't know if the standard of the tests was the same.

Even though you might not agree with the first statement: 'The students at Oyster Bay Academy are more intelligent than the students at Crescent Moon High', it is an example of *inference*. Specifically, *statistical inference* is the action of making generalizations or drawing conclusions about a population based on a sample from that population.

> A **population** is a set of objects under consideration in a statistical context. It could be a group of people, or a collection of objects.
>
> A **sample** is a subset of a population.
>
> **Inference** is the act of making generalizations or drawing conclusions about a population based on a sample.

Any set of objects could form a population, for example the bags of sugar filled by a machine could be a population, as could all the cars sold in Japan in 2014.

Reflect and discuss 3

Suppose you believe that the students in one school are better at mathematics than the students at another school. What sort of evidence would you need to collect to validate such a claim?

> A **census** is a collection of data from every member of a population.
>
> A sample is **representative** if its properties reflect those of the population that it comes from.

Often a sample is taken because it is not practical to conduct a census. It is important to ensure that a sample is representative of the population. In the example concerning the two schools, the sample would be representative only if it covered the whole ability range within the school.

Response rate

The response rate is defined as the number of people who complete the survey as a percentage of the number people who were sent the survey.

It can be calculated as:

$$\frac{\text{number of people who completed the survey}}{\text{number of people who were sent the survey}} \times 100\%$$

Objective: D. Applying mathematics in real-life contexts
i. identify relevant elements of authentic real-life situations

You will need to draw on your general knowledge to help answer the questions in Exploration 1. Trying to find underlying assumptions even when you don't know everything about the context is a key mathematical skill.

Exploration 1

The managers of a large factory, which has around 10000 workers, would like to know more about the commuting times of their staff.

1 Explain why it might not be sensible to ask every single employee.

2 The managers decide to conduct a survey of a sample of the employees. They brainstorm a number of ideas for ways of gathering the information.

   a They could ask each employee individually as they arrived at work.

   b They could put up a notice asking employees to respond by email.

   c They could ask one person in each department to estimate an average commuting time for that department.

   d They could ask every 200th person on the company's staff list, having sorted it alphabetically.

   e They could ask every 200th person on the company's staff list, having sorted it by salary.

   f They could put every employee's name into a bag and draw out 50 names at random.

Comment on each of these ideas. Explain how useful you think the surveys would be for finding out representative information about the commute times of the factory's employees.

There are good reasons why a company might conduct a survey of a sample, rather than the whole workforce, two of which are cost and practicality. There are, as you have seen in Exploration 1, problems that can arise when taking a sample, however. Most of these are to do with the idea of bias. A sample is biased if it is not a fair representation of the population.

You will notice that some of the samples above required having a list of all the employees, whereas others did not. This list is known as a *sampling frame*. A sampling frame is any list that identifies every member of the population. In a case like this one, where we are surveying employees, it is quite likely that we would be able to obtain such a list. If, however, the company wished to run a customer satisfaction survey, they would probably not be able to obtain a list of everybody who had bought their products.

> A **sampling frame** is a list of every member of the population.

Different sampling methods are available to us depending on whether it is possible, or practical, to obtain a sampling frame. The following three sampling methods all require a sampling frame.

- A **simple random sample** is a sample such that every member of the population is equally likely to be included in the sample, independent of any other member of the population.
- A **systematic sample** takes members of the population at regular intervals from an ordered sampling frame – for example, taking every 10th person from a list sorted alphabetically.
- A **stratified sample** identifies different sections of the population and ensures that those groups are represented in appropriate proportions in the sample.

Simple random samples

When creating a simple random sample it is important that the selections you make are genuinely random. This could be done by pulling names from a hat or by using the random number generator on a calculator.

Systematic sampling

A systematic sample is formed by taking an ordered sampling frame and then – having first picked a random starting point – taking items from the sampling frame at regular intervals.

Stratified sampling

To form a stratified sample, you first have to divide the population into groups that you want to represent. For example, if you were surveying a group of people, you might want to make sure that men and women were fairly represented, or that different age ranges were fairly represented.

In this case, 'fairly represented' means that the proportion of men in the sample should match the proportion of men in the population, and likewise for women; or that the proportions of people in different age ranges in the sample reflected the proportions in the population.

Surveying 10 students from a year group of 80 after an IB exam to see how difficult they thought it was. The students were taught in five different classes of 16 students.	You are sampling $\frac{10}{80} = \frac{1}{8}$ of the students. From each class of 16, you need $\frac{1}{8}$ of $16 = 2$ students. From each class, pick a simple random sample of 2 students.
Checking 20 of the cars in a full lot of 500 cars to see whether their tires meet regulation requirements. 100 cars were compacts, 250 cars were estates and 150 cars were saloons.	You need $\frac{20}{500} = \frac{1}{25}$ of the cars. So you need $\frac{1}{25}$ of $100 = 4$ compacts; $\frac{1}{25}$ of $250 = 10$ estates; $\frac{1}{25}$ of $150 = 6$ saloons. Pick a simple random sample of 4 of the compacts, 10 of the estates and 6 of the saloons.

Reflect and discuss 4

- What are the advantages and disadvantages of the three types of sampling described above?

- Suggest some situations in which you would use each of the sampling techniques.

- Describe the difficulties you might encounter when trying to apply them.

Example 1

Javier is going to sample 50 students at his school.

The school secretary provides a list of the 500 total students in the school. There are five year groups, each with 100 students, and each year group has 60 boys and 40 girls.

Explain how Javier could create:

a a simple random sample

b a systematic sample

c a stratified sample.

a   Method 1

Cut up a printed list to separate all the names and place them in a bag. Shuffle its contents and then randomly draw out 50 names.

Method 2

Number each student from 1 to 500 in alphabetical order. Use a random number generator to pick 50 numbers between 1 and 500 (ignoring any duplicates).

b   List the students in alphabetical order. Use a random number generator to pick a random starting point. From that point, take every 10th name until you get back to the starting point.

> 50 students out of a total of 500 means taking every 10th name.

c   Each year group is $\frac{100}{500} = \frac{1}{5}$ of the school, so each group should be a sample of 10 students. Within each group 60% are boys and 40% girls, so from each year group take a simple random sample of 6 boys and 4 girls.

Practice 1

1 You are concerned that the eggs in your kitchen are rotting.
You can tell if an egg is rotten by breaking it open and smelling the contents. If the egg is rotten, there will be a pungent smell.

  a Explain why you might wish to sample the eggs, rather than conduct a census.

  b Explain how you could conduct a simple random sample of the eggs.

2 Alex lives in a high-rise apartment building containing 80 apartments, numbered 1–80. He wants to conduct a survey to find out how many people on average live in each apartment.

  a Explain how he could create a simple random sample of 20 apartments.

  b Explain why a systematic sample of 20 apartments starting with apartment 3 and then selecting every fourth apartment might lead to bias.

  c Describe any factors that would be relevant if Alex wished to take a stratified sample.

> There is information relevant to the situation that is not contained within the question. Could the design of the building be relevant here?

ATL

3 A teenager wants to know how many of his friends watch cartoons.
He sends a message to every 20th person in the contact list on his phone.
  a Determine what sort of sample this is.
  b Comment on the suitability of this sampling method.
  c He sends the message to 36 of his friends and 30 validate reply. Find the response rate

4 A company employs 900 people, employed on different pay grades.
The number of men and women at each pay grade is as follows:

Pay grade	Men	Women
A	1	2
B	12	15
C	40	30
D	80	320
E	240	160

A full list of the employees has been made available for a survey on childcare provision at work.

  a Describe how the company could construct a simple random sample of 40 employees.

  b Describe how the company could construct a systematic sample of 45 employees.

  c Describe how the company could construct a stratified sample of 90 employees. Explain clearly why it would be necessary to combine pay grades A and B.

5 Explain in which of the following scenarios it would be possible to conduct a random sample by selecting people at random from a sampling frame.

  a A survey of the students in a school to find out the proportion of students who are vegetarian.

  b A survey of the supporters of a particular ice hockey team to find out whether or not they thought the manager was doing a good job.

  c A survey of the voters in a particular town to see if they would vote in favour of re-electing the town mayor.

  d A survey of the civil servants in an American city to see if they attended fire safety training sessions regularly.

- -

In situations where a sampling frame cannot be obtained, or it is not possible to guarantee responses, *quota sampling* is often used. To create a quota sample, first decide how big your sample is to be. If desired, the sample can still be split into different subgroups as in stratified sampling. Then collect data by any means possible until you have as many as needed to fill your quota.

Suppose you wish to know what local shoppers think of public transport in your town. You could decide to survey 30 people. You want your sample to be representative of the people who live in your town, so you are going to ask questions only of people who live locally, and want to represent men's and women's views equally.

An appropriate way to conduct the survey might be to stand in the downtown area and ask the first people that were willing to talk to you. When you have received responses from 15 local men and 15 local women, you can stop.

Reflect and discuss 5

- Why might the choice of where you stand to conduct the survey be important (and thus have unwanted influence on the survey)?

- What problems might you encounter when taking a quota sample?

A **quota sample** is used when the sampling frame is unknown, or does not exist. It involves collecting data until enough pieces of data are found.

Example 2

An interviewer is asked to find a sample of 50 students, to produce a survey on methods of transport used by young people. They decided to go to the bus stop near a school and ask the first 50 students they saw.

a Decide what method of sampling is used.

b Discuss the benefits and limitations of this method of sampling.

a This method of sampling is quota sampling – it is used to overcome difficulties of non-response and inability to find sufficient people

b The limitations lie in the non-random selection of individuals. In this case the students are probably:

- the same age range

- from the same school

- using the bus as their preferred method of transportation.

The benefits are:

- they will have time to answer the questions

- there will be a large number of students available to answer the questions.

Practice 2

1 Identify a suitable sampling method for each of the following scenarios. Give as much detail as possible.

a A botanist wants to find the mean length of the leaves on a type of tree.

b You want to find out how students at your school travel to school each day.

c You want to find the average mark obtained by students in your year group in a recent test, but don't want to collect everybody's scores.

d A school principal wishes to sample 20 employees in a school which employs 150 teachers, 20 administrative staff and 30 facilities staff.

e An event organizer wishes to find the average time taken by runners to complete a 10 km charity race.

2 A company wants to assess customer satisfaction with their latest style of coffee machine. Some different plans are proposed.

One plan is to put a feedback form in the box for every product that is sold and ask customers to return the form by post.

Another plan is to call a random sample of customers based on the telephone numbers filled in on the guarantee registration forms.

Describe the advantages and disadvantages of the plans. Determine whether they are random samples.

3 a A student wishes to estimate the average height of students in his year group of 150 students. He uses the 25 members of his school athletics team as a sample and records their heights correct to the nearest cm. Comment on the suitability of his sample.

b Another student wishes to estimate the average height of the 150 students in her year group. She uses her MYP History class of 25 students as a sample and records their heights correct to the nearest cm. Comment on the suitability of her sample.

c Explain how a simple random sample of 25 students could be taken from this year group of 150 students.

d Explain how a stratified sample of 25 students could be taken from this year group.

- -

C Generalization and inference

- How are generalizations made from experimental data?

If a sample is representative of the population from which it is drawn, its properties should reflect the properties of the population. This means that you can use the properties of the sample to make deductions about the whole population. In doing so, you are generalizing – taking specific knowledge from the sample data you have obtained and using it to make broader conclusions about the whole population.

Exploration 2

Antonia thinks that boys who make the school rowing team are taller on average than the rest of their year group.

She measures the height of each of the 8 boys on the rowing team, and takes a random sample of 16 other boys from the year group.

The rowers have the following heights, each measured to the nearest whole centimeter: 173, 192, 181, 192, 174, 184, 182, 179.

The other students have the following heights: 170, 154, 192, 165, 168, 190, 188, 167, 187, 181, 194, 180, 167, 157, 193, 165.

1 Calculate the mean height of the rowers.

2 Calculate the mean height of the non-rowers.

3 Comment on her claim that boys who make the school rowing team are taller on average than the rest of their year group.

Reflect and discuss 6

- Where have you generalized in Exploration 2?

- Is the generalization reasonable?

- In this problem you have used the mean of a sample as a way of estimating the mean of the population. Explain why it might not be sensible to use the range of the sample to estimate the range of the population.

In this context, you should have made two generalizations: first, that the information gained from the sample told you something about the population from which it came; second, that by comparing the means of two groups you could draw conclusions about which group contained taller students. Both of these generalizations are types of inference.

Practice 3

1 Your tutor says that your test scores in Physics are better than your test scores in Chemistry. Your results (out of 100) for the last six tests in each subject are presented in this table:

Chemistry	56	64	66	58	72	81
Physics	64	62	72	73	60	70

a Calculate your mean test score in Chemistry and in Physics.

b Comment on your tutor's claim.

c Explain how you have used generalization in this problem.

2 You suspect that boys are spending more money than girls in your school canteen. You stand by the cashier one lunch time and record the amount spent by the first ten girls and by the first ten boys. The amounts you record are as follows:

Boys		Girls	
$3.12	$1.00	$4.00	$2.51
$4.00	$6.37	$1.37	$0.88
$4.00	$4.00	$4.00	$4.00
$5.16	$3.82	$4.00	$4.80
$2.13	$3.65	$2.32	$3.55

a Describe the type of sampling used.

b Outline one way in which this manner of sampling might have introduced bias.

c Comment on the claim that boys spend more than girls in the canteen.

d Explain where you have generalized in your answer.

Why does $4.00 appear so frequently in the table? Something that stands out like this should cause you to reflect on what other information you can infer from the data you have, and then question whether it is likely to have an impact on the validity of the sample.

Exploration 3

GDP per capita is a measure of the average income per person in a country. You can find this data in annual tables in the World Bank database (data.worldbank.org). Ask your teacher if you need help with this.

GDP stands for Gross Domestic Product.

1 There are a large number of countries in this table so it will be necessary to select a sample. Make a simple random sample of 10 countries with the GDP per capita for the years 2000 and 2010.

2 Calculate the mean GDP per capita for each year and determine whether it rose over the period from 2000 to 2010.

3 Determine if the selection of countries you made is fair for you to generalize about the GDP per capita for the whole world. Explain whether it would be better to use a stratified sample. Plan how to do this and see how your results compare using this method.

Exploration 4

A factory owner wishes to compare the output of two employees. The number of components they each produce per day is recorded for ten days:

Employee A	108	101	100	99	93	108	100	106	90	95
Employee B	116	102	100	98	86	116	100	112	80	90

1 Present each employee's production using two side-by-side box-and-whisker diagrams.

2 Compare the performance of the two employees.

3 If the factory owner was able to keep only one of the two employees, suggest which you would recommend keeping. Justify your decision.

Reflect and discuss 7

- The factory owner asks you to comment on the consistency of his employees. What does 'consistent' mean in this context?

- Why might consistency be considered a positive attribute?

- What statistical measures are you able to calculate that describe how consistent a set of data is?

Measures of spread such as the range and interquartile range are appropriate ways of comparing how densely a set of data is packed together – how consistent it is.

Look back at the eAssessment data for Crescent Moon High School and Oyster Bay Academy (page 462).

You have already looked at how you might compare the location of the data by examining the median. What do the range and interquartile range tell you about the spread of the data?

Crescent Moon High School has range 67 and interquartile range 19.5. Oyster Bay Academy has range 41 and interquartile range 16. Both pairs of statistics (the range and the IQR) suggest that the marks at Oyster Bay Academy are grouped together within a smaller interval. You might say that the performance of the students at Oyster Bay Academy was more consistent, or that the results at Crescent Moon High School showed greater variety.

In general, you will be more interested in comparing the IQR than the range; this is because the range is easily affected by outliers, whereas the IQR is not. In general, however, if your measures of spread have smaller values, then the data is more densely packed together. You should always try to interpret this in the context of the data as has been done here – so rather than saying simply that the IQR is smaller, you should observe that the marks at Oyster Bay Academy were more consistent.

> An outlier is a piece of data that lies far outside the overall distribution pattern of the rest of the data.

Practice 4

1 Joe can travel to work by bus or by train. The total journey times for 40 bus journeys and 40 train journeys are illustrated in the box-and-whisker diagrams below:

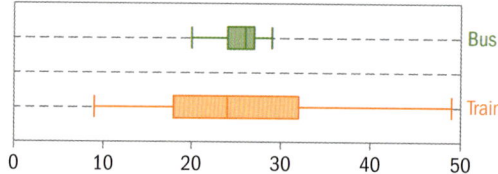

a Determine which mode of transport is faster on average.

b Determine which mode of transport has a more predictable journey time.

c Explain, with reference to these statistics, why Joe might prefer to take the bus than the train.

2 Two computer scientists write programs designed to crack encoded messages. The two programs (A and B) work in different ways, and so their speed can be assessed. Both programs are timed for decoding 11 messages. The times taken (in seconds) are as follows:

A	12.1	11.8	12.4	12.3	12.5	12.1	12.1	12.5	12.1	12.3	12.5
B	10.9	12.4	14.2	13.2	13.7	14.4	13.3	11.8	14.2	13.8	10.8

a Determine which program is faster on average.

b The program is to be used in a coding competition. The program which decodes a new message the fastest will win a prize. Select which program you would choose to use under the following scenarios. Justify your answer.

i You are the last programmer to compete and the current best time is 12.5 seconds.

ii You are the last programmer to compete and the current best time is 11.5 seconds.

iii You are the first programmer to compete.

3 In a factory, two machines are used to fill sugar bags. They are expected to fill them to a mass of 1000 g. To compare the two machines, 12 bags are taken from each and their contents weighed. The results found, in grams, are as follows:

Machine A	995.0	999.6	1005.3	996.7	997.1	999.5	1005.4	1002.0	1005.2	1001.1	994.7	1000.7
Machine B	1009.5	991.3	1022.3	1005.9	1000.0	994.7	1002.4	1016.2	996.2	1010.1	1009.6	1005.3

a Find the mean mass for each machine.

b Find the interquartile range for each sample.

c Compare the output of the two machines.

- -

D The effect of sample size

- How do we know when to say 'when'?

In spite of using sampling techniques with great care, the sample may still, by chance, end up being unrepresentative. Another factor that affects the reliability of a sample is its size.

Exploration 5

1 Use a spreadsheet or your GDC to generate a list of 400 randomly selected integers between 1 and 20.

> In Microsoft Excel or Google Sheets the command to generate a random integer between 1 and 20 is '=RANDBETWEEN(1, 20)'.

2 Select a random sample of 5 numbers from this list.

3 Calculate the mean of your sample.

4 Collect all the sample means that have been calculated in your class and organize them in a stem-and-leaf diagram and then present the data using a box-and-whisker diagram.

5 Repeat the experiment using a sample size of 20 instead of 5, gathering your class data as before.

6 Explain why different members of the class have found different values for the sample mean.

7 Compare the box-and-whisker diagrams for the two sample sizes. Suggest what effect varying the sample size would have on the consistency of the estimates found.

8 Predict what the mean value would be for the whole set of data. Suggest whether the mean of a large sample or the mean of a small sample is a better estimate for the mean of the population.

Reflect and discuss 8

Given that larger sample sizes produce less variation in the estimated mean value, why would we ever use small samples? Consider the following scenarios and explain why taking large samples might be problematic:

- A manufacturer wants to know long their light bulbs last before failing.

- A marine biologist wants to study the mass of a particular species of crab in different areas of the Mediterranean Sea.

Summary

- A **population** is a set of objects under consideration in a statistical context. It could be a group of people, or a collection of objects.

- A **census** is a collection of data from every member of a population.

- A **sampling frame** is a list of every member of the population.

- A **sample** is a subset of a population.
  - A sample is **representative** if its properties reflect those of the population from which it comes.
  - A **simple random sample** is a sample such that every member of the population is equally likely to be included in the sample, independent of any other member of the population.
  - A **systematic sample** takes members of the population at regular intervals from the sampling frame.

- A **stratified sample** identifies different sections of the population and ensures that those groups are represented in appropriate proportions in the sample.

- A **quota sample** is used when the sampling frame is unknown, or does not exist. It involves collecting data until enough pieces of data are found.

- A sample is **biased** if it is not a fair representation of the population.

- **Inference** is the act of making generalizations drawing conclusions about a population based on a sample.
  - You can use the sample mean to estimate the mean of a population.
  - Larger samples provide more reliable estimates.

Mixed practice

1 Tom and Jo are comparing their marks in recent English assessments. The IQR for Tom's marks is 13 and the IQR for Jo's marks is 18. Tom says that because his IQR is smaller he has performed better in the assessments. Jo says that because her IQR is larger she has performed better in the assessments.

Comment on their claims.

2 A school's ballet class has 11 students, with a mean height of 1.51 m and a range of heights of 21 cm. The school's chess club also has 11 students, with a mean height of 1.73 m and a range of heights of 43 cm.

a **Comment** on the differences between the heights of the members of the ballet class and the chess club.

b **Explain** why it would be preferable to know the interquartile range rather than the range of the data sets.

c Claire proposes to use the data to make predictions concerning adult ballet dancers and adult chess players. **Explain** why these clubs may not be a suitable sample.

3 Paul wants to estimate the average length of the fish in a lake.

He knows that roughly 40% of the fish in the lake are salmon and 60% of the fish are trout. To measure the fish, he will catch them with a large net and measure them on the shore before returning them to the water. He plans to take a sample of size 50.

   a **Suggest** a suitable sampling method for Paul to use.

   b **Explain** how he would take such a sample.

4 A polling company would like to conduct a survey to determine the extent to which the residents of a city feel that they are subject to unwanted advertising. The company proposes to conduct a simple random sample using the local phone directory as a sampling frame.

   Evaluate the company's plan.

Review in context

Identities and relationships

1 The average household income in two neighboring towns is assessed by taking a random sample of residents using a recent census as a sampling frame. The data obtained is as follows:

Income range ($)	Town A	Town B
$20\,000 \leq x < 30\,000$	4	1
$30\,000 \leq x < 40\,000$	7	4
$40\,000 \leq x < 50\,000$	11	7
$50\,000 \leq x < 60\,000$	15	6
$60\,000 \leq x < 70\,000$	5	12
$70\,000 \leq x < 80\,000$	4	9
$80\,000 \leq x < 90\,000$	4	7
$90\,000 \leq x < 100\,000$	0	3
$100\,000 \leq x < 110\,000$	0	1

   a **Present** this information using a pair of cumulative frequency graphs on the same axes.

   b **Comment** on the differences between the earnings of households in towns A and B.

   c The statistician conducting the survey claims that the samples are representative of the towns they came from. **Explain** what is meant by the word *representative* in this context.

2 To assess the impact of a new literacy strategy in 50 primary schools, a local education authority assesses the reading age of all 11-year-olds in three of the schools before and after implementation. The following table summarizes the data.

	Before	After
Minimum	8.4	8.2
Q_1	9.2	10.3
Q_2	10.1	10.8
Q_3	10.5	11.1
Maximum	13.2	12.8

   a **Present** the data with over-and under box-and-whisker diagrams.

   b **Describe** the similarities and differences between the two sets of data.

   c **Comment** on the effectiveness of the education authority's intervention.

   d **Evaluate** the authority's sampling method.

3 You will be able to find data about the representation of women in national parliaments online from the Inter-Parliamentary Union (www.ipu.org) or from the World Bank (data.worldbank.org). You are to investigate the proposition that the percentage of women's representation varies in different continents.

a Take a random stratified sample of 5 countries from Africa, Asia and Europe. **Compare** the means of these samples.

b **Comment** on whether the samples are representative of the data in this case.

c **Describe** how you would take a *census* from this data to compare the average representation from the three continents.

4 Elderly people were surveyed about the number of hours, t, of social contact they have with volunteers after the introduction of a new assistance scheme.

Hours	Before	After
$0 \leq t < 2$	4	0
$2 \leq t < 4$	10	8
$4 \leq t < 5$	7	9
$5 \leq t < 6$	5	8
$6 \leq t < 8$	6	5
$8 \leq t < 10$	4	5
$10 \leq t < 12$	3	2
$12 \leq t < 16$	0	2
$16 \leq t < 20$	1	1

a **Interpret** the data and **suggest** whether or not the scheme was successful.

The sample was obtained by collecting contact details for 40 elderly people. The researcher waited in the local bus depot and asked people who he thought were over 75 whether they would be interested in such a scheme and whether he could have their contact details to evaluate the success of the scheme.

b **Determine** the type of sampling used.

c **Evaluate** the researcher's methods.

d **Suggest** a more appropriate way of constructing the sample.

5 You want to find out if students in your school are more likely to donate to local, national or international causes.

a **Outline** difficulties you expect to encounter in obtaining data relevant to your inquiry.

You decide that the easiest way to collect reliable data is to give people forms to keep for a whole year, which they can fill in when they donate money to charity.

You give a form to every student in your school to take home.

You believe that donation trends will vary depending on whether the parents in the family grew up locally, grew up elsewhere in the country, or grew up in a different country.

Separate research suggests that 30% of families had parents that grew up locally, 45% grew up elsewhere in the country and 25% grew up in a different country.

b **Explain** how you would use this information to try to make your sample representative.

After a year, you receive 40 responses from families with parents that grew up locally, 75 from those that grew up elsewhere in the country and 50 from those that grew up in a different country.

c **Calculate** the number of responses you should use from each category of respondent in order to obtain the largest representative sample possible.

Reflect and discuss 9

How have you explored the statement of inquiry? Give specific examples.

Statement of inquiry:

Generalizing and representing relationships can help to clarify trends among individuals.

9.2 Bivariate data

Global context: Identities and relationships

Related concept: Representation

Objectives

- Drawing a scatter diagram for bivariate data
- Drawing a line of best fit (regression line) by eye
- Qualitative handling of data
- Understanding and interpreting the correlation between two sets of data

Inquiry questions

- How can you describe a relationship between two sets of data?
- How do you draw and use a line of best fit?

- How does the way data is represented affect our ability to make predictions?

- Does correlation indicate causation?
- Do I want to be like everybody else?

RELATIONSHIPS

ATL Critical-thinking

Identify trends and forecast possibilities

Statement of inquiry:

Generalizing and representing relationships can help to clarify trends among individuals.

Launch additional digital resources for this chapter.

You should already know how to:

• represent data by plotting points on the Cartesian plane	**1** The table shows the cost of different masses of potatoes. Plot points on a Cartesian plane to represent this data. | **Mass (kg)**	**Price (£)** | |---|---| | 0.5 | 0.40 | | 3.4 | 2.70 | | 5 | 4 | | 2.1 | 1.70 | | 4.5 | 3.60 | | 3.8 | 2.90 | | 2 | 1.60 |
• calculate the mean of a set of data	**2** Calculate the mean of this set of numbers: 2, 4, 6, 2, 7, 1, 9, 4, 6, 2
• identify an outlier in a set of data	**3** Determine whether any of these data values can be classified as outliers. Explain your answer. 1, 6, 6, 6, 8, 8, 9, 9, 11, 15, 20

> A data point is an outlier if it is more than $1.5 \times \text{IQR}$ above the third quartile or below the first quartile.

Introduction to correlation

- How can you describe a relationship between two sets of data?
- How do you draw and use a line of best fit?

Investigating the relationship between variables is a key topic in Statistics. If you can identify a relationship between two variables, you can often use the value of one variable to predict the value of the other.

Exploration 1

The table shows 12 students' marks for Mathematics and Physics tests. The maximum possible score on each test was 8.

Student	A	B	C	D	E	F	G	H	I	J	K	L
Mathematics	8	6	7	5	4	8	5	6	7	7	3	2
Physics	8	7	6	4	4	7	5	5	7	6	3	3

1 Draw a graph with Mathematics scores on the *x*-axis and Physics scores on the *y*-axis. Use a sensible scale, and label the axes. Plot points (Mathematics score, Physics score) to represent each student's scores. For example, for student A, plot the point (8, 8). For student B, plot (6, 7), and so on. Do not join the points.

2 Explain whether your graph suggests that there might be a relationship between the students' Mathematics and Physics marks.

▶ Continued on next page

3 Describe any patterns you see in the data. Determine whether these patterns apply to every student in the class.

4 The teacher claimed that students who got a good mark in one subject also got a good mark in the other. Is this claim justified?

5 Draw a straight line on your graph that best shows the relationship between the marks for Mathematics and Physics. Which way does the line slope? Discuss how close the points are to the line.

A scatter diagram shows the relationship between two quantitative variables. The independent variable is represented on the x-axis and the dependent variable on the y-axis. Data from two variables is called **bivariate data**.

Scatter diagrams are also called scatter plots or scatter graphs.

Correlation is a measure of the association between two variables.

When one variable increases as the other increases, there is positive correlation.

When one variable decreases as the other increases, there is negative correlation.

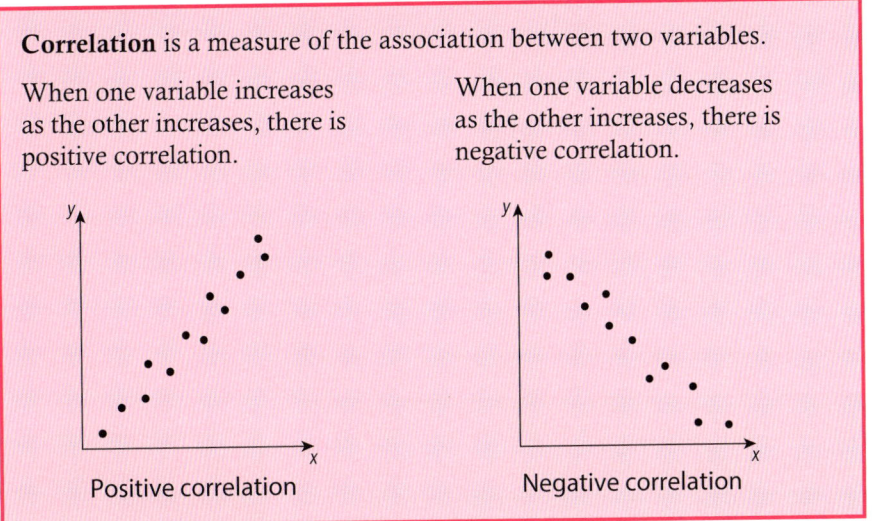

Positive correlation   Negative correlation

When the plotted points are close to a straight line drawn through the middle of the points, you say there is a linear correlation between the variables.

The closer the points are to a straight line, the stronger the correlation between the variables.

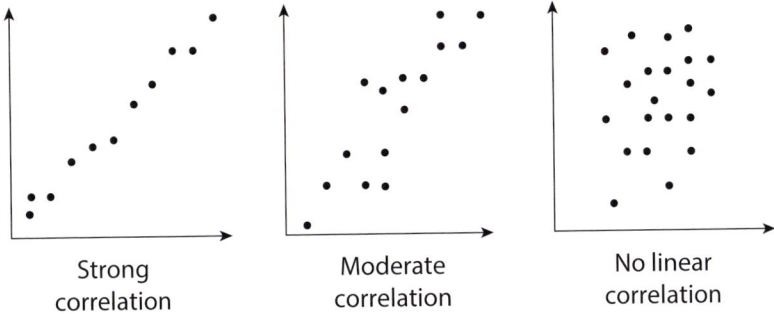

Strong correlation   Moderate correlation   No linear correlation

The scatter diagram you drew in Exploration 1 shows strong linear correlation between Mathematics and Physics scores. The higher the Mathematics score, the higher the Physics score.

Practice 1

For each scatter diagram, describe the form, direction and strength of the association between the variables. Interpret your description in the context of the data.

'Form' is linear or non-linear. 'Direction' is positive or negative.

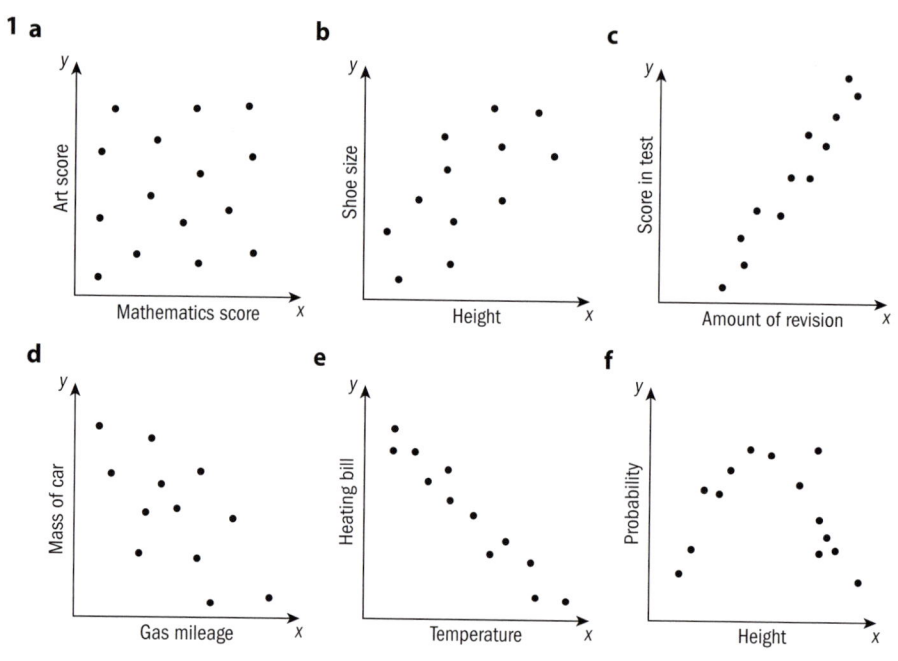

A line of best fit is a straight line drawn through the middle of a set of data points so that they are equally distributed on either side of the line. The line of best fit passes through the point $(\bar{x}, \bar{y})$ where $\bar{x}$ is the mean of the x-values and $\bar{y}$ is the mean of the y-values.

The line of best fit can also be called a *trend line*.

You can draw a line of best fit by eye.

Under some conditions you can use of the line of best fit to predict a y-value when you know an x-value, and vice versa.

C Making predictions

- How does the way data is represented affect our ability to make predictions?

When there is reasonable correlation between the two variables on the scatter diagram, it is possible to draw a *line of best fit*. This line represents the underlying relationship between the two quantities on the x- and y-axes. When drawing a line of best fit by eye it is important to consider qualitative techniques. These qualities are:

- Ensure that there are sufficient data points to be confident that there is a relationship.
- The line should pass through the data point $(\bar{x}, \bar{y})$ where $\bar{x}$ is the mean of the x-values and $\bar{y}$ is the mean of the y-values.

- There should be approximately the same number of data points on each side of the line.
- The points should be evenly distributed, either side of the line, both at the top and the bottom of the line.
- The line should be near as many points as possible.

The line of best fit can therefore be used to make predictions. The accuracy and reliability of the predictions will depend on the form, direction and strength between the two variables.

Example 1

The table shows the average daily temperature in °C for a week and the daily sales of ice cream in dollars.

	Mon	Tue	Wed	Thu	Fri	Sat	Sun
Temperature, x (°C)	17	22	18	23	25	19	22
Sales, y ($)	408	445	421	544	614	412	522

a Draw a scatter diagram of this data and draw a line of best fit through the points.

b Use the line of best fit to predict the sales of ice cream on a day when the temperature is 20°C.

a $\bar{x} = \dfrac{17+22+18+23+25+19+22}{7} = 20.9$ —— Calculate the mean temperature ($\bar{x}$).

$\bar{y} = \dfrac{408+445+421+544+614+412+522}{7} = 480.9$ —— Calculate the mean sales ($\bar{y}$).

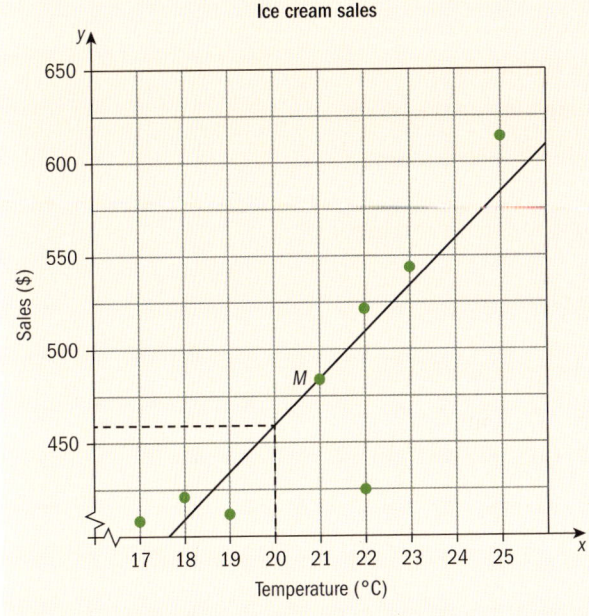

Plot the points from the table and the point $M = (\bar{x}, \bar{y})$.

Draw a line through M and through the middle of the other points.

Use a transparent ruler so you can see all the points above and below it. Pivot the ruler through the point $(\bar{x}, \bar{y})$ to find the best position.

b When the temperature is 20°C, predicted sales are $460. —— Draw a line from $x = 20$ and read off the y value.

> To draw a line of best fit by eye:
>
> - Calculate the mean of x ($\bar{x}$) and the mean of y ($\bar{y}$).
>
> - Plot the point $M = (\bar{x}, \bar{y})$ on the scatter diagram.
>
> - Draw a line through $M(\bar{x}, \bar{y})$ and through the middle of the other points. The points should be evenly distributed above and below the line.

ATL

Practice 2

1 The table shows data on 10 students:

- Reaction distance, in a test to measure visual responses
- Height, in meters
- Mass, in kilograms
- Time, in seconds, taken to fasten their shoelaces.

	A	B	C	D	E	F	G	H	I	J
Reaction distance (cm)	5.3	4.6	7.7	3.7	4.6	3.6	4.2	4.8	5.3	4.6
Height (m)	1.64	1.50	1.67	1.75	1.45	1.35	1.87	1.67	1.56	1.70
Mass (kg)	60	60	64	76	48	45	75	75	52	60
Fastening time (s)	9.1	10.5	13.4	9.6	10.5	9.2	8.8	8.5	10.4	6.3

- **a** Draw four separate scatter diagrams:
  - **i** Plot height on the x-axis and mass on the y-axis.
  - **ii** Plot mass on the x-axis and reaction distance on the y-axis.
  - **iii** Plot reaction distance on the x-axis and fastening time on the y-axis.
  - **iv** Plot height on the x-axis and fastening time on the y-axis.
- **b** Draw a line of best fit on each scatter diagram.
- **c** Comment on the form, direction and strength of the correlation in each scatter diagram.
- **d** Use the line of best fit to estimate the mass of a person who is 1.68 m tall.
- **e** Use the line of best fit to estimate the reaction distance of a student who took 12 seconds to fasten their shoelaces.
- **f** Explain which of your graphs would give the most accurate predictions.

2 The table shows information on road deaths and vehicle ownership in ten countries.

Country	Vehicles per 100 population	Road deaths per 100 000 population
UK	31	14
Belgium	32	29
Denmark	30	22
France	47	32
Germany	30	25
Ireland	19	20
Italy	36	21
Netherlands	40	22
Canada	47	30
USA	58	35

a Draw a scatter diagram with vehicles per 100 population on the x-axis and road deaths per 100 000 population on the y-axis. Does the graph show any correlation?

b Draw a line of best fit to represent the pattern in the data.

c The road death data for Switzerland is missing. Switzerland has 25 vehicles per 100 population. Use your line of best fit to estimate the number of road deaths per 100 000 population in Switzerland.

- -

D ## How reliable is the line of best fit?

- Does correlation indicate causation?
- Do I want to be like everybody else?

You have already learned how to do the following for a set of bivariate data:

- represent data set from the two variables in a table
- represent the data on a scatter diagram
- calculate the mean of each variable and plot the point $(\bar{x}, \bar{y})$
- draw a line of best fit by eye.

Depending on the strength of the association, form of the data, and the number of data points, you can make predictions from the data.

It is also possible to find an equation for the line of best fit, which will allow you to make predictions without using your scatter diagram.

Exploration 2

1 A line passes through the points with coordinates (2, 2) and (5, 7). Determine the equation of this line.

2 The following data on the ages in weeks of a tadpole and the length of its tail was collected from eight tadpoles and the line of best fit was drawn by eye

▶ Continued on next page

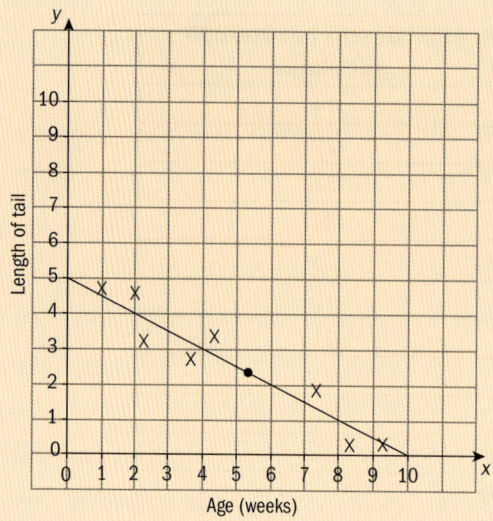

a Given that $(\overline{x}, \overline{y}) = (5.3, 2.5)$ and the line of best fit was as drawn on the diagram, state the coordinates of the y-intercept.

b Find the equation of the line of best fit.

c Use this equation to predict the length of the tail when the tadpole is 7.9 weeks old.

Reflect and discuss 1

Would it make sense to use the equation from step **2b** in Exploration 2 to predict the length when the tadpole is 15 weeks old?

Practice 3

In questions **1** to **3**:

    a draw a scatter diagram to represent the points

    b calculate the mean of x and y

    c draw a line of best fit.

Use $(\overline{x}, \overline{y})$ and the y-intercept to calculate the equation of the line of best fit. Use this equation to make predictions for y when $x = 10$ in each question.

1 Data was collected from 8 students where x was the number of electrical devices they had in their room and y was the average number of hours of screen time per week.

x	2	14	14	4	12	18	12	6
y	5	15	16	6	12	18	13	7

2 Data was collected from 7 students to determine a relationship between x, the number of laps of the athletics track which a student could run, and y, the amount of hours of television a student watched each week.

x	2	15	17	3	20	3	6
y	13	7	5	12	4	13	11

3 The data in the table shows the grades for 11 students in both x, music exams and y, art exams. Both exams were marked out of 50.

x	15	36	36	22	23	27	43	22	43	40	26
y	6	28	35	18	28	28	37	9	41	45	17

In question **3**, determine why it would not be valid to predict the art score, when the music score was 10.

Summary

A scatter diagram shows the relationship between two quantitative variables. The independent variable is represented on the x-axis and the dependent variable on the y-axis. Data from two variables is called **bivariate data**.

Correlation is a measure of the association between two variables. When one variable increases as the other increases, there is positive correlation. When one variable decreases as the other increases, there is negative correlation.

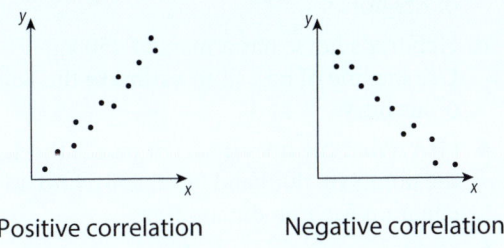

Positive correlation   Negative correlation

The closer the points are to a straight line, the stronger the correlation between the variables.

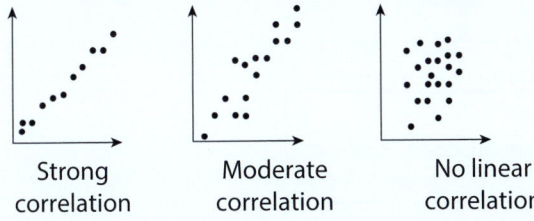

Strong   Moderate   No linear
correlation   correlation   correlation

A **line of best fit** is a straight line drawn through the middle of a set of data points so that they are equally distributed on either side of the line. The line of best fit passes through the point $(\bar{x}, \bar{y})$ where $\bar{x}$ is the mean of the x-values and $\bar{y}$ is the mean of the y-values.

To draw a line of best fit by eye:

- Calculate the mean of x $(\bar{x})$ and the mean of y $(\bar{y})$.
- Plot the point $M(\bar{x}, \bar{y})$ on the scatter diagram.
- Draw a line through M and through the middle of the other points. The points should be evenly distributed above and below the line.

An **outlier** is an anomaly in the data. To identify outliers in bivariate data, look at the distance of the data point from the line of best fit.

Mixed practice

1 The table gives the length and width of 10 oak leaves that fell to the ground.

Length (mm)	Width (mm)
103	38
146	44
119	38
149	53
89	36
135	38
151	51
147	43
123	33
128	42

a Represent the data on a scatter diagram, with length on the x-axis and width on the y-axis.

b Comment on the correlation between length and width of the leaves.

c By finding the mean length and mean width, **draw** a line of best fit.

2 The following data was collected during a science experiment:

Mass (kg)	0.7	1.0	1.3	2.4	2.6	3.0
Force (N)	2.1	3.5	4.8	6.2	7.8	11.2

a Draw a scatter diagram to represent the data.

b Calculate $\bar{x}$ and $\bar{y}$.

c Draw the line of best fit by eye.

d Determine whether this data allows for predictions to be made.

e Use the line of best fit to **determine** the force corresponding to a mass of 1.5 kg

3 The following scatter diagram represents the heights and masses of the horses at an equine therapy retreat.

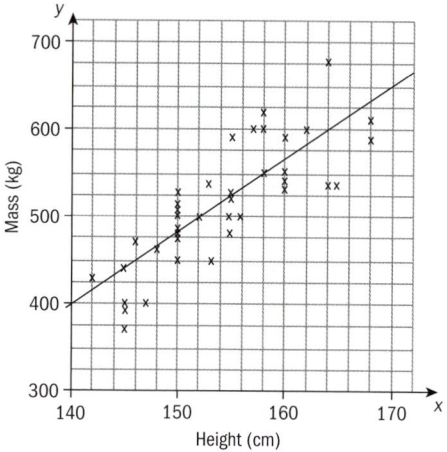

a Describe the association, form and strength of the relationship.

b Determine whether the line of best fit drawn is appropriate.

c The height of Bella's horse is 165 cm. Use the line of best fit to **estimate** the mass of her horse.

d Hendrix's horse has a mass of 450 kg, Use the line of best fit to **estimate** the height of his horse.

e Given that the line of best fit passes through the points (0, 400) and (158, 550), **find** an equation for a prediction line.

f Use the equation to **predict** the mass of a horse given that the height is 138 cm.

g Comment on the limitations of your line of best fit.

Objective: D. Applying mathematics in real-life contexts
ii. select appropriate mathematical strategies when solving authentic real-life situations

In this review you will have to use the mathematical strategies of drawing scatter diagrams, using technology to extract information and determining the reasons for outliers, in real-life situations.

Review in context

Identities and relationships

1 Florence's parents were concerned that she seemed short for her age and they recorded her height over a 36-month period:

Age (months)	36	48	51	58	66	72
Height (cm)	86	90	91	93	94	95

a **Draw** a scatter diagram of this data.

b **Use** this scatter diagram to **estimate** her height at age 42 months.

c Could you use this data and the scatter diagram to **predict** her height at age 18?

2 There are 12 students training for a charity 10 km run. The table shows the average number of hours of training per week and the time taken to complete the run.

Training time (hours)	Time to complete run (minutes)
10	56
9	54
13	53
4	62
26	42
7	66
11	54
6	66
7	68
22	39
5	70
10	67

a **Comment** on the correlation between training time and the time to complete the run.

b **Estimate** how long the run would take a student who trains 18 hours per week.

c **Determine** whether you could use this data to **predict** how long the run would take a student who trained 50 hours per week.

Reflect and discuss 2

How have you explored the statement of inquiry? Give specific examples.

Statement of inquiry:

Generalizing and representing relationships can help to clarify trends among individuals.

Index

24 game   19